1550
十

ordered 10/26/52

D1407015

MATHEMATICS

FOR

ELECTRICIANS AND RADIOMEN

MATHEMATICS

for

Electricians and Radiomen

BY

NELSON M. COOKE

Lieutenant Commander, United States Navy (Retired)
President, Cooke Engineering Company
Senior Member, Institute of Radio Engineers

McGRAW-HILL BOOK COMPANY, Inc.

NEW YORK AND LONDON

1942

42-3824

ACKNOWLEDGMENTS

In common with many text books, this book is based upon lecture notes which were compiled over a period of years. During this time, with no thought of eventual publication, material was drawn from many excellent sources which, with the passage of time, have become obscure or of unknown origin. It is impossible, therefore, to list these sources or to give credit where it is so justly due.

The author is indebted to the instructors of the Radio Matériel School, Naval Research Laboratory, and former students for much helpful criticism and suggestions. In particular, Classes Thirty-two, Thirty-three and Thirty-four of the Radio Matériel School deserve credit for their efforts in mimeographing the final material and offering valuable suggestions while using it as a text.

Special credit is due Lt. Comdr. Wallace J. Miller, U.S. Navy, officer in charge of the Radio Matériel School, for his sympathetic attitude, encouragement, and many helpful suggestions.

The students of Class Fourteen of the Warrant Officers Radio Engineering Course, Radio Matériel School, offered invaluable criticism and suggestions for the improvement of the text. Three of these are deserving of special mention: Radio Electrician I. L. McNally, U.S. Navy, for submitting many original problems; Radio Electrician J. R. True, U.S. Navy, and Radio Electrician A. J. Beaudoin, U.S. Navy, for proofreading the manuscript and offering much valuable comment.

The author is indebted to M. E. Beard, radioman first class, U.S. Navy, for his aid in compiling the answers.

Last, but by no means least, the author is much indebted to his wife for her untiring assistance in preparing the manuscript and for her constant encouragement.

The author welcomes any corrections or suggestions for improvement.

NELSON M. COOKE.

WASHINGTON, D.C.,
January, 1942.

v

CONTENTS

APPENDIX

MATHEMATICS FOR ELECTRICIANS AND RADIOMEN

CHAPTER I

INTRODUCTION

In the legions of textbooks on the subject of mathematics, all the basic principles contained here have been expounded in admirable fashion. However, electrical and radio engineering students have need for a course in mathematics that is directly concerned with application to electrical and radio circuits. This book is intended to provide those students with a sound mathematical background and to further their understanding of the basic principles of electricity.

1-1. Preparation Required. Any student who can perform arithmetical computations rapidly and accurately is capable of mastering the principles laid down in this text, if he applies himself properly. The student who has had some high-school mathematics will find that the earlier chapters form a comprehensive review and will aid him in applying mathematics to radio and electric-circuit theory.

1-2. Scope and Arrangement. This textbook is intended to provide a mathematical background adequate for the solving of practically all everyday electrical and radio problems. If the student desires to proceed into the realm of higher mathematics in the study of radio and electrical design problems, he will find that this subject matter will give him a firm foundation on which to build.

The text follows an electrical rather than a purely mathematical arrangement, although there is no loss of mathematical continuity.

A double system of article, problem, and figure numbering has been followed in order to facilitate cross reference to a given article, problem, or figure in a minimum of time.

1

1-3. Mathematics—a Language. The study of mathematics may be likened to the study of a language. In fact, mathematics is a language, the language of number and size. Just as the rules of grammar must be studied in order to master English, so must certain concepts, definitions, rules, terms, and words be learned in the pursuit of mathematical knowledge. These form the vocabulary or structure of the language. The more a language is studied and used, the greater becomes the vocabulary; the more mathematics is studied and applied, the greater becomes its usefulness.

There is one marked difference, however, between the study of a language and the study of mathematics. A language is based on words, phrases, expressions, and usages that have been brought together through the ages in haphazard fashion according to the customs of the times. Mathematics is built upon the firm foundation of sound logic and orderly reasoning, and progresses smoothly, step by step, from the simplest numerical processes to the most complicated and advanced applications, each step along the way resting squarely upon those which have gone before. This makes mathematics the fascinating subject that it is.

1-4. Mathematics—a Tool. As the builder works with his square and compasses, so does the engineer employ mathematics. A thorough grounding in this subject is essential to proficiency in any of the numerous branches of engineering. In no other branch is this more apparent than in the study of electricity and radio, for most of our basic ideas of electrical phenomena are based upon mathematical reasoning and stated in mathematical terms. This is a fortunate circumstance, for it enables us to build a structure of electrical knowledge with precision, assembling and expressing the components in clear and concise mathematical terms and arranging the whole in logical order. Without mathematical assistance, the electrician or radioman must content himself with the long and painful process of accumulating bits of information, details of experience, etc., and he may never achieve a thorough understanding of the field in which he lives and works.

1-5. Mathematics—a Teacher. In addition to laying a foundation for technical knowledge and assisting in the practical application of knowledge already possessed, mathematics offers unlimited advantages in respect to mental training. The solution of a problem, no matter how simple, demands logical thinking

for it to be possible to state the facts of the problem in mathematical terms and then proceed with the solution. Continued
study in this orderly manner will increase the mental capacity
of the student, enabling him to solve more difficult problems, to
understand more complicated engineering principles, and to cope
more successfully with the everyday problems of life.

1-6. Methods of Attack. Before beginning detailed study of
this text the student should carefully analyze it, in its entirety, in
order to form a mental outline of its contents, scope, and arrangement. Another preliminary survey of individual chapters should
be made before attempting detailed study of their subject matter.
After such detailed study, problems should be worked until all
principles are fixed firmly in mind before proceeding to new
material.

In working problems, the same general procedure is recommended. First, a problem should be analyzed in order to determine the best method of solution. The problem should then be
stated in mathematical terms, the principles that are applicable
being utilized. If but little progress is made, it is probable the
student has not completely mastered the principles explained
in the text, and a review is in order.

The author is a firm believer in the use of a workbook, preferably in the form of a loose-leaf notebook, which contains all
the problems the student has worked, together with the numerous
notes made while studying the text. Such a book is an invaluable
aid for purposes of review. The habit of jotting down notes during reading or studying should be cultivated. Such notes in the
student's own words will provide a better understanding of a
concept.

1-7. Rate of Progress. Home-study students should guard
against too rapid progress. There is a tendency, especially in
studying a chapter whose contents are familiar or easy of com-
prehension, to hurry to the next chapter. Hasty reading may
cause the loss of a particular meaning that a section or a paragraph
is intended to convey. Proficiency in mathematics depends upon
thorough understanding of each step as it is encountered, so that
it can be used to master that which follows.

1-8. Importance of Problems. Full advantage should be
taken of the many problems distributed throughout the text.
There is no approach to a full and complete understanding of any

branch of mathematics other than the solution of numerous problems. Application of what has been learned from the text to practical problems in which the student is primarily interested not only will help with the subject matter of the problem but will serve the purpose of fixing in mind the mathematical principles involved.

The arrangement of problems is such that the most difficult appear at the end of each group. It is apparent that the working of the simpler problems first will tend to make the more difficult ones easier of solution. The home-study student is therefore urged to work all problems in the order given. At times, this may appear to be useless, and the student may have the desire to proceed to more interesting things; but time spent in working problems will amply repay the student in giving him a depth of understanding to be obtained in no other manner. This does not mean that progress should cease if a problem appears impossible of solution. Return to such problems when the mind is fresh, or mark them for solution during a review period.

1-9. Illustrative Examples. Each of the illustrative examples in this book is intended to make clear some important principle or method of solution. The subject matter of these examples will be more thoroughly assimilated if, after careful analysis of the problem set forth, an independent solution is made and the method and results are compared with the illustrative example.

1-10. Review. Too much stress cannot be placed upon the necessity for frequent and thorough review. Often points that have been missed in the original study of the text will stand out clearly upon careful review. A review of each chapter before proceeding with the next is recommended.

CHAPTER II

LITERAL NUMBERS

In general, arithmetic consists of the operations of addition, subtraction, multiplication, and division of a type of numbers represented by the digits 1, 2, 3, $\cdots$ 9, 0. By using the above operations or combinations of them, we are able to solve many problems. However, a knowledge of mathematics limited to arithmetic is inadequate and a severe handicap to a man interested in acquiring an understanding of electric circuits. Proficiency in performing even the most simple operations of algebra enables the student to solve problems and determine relations that would be impossible with arithmetic alone.

2-1. The General Number. Algebra may be thought of as a continuation of arithmetic in which letters and symbols are used to represent definite quantities whose actual values may or may not be known. For example, in electrical and radio texts, it is customary to represent currents by the letters I or i; voltages by E, e, V, or v; resistances by R or r; etc. The base of a triangle is often represented by b, and the altitude may be specified as a. Such letters or symbols used for representing quantities in a general way are known as *general numbers* or *literal numbers*.

The importance of the general-number idea cannot be overemphasized. Although it is possible to express in English the various laws and facts concerning electricity, they are more concisely and compactly expressed in mathematical form in terms of general numbers. As an example, Ohm's law states, in part, that the current in a certain part of a circuit is proportional to the potential difference (voltage) across that part of the circuit and inversely proportional to the resistance of that part. This same statement, in mathematical terms, says

$$I = \frac{E}{R}$$

where I represents the current, E is the potential difference, and R is the resistance. Such an expression is known as a *formula*.

5

Although the expression (as formulas) of various laws and relationships of science, in the language of mathematics, gives a more compact form of notation, therein is not the real value of the formula. As we attain proficiency in algebra, the value of general formulas will become more apparent. Our studies of algebra will consist mainly in learning how to add, subtract, multiply, divide, and solve such general algebraic expressions, or formulas, in order to attain a better understanding of the fundamentals of electricity and radio.

2-2. Algebraic Expressions. An *algebraic expression* is one that expresses or represents a number by the signs and symbols of algebra. A *numerical algebraic expression* is one consisting entirely of signs and numerals. A *literal algebraic expression* is one containing general numbers or letters. An example of a numerical algebraic expression is $8 - (6 + 2)$; I^2R is a literal algebraic expression.

2-3. The Product. A *product* is the result obtained in multiplying two or more numbers. Thus, 12 is the product of 6×2.

2-4. The Factor. If two or more numbers are multiplied together, each of them or the product of any combination of them is called a *factor* of the product. For example, in the product $2xy$, 2, x, y, $2x$, $2y$, and xy are all factors of $2xy$.

2-5. Coefficients. Any factor of a product is known as the *coefficient* of the product of the remaining factors. In the foregoing example, 2 is the coefficient of xy, x is the coefficient of $2y$, y is the coefficient of $2x$, etc. It is common practice to speak of the numerical part of an expression as the *coefficient* or as the *numerical coefficient*. If an expression contains no numerical coefficient, 1 is understood to be the numerical coefficient. Thus, $1abc$ is the same as abc.

2-6. Signs of Operation. In algebra the signs of operation $+$, $-$, $\times$, and $\div$ have the same meanings as in arithmetic. The sign $\times$ is generally omitted between literal numbers. For example, $I \times R$ is written IR and means that I is to be multiplied by R. Similarly, $2\pi fL$ means 2 times π times f times L. Sometimes the symbol $[\cdot]$ is used to denote multiplication. Thus $I \times R$, $I \cdot R$, and IR all mean I times R.

2-7. Evaluation. To *evaluate* an algebraic expression is to find its numerical value. In Art. 2-1, it was stated that in algebra certain signs and symbols are used to represent definite quantities.

Also, in Art. 2-2, an algebraic expression was defined as one that represents a number by the signs and symbols of algebra. We can find the numerical, or definite, value of an expression only when we know the values of the letters in the expression.

Example 1. Find the value of $2ayz$ if $a = 1$, $y = 2$, and $z = 4$.

Solution: $2ayz = 2 \times 1 \times 2 \times 4 = 16$

Example 2. Evaluate the expression $4z - 2az$ if a, y, and z have the same values as in Example 1.

Solution: $4z - 2az = 4 \times 4 - 2 \times 1 \times 4$
$$= 16 - 8$$
$$= 8$$

PROBLEMS 2-1

1. What does $8E$ mean?   What does $3i$ mean? $11R$?

2. How much is $4E$ when E is 8 volts?   When E is 0.5 volt?

3. If one resistor costs $3.00, what will seven resistors cost?   What will n resistors cost?

4. Sixteen resistors cost a total of $4.00. What is the cost of each resistor?

5. n resistors cost $2.50. What is the cost of 1 resistor? q resistors?

6. The voltage across a certain circuit is $12E$ volts. What is the value if the voltage is doubled?

7. A certain power company charges x cents per kilowatt-hour for lighting power, and another company charges half as much. Indicate the second company's charge per kilowatt-hour.

8. What part of $24R$ is

(a) $3R$?   (b) $4R$?   (c) $8R$?   (d) 24?   (e) R?

9. There are three voltages of which the second is five times the first and the third is six times the second. Let E represent the first voltage, in volts, and then represent the others in terms of E.

10. There are four currents of which the second is one-half the first, the third is three times the second, and the fourth is ten times the third. Let I represent the first current, in amperes, and then represent the others in terms of I.

If $a = 2$, $b = 8$, and $c = 5$, find the value of each of the following:

11. $b + c$.   **12.** $b + a - c$.   **13.** abc.

14. $\dfrac{b}{a}$.   **15.** $\dfrac{a + b}{c}$.   **16.** $2b - 3a$.

17. $\dfrac{b + 6a}{2c}$.   **18.** $\dfrac{2abc}{5b}$.   **19.** $\dfrac{1 + c + b + a}{a + 6 + b}$.

20. $\dfrac{24cba}{48bc}$.

21. Express a voltage 10 volts greater than E volts.

22. Express a current that is 6 amperes less than $60I$ amperes.

23. A certain resistor is 25 ohms. What is a resistance of R ohms less than this?

24. A circuit has a current of 12 amperes. Express a current five times this value diminished by I amperes.

25. A voltage E exceeds another voltage E_1 by 220 volts. Express the voltage E_1 in terms of E.

2-8. Exponents. If we want to express "x is to be taken as a factor four times," instead of writing $xxxx$, it has been generally agreed to express this as x^4.

An *exponent*, or *power*, is a number written at the right of and above another number to indicate how many times the latter is to be taken as a factor. The number to be multiplied by itself is called the *base*.

Thus, I^2 is read "I square" or "I second power" and means that I is to be taken twice as a factor; e^3 is read "e cube" or "e third power" and means that e is to be taken as a factor three times. Likewise, 5^4 is read "5 fourth power" and means that 5 is to be taken as a factor four times; thus,

$$5 \times 5 \times 5 \times 5 = 625$$

When no exponent, or power, is indicated, the exponent is understood to be 1. Thus, x is the same as x^1.

2-9. The Radical Sign. The radical sign $\sqrt{}$ has the same meaning in algebra as in arithmetic. $\sqrt{e}$ means the square root of e, $\sqrt[3]{x}$ means the cube root of x, $\sqrt[4]{i}$ means the fourth root of i, etc. The small number in the angle of a radical sign, like the 4 in $\sqrt[4]{i}$, is known as the *index* of the root.

2-10. Terms. A *term* is an expression or portion of an expression whose parts are not separated by a plus or a minus sign. $3E^2$, IR, and $-2e$ are terms of the expression $3E^2 + IR - 2e$.

Although the value of a term depends upon the values of its literal factors, it is customary to refer to a term whose sign is plus as a *positive term*. Likewise, we refer to a term whose sign is minus as a *negative term*.

Terms having the same literal parts are called *like terms* or *similar terms.* $2a^2bx$, $-a^2bx$, $18a^2bx$, and $-4a^2bx$ are like terms.

Terms that are not alike in their literal parts are called *unlike terms* or *dissimilar terms.* $5xy$, $6ac$, $9I^2R$, and EI are *unlike terms.*

An algebraic expression consisting of but one term is known as a *monomial.*

A *polynomial,* or *multinomial,* is an algebraic expression consisting of two or more terms.

A *binomial* is a polynomial of two terms. $e + ir$, $a - 2b$, and $2x^2y + xyz^2$ are binomials.

A *trinomial* is a polynomial of three terms. $2a + 3b - c$, $IR + 3e - E^2$, and $8ab^3c + 3d + 2xy$ are trinomials.

2-11. The Order of Signs of Operation. In performing a series of different operations, it has been agreed that the multiplications must be performed first, next the divisions, and then the additions and subtractions. Thus,

$$16 \div 4 + 8 + 4 \times 5 - 3 = 4 + 8 + 20 - 3 = 29$$

PROBLEMS 2-2

If $e = 3$, $i = 2$, and $r = 5$, find the value of the following expressions:

1. $15\dfrac{e^2}{r}$.

2. $3i^2r$.

3. $6eir^2$.

4. $2e^3i^2r$.

5. $\dfrac{3e^2i^4r}{ei^3r}$.

6. $\dfrac{20ei - i^2r}{13ir - 10e}$.

7. $\dfrac{10i^3r^2}{16r^3} - \dfrac{i^6r}{16i^2r}$.

8. $\dfrac{4}{ir^2} - \dfrac{1}{i^3r}$.

9. $\sqrt{e^2i^6r^2} - \dfrac{2.5r^3i}{\sqrt{25r^2}}$.

10. $4r^2 + \dfrac{i^3e^2}{36} - ir^2$.

State which of the following are monomials, binomials, and trinomials:

11. $\dfrac{E^2}{R}$.

12. $E + IR$.

13. $ab + bc + cd$.

14. $\dfrac{E^2}{R} - I^2R + P_1$.

15. πr^2.

16. $\frac{1}{2}at^2$.

17. $8ax^2y - 3axy^2 + 4xyz^3$.

18. $r^2 + x^2$.

19. EI (p.f.).

20. $\dfrac{E}{I} + Z$(p.f.) $+ R$.

21. $\dfrac{h\pi r^2}{3}$.

22. $3x + 2ny - 8z^2$.

23. $\frac{1}{2}mv^2$.

24. $e_1 + iZ + 36e_2$.

25. $Z_1 + \dfrac{e}{i} - \dfrac{R}{\text{p.f.}}$.

26. In Probs. 1 to 25, state which expressions are polynomials.

27. The area of a circle is given by the formula $A = \pi r^2$ in which A is the area, π is 3.14 (approximately), and r is the radius. Find the area of a circle whose radius is

(a) 2 inches. (b) 0.5 inch.

28. The power in any part of an electric circuit is given by $P = I^2R$ in which P is the power in watts, I is the current in amperes through that part, and R is the resistance in ohms of that part. Find the power expended when

(a) Current = 5 amperes, resistance = 6 ohms.
(b) Current = 0.020 ampere, resistance = 5000 ohms.

29. The distance a body falls from rest is given by the formula $s = \frac{1}{2}gt^2$, in which s is the distance in feet, g is the acceleration due to gravity (32 approximately), and t is the time in seconds that the body falls. How far will a body fall from rest in

(a) 1 second? (b) 5 seconds? (c) t seconds?

30. The power in any part of an electric circuit is given by $P = \dfrac{E^2}{R}$, in which P is the power in watts, E is the voltage across that part, and R is the resistance of that part. Find the power expended when

(a) Voltage = 110 volts, resistance = 200 ohms.
(b) Voltage = 220 volts, resistance = 50 ohms.

Write the following in algebraic symbols:

31. The product of I square times R.

32. The quotient of E square divided by R.

33. E minus the product of I times R.

34. Z is equal to the square root of the sum of R square plus X square.

35. The product of four times x cube minus y square.

36. The square of the sum of x and y.

37. R square equals Z square minus X square.

38. The quotient of the sum of R and X divided by the difference when X is subtracted from R.

39. What is the coefficient in

(a) Prob. 1?
(b) Prob. 3?
(c) Prob. 15?
(d) Prob. 21?
(e) Prob. 23?

40. What is the value of 628×10^5?

41. What is the value of 0.00345×10^6?

42. In Prob. 27, how much larger is the area of a circle whose radius is twice that of another circle?

43. In Prob. 28, everything else remaining constant, what happens to the power in an electric circuit when the current is

(a) Doubled?

(b) Tripled?

44. In Prob. 30, everything else remaining constant, what happens to the power when the voltage is

(a) Doubled?

(b) Tripled?

(c) Quadrupled?

45. In Prob. 30, everything else remaining constant, what happens to the power when the resistance is doubled?

CHAPTER III

ADDITION AND SUBTRACTION

The problems of arithmetic deal with positive numbers only. A *positive number* may be defined as any number greater than zero. Accepting this definition, we know that when such numbers are added, multiplied, and divided the results are always positive. Such is the case in subtraction if a number be subtracted from a larger one. However, if we attempt to subtract a number from a smaller one, arithmetic furnishes no rule for carrying out this operation.

3-1. Negative Numbers. Limiting our knowledge of mathematics to positive numbers would place us under a severe handicap, for there are many instances when it becomes necessary to deal with negative numbers. For the time being, we shall define a *negative number* as a number less than zero. Negative numbers are prefixed with the minus sign. Thus, negative 2 is written -2, negative $3ac$ is written $-3ac$, etc. If no sign precedes a number, it is assumed to be positive.

Numerous examples of the uses of negative numbers could be cited. For example, zero degrees on the centigrade thermometer has been chosen as the temperature of melting ice—commonly referred to as freezing temperature. Now everyone knows, that in some climates, it gets much colder than "freezing." Such temperatures are referred to as so many "degrees below zero." How shall we state, in the language of mathematics, a temperature of "10 degrees below zero"? Ten degrees *above* zero would be written 10°. Because 0° is the reference point, it is logical to assume that 10° *below* zero would be written as $-10°$, which, for our purposes, makes it a negative number.

3-2. Practical Need for Negative Numbers. The need for negative numbers often arises in the consideration of voltages or currents in electrical and radio circuits. It is common practice to select the ground, or earth, as a point of zero potential. This does not mean, however, that there can be no potentials below

12

ground, or zero, potential.   Consider the case of a battery connected to two equal resistors by wires of negligible resistance with a ground connection as shown in Fig. 3-1.

A voltmeter connected across the battery at points A and B would read a potential difference of 6 volts across the battery, which would be the same as connecting the voltmeter across points C and H.   Then, according to the distribution of potential differences (voltages) in series circuits, when the voltmeter was connected across points C and D and also across points F and H a reading of 3 volts would be obtained in each case, for, as stated, the two resistances are equal. Now, point C is 3 volts positive with respect to ground because D is at ground potential.   Because F is also at ground potential, it follows that H is 3 volts negative with respect to ground.   As long as the ground was considered as the reference point, or zero potential, the voltage at C with respect to ground would be denoted as 3 volts,

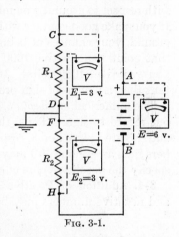

FIG. 3-1.

and the voltage at H with respect to ground would be -3 volts. This is an interesting little experiment.   Try it and carefully note the polarity of the voltmeter connections when changing from one resistor to the other.

The student can think of many other instances in everyday life where the use of negative numbers is helpful.

3-3. The Mathematical Need for Negative Numbers.   From a purely mathematical viewpoint the need for negative numbers may be seen from a succession of subtractions where we subtract successively larger numbers from 5 as shown below.

5	5	5	5	5	5	5	5	5
0	1	2	3	4	5	6	7	8
5	4	3	2	1	0	−1	−2	−3

The above subtractions result in the remainders becoming less until zero is reached.   When the remainder becomes less than zero, this is indicated by placing the negative sign before it.   This is one reason for defining a negative number as a number less than zero. Mathematically, the definition is correct if we consider only the signs that precede the numbers.

The student must not lose sight of the fact, however, that as far as magnitude, or size, is concerned a negative number may represent a larger absolute value than some positive number. *The positive and negative signs simply denote reference from zero.* For example, if some point in an electric circuit is 1000 volts negative with respect to ground, you may denote it by writing −1000 volts. If you make good contact with your body between that point and ground, your chances of being electrocuted are just as good as if that point was positive 1000 volts with respect to ground—and you wrote it +1000 volts! In this case, *how much* is more important than a matter of sign preceding the number.

The numerical, or *absolute*, value of a number is its value without regard to sign. Thus, the absolute values of −1, +4, −6, and +3 are 1, 4, 6, and 3, respectively. Note that different numbers such as −9 and +9 may have the same absolute value. To specify the absolute value of a number, such as Z, we write $|Z|$.

3-4. Addition of Positive and Negative Numbers. Positive and negative numbers may be represented graphically as in Fig.

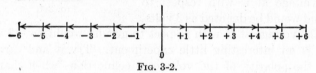

FIG. 3-2.

3-2. Positive numbers are shown as being directed toward the right of zero, which is the reference point, whereas negative numbers are directed toward the left.

Such a scale of numbers may be used to illustrate both addition and subtraction as performed in arithmetic. Thus, in adding 3 to

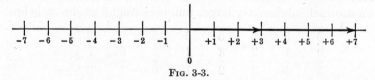

FIG. 3-3.

4, we may begin at 3 and count 4 units to the right, obtaining the sum 7. Or, because these are positive numbers directed toward the right, we could draw them to scale, place them end to end, and measure their total length to obtain a length of 7 units in the positive direction.   This is illustrated in Fig. 3-3.

In like manner, -2 and -3 may be added to obtain -5 as shown in Fig. 3-4.

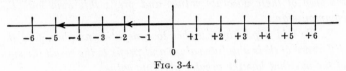

FIG. 3-4.

Note that adding -3 and -2 is the same as adding -2 and -3 as in the foregoing example.   The sum -5 is obtained, as shown in Fig. 3-5.

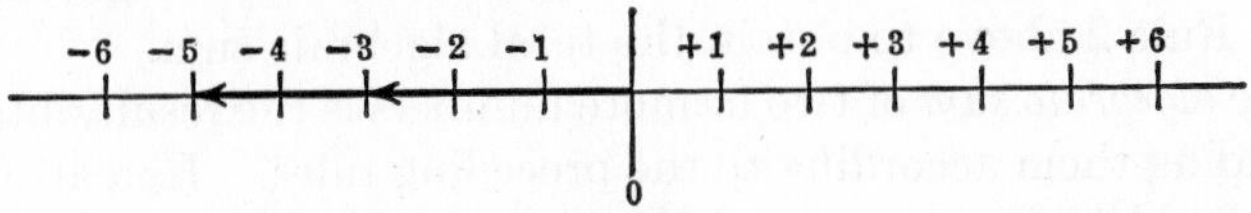

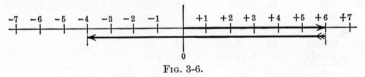

FIG. 3-5.

Suppose we add $+6$ and -10.   This could be accomplished on the scale by first counting 6 units to the right and from *that* point counting 10 units to the left.   In so doing, we end up at -4, which is the sum of $+6$ and -10.   Similarly, we could have started by first counting 10 units to the left, from zero, and from that point could have counted 6 units to the right for the $+6$. Again we should have arrived at -4.

FIG. 3-6.

Adding $+6$ and -10 may be accomplished graphically as in Fig. 3-6.   The $+6$ is drawn to scale, and then the tail of the -10 is joined with the head of $+6$.   The head of the -10 is then on -4.   As would be expected, the same result is obtained by first drawing in the -10 and then the $+6$.

The following problems may be checked graphically in order to verify their correctness:

$$
\begin{array}{rrrrrr}
+8 & +9 & +6 & -5 & -7 & -17 \\
+4 & -3 & -9 & +2 & +9 & -14 \\
\hline
+12 & +6 & -3 & -3 & +2 & -31 \\
\end{array}
$$

Consideration of the above examples enables us to establish the following rule:

Rule: 1. *To add two or more numbers with like signs, find the sum of their absolute values and prefix this sum with the common sign.*

2. *To add a positive number to a negative number, find the difference of their absolute values and prefix to the result the sign of the one that has the greater absolute value.*

When three or more algebraic numbers are to be added, differing in signs, find the sum of the positive numbers and then the sum of the negative numbers. Add these sums algebraically using Rule 2 above to obtain the total algebraic sum.

The *algebraic sum* of two or more numbers is the result obtained by adding them according to the preceding rules. Hereafter, the word "add" will mean "find the algebraic sum."

PROBLEMS 3-1

Add:

1. -9 -2	2. 16 -30	3. 23 -6	4. -63 46
5. 21 37	6. -54 33	7. -83 -24	8. -43 -96
9. 682 -934	10. -347 405	11. -382 590	12. -34.03 16.98
13. 0.0025 -0.1024	14. 0.206 -38.802	15. $3\frac{1}{3}$ $-2\frac{2}{3}$	16. $-\frac{1}{2}$ $\frac{1}{6}$
17. 3.02 -4.68	18. $-64\frac{2}{3}$ $8\frac{1}{8}$	19. $-2\frac{1}{4}$ $6\frac{5}{6}$	

20. Is it possible to decrease the absolute value of a number by addition? Explain your answer.

3-5. The Subtraction of Positive and Negative Numbers. We may think of subtraction as the process of determining what number must be added to a given number in order to produce another given number. Thus, when we subtract 5 from 9 and get 4, we have found that 4 must be added to 5 in order to obtain 9. From this it is seen that subtraction is the inverse of addition.

Example 1. $(+5) - (+2) = ?$

Solution: In the above the question is asked, "What number added to +2 will give +5?" Using the scale of Fig. 3-7, start at +2 and count to the

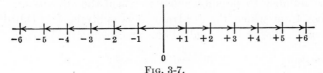

FIG. 3-7.

right (positive direction), until +5 is reached. This requires 3 units. Therefore, the difference is +3, or $(+5) - (+2) = +3$.

Example 2. $(+5) - (-2) = ?$

Solution: In the above the question is asked, "What number added to −2 will give +5?" Using the scale, start at −2 and count the number of units to +5. This requires 7 units; and because it was necessary to count in the positive direction, the difference is +7, or $(+5) - (-2) = +7$.

Example 3. $(-5) - (+2) = ?$

Solution: In this example the question is, "What number added to +2 will give −5?" Again using the scale, we start at +2 and count the number of units to −5. This requires 7 units; but because it was necessary to count in the negative direction, the difference is −7, or $(-5) - (+2) = -7$.

Example 4. $(-5) - (-2) = ?$

Solution: Here the question is, "What number added to −2 will give −5?" Using the scale, we start at −2 and count the number of units to −5. This requires 3 units in the negative direction. Hence, $(-5) - (-2) = -3$.

Summing up the foregoing examples, we have the following subtractions:

$$\begin{array}{cccc} +5 & +5 & -5 & -5 \\ +2 & -2 & +2 & -2 \\ \hline +3 & +7 & -7 & -3 \end{array}$$

A careful study of the examples illustrates the following principles:

1. *Subtracting a positive number is equivalent to adding a negative number of the same absolute value.*

2. *Subtracting a negative number is equivalent to adding a positive number of the same absolute value.*

These principles may be used for the purpose of establishing the following rule:

Rule : *To subtract one number from another, change the sign of the subtrahend and add algebraically.*

The number to be subtracted is called the *subtrahend.* The number from which the subtrahend is subtracted is called the *minuend.* The result is called the *remainder* or *difference.*

Example 5.
$$\begin{aligned}\text{Minuend} &= -642 \\ \text{Subtrahend} &= \underline{403} \\ \text{Remainder} &= -1045\end{aligned}$$

PROBLEMS 3-2[1]

Subtract:

1. 16
66

2. -34
23

3. -78
-47

4. 147
-104

5. -35
15

6. -45
-37

7. 64.06
-9.83

8. 0.0025
0.64

9. $3\frac{2}{3}$
$-4\frac{1}{8}$

10. $-9\frac{3}{8}$
$-8\frac{1}{2}$

11. -10.63
21.36

12. 0.824
-0.986

13. -1054
8623

14. $16\frac{1}{5}$
$-8\frac{2}{3}$

15. 106.25
-6.07

16. $-8\frac{5}{8}$
$4\frac{2}{3}$

How many degrees must the temperature rise to change from

17. $+3°$ to $+14°$?

18. $-20°$ to $-4°$?

19. $-6°$ to $+18°$?

20. $+13°$ to $+40°$?

How many degrees must the temperature fall to change from

21. $+6°$ to $-4°$?

22. $-3°$ to $-14°$?

23. $0°$ to $-21°$?

24. $+98°$ to $+20°$?

25. Is it possible to increase the absolute value of a number by subtraction? Explain your answer.

26. Is subtraction always possible in arithmetic? Explain your answer.

27. Is subtraction always possible in algebra? Explain your answer.

28. A certain point in a circuit is 440 v positive with respect to ground. Another point in the same circuit is 220 v negative with respect to ground. What is the potential difference between the two points?

29. A point in a circuit is 110 v negative with respect to ground. Another point in the circuit is 50 v negative with respect to ground. What is the potential difference between the two points?

[1] The reader is referred to Table III (p. 501) which contains a list of abbreviations used henceforth in problems, answers to problems, centered equations, and tables.

3-6. Addition and Subtraction of Like Terms. In arithmetic, it is never possible to add unlike quantities. For example, we should not add inches and gallons and expect to obtain a sensible answer. Neither should we attempt to add volts and amperes, kilocycles and microfarads, ohms and watts, etc. So it goes on through algebra—we can never add quantities unless they are expressed in the same units.

The addition of two like terms such as $6ab + 12ab = 18ab$ may be checked by substituting numbers for the literal factors. Thus, if $a = 1$ and $b = 2$,

$$
\begin{array}{rcccl}
6ab &=& 6 \times 1 \times 2 &=& 6 \times 2 = 12 \\
12ab &=& 12 \times 1 \times 2 &=& 12 \times 2 = 24 \\
\hline
18ab &=& 18 \times 1 \times 2 &=& 18 \times 2 = 36
\end{array}
$$

From the foregoing, it is apparent that like terms may be added or subtracted by adding or subtracting their coefficients.

The addition or subtraction of unlike terms cannot be carried out but can only be indicated, because the unlike literal factors may stand for entirely different quantities.

Example 1. Addition of like terms:

$$
\begin{array}{rrr}
-3x^2y & -16IR & 13ab^2cd \\
8x^2y & 14IR & -20ab^2cd \\
\hline
5x^2y & -3IR & -32ab^2cd \\
\hline
& -5IR & -39ab^2cd
\end{array}
$$

Example 2. Subtraction of like terms:

$$
\begin{array}{rrr}
-8e_1 & 6iZ & -28xyz^2 \\
3e_1 & -13iZ & -29xyz^2 \\
\hline
-11e_1 & 19iZ & xyz^2
\end{array}
$$

Example 3. Addition of unlike terms:

$$
\begin{array}{lll}
3e & -3b & 3EI \\
-3IX & 4a & 10I^2R \\
4E & -16xy & -46W \\
\hline
3e - 3IX + 4E & 4a - 3b - 16xy & 3EI + 10I^2R - 46W
\end{array}
$$

3-7. Addition and Subtraction of Polynomials. Polynomials are added or subtracted by arranging like terms in the same column and then combining terms in each column, as with monomials.

Example 1.   Addition of polynomials:

$$-3ab + 6cd + x^2y$$
$$14ab \qquad - 5x^2y$$
$$\underline{ab - 3cd}$$
$$12ab + 3cd - 4x^2y$$

$$6E + 3RI - 8IZ$$
$$RI - 2IZ$$
$$\underline{-7E \qquad + 3IZ}$$
$$-E + 4RI - 7IZ$$

Example 2.   Subtraction of polynomials:

$$3mn + 16pq - xy^2$$
$$\underline{-9mn \qquad + 7xy^2}$$
$$12mn + 16pq - 8xy^2$$

$$11R + 4x$$
$$\underline{15R \qquad - 18Z}$$
$$-4R + 4x + 18Z$$

PROBLEMS 3-3

Add:

1. $5x$, $6x$, $-18x$, $40x$.
2. $3a^2b$, $-13a^2b$, a^2b, $-4a^2b$.
3. $11I^2R$, I^2R, $4I^2R$.
4. $17ei$, $-14ei$, ei, $-4ei$.
5. $12iz$, $-iz$, $-6iz$, $8iz$.
6. $3a^2b + 6ab^2$, $-6a^2b + 2ab^2$.
7. $-6E - 4IX$, $10E + 2IX$.
8. $-9a^3b + 6a^2b^2 - 5ab^3$, $14a^3b + 6a^2b^2 - 5ab^3$, $a^3b - 3a^2b^2 - a^3b$.
9. $2(R + r)$, $-6(R + r)$, $6(R + r)$.
10. $13xyz^2 - 12xyz$, $-3xyz^2 + 18xyz$, $6xyz^2 - 6xyz$.
11. $2x - 2y + z$, $x - 2y - 3z$.
12. $4x - 3a - 3c - 11$, $2a - 3x + 4c$
13. $x^2 - 7x - 10$, $14x - 8 + 3x^2$.
14. $x^2 + 5x - 6$, $8x^2 - 4$.
15. $2c^4 - 3a^2c^2 - 4a^2$, $a^4 + a^2c^2 + c^4$.
16. $3x - 3y - 3z$, $6z + 4x - 9y$, $5x - 5y$.
17. $7c - 2a + 10$, $c - a - 2x - 11$, $a - x - 3c$, $4 - 7 + 3a$.
18. $6d - 12a + 7(b - c)$, $11a - 5(b - c)$, $2(b - c) - a + d$.
19. $r + 3\sqrt{R^2 + X^2}$, $6\sqrt{R^2 + X^2} + Z - r$, $6 - \sqrt{R^2 + X^2} + 3Z + 4r$.
20. $-3(x - y) + 6$, $10a - 5 + 4(x - y)$, $a - 3(x - y) + z$.

Simplify by uniting like terms:

21. $5IR + E - 6IX - 3IR + 2IX - 3IR + 8E - 6 + 9IR$.
22. $3W + EI - W + 6I^2R - 3 + 2W - 8I^2R + 4 + W - 10EI + I^2R$.
23. $8x - 5x^2 + 2x^2 - 3x - 4x + 3$.
24. $2.5xy - 0.6x + 3.04xy - 1.2x + 8.3x$.
25. $\frac{1}{4}y^3 + \frac{1}{2}x - \frac{3}{10}x + \frac{7}{10}y^3 + \frac{2}{5}x$.
26. From $4IX + 6E$, subtract $10E - 21IX$.

27. From $-8xy + 3ab$, subtract $6xy - 14ab$.

28. From $6\sqrt{R^2 + X^2} + r - Z$, subtract $3Z - 5r + 9\sqrt{R^2 + X^2}$.

29. From $16Ix + 2E - 10IR$, subtract $-3E + 8IR + 6Ix$.

30. From $2W + 4EI - 13I^2R$, subtract $-14I^2R - 4W + 8EI$.

31. From the sum of $1 + a^3 - a^2 - a$ and $3a - 3a^2 + 1 - a^3$, subtract $2 + 3a^3 - a^2 + 4a$.

32. By how much does $36x^2 + 3y^2 - 21xy$ exceed $9y^2 - 2xy + 16x^2$?

33. By how much does 0 exceed $x^2 - y^2$?

34. By how much does 1 exceed $a^3 - 4ab + b^2$?

35. Subtract $\frac{1}{3}p + \frac{2}{5}q - \frac{3}{4}s$ from $\frac{1}{2}s - \frac{1}{6}p + \frac{1}{10}q$.

36. Subtract $2e + 3ir - 8iz$ from the sum of $4iz - 6e + ir$ and $8ir - 6e - 7iz$.

37. Take $3.4a^2 + 6.02ab - 0.01b^2$ from $0.002b^2 - 2.1a^2 + 4.68ab$.

38. Subtract the sum of $W - I^2R - 6.2EI$ and $7I^2R + 9EI - 8W$ from $8EI - 2W + 11I^2R$.

39. Subtract $\frac{1}{4}e - \frac{1}{2}ir - \frac{2}{5}ix$ from the sum of $\frac{2}{3}ir + \frac{1}{10}ix - e$ and $-\frac{3}{10}ix + \frac{5}{8}e - \frac{1}{3}ir$.

40. From $0.0025t + 60.02s^2 - 3.46u$, subtract $8.63u - 3.09s^2 + 0.0036t$.

3-8. Signs of Grouping.

Often it is necessary to express, or group together, quantities that are to be affected by the same operation. Also, it is desirable to be able to represent that two or more terms are to be considered as one quantity.

In order to meet the above requirements, signs of grouping have been adopted. These signs are the *parentheses* ( ), the *brackets* [ ], the *braces* { }, and the *vinculum* ———. The first three are placed around the terms to be grouped, as $(E - IR)$, $[a + 3b]$, and $\{x^2 + 4y\}$. All have the same meaning, that the enclosed terms are to be considered as one quantity.

Thus, $16 - (12 - 6)$ means that the quantity $(12 - 6)$ is to be subtracted from 16. That is, 6 is to be subtracted from 12, and then the remainder 6 is to be subtracted from 16 to give a final remainder of 10. In like manner, $E - (IR + e)$ means that the sum of $IR + e$ is to be subtracted from E.

The student should carefully note that the sign preceding a sign of grouping, as the minus sign between E and $(IR + e)$ above, is a sign of operation and does not denote that $(IR + e)$ is a negative quantity.

The vinculum is used mainly with radical signs and fractions, as $\sqrt{7245}$ and $\dfrac{a + b}{x - y}.$ In the latter case the vinculum denotes the division of $a + b$ by $x - y$, in addition to grouping the terms in the numerator and denominator.   When studying later chapters, many mistakes will be avoided by remembering that *the vinculum is a sign of grouping*.

In working problems involving signs of grouping, the operations within the signs of grouping should be performed first.

Example 1. $a + (b + c) = ?$

Solution: This means, "What result will be obtained when the sum of $b + c$ is added to a?"   Because both b and c are denoted as positive, it follows that we may write

$$a + (b + c) = a + b + c$$

because it makes no difference in which order we add.

Example 2. $a + (b - c) = ?$

Solution: This means, "What result will be obtained when the difference of $b - c$ is added to a?"   Again, because it makes no difference in which order we add, we may write

$$a + (b - c) = a + b - c$$

Example 3. $a - (b + c) = ?$

Solution: Here the sum of $b + c$ is to be subtracted from a.   This is the same as if we first subtract b from a and from this remainder subtract c. Therefore,

$$a - (b + c) = a - b - c$$

or, because this is subtraction, we could change the signs and add algebraically, remembering that b and c are denoted as positive, as shown below.

$$\begin{array}{r} a \\ b + c \\ \hline a - b - c \end{array}$$

Example 4. $a - (-b - c) = ?$

Solution: This means that the quantity $-b - c$ is to be subtracted from a. Performing this subtraction, we obtain

$$\begin{array}{r} a \\ -b - c \\ \hline a + b + c \end{array}$$

Therefore, $a - (-b - c) = a + b + c$

A study of the foregoing examples enables us to set up the following:

Rule : 1. *Parentheses or other signs of grouping preceded by a plus sign may be removed without any other change.*

·2. *To remove parentheses or other signs of grouping preceded by a minus sign, change the sign of every term that was included in the sign of grouping.*

Although not apparent in the examples, another rule may be added as follows:

3. *If parentheses or other signs of grouping occur one within another, remove the inner grouping first.*

Examples. $(x + y) + (2x - 3y) = x + y + 2x - 3y = 3x - 2y$

$$3a - \overline{2b + c} - a = 3a - 2b - c - a = 2a - 2b - c$$

$$10x - (-3x - 4y) + 2y = 10x + 3x + 4y + 2y = 13x + 6y$$

$$x - [2x + 3y - (3x - y) - 4x] = x - [2x + 3y - 3x + y - 4x]$$
$$= x - 2x - 3y + 3x - y + 4x$$
$$= 6x - 4y$$

PROBLEMS 3-4

Simplify by removing signs of grouping and combining similar terms:

1. $(3x + 4y - 3z) - (2y + 5x - 2z)$.

2. $(2x^2 - 5xy) - \overline{-6xy - x^2}$.

3. $-(ab - b^2 + a^2) + (2a^2 - 3b^2 - 4ab)$.

4. $(-9a + 2b) - (-16b + 10a - 4b)$.

5. $x - y + z - \underline{x - y + z} - (-y - z + x)$.

6. $5x + [2x + 4y - (6y - 3x)]$.

7. $3p - 2q \sim (3q + 8p - \overline{7p + q} + 10q)$.

8. $x - \{x - [x - (2x - x)]\}$.

9. $x + y - \{x - y + [x + y - (x - y)]\}$.

10. $a^3 - b^3 + 3ab^2 - 3a^2b - (a^3 + b^3 - 2a^2b - 4ab^2)$.

11. $-\{e - [e + \underline{ir - e} - (ir - e) - e] - 2e\}$.

12. $8ei - [16w - \underline{3ei - (12w - ei) - 8w} + ei]$.

13. $\frac{1}{2}x - (\frac{2}{3}y - \frac{1}{2}z) - \{x - [\frac{1}{2}x - (\frac{1}{3}y - \frac{1}{4}z)] - (\frac{2}{3}y - \frac{1}{2}z)\}$.

14. $-2E - [3IR + (3e - \overline{4e + 3IR + 2E})]$.

15. $-[-(-\underline{a + b} - x)] + \{-[-(x + a - b)]\}$.

3-9. Inserting Signs of Grouping.

To enclose terms within signs of grouping preceded by a plus sign, rewrite the terms without changing their signs.

Example 1. $a + b - c + d = a + (b - c + d)$

To enclose terms within signs of grouping preceded by a minus sign, rewrite the terms changing the signs of the terms enclosed.

Example 2. $a + b - c + d = a + b - (c - d)$

No difficulty need be encountered when inserting signs of grouping because, by removing the signs of grouping from the result, the original expression should be obtained.

Example 3. $x - 3y + z = x - (3y - z) = x - 3y + z$

PROBLEMS 3-5

Enclose the last three terms of the following expressions in parentheses preceded by a plus sign:

1. $a + b - c + d$.

2. $e + E - ir - ix$.

3. $\dfrac{E}{R} + \dfrac{e}{z} + 3I - 2i$.

4. $\dfrac{E^2}{R} - i^2 r + 6EI - 5W$.

5. $\omega L - \dfrac{1}{\omega C} - X + Z$.

6. $Z^2 + R^2 - 2RX + X^2$.

7. $y^2 - x^2 + 2xy - y^2$.

8. $p - q - r - s$.

9. $\dfrac{1}{\omega C} - \omega L + 2\omega M - X$.

10. $a - y + b - c$.

11. Write the amount by which E is greater than $(e - IR)$.

12. Write the amount by which P exceeds $(I^2 R + EI)$.

13. The sum of two numbers is 65; the larger is x. Express the smaller number.

14. Write the larger part of $10e$ if $(E + 3IR)$ is the smaller part.

15. Write the smaller part of $12ei$ if $(4P + I^2 R)$ is the larger part.

16. The difference between two numbers is 16; the smaller is p. Express the larger.

CHAPTER IV

MULTIPLICATION

Multiplication is often defined as the *process of continued addition.* Thus, 2×3 may be thought of as adding 2 three times, or $2 + 2 + 2 = 6$.

Considering multiplication as a shortened form of addition is not satisfactory, however, when the multiplier is a fraction. For example, it would not be sensible to say that $5 \times \frac{2}{7}$ was adding 5 two-sevenths of a time. This problem could be rewritten as $\frac{2}{7} \times 5$ which would be the same as adding $\frac{2}{7}$ five times. But this is only a temporary help; for if two fractions are to be multiplied together, as $\frac{3}{4} \times \frac{5}{6}$, the original definition of multiplication will not apply. However, the definition has been extended to include such cases, and the product of $5 \times \frac{2}{7}$ is taken to mean 5 multiplied by 2 and this product divided by 7; that is, by $5 \times \frac{2}{7}$ is meant $\dfrac{5 \times 2}{7}$.

Also, $$\frac{3}{4} \times \frac{5}{6} = \frac{3 \times 5}{4 \times 6} = \frac{15}{24}$$

4-1. Multiplication of Positive and Negative Numbers. Because we are now dealing with both positive and negative numbers, it becomes necessary to determine what sign the product will have when combinations of these numbers are multiplied.

When two numbers only are to be multiplied there can be but four possible combinations of signs, as follows:

(1) $\qquad\qquad (+2) \times (+3) = ?$
(2) $\qquad\qquad (-2) \times (+3) = ?$
(3) $\qquad\qquad (+2) \times (-3) = ?$
(4) $\qquad\qquad (-2) \times (-3) = ?$

(1) means that $+2$ is to be added three times:

$$(+2) + (+2) + (+2) = +6$$
or $\qquad\qquad (+2) \times (+3) = +6$

In the same manner, (2) means that -2 is to be added three times:

$$(-2) + (-2) + (-2) = -6$$

or
$$(-2) \times (+3) = -6$$

(3) means that $+2$ is to be subtracted three times:

$$-(+2) - (+2) - (+2) = -6$$

or
$$(+2) \times (-3) = -6$$

Note that this is the same as subtracting 6 once, -6 being thus obtained.

(4) means that -2 is to be subtracted three times:

$$-(-2) - (-2) - (-2) = +6$$
$$(-2) \times (-3) = +6$$

or

This may be considered to be the same as subtracting -6 once; and because subtracting -6 once is the same as adding $+6$, we obtain $+6$ as above.

From the foregoing we have these rules:

Rules: 1. *The product of two numbers having like signs is positive.*

2. *The product of two numbers having unlike signs is negative.*

3. *If more than two factors are multiplied, the foregoing rules are to be used successively.*

4. *The product of an even number of negative factors is positive. The product of an odd number of negative factors is negative.*

These rules may be summarized in general terms as follows:

(1) $\qquad (+a)(+b) = +ab$

(1) $\qquad (-a)(-b) = +ab$

(2) $\qquad (+a)(-b) = -ab$

(2) $\qquad (-a)(+b) = -ab$

(3) $\qquad (-a)(+b)(-c) = +abc$

(4) $\qquad (-a)(-b)(-c)(-d) = +abcd$

(4) $\qquad (-a)(-b)(-c) = -abc$

PROBLEMS 4-1

Find the products of the following:

1. $5, -4.$

2. $-6, 3.$

3. $-6.4, 2.8.$

4. $-\frac{2}{3}, -\frac{3}{5}.$

5. $3, -6, 4.$

6. $3.01, -0.02, -1.26.$

7. $-\frac{3}{2}, -\frac{6}{7}, -\frac{2}{5}.$

8. $-4, -7, -1, -\frac{1}{2}.$

9. $\frac{2}{3}, -\frac{1}{6}, -\frac{3}{5}, \frac{3}{8}.$

10. $-0.0025, 150, -0.10, 0.075.$

11. $-x, -y, z.$

12. $-p, q, r, -s, t.$

13. $a^2, -b^2, -c.$

14. $-\frac{1}{\omega}, \frac{1}{c}.$

15. $\frac{1}{a}, -\frac{1}{b}, \frac{1}{d}, -\frac{1}{c}, -\frac{1}{c}.$

4-2. Graphical Representation. Our system of representing numbers is a graphical one, as illustrated in Fig. 3-2. It might be well at this time to consider certain facts regarding multiplication.

When a number is multiplied by any other number, except 1, we may think of the operation as having changed the absolute value of the multiplicand. Thus, 3 inches $\times$ 4 becomes 12 inches, 6 amperes $\times$ 3 becomes 18 amperes, etc. Such multiplications could be represented graphically by simply extending the multiplicand the proper amount, as shown in Fig. 4-1.

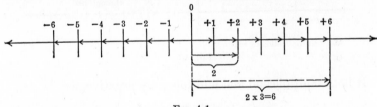

Fig. 4-1.

The case of multiplying a negative number by a positive number is shown in Fig. 4-2.

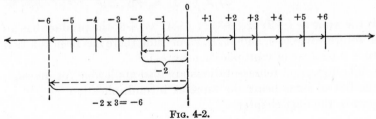

Fig. 4-2.

From these examples, it is evident that a positive multiplier simply changes the absolute value, or magnitude, of the number being multiplied. What happens if the multiplier is negative? As an example, consider the case of $2 \times (-3) = -6$. How shall this be represented graphically?

Now, $2 \times (-3) = -6$ is the same as

$$2 \times (+3) \times (-1) = -6$$

Therefore, let us first multiply 2×3 to obtain $+6$ and represent it as shown in Fig. 4-1. We must multiply by -1 to complete the problem and in so doing should obtain -6; but -6 must be represented as a number 6 units in length and directed toward the left, as illustrated in Fig. 4-2. We therefore agree that multiplication by -1 rotates a number so that it will be directed oppositely from its original direction. This is illustrated in Fig. 4-3.

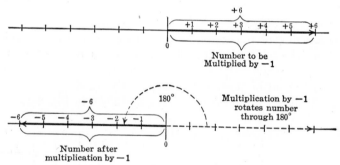

FIG. 4-3.

If both multiplicand and multiplier are negative, as

$$(-2) \times (-3) = +6$$

the representation is as illustrated in Fig. 4-4. Again,

$$(-2) \times (-3) = +6$$

is the same as $(-2) \times (+3) \times (-1) = +6$; the product has an absolute value of 6, and at the same time there has been rotation to $+6$ because of multiplication by -1.

The foregoing representations are also applicable for division, the law of signs being the same as in multiplication, as will be seen in the next chapter.

The important thing to bear in mind is that multiplication or division by -1 causes rotation of a number to an exactly opposite direction from its original direction.   The number -1, when used as a multiplier or divisor, should be considered as an *operator* for the purpose of rotation.   It is important that the student clearly understand this concept, for he will encounter it later on.

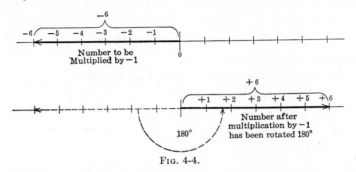

FIG. 4-4.

4-3. Law of Exponents in Multiplication.   As explained in Art. 2-8, an exponent indicates how many times a number is to be taken as a factor.   Thus $x^4 = x \cdot x \cdot x \cdot x$, $a^3 = a \cdot a \cdot a$, etc.

Because $x^4 = x \cdot x \cdot x \cdot x$
and $x^3 = x \cdot x \cdot x$
then $x^4 \cdot x^3 = x \cdot x \cdot x \cdot x \cdot x \cdot x \cdot x = x^7$
or $x^4 \cdot x^3 = x^{4+3} = x^7$

Thus, we have the rule:

Rule: *To find the product of two or more powers having the same base, add the exponents.*

Examples.
$$a^3 \cdot a^2 = a^{3+2} = a^5$$
$$x^4 \cdot x^4 = x^{4+4} = x^8$$
$$6^2 \cdot 6^3 \cdot 6^5 = 6^{2+3+5} = 6^{10}$$
$$a^2 \cdot b^3 \cdot b^3 \cdot a^5 = a^{2+5} \cdot b^{3+3} = a^7 b^6$$
$$e \cdot e^3 = e^{1+3} = e^4$$
$$3^2 \cdot 3^4 = 3^{2+4} = 3^6$$
$$e^a \cdot e^b = e^{a+b}$$

From the foregoing examples, it is seen that the law of exponents may be expressed in the well-known general form

$$a^m \cdot a^n = a^{m+n}$$

where $a \neq 0$ and m and n are literal numbers and may represent any number of factors.

4-4. Multiplication of Monomials.

Rule: 1. *Find the product of the numerical coefficients, giving it the proper sign, plus or minus, according to the rules for multiplication.* (Art. 4-1.)

2. *Multiply this numerical product by the product of the literal factors, using the law of exponents as applicable.*

Example 1.   Multiply $3a^2b$ by $4ab^3$.

Solution: $(3a^2b)(4ab^3) = +(3 \cdot 4) \cdot a^{2+1} \cdot b^{1+3}$
$$= 12a^3b^4$$

Example 2.   Multiply $-6x^3y^2$ by $3xy^2$.

Solution: $(-6x^3y^2)(3xy^2) = -(6 \cdot 3) \cdot x^{3+1} \cdot y^{2+2}$
$$= -18x^4y^4$$

Example 3.   Multiply $-5e^2x^4y$ by $-3e^2x^2p$.

Solution: $(-5e^2x^4y)(-3e^2x^2p) = +(5 \cdot 3)e^{2+2} \cdot p \cdot x^{4+2} \cdot y$
$$= 15e^4px^6y$$

PROBLEMS 4-2

Find the product of the following:

1. $x^3 \cdot x^5$.

2. $-a^2 \cdot a^3$.

3. $b \cdot b^3 \cdot b^6$.

4. $-r^2 \cdot r^3 \cdot (-r) \cdot r^4$.

5. $(2x^2)(7x)$.

6. $(-6a^2x)(2a^3)$.

7. $(3x)(-6x^3)$.

8. $(10b)(-9)$.

9. $(-a)^2$.

10. $(5a^4)(-6x^3)$.

11. $(13b^a)(-2b^n)$.

12. $(3a^2b)^2$.

13. $(4e^3)(-2x^2y)$.

14. $(-5a^3b^2cd^4)(-3abc^3d^2x)$.

15. $(2ay^2)^3$.

16. $(\frac{1}{2}a^2b)(-\frac{2}{3}ab^3c)$.

17. $(0.5s^3t)(1.5st^2u)$.

18. $(10e^2r)(-\frac{2}{3}e^3r^2i)$.

19. $(-\frac{3}{2}abc)(\frac{1}{3}d)(-\frac{1}{3}a^2b^3e)$.

20. $(\frac{3}{8}p^2qr)(-\frac{2}{3}r^2s)(-4ps)$.

21. $(0.002x^2yz)(0.05xy)(-10,000y^2z)$.

22. $(10^3)(10^2)$.

23. $(10^2)^2$.

24. $(\frac{3}{4}IZ^2)(-\frac{2}{3}I)(-2ZR^2)$.

25. $(-3.5W^2)(2WX^2Y)(-XYZ)$.

26. $(14a^3b^2cd)(-\frac{3}{7}abc^2e)$.

27. $(20xyz^3)(\frac{3}{10}ax^2y)$.

28. $(-15c^2d^3e)(-\frac{6}{5}a^2b^3e^2f)$.

29. $(0.5e^2i)(5i^2x)(-0.05e^3xy)(10e^2y^3)$.

30. $(-\frac{3}{10}ad^2)(\frac{2}{3}c^2e)(-\frac{5}{2}a^2b^3)(2abc^2d^2e^3)$.

4-5. Multiplication of Polynomials by Monomials.   Another method of graphically representing the product of two numbers

is as shown in Fig. 4-5.   The product $5 \times 6 = 30$ is shown as a rectangle whose sides are 5 and 6 units in length; therefore, the rectangle contains 30 square units.

FIG. 4-5.

Similarly, the product of $5(6 + 9)$ may be represented as illustrated in Fig. 4-6.

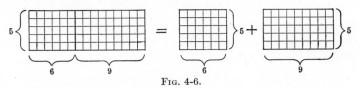

FIG. 4-6.

Thus, $5(6 + 9)$
$\quad = 5 \times 15$
$\quad = 75$

Also, $5(6 + 9)$
$\quad = (5 \times 6) + (5 \times 9)$
$\quad = 30 + 45$
$\quad = 75$

In like manner the product $a(c + d) = ac + ad$ may be illustrated as in Fig. 4-7.

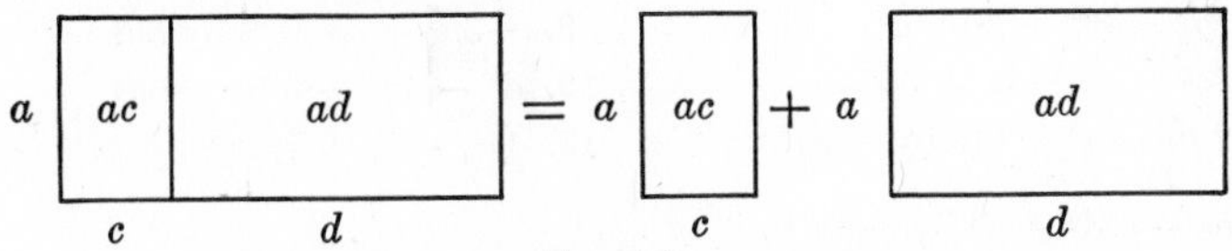

a | ac | ad | $= a$ | ac | $+ a$ | ad

$c \qquad\qquad d \qquad\qquad\qquad c \qquad\qquad\qquad d$

FIG. 4-7.

From the foregoing, the student may show that

(1) $3(4 + 2) = 3 \times 4 + 3 \times 2 = 12 + 6 = 18$
(2) $4(5 + 3 + 4) = 4 \times 5 + 4 \times 3 + 4 \times 4$
$\qquad\qquad\qquad\qquad = 20 + 12 + 16 = 48$
(3) $x(y + z) = xy + xz$
(4) $p(q + r + s) = pq + pr + ps$

Note that, in all cases, each term of the polynomial (the terms enclosed in parentheses) is multiplied by the monomial.   From these examples, we develop the following rule:

Rule: *To multiply a polynomial by a monomial, multiply each term of the polynomial by the monomial and write in succession the resulting terms with their proper signs.*

Example 1. $3x(3x^2y - 4xy^2 + 6y^3) = ?$
Solution: Multiplicand $= 3x^2y - 4xy^2 + 6y^3$
               Multiplier $= 3x$
               Product $= \overline{9x^3y - 12x^2y^2 + 18xy^3}$

Example 2. $-2ac(-10a^3 + 4a^2b - 5ab^2c + 7bc^2) = ?$
Solution: Multiplicand $= -10a^3 + 4a^2b - 5ab^2c + 7bc^2$
           Multiplier $= -2ac$
           Product $= \overline{20a^4c - 8a^3bc + 10a^2b^2c^2 - 14abc^3}$

Example 3. Simplify $5(2a - 3) - 3(a + 4)$.
Solution: First multiply $5(2a - 3)$ and $3(a + 4)$, and then subtract the second result from the first, thus:

$$5(2a - 3) - 3(a + 4) = (10a - 15) - (3a + 12)$$
$$= 10a - 15 - 3a - 12$$
$$= 7a - 27$$

PROBLEMS 4-3

Multiply:

1. $4 + jx$ by x.
2. $x^2 - 3$ by $2x$.
3. $R_1 + 2R_2$ by $3I$.
4. $2i^2 - 3I^2$ by $2R$.
5. $x^2 - 4y - 2$ by $4y$.
6. $2y^3 - 3y^2 + 4y - 3$ by y^3.
7. $5a^3 - 3a + 4$ by a^3.
8. $-3b^2 + 4b - 3$ by $5b^2$.
9. $2c^2 - 4c - 3$ by $5c^2$.
10. $d^3 - 4d^2 - 3$ by $-6d^4$.
11. $2y - 4y^2 - 3y^3$ by $-2y^3$.
12. $4jx - jy + 2jx^2y^2$ by jx.

13. $b^4 - b^2d^2 + d^4$ by $-b^2d^2$.
14. $-4r^2s + 2rs - 3s^2 - s^3$ by $-3ars$.
15. $-\dfrac{a^3b}{2} + \dfrac{2a^2b^2}{3} - \dfrac{4ab^3}{6}$ by $-\dfrac{ab}{2}$.
16. $\dfrac{a^2x}{3} - \dfrac{3ax^2}{2} + \dfrac{2x^3}{3}$ by $\dfrac{a^2x^2}{2}$.

Simplify:

17. $3(3x + 4y) + 4(2x + y)$.
18. $2(6a - 5b) - 3(a + 4b)$.
19. $s(a - jx) - s(a + jx)$.
20. $x(x^2 - y) + y(x - y^2)$.

21. $3a(4a - 2b + 3c) - 4(a^2 + ab - 2ac)$.
22. $4x(3x^2 + 2xy - 3y^2) - 2(6x^3 + 4x^2y - 6xy^2)$.

23. $4\left(\dfrac{a}{2} - \dfrac{b}{4} + \dfrac{c}{8}\right).$ **24.** $16\left(\dfrac{x}{4} + \dfrac{1}{8} - \dfrac{3x}{2}\right).$

25. $15\left(\dfrac{3b^2}{5} + \dfrac{b^2}{2} - \dfrac{2}{3}\right).$ **26.** $12\left(\dfrac{s}{3} - \dfrac{s}{2} + \dfrac{2s}{3}\right).$

27. $24\left(\dfrac{x^2}{6} + \dfrac{x^2}{4} - \dfrac{1}{3}\right).$ **28.** $\dfrac{1}{6}\,ax\,(6a^2 - 12ax - 24x^2).$

29. $-\frac{1}{3}x^2y(9x^3y - 3x^2y^2 + 6xy^3).$

30. $-\frac{1}{4}ab^2(8ab + 4ab^2 - 12b^3 - 4).$

4-6. Multiplication of a Polynomial by a Polynomial. It is apparent that

$$(3 + 4)(6 - 3) = 7 \times 3 = 21$$

The above multiplication may also be accomplished in the following manner:

$$\begin{aligned}
(3 + 4)(6 - 3) &= 3(6 - 3) + 4(6 - 3) \\
&= (18 - 9) + (24 - 12) \\
&= 9 + 12 \\
&= 21
\end{aligned}$$

Similarly,

$$\begin{aligned}
(2a - 3b)(a + 5b) &= 2a(a + 5b) - 3b(a + 5b) \\
&= (2a^2 + 10ab) - (3ab + 15b^2) \\
&= 2a^2 + 10ab - 3ab - 15b^2 \\
&= 2a^2 + 7ab - 15b^2
\end{aligned}$$

From the foregoing, we have this rule:

Rule: *To multiply polynomials, multiply every term of the multiplicand by each term of the multiplier, and add the partial products.*

Example 1.   Multiply $2a - 3$ by $a + 2$.

Solution:

Multiplicand	$= 2a - 3$
Multiplier	$= \underline{a + 2}$
a times $(2a - 3) =$	$2a^2 - 3a$
2 times $(2a - 3) =$	$\underline{\qquad 4a - 6}$

Adding,   Product $= 2a^2 + a - 6$

Example 2.   Multiply $a^2 - 3ab + 2b^2$ by $2a^2 - 3b^2$.

Solution:

Multiplicand	$=$	$a^2 - 3ab + 2b^2$
Multiplier	$=$	$2a^2 - 3b^2$
$2a^2$ times $(a^2 - 3ab + 2b^2)$	$=$	$2a^4 - 6a^3b + 4a^2b^2$
$-3b^2$ times $(a^2 - 3ab + 2b^2)$	$=$	$\qquad\qquad - 3a^2b^2 + 9ab^3 - 6b^4$

Adding,

Product	$=$	$2a^4 - 6a^3b + a^2b^2 + 9ab^3 - 6b^4$

Products obtained by multiplication can be tested by substituting any convenient numerical values for the literal numbers. It is not good practice to substitute the number 1; if there are exponents, the test will not be a proof of correct work, for 1 to any power is still 1.

Example. Multiply $a^2 - 4ab - b^2$ by $a + b$, and test by letting $a = 2$ and $b = 2$.

Solution:
$$\begin{array}{ll} a^2 - 4ab - b^2 & = 4 - 16 - 4 = -16 \\ \underline{a + b} & = 2 + 2 \qquad = \underline{\quad 4} \\ a^3 - 4a^2b - ab^2 & \qquad\qquad\quad = -64 \\ \underline{\quad a^2b - 4ab^2 - b^3} & \\ a^3 - 3a^2b - 5ab^2 - b^3 & = 8 - 24 - 40 - 8 = -64 \end{array}$$

PROBLEMS 4-4

Multiply:

1. $c + 1$ by $c + 1$.
2. $c - 1$ by $c - 1$.
3. $c + 1$ by $c - 1$.
4. $r + 2$ by $r + 2$.
5. $r - 2$ by $r - 2$.
6. $r + 2$ by $r - 2$.
7. $i + 2$ by $i + 3$.
8. $i + 3$ by $i - 2$.
9. $j + 5$ by $j - 7$.
10. $x - 8$ by $x - 9$.

NOTE: Parentheses or other signs of grouping are often used to indicate a product. Thus, $(x^2 + 2y)(x - y)$ means $(x^2 + 2y)$ times $(x - y)$.

Simplify:

11. $(a + 4)(a + 3)$.
12. $(4C + 7)(3C + 2)$.
13. $(3i - 5)(3i + 8)$.
14. $(3r - 2)(2r + 4)$.
15. $(6 - 3y)(5 - 4z)$.
16. $(2x + y)(x - 4y)$.
17. $(2a - 3b)(3a - 2b)$.
18. $(3b - 2)(2b - 6)$.
19. $(ax - bx)(cx + dx)$.
20. $(3a + 2b^2)(4a - b)$.
21. $(2a^2 - 6b)(5a - 3b^2)$.
22. $(3a^2 - 4x - 7)(a + 3)$.
23. $(x^2 - xy + y^2)(x + y)$.
24. $(a^2 + 2ab + b^2)(a + b)$.
25. $(a + b)(a + b)(a + b)$.
26. $(3a^2 - 5a - 1)(a + b)$.
27. $(a^2 - 2a + 1)(3a^2 + a - 2)$.
28. $(2a + b - 1)^2$.
29. $(3a^2 - 3x + 5)^2$.
30. $3(a^2 + 5ab - b^2)(a - b)$.
31. $(\tfrac{1}{3}x - \tfrac{1}{4}y)(\tfrac{1}{3}x - \tfrac{1}{4}y)$.
32. $(\tfrac{2}{3}a - \tfrac{3}{8}b)(\tfrac{2}{3}a - \tfrac{1}{8}b)$.

33. $(2m - \frac{1}{3}n)(m + \frac{1}{2}n)$.

34. $(3x + 7)(x - 5) + (2x - 3)(4x - 1)$.

35. $(2a - 7)(3a - 4) - (3a + 4)(a - 2)$.

36. $5(b - 3)(b + 1) - 3(b + 2)(b - 4)$.

37. $2(3y + 1)(4y - 5) - 4(2y - 2)(y + 3)$.

38. $(a + b)^2 - 2(a + 2b)(a - 3b)$.

39. $(x + y)(x^2 + y^2) - (x - y)(x^2 - y^2)$.

40. $3(2a - 3b - c)(5a + 2b - 4c) - (a + b - c)$.

CHAPTER V

DIVISION

The division of algebraic expressions requires the development of certain rules and new methods in connection with operations involving exponents. However, if the student has mastered the processes of the preceding chapter, algebraic division will be an easy subject.

For the purpose of review the following definitions are given:

1. The *dividend* is a number, or quantity, that is to be divided.

2. The *divisor* is a number by which a number, or quantity, is to be divided.

3. The *quotient* is the result obtained by division.

That is,
$$\frac{\text{Dividend}}{\text{Divisor}} = \text{quotient}$$

5-1. Division of Positive and Negative Numbers. Because division is the inverse of multiplication, the methods of the latter will serve as an aid in developing methods for division. For example,

because	$6 \times 4 = 24$
then	$24 \div 6 = 4$
and	$24 \div 4 = 6$

These relations can be used in applying the rules for multiplication to division.

All the possible cases may be represented as follows:

(1)	$(+24) \div (+6) = ?$
(2)	$(-24) \div (+6) = ?$
(3)	$(+24) \div (-6) = ?$
(4)	$(-24) \div (-6) = ?$

Because division is the inverse of multiplication, we apply the rules for multiplication of positive and negative numbers and obtain the following:

36

(1) $(+24) \div (+6) = +4$ because $(+4) \times (+6) = +24$
(2) $(-24) \div (+6) = -4$ because $(-4) \times (+6) = -24$
(3) $(+24) \div (-6) = -4$ because $(-4) \times (-6) = +24$
(4) $(-24) \div (-6) = +4$ because $(+4) \times (-6) = -24$

Therefore, we have the following:

Rule: *To divide positive and negative numbers,*
1. *If both numbers have like signs, the quotient is positive.*
2. *If both numbers have unlike signs, the quotient is negative.*

PROBLEMS 5-1

Divide the first number by the second in Probs. 1 to 10:

1. $6, -3$.   **2.** $-16, 4$.   **3.** $-20, -5$.

4. $36, 4$.   **5.** $-5.6, -0.008$.   **6.** $\frac{1}{3}, -\frac{1}{2}$.

7. $-\frac{5}{7}, \frac{3}{4}$.   **8.** $-a, -b^2$.   **9.** $xy, -36$.

10. $1, -\omega c$.

Supply the missing divisors:

11. $-\dfrac{16}{?} = 4$.   **12.** $\dfrac{32}{?} = -8$.   **13.** $\dfrac{50}{?} = \dfrac{1}{2}$.

14. $-\dfrac{64}{?} = -\dfrac{1}{4}$.   **15.** $-\dfrac{27}{?} = \dfrac{1}{3}$.

5-2. The Law of Exponents in Division.   By previous definition of an exponent (Art. 2-8),

$$x^6 = x \cdot x \cdot x \cdot x \cdot x \cdot x$$

and

$$x^3 = x \cdot x \cdot x$$

Then,

$$x^6 \div x^3 = \frac{x^6}{x^3} = \frac{\not{x} \cdot \not{x} \cdot \not{x} \cdot x \cdot x \cdot x}{\not{x} \cdot \not{x} \cdot \not{x}} = x^3$$

This result is obtained by canceling common factors in numerator and denominator.   The above could be expressed as

$$x^6 \div x^3 = \frac{x^6}{x^3} = x^{6-3} = x^3$$

In like manner,

$$\frac{a^7}{a^3} = a^{7-3} = a^4$$

From the foregoing, it is seen that the law of exponents may be expressed in the general form

$$a^m \div a^n = \frac{a^m}{a^n} = a^{m-n}$$

where $a \neq 0$ and m and n are general numbers.

5-3. The Zero Exponent. Any number, except zero, divided by itself results in a quotient of 1. Thus,

$$\frac{6}{6} = 1$$

Also, $$\frac{a^3}{a^3} = 1$$

Therefore, $$\frac{a^3}{a^3} = a^{3-3} = a^0 = 1$$

Then, in the general form, $\dfrac{a^m}{a^n} = a^{m-n}$

If $$m = n$$
then $$m - n = 0$$
and $$\frac{a^m}{a^n} = a^{m-n} = a^0 = 1$$

The foregoing leads to the definition that *any base, except zero, affected by zero exponent is equal to 1.* Thus, a^0, x^0, y^0, 3^0, 4^0, etc., all equal 1.

5-4. The Negative Exponent. If the law of exponents in division is to apply to all cases, it must apply when n is greater than m. Thus,

$$\frac{a^2}{a^5} = \frac{\cancel{a} \cdot \cancel{a}}{\cancel{a} \cdot \cancel{a} \cdot a \cdot a \cdot a} = \frac{1}{a^3}$$

or $$\frac{a^2}{a^5} = a^{2-5} = a^{-3}$$

Therefore, $$a^{-3} = \frac{1}{a^3}$$

Also, $$a^{-n} = \frac{1}{a^n}$$

This leads to the definition that *any base affected by a negative exponent is the same as 1 divided by that same base but affected by a positive exponent of the same absolute value as the negative exponent.*

Examples. $$x^{-4} = \frac{1}{x^4}$$
$$2^{-2} = \frac{1}{2^2} = \frac{1}{4}$$
$$3^{-3} = \frac{1}{3^3} = \frac{1}{27}$$
$$\frac{4^3}{4^5} = \frac{\cancel{4} \times \cancel{4} \times \cancel{4}}{\cancel{4} \times \cancel{4} \times \cancel{4} \times 4 \times 4} = \frac{1}{4 \times 4} = \frac{1}{4^2} = 4^{-2}$$

or $$\frac{4^3}{4^5} = 4^{3-5} = 4^{-2}$$

It follows, from the consideration of negative exponents, that *any* **factor** *of an algebraic term may be transferred from numerator to denominator, or vice versa, by changing the sign of the exponent of the* **factor.**

Example. $$3a^2x^3 = \frac{3a^2}{x^{-3}} = \frac{3}{a^{-2}x^{-3}} = \frac{3x^3}{a^{-2}}$$

5-5. Division of One Monomial by Another.

Rule : *To divide one monomial by another,*

1. *Find the quotient of the absolute values of the numerical coefficients, affixing the proper sign according to the rules for division of positive and negative numbers.* (Art. 5-1.)

2. *Determine the literal coefficients with their proper exponents, and write them after the numerical coefficient found in 1 above.*

Example 1. Divide $-12a^3x^4y$ by $4a^2x^2y$.

Solution: $$\frac{-12a^3x^4y}{4a^2x^2y} = -3ax^2$$

Example 2. Divide $-7a^2b^4c$ by $-14ab^2c^3$. Express the quotient with positive exponents.

Solution: $$\frac{-7a^2b^4c}{-14ab^2c^3} = \frac{ab^2}{2c^2}$$

Example 3. Divide $15a^{-2}b^2c^3d^{-4}$ by $-5a^2bc^{-1}d^{-2}$. Express the quotient with positive exponents.

Solution: $$\frac{15a^{-2}b^2c^3d^{-4}}{-5a^2bc^{-1}d^{-2}} = -\frac{3bc^4}{a^4d^2}$$

Division may be checked by substituting convenient numerical values for the literal factors or by multiplying the divisor by the quotient, the product of which should result in the dividend.

PROBLEMS 5-2

Divide:

1. $-15xy^2$ by $5xy$.

2. $-24x^4y^2z$ by $-8x^4y^2$.

3. $28a^2b^4c^3$ by $-7b^3c^3$.

4. $144m^4n^3p^8$ by $-12m^2n^3p^5$.

5. $-16e^3i^2r^5$ by $-4e^2i^2r^3$.

6. $10a^8b^6c^3d^2$ by $5a^7b^6c^2d^2$.

7. $14x^{10}y^2z^7$ by $-7x^8yz^6$.

8. $-18c^9d^2e^3$ by $-2c^8d^2e^2$.

9. $-26p^4q^2r^5$ by $-2p^4qr^4$.

10. $-33a^3b^4cd^2$ by $11a^2b^2cd$.

Simplify, expressing literal factors with positive exponents:

11. $\dfrac{-16a^3b^2cd}{4ab^2c}.$ 　　**12.** $\dfrac{10x^2y^4z}{-5x^4y^2z}.$

13. $\dfrac{-4r^2s^3t^5}{-8r^4st^6}.$ 　　**14.** $\dfrac{a^2b^3cd^4}{3a^4b^3cd^5}.$

15. $\dfrac{11e^4i^2r^8}{-44e^3ir^9}.$ 　　**16.** $\dfrac{-9a^{-2}b^4c^{-3}d^2}{-27a^{-2}b^{-3}c^2d^2}.$

17. $\dfrac{-42w^{-2}x^3y^5z^{-3}}{14w^2x^2y^{-1}z^{-3}}.$ 　　**18.** $\dfrac{-21r^{-1}s^2t^4u^{-6}}{-63r^{-2}s^2t^{-4}u^{-5}}.$

19. $\dfrac{13a^4b^{-6}cd^{-1}}{-52a^{-4}b^6cd}.$ 　　**20.** $\dfrac{-105x^3y^2z^{-8}}{15x^7y^{-2}z}.$

5-6. Division of a Polynomial by a Monomial.

Because 　　　　　　　$2 \times 8 = 16$

then 　　　　　　　$\dfrac{16}{2} = 8$

Also, because 　　　$3(a + 4) = 3a + 12$

then 　　　　　　　$\dfrac{3a + 12}{3} = a + 4$

Similarly, because 　$3x(2x + 3y) = 6x^2 + 9xy$

then 　　　　　　　$\dfrac{6x^2 + 9xy}{3x} = 2x + 3y$

From the foregoing, we have the following:

Rule: *To divide a polynomial by a monomial,*
1. Divide each term of the dividend by the divisor.
2. Unite the results with the proper signs obtained by the division.

Example 1. Divide $8a^2b^3c - 12a^3b^2c^2 + 4a^2b^2c$ by $4a^2b^2c$.

Solution: $\dfrac{8a^2b^3c - 12a^3b^2c^2 + 4a^2b^2c}{4a^2b^2c} = 2b - 3ac + 1$

Example 2. Divide $-27x^3y^2z^5 + 3x^4y^2z^4 - 9x^4y^3z^5$ by $-3x^3y^2z^4$.

Solution: $\dfrac{-27x^3y^2z^5 + 3x^4y^2z^4 - 9x^4y^3z^5}{-3x^3y^2z^4} = 9z - x + 3xyz$

PROBLEMS 5-3

Divide:

1. $4x - 6y$ by 2. 　　　　　**2.** $12a - 6b$ by 3.

3. $16m^2 - 12n^2$ by 4. 　　　**4.** $20z - 10z^2$ by $5z$.

5. $a^6 - a^4 + a^2$ by a^2. 　　　**6.** $x^3yz^2 - x^2y^3 + x^2yz^2$ by x^2y.

7. $am^4 - bm^3 + cm^2$ by $-m^2$. 　**8.** $4a^4b - 8a^6b^2 + 12a^8b^4$ by $4a^4b$.

9. $15r^2s^2 + 9r^4s^3 - 30r^6s^4$ by $-3r^2s^2$.

10. $102abc + 170a^2bc^2 - 85a^3bc^3 - 51a^5b^5c$ by $17abc$.

11. $\frac{1}{3}r^3s^2t - \frac{5}{6}rs^3t^2 + \frac{2}{3}rs^2t^3$ by $-\frac{1}{3}rst$.

12. $20x^8y^5 - 35x^4y^3 - 30x^4y^9$ by $-5x^4y^3$.

13. $\frac{3}{20}m^{10} - \frac{7}{10}m^8 + \frac{3}{8}m^6 + \frac{1}{4}m^4 - \frac{1}{2}m^2$ by $\frac{1}{2}m^2$.

14. $3(a + b) + c(a + b)$ by $(a + b)$.

15. $4(x + 1) + 2x(x + 1)$ by $(x + 1)$.

16. $R(I + i) - r(I + i)$ by $(I + i)$.

17. $I(R + r)^2 + i(R + r)^2$ by $(R + r)^2$.

18. $6(c + d)^4 - a(c + d)^2$ by $(c + d)^2$.

19. $a(x^2 - y^2)^2 - b(x^2 - y^2)^2$ by $-(x^2 - y^2)^2$.

20. $4(a + b)(a - b) - 2(a - b)(a + b)$ by $2(a - b)$.

5-7. Division of One Polynomial by Another.

Rule: *To divide one polynomial by another,*

1. Arrange the dividend and divisor in ascending or descending powers of some common literal factor.

2. Divide the first term of the dividend by the first term of the divisor, and write the result as the first term of the quotient.

3. Multiply the entire divisor by the first term of the quotient, write the product under the proper terms of the dividend, and subtract it from the dividend.

4. Consider the remainder a new dividend, and repeat 1, 2, and 3 until there is no remainder, or until there is a remainder that cannot be divided by the divisor.

Example 1.   Divide $x^2 + 5x + 6$ by $x + 2$.

Solution:

$$
\begin{array}{r|l}
\text{Dividend} = x^2 + 5x + 6 & x + 2 = \text{divisor} \\
\phantom{\text{Dividend} = }x^2 + 2x & x + 3 = \text{quotient} \\
\hline
\phantom{\text{Dividend} = x^2}3x + 6 & \\
\phantom{\text{Dividend} = x^2}3x + 6 &
\end{array}
$$

x, the first term of the divisor, divides into x^2, the first term of the dividend, x times. Therefore, x is written as the first term of the quotient. The product of the first term of the quotient and the divisor ($x^2 + 2x$) is then written under like terms in the dividend and subtracted. The first term of the remainder then serves as a new dividend, and the process of division is continued.

This result may be checked by multiplying the divisor by the quotient.

$$
\begin{array}{rl}
\text{Divisor} & = x + 2 \\
\text{Quotient} & = x + 3 \\
\hline
& x^2 + 2x \\
& 3x + 6 \\
\hline
\text{Dividend} & = x^2 + 5x + 6
\end{array}
$$

Example 2.　Divide $a^2b^2 + a^4 + b^4$ by $-ab + b^2 + a^2$.

Solution: First arrange the dividend and divisor according to step 1 of the rule. Because there are no a^3b or ab^3 terms, allowance is made for them by supplying 0 terms. Thus,

$$
\begin{array}{l}
a^4 + 0 + a^2b^2 + 0 + b^4 \,\big|\, a^2 - ab + b^2 = \text{divisor} \\
\underline{a^4 - a^3b + a^2b^2} \qquad\;\; \big|\underline{\,a^2 + ab + b^2\,} = \text{quotient} \\
\qquad a^3b \\
\qquad \underline{a^3b - a^2b^2 + ab^3} \\
\qquad\qquad a^2b^2 - ab^3 + b^4 \\
\qquad\qquad \underline{a^2b^2 - ab^3 + b^4}
\end{array}
$$

Example 3.　Divide $x^4 + 3x^2 + 4$ by $x^2 - 2$.

Solution:

$$
\begin{array}{l}
x^4 + 3x^2 + 4 \,\big|\, x^2 - 2 = \text{divisor} \\
\underline{x^4 - 2x^2} \qquad\;\; \big|\underline{\,x^2 + 5\,} = \text{quotient} \\
\qquad 5x^2 + 4 \\
\qquad \underline{5x^2 - 10} \\
\qquad\qquad 14 = \text{remainder}
\end{array}
$$

This result is written $x^2 + 5 + \dfrac{14}{x^2 - 2}$, which is as it would be written in an arithmetical division that did not divide out evenly.

PROBLEMS 5-4

Divide:

1. $x^2 + 3x + 2$ by $x + 1$.
2. $a^2 - 7a + 12$ by $a - 3$.
3. $x^2 - 11x + 30$ by $x - 5$.
4. $b^2 - 49b + 600$ by $b - 25$.
5. $3t^2 + 10t + 3$ by $t + 3$.
6. $2a^2 + 11a + 5$ by $1 + 2a$.
7. $100n^3 - 13n^2 - 3n$ by $3 + 25n$.
8. $6b^2 - 7b - 3$ by $2b - 3$.
9. $21t^2 + 24s^2 - 65st$ by $8s - 3t$.
10. $12x^2 - 36y^2 - 11xy$ by $4x - 9y$.
11. $a^3 + 6a^2 + 7a - 8$ by $a - 1$.
12. $x^4 + 1$ by $x^2 + 1$.
13. $x^2 - y^2$ by $x - y$.
14. $x^3 - y^3$ by $x - y$.
15. $x^4 - y^4$ by $x - y$.
16. $x^3 + y^3$ by $x + y$.
17. $x^5 + y^5$ by $x + y$.
18. $x^7 + y^7$ by $x + y$.
19. $x^2 - y^2$ by $x + y$.
20. $x^4 - y^4$ by $x + y$.
21. $x^6 - y^6$ by $x + y$.
22. $6a^3 - a^2 - 14a + 3$ by $3a^2 + 4a - 1$.
23. $2 + b^5 + 3b^3 + 3b^2 - 4b^4 - 3b$ by $b^2 - b - 2$.
24. $1 + 2x^4 + 4x^2 - x^3 + 7x$ by $3 + x^2 - x$.
25. $30c^4 + 3 - 82c^2 - 5c + 11c^3$ by $3c^2 - 4 + 2c$.
26. $\frac{1}{8}x^3 - \frac{9}{4}x^2y + \frac{27}{2}xy^2 - 27y^3$ by $\frac{1}{2}x - 3y$.
27. $\frac{1}{27}b^3 - \frac{1}{12}b^2 + \frac{1}{16}b - \frac{1}{64}$ by $\frac{1}{3}b - \frac{1}{4}$.
28. $6a^2 - \frac{5}{8}a - \frac{1}{6}$ by $2a - \frac{1}{2}$.
29. $n^2 - \frac{10}{3}n + 1$ by $n - \frac{1}{3}$.
30. $36d^2 + \frac{1}{9}e^2 + \frac{1}{4} - 4de - 6d + \frac{1}{3}e$ by $6d - \frac{1}{3}e - \frac{1}{2}$.

CHAPTER VI

EQUATIONS

In the preceding chapters, considerable time has been spent in the study of the fundamental operations of algebra. These fundamentals will be of little value unless they can be put to practical use in the solution of problems. This is accomplished by use of the equation, the most valuable tool in mathematics.

6-1. Definitions. An *equation* is a mathematical statement that two numbers, or quantities, are equal. The *equality sign* ($=$) is used to separate the two equal quantities. The terms to the left of the equality sign are known as the *left member* of the equation, and the terms to the right are the *right member* of the equation. For example, in the equation

$$3x + 4 = 2x + 6$$

$3x + 4$ is the left member, and $2x + 6$ is the right member.

An *identical equation,* or *identity,* is an equation whose members are equal for all values of the literal numbers contained in the equation. The equation

$$4I(r + R) = 4Ir + 4IR$$

is an identity because if

$$I = 2, \qquad r = 3, \qquad \text{and} \qquad R = 1$$

then $4I(r + R) = 4 \cdot 2(3 + 1) = 32$

Also, $4Ir + 4IR = 4 \cdot 2 \cdot 3 + 4 \cdot 2 \cdot 1 = 24 + 8 = 32$

Any other values of I, r, and R substituted in the equation will produce equal numerical results in the two members of the equation.

An equation is said to be *satisfied* if, when numerical values are substituted for the literal numbers, the equation becomes an identity. Thus, the equation

$$ir - iR = 3r - 3R$$

43

is satisfied by $i = 3$, because when this value is substituted in the equation we obtain

$$3r - 3R = 3r - 3R$$

which is an identity.

6-2. Conditional Equations. A *conditional equation* is one consisting of one or more literal numbers that is not satisfied by all values of the literal numbers. Thus, the equation

$$e + 3 = 7$$

is not satisfied by any value of e except $e = 4$.

6-3. Solution. To *solve* an equation is to find the value or values of the unknown number that will satisfy the equation. This value is called the *root* of the equation. Thus, if

$$i + 6 = 14$$

the equation becomes an identity only when i is 8, and therefore 8 is the root of the equation.

6-4. Axioms. An *axiom* is a truth, or fact, that is self-evident and needs no formal proof. The various methods of solving equations are derived from the following axioms:

1. *If equal numbers are added to equal numbers, the sums are equal.*

Example 1. If $x = x$,
then $\qquad\qquad\qquad x + 2 = x + 2$
because, if $x = 4$, $\qquad\quad 4 + 2 = 4 + 2$
or $\qquad\qquad\qquad\qquad 6 = 6$

Therefore, *the same number may be added to both members of an equation without destroying the equality.*

2. *If equal numbers are subtracted from equal numbers, the remainders are equal.*

Example 2. If $x = x$,
then $\qquad\qquad\qquad x - 2 = x - 2$
because, if $x = 4$, $\qquad\quad 4 - 2 = 4 - 2$
or $\qquad\qquad\qquad\qquad 2 = 2$

Therefore, *the same number may be subtracted from both members of an equation without destroying the equality.*

3. *If equal numbers are multiplied by equal numbers, their products are equal.*

Example 3. If $x = x$,

then $3x = 3x$
because, if $x = 4$, $3 \cdot 4 = 3 \cdot 4$
or $12 = 12$

Therefore, *both members of an equation may be multiplied by the same number without destroying the equality.*

4. *If equal numbers are divided by equal numbers, their quotients are equal.*

Example 4. If $x = x$,

then $\dfrac{x}{2} = \dfrac{x}{2}$

because, if $x = 4$, $\dfrac{4}{2} = \dfrac{4}{2}$

or $2 = 2$

Therefore, *both members of an equation may be divided by the same number without destroying the equality.*

5. *Numbers that are equal to the same number or equal numbers are equal to each other.*

Example 5. If $a = x$ and $b = x$,

then $a = b$
because, if $x = 4$, $a = 4$ and $b = 4$

Therefore, *an equal quantity may be substituted for any term of an equation without destroying the equality.*

6. *Like powers of equal numbers are equal.*

Example 6. If $x = x$,

then $x^3 = x^3$
because, if $x = 4$, $4^3 = 4^3$
or $64 = 64$

Therefore, *both members of an equation may be raised to the same power without destroying the equality.*

7. *Like roots of equal numbers are equal.*

Example 7. If $x = x$,

then $\qquad\qquad\qquad \sqrt{x} = \sqrt{x}$

because, if $x = 4$, $\qquad\quad \sqrt{4} = \sqrt{4}$

or $\qquad\qquad\qquad\qquad 2 = 2$

Therefore, *like roots may be extracted of both members of an equation without destroying the equality.*

8. *The whole of anything equals the sum of all its parts.*

Example 8. The sum of two numbers is 45. One number is two times the other. Express the numbers.

Solution: Let x = smaller number.

Then $\qquad\qquad\qquad 2x$ = larger number

$\qquad\qquad\qquad\qquad 45 = x + 2x \qquad\qquad\qquad$ (Axiom 8)

The method of solving for x will be considered later.

6-5. Notation. In order to shorten the **explanations** of the solutions of various equations, we shall employ the letters **A, S, M,** and **D** for "add," "subtract," "multiply," and "divide," respectively.

Thus, **A :** 6 will mean "add 6 to both members of the equation."

S : $-6x$ will mean "subtract $-6x$ from both members of the equation."

M : $-3a$ will mean "multiply both members of the equation by $-3a$."

D : 2 will mean "divide both members of the equation by 2."

6-6. The Solution of Equations. A considerable amount of time and drill must be spent in order to become proficient in the solution of equations. It is in this branch of mathematics that the student will find he must be familiar with the more elementary parts of algebra.

Some of the methods used in the solutions are very easy, so easy, in fact, that there is a tendency to employ them mechanically. This is all very well, but one should not let himself become so mechanical that he forgets the reason for performing certain operations.

We shall begin the solution of equations with very easy cases and attempt to build up general methods of procedure for all equations as we proceed to the more difficult problems.

The student who is studying equations for the first time is urged to study the following examples carefully until he thoroughly understands the methods and the reasons behind them.

Example 1.   Find the value of x, if $x - 3 = 2$.

Solution: In this simple equation, it is seen by inspection that x must be equal to 5.   However, to make the solution by the methods of algebra, proceed as follows:

Given	$x - 3 = 2$	
A∴3,	$x = 2 + 3$	(Axiom 1)
Collecting terms,	$x = 5$	

Example 2.   Solve for e, if $e + 4 = 12$.
Solution:

Given	$e + 4 = 12$	
S:4,	$e = 12 - 4$	(Axiom 2)
Collecting terms,	$e = 8$	

Example 3. $3i + 5 = 20$
Solution:

Given	$3i + 5 = 20$	
S:5,	$3i = 20 - 5$	(Axiom 2)
Collecting terms,	$3i = 15$	
D:3,	$i = 5$	(Axiom 4)

Example 4.   Solve for r, if $40r - 10 = 15r + 90$.
Solution:

Given	$40r - 10 = 15r + 90$	
S:15r,	$40r - 10 - 15r = 90$	(Axiom 2)
A:10,	$40r - 15r = 90 + 10$	(Axiom 1)
Collecting terms,	$25r = 100$	
D:25,	$r = 4$	(Axiom 4)

From the foregoing examples, it will be noted that adding or subtracting a term from both members of an equation is equivalent to *transposing* that number from one member to the other and changing its sign.   This fact leads to the

Rule : *A* **term** *may be transposed from one member of an equation to the other, provided that its sign is changed.*

By transposing all terms containing the unknown to the left member and all others to the right member; by collecting terms and dividing both members by the numerical coefficient of the unknown, the equation has been solved for the value of the unknown.

6-7. Canceling Terms in an Equation.

Example. Solve for x, if $x + y = z + y$.
Solution:

Given $\qquad\qquad\qquad x + y = z + y$
S$:y$, $\qquad\qquad\qquad\qquad x = z$ $\qquad\qquad$ (Axiom 2)

The term y in both members of the given equation does not appear in the next equation as the result of subtraction. The result is the same as if the term were dropped from both members. This fact leads to the

Rule: *If the same* **term,** *preceded by the same sign, occurs in both members of an equation, it may be canceled.*

6-8. Changing Signs in an Equation.

Example. Solve for x, if $8 - x = 3$.
Solution:

Given $\qquad\qquad\qquad 8 - x = 3$
S$:8$, $\qquad\qquad\qquad\quad -x = 3 - 8$ $\qquad$ (Axiom 2)
M$:-1$, $\qquad\qquad\qquad\quad x = -3 + 8$ $\qquad$ (Axiom 3)
Collecting terms, $\qquad\qquad x = 5$

Note that multiplication by -1 has the effect of changing the signs of all terms. This gives the

Rule: *The signs of all the* **terms** *of an equation may be changed without destroying the equality.*

Although the foregoing rules involving mechanical methods are valuable, the student should not lose sight of the fact that they are all derived from fundamentals, or axioms, as outlined in Art. 6-4.

6-9. Checking the Solution. If there is any doubt that the value of the unknown is correct, the solution may be checked by substituting the value of the unknown in the original equation. If the two members reduce to an identity, the value of the unknown is correct.

Example. Solve and test $3i + 14 + 2i = i + 26$.
Solution:

Given $\qquad\qquad\qquad 3i + 14 + 2i = i + 26$

Transposing, $3i + 2i - i = 26 - 14$
Collecting terms, $4i = 12$
D : 4, $i = 3$

Test by substituting $i = 3$ in given equation.

Check. $(3 \cdot 3) + 14 + (2 \cdot 3) = 3 + 26$
                                 $9 + 14 + 6 = 3 + 26$
                                         $29 = 29$

PROBLEMS 6-1

Solve for the unknowns in the following equations:

1. $4y - 1 = 3y + 3$.   **2.** $r - 10 = 5 + 4r$.
3. $1 - 9i = -6i - 2$.   **4.** $6e + 3 - 2e = 27$.
5. $5x + 2 = 3 + 4x$.   **6.** $11e - 22 = 4e + 13$.
7. $16 - 9r = 5r - 12$.   **8.** $21 - 15x = -8x - 7$.
9. $27Z + 22 = 30 + 17Z$.   **10.** $27 - 28i = 19 - 16i$.
11. $16p - 3 = 6p + 8 - 23p$.   **12.** $4 + 3(r - 7) = 16 + 2(5r + 1)$.
13. $8e - 5(4e + 3) = -3 - 4(2e - 7)$.
14. $3(i - 2) - 10(i - 6) = 5$.
15. $4(p - 5) - 3(p - 2) = 2(p - 1)$.
16. $0 = 18 - 4r + 27 + 9r - 3 + 16r$.
17. $5p - 8 + 4p + 5 = 7p - 3 - 2p + 5$.
18. $18 + 5R - 6 - 2R + 1 + 3R - 25 = 0$.
19. $3I - 15 - 10I - 9 + 16I - 21 = 0$.
20. $19 - 5E(4E + 1) = 40 - 10E(2E - 1)$.

6-10. Forming and Solving Equations. As previously stated, we are continually trying to express certain laws and relations in the language of mathematics. The solution of most problems consists in writing an equation that connects various observed data with known facts. This, then, is nothing more than translating from ordinary English, or speech, into the language of mathematics. In relatively simple problems the translation may be made directly, almost word by word, into algebraic symbols.

Example 1.   Five times a certain voltage diminished by 3,
                 5   ×   E   −   3

gives the same result as the voltage increased by 125.
                 =   E   +   125

That is, $5E - 3 = E + 125$
or $E = 32$ volts.

Example 2.   What number increased by 42 is equal to 110?

$$x \quad + \quad 42 \quad = \quad 110?$$

That is, $x + 42 = 110$
or $x = 68$
Check. $68 + 42 = 110$

It is impossible to lay down a set of rules for the solution of general problems, for they could not be made applicable to all cases.   However, no rules will be needed if the student thoroughly understands what is to be translated into the language of mathematics from the wording or facts of the problem at hand. The following outline will serve as a guide:

   1. *Read the problem so carefully that every fact contained therein is understood.*

   2. *Determine what is to be found (the unknown quantity), and denote it by some letter.   If there are two or more unknowns, try to represent them in terms of the first one.*

   3. *Find two expressions that, according to the facts of the problem, represent the same quantity, and set them equal to each other. The resulting equation may then be solved for the unknown.*

PROBLEMS 6-2

   1. The sum of two resistances is R Ω.   One resistance is 10 Ω.   What is the other?

   2. The difference of two resistances is R Ω.   If the smaller resistance is 6 Ω, what is the other?

   3. The difference of two numbers is E.   The smaller is e.   What is the other?

   4. A certain man is x years of age.   (*a*) How old was he y years ago? (*b*) How old will he be z years from now?

   5. A man is x years of age.   (*a*) When will he be 40 years of age?   (*b*) When was he y years of age?

   6. From what number must 13 be subtracted so that the result may be 36?

   7. If a certain number is doubled and the result diminished by 12, the remainder is 50.   What is the number?

   8. If a certain voltage is trebled and the result is diminished by 220 v, the remainder is equal to the original voltage.   What is the voltage?

   9. Three times a certain number, less 38, equals twice the number, less 26.   Find the number.

   10. If four times a number is added to five times that number, the sum is 108.   What is the number?

   11. A room is twice as long as it is wide, and its perimeter (sum of the lengths of the sides) is 144 ft.   Find (*a*) the length and (*b*) the width.

Suggestion:

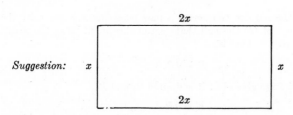

12. An ohmmeter and a wattmeter cost together $75.00. The wattmeter cost $26.00 more than the ohmmeter. Find the cost of (*a*) the wattmeter and (*b*) the ohmmeter.

13. A rectangular lot is 75 ft longer than it is wide. The perimeter is 600 ft. Find (*a*) the length and (*b*) the width.

14. The three sides of a triangle are $3x + 1$, $x + 8$, and $4x$ in., respectively, and the perimeter is 33 in. Find the length of each side.

15. Find the three sides of a triangle with a perimeter of 45 ft, if the second side is twice the third side, and if the first side exceeds the third by 5 ft.

16. Write in symbols that x exceeds y as much as a is less than b.

17. If x years ago a man was b years old, express his age 13 years hence.

18. The volume of a box is y cu ft. The width is x ft, and the length is b ft. Express the height.

19. Write in symbols one-half the square of x plus twice the square of y.

20. The sum of two consecutive numbers is 47. What are the numbers?

21. The second angle of a triangle exceeds the first by 30°; the third angle exceeds the second by 15°. Find the three angles. (The sum of all angles in any triangle is 180°.)

22. John is 4 years older than Charles. Eight years ago, twice Charles's age exceeded John's age then by 1 year. How old is each now?

23. The angles of a certain triangle are $6x + 60$, $x + 25$, and $5x + 35$, respectively; find the angles of the triangle.

24. Find three consecutive even numbers whose sum is 126.

25. The age of Paul is now four times the age of Frank. Four years from now, Paul's age will be 1 year more than Frank's age then. What are their present ages?

6-11. Literal Equations—Formulas.

A *formula* is a rule, or law, generally pertaining to some scientific relationship, expressed as an equation by means of letters, symbols, and constant terms. The ability to handle formulas is of the utmost importance. The usual formula is expressed in terms of other quantities, and it is often desirable to solve for *any* quantity contained in a formula. This is readily accomplished by using the knowledge gained in solving equations.

Example 1.   The voltage (E) across a part of a circuit is given by the product of the current (I) through that part of the circuit times the resistance (R) of that part.   That is,

$$E = IR$$

Suppose E and I are given but it is desired to find R.

Given	$E = IR$	
D : I,	$\dfrac{E}{I} = R$	(Axiom 4)
or	$R = \dfrac{E}{I}$	

Similarly, if we wanted to solve for I,

Given	$E = IR$	
D : R,	$\dfrac{E}{R} = I$	(Axiom 4)
or	$I = \dfrac{E}{R}$	

Example 2.   Solve for I, if $e = E - IR$.
Solution:

Given	$e = E - IR$	
Transposing,	$IR = E - e$	
D : R,	$I = \dfrac{E - e}{R}$	(Axiom 4)

Example 3.   Solve for C, if $X_c = \dfrac{1}{2\pi f C}$.

Solution:

Given	$X_c = \dfrac{1}{2\pi f C}$	
D : X_c,	$1 = \dfrac{1}{2\pi f C X_c}$	(Axiom 4)
M : C,	$C = \dfrac{1}{2\pi f X_c}$	(Axiom 3)

It will be noted from the foregoing examples that if the numerator of a member of an equation contains but one term, any factor of that term may be transferred to the denominator of the other member as a factor.   In like manner if the denominator of a member of an equation contains but one term, any factor of that term may be transferred to the numerator of the other member as a factor.   These mechanical transformations simply make use of Axioms 3 and 4, and the student should not lose sight of the real reasons behind them.

6-12. Primes and Subscripts. In a formula in which, for example, two resistances are being compared or where it is desirable to make a distinction between them, the resistances may be represented by R_1 and R_2 or R_a and R_b. The small numbers or letters written at the right of and below the R's are called *subscripts*. They are generally used to denote different values of the same units.

R_1 and R_2 are read "R sub one" and "R sub two" or simply "R one" and "R two."

Care must be used in distinguishing between subscripts and exponents. Thus E^2 is an indicated operation that means $E \cdot E$, whereas E_2 is used to distinguish one quantity from another of the same kind.

Primes and *seconds*, instead of subscripts, are often used to denote quantities. Thus one current might be denoted by I' and another by I''. The first is read "I prime" and the latter is read "I second." I' resembles I^1 (I to the first power), but in general this causes little confusion.

In the following problems an attempt has been made to group formulas according to their field of usage. However, because the study of physics includes mechanics and electricity, there can be no sharp line of division for all formulas, and it is possible the student will find certain formulas under one heading that he believes should be under another. The drill in *solving* the formulas is the important consideration.

PROBLEMS 6-3

Given	Solve for	Given	Solve for
		Electrical and Radio Formulas	
1. $R_t = R_1 + R_2 + R_3$.	R_2.	**2.** $Z^2 = R^2 + X^2$	R^2.
3. $E = IZ$.	I.	**4.** $f = \dfrac{PN}{120}$.	P.
5. $R = \dfrac{KL}{m}$.	L.	**6.** $X_c = \dfrac{1}{2\pi f C}$.	f.
7. $X_L = 2\pi f L$.	L.	**8.** $\dfrac{E_p}{E_s} = \dfrac{N_p}{N_s}$.	N_s.
9. $\dfrac{I_p}{I_s} = \dfrac{N_s}{N_p}$.	N_s.	**10.** $I_p E_p = I_s E_s$.	I_s.
11. $Q = \dfrac{\omega L}{R}$.	R.	**12.** $C = \dfrac{Q}{V}$.	Q.
13. $F = HLi$.	L.	**14.** $E = \dfrac{BLv}{10^8}$.	B.

15. $I = \dfrac{E - e}{R}$.   *R.*   **16.** $P = I^2R$.   *R.*

17. $P = \dfrac{E^2}{R}$.   *R.*   **18.** $H = \dfrac{4\pi Ni}{l}$.   *N.*

19. $\phi = HA$.   *H.*   **20.** $w = \dfrac{B^2Al}{8\mu}$. μ.

21. $Q = 0.24EIt$.   *t.*   **22.** $E + e_2 = IR_1 + IR_2 + e_1$. e_1.

23. $\lambda = \dfrac{v}{f}$ *v.*   **24.** $L = 1.25N^2P \cdot 10^{-8}$ *P.*

25. $C = 0.08842K\dfrac{A}{d}$.   *K.*   **26.** $G_m = \dfrac{\mu}{R_p}$. μ.

27. $E_c = \dfrac{-E_{sg}}{\mu_{sg}}$. μ_{sg}.   **28.** $e_b = E_b - iR_L$. R_L.

29. $H = 0.057I^2Rt$.   *R.*   **30.** $Y_f = Y_b - 2m$. Y_b.

Physics Formulas

31. $F = \dfrac{mm'}{\mu d^2}$.   *m.*   **32.** $W = \dfrac{2\pi}{T}$.   *T.*

33. $\omega = \dfrac{\theta}{t}$. θ.   **34.** $\omega = 2\pi n$.   *n.*

35. $V^2 = 2gh$.   *h.*   **36.** K.E. $= \frac{1}{2}mv^2$.   *m.*

37. $V = \dfrac{V_t + V_0}{2}$. V_0.   **38.** $\dfrac{2\text{K.E.}}{I} = W^2$.   K.E.

39. $F = m\omega^2r$.   *m.*   **40.** $m = \dfrac{F}{4\pi^2n^2r}$.   *r.*

Mechanical Formulas

41. $P = \dfrac{N + n}{2C}$.   *C.*   **42.** $I = \dfrac{N - 2}{P}$.   *P.*

43. $C = D + 2K$.   *K.*   **44.** $C = \dfrac{D + d}{2}$.   *D.*

45. $d = 2C - D$.   *C.*   **46.** $L = nP$.   *P.*

47. $DP = N$.   *P.*   **48.** $t = \dfrac{T(C - F)}{C}$.   *T.*

49. $d = a + b - c$.   *c.*   **50.** $P = \dfrac{N + 2}{H}$.   *H.*

Miscellaneous Formulas

51. $P = A - I$.   *I.*   **52.** $I = Prt$.   *r.*

53. $M = \dfrac{Kl}{r}$.   *l.*   **54.** $I = Adt$.   *t.*

55. $G^2 = ab$.   *a.*   **56.** $A = \pi ab$.   *a.*

57. $T = ph + 2A$.   *A.*   **58.** $S = 2\pi rh$.   *r.*

59. $b^2 = c^2 - a^2$. a^2.   **60.** $a = \dfrac{2A}{b}$.   *A.*

CHAPTER VII

THE SLIDE RULE—POWERS OF TEN

The slide rule is an instrument, or tool, designed for the purpose of saving time and labor in calculating.

A complete description of various slide rules or of a particular type of rule is not within the scope of this book. Briefly, the slide rule is a mechanical equivalent of a table of logarithms. Each rule consists of a number of scales so graduated and arranged that the operations of multiplication, division, squaring, cubing, extracting roots, and many others may be performed with great facility. Furthermore, problems involving trigonometry, logarithms, etc., may be worked on the slide rule. However, addition and subtraction are not feasible except on specially constructed rules.

Every technical man, especially the electrician and radioman, should be proficient in the operation of some type of slide rule. The solution of every practical problem, where a concrete answer is desired, eventually reduces to an arithmetical computation. Much valuable time is wasted performing a series of multiplications, divisions, square roots, etc., with a pencil and paper, when there is an instrument available that will do the work satisfactorily in a fraction of the time and with a fairly high degree of accuracy. Very few people enjoy performing numerical computations simply for the joy of "figuring." The practical man wants concrete answers; therefore, he should use whatever tools or devices are available to assist him in arriving at those answers with a minimum expenditure of time and effort.

7-1. Types of Slide Rule. Types of slide rule range from inexpensive beginner's slide rules to those comparable with calculating machines. Most of them are designed for use in general mathematical operations; some are designed especially for use in specific professions or trades.

The prospective purchaser who is unfamiliar with slide rules should exercise considerable caution when choosing a rule. Too many men have purchased slide rules without benefit of advice, only to learn later there was another type of rule better suited to their individual use. There is *one* type of slide rule best suited to your particular need.

No attempt is made here to advise the student as to just what type of rule is best suited to his use. If you are attending a technical school, your instructors are qualified to advise as to the type of rule they believe best. If you are professionally employed, your technical associates will be able to assist in your selection of a rule. Needless to say, the average salesman is rarely qualified to suggest the type of rule best suited for a specific profession.

Among the many types developed, the Cooke Radio Slide Rule has met with moderate success. This rule employs a minimum number of scales but at the same time allows almost as wide a mathematical scope as may be desired. The scales have been designed and arranged for the express purpose of completing the more common radio and electrical problems in a simple and straightforward manner. The instruction book furnished with this rule has been written so that the examples and exercises follow these subjects as closely as is consistent with clarity.

Instruction books are furnished with all slide rules; thus, the beginner needs no instructor but merely a reasonable amount of practice in order to become proficient in using them.

It is therefore strongly recommended that the student acquire a rule and learn to use it while studying this text. Many hours devoted to figuring with a pencil will be saved that can be well spent in the study of mathematics or other essential subjects, to say nothing of lightening otherwise tedious computations.

7-2. Accuracy of Slide Rules. From a radio or electrical viewpoint, except possibly where extremely accurate radio-frequency measurements are needed, the accuracy of a slide rule leaves nothing to be desired. Its accuracy is nearly proportional to the length of scales used. The 10-inch scales give results accurately to within 1 part in 1000, or one-tenth of 1 per cent.

When practical radio or electric circuits are taken into consideration, slide-rule computations are more accurate than the circuit components involved. For example, the tolerances of resistors, inductances, and condensers used in the usual receiver and transmitter average ± 10 per cent. Also, the average switchboard meter is seldom correct to within 3 per cent throughout its calibration.   Suppose we go into a store to buy a 10,000-ohm resistor and ask the salesman to check the resistance on his ohmmeter.   According to present standards, if this resistance measures anywhere between 9000 and 11,000 ohms, which is within the ± 10 per cent tolerance, we should be satisfied.   However, if his ohmmeter has an accuracy within ± 2 per cent, he is to be congratulated on having a good meter.   Because, in all probability, he does not know just how accurate the meter is, we leave the store *hoping* we have a resistor somewhere near the correct value.   Actually, such a resistor would be entirely satisfactory for ordinary requirements, as we shall see later.

Other circuit components, except those used in the laboratory, vary in much the same manner; and when temperature, humidity, and other variations are taken into consideration, the slide-rule results more than meet all practical needs.

From the foregoing, it might appear that mathematical accuracy in the calculation of electric circuits is unnecessary.   Far from it—the laws of electricity follow concise mathematical concepts and we *can* construct circuit components and measuring equipment that are very precise.   However, mainly for economical reasons, it is neither practical nor necessary to maintain such a high degree of accuracy in the average circuits.

The important point is that we must first know how accurate our available circuit components and measuring equipment are and then depend upon this accuracy to a reasonable extent.   In general, students thoughtlessly make computations of quantities that have been found by measurements, instrument readings, etc., and carry the operations to several unnecessary decimal places. Not only does this computation consume a considerable amount of time; worse still, the results often give a false impression of accuracy.   In this connection, it is safe to assume that the constants of any radio- or electric-circuit components or the calibration of meters, excluding precision measuring equipments, are generally not correct beyond three significant figures.

7-3. Rounded Numbers.   A number is *rounded off* by dropping one or more figures at its right.   If the last figure dropped is 6 or more, we increase the last figure retained by 1.   Thus 3867 would be rounded off to 3870, 3900, or 4000.   If the last figure dropped is 4 or less, we leave the last figure retained as it is.   Thus, 5134 would be rounded off to 5130, 5100, or 5000.   If the last figure dropped is just 5, add 1 if it will make the last figure retained *even*, otherwise no. Thus, 55.7$\not{5}$ = 55.8, but 67.6$\not{5}$ = 67.6.

7-4. Significant Figures. In mathematics, a number is generally considered as being exact. For example, 220 would mean 220.0000, etc., for as many added zeros as desired. However, a meter reading, for example, is always an *approximation*. We might read 220 volts on a certain switchboard type of voltmeter; but a precision instrument might show the voltage to be 220.3 volts, and a series of precise measurements might show the voltage to be 220.36 volts. It should be noted that the position of the decimal point does not determine the accuracy of a number. For example, 115 volts, 0.115 kilovolt, and 115,000 millivolts are of identical value and equally accurate.

Any number representing a measurement, or the amount of some quantity, expresses the accuracy of the measurement. The figures required are known as *significant figures*.

The *significant figures* of any number are the figures 1, 2, 3, 4, $\cdots$ 9, in addition to such ciphers, or zeros, as may occur between them or as may have been retained in properly rounding them off.

Examples.	0.00236	is correct to *three* significant figures.
	3.14159	is correct to *six* significant figures.
	980,000.0	is correct to *seven* significant figures.
	24.	is correct to *two* significant figures.
	24.0	is correct to *three* significant figures.
	0.02500	is correct to *four* significant figures.

After studying the powers of ten, we shall return to a more detailed discussion of significant figures and how to express them.

7-5. Decimals. Two important considerations arise in making computations involving decimals:

1. A slide rule gives only the significant figures of the result of a mathematical operation. For example, suppose that we have performed some operation on the slide rule and read as the result the significant figures 432. Now the slide rule does not indicate whether this answer is 0.0432, 0.432, 4.32, 4320, 43,200, etc. Therefore, it becomes necessary for the slide-rule operator to fix the decimal point; that is, the operator must first determine the *approximate* answer in order that he may use the more accurate figures taken from the slide-rule scales.

2. Unfortunately, electrical engineers and particularly radio engineers are required to handle cumbersome numbers, the numbers ranging from extremely small fractions of electrical units to very large numbers, as represented by radio frequencies. The fact that these wide limits of numbers are encountered in the same problem does not simplify matters. This situation is becoming more complicated owing to the trend to the ultra-high radio frequencies with attendant smaller fractions of units represented by circuit components.

For these reasons, in using a slide rule, the decimal point *cannot* be fixed "by inspection" except in the simpler problems. This important item has not been sufficiently stressed by most writers of slide-rule instruction books. Accordingly, many beginners interested in using the slide rule for solving radio and electrical problems have become discouraged by the difficulty of placing the decimal points owing to the above-mentioned wide range of numbers encountered in the average problem.

The man who does not use a slide rule is far less efficient than the man who does; for the former, using only the rules of ordinary arithmetic, must write out and perform the necessary operations with the very small decimal quantities as well as with the large numbers. This is laborious and time-consuming and spreads out the problem over so much territory that sometimes the real point of the problem is obscured. In addition, there is always the chance of making errors in performing computations in this manner.

The problem of properly placing the decimal point and thus reducing unnecessary work presents little difficulty to the man who has a working knowledge of the powers of ten.

7-6. Powers of Ten. The powers of ten are sometimes termed the "engineer's shorthand." A thorough knowledge of the powers of ten and the ability to apply the theory of exponents will greatly assist in determining an approximation. If a slide rule is used with the powers of ten, the average problem reduces to the usual slide-rule operations plus simple mental arithmetic. If a slide rule is not used for computation, the powers of ten enable one to work all problems by using convenient whole numbers. Either offers a convenient method for obtaining a final answer with the decimal point in its proper place.

Some of the multiples of 10 may be represented as follows:

Number		Power of Ten		Expressed in English
0.000001	=	10^{-6}	=	ten to the negative *sixth* power.
0.00001	=	10^{-5}	=	ten to the negative *fifth* power.
0.0001	=	10^{-4}	=	ten to the negative *fourth* power.
0.001	=	10^{-3}	=	ten to the negative *third* power.
0.01	=	10^{-2}	=	ten to the negative *second* power.
0.1	=	10^{-1}	=	ten to the negative *first* power.
1	=	10^{0}	=	ten to the *zero* power.
10	=	10^{1}	=	ten to the *first* power.
100	=	10^{2}	=	ten to the *second* power.
1000	=	10^{3}	=	ten to the *third* power.
10,000	=	10^{4}	=	ten to the *fourth* power.
100,000	=	10^{5}	=	ten to the *fifth* power.
1,000,000	=	10^{6}	=	ten to the *sixth* power.

From the above, it is seen that any decimal may be expressed as a whole number times some negative power of ten. This may be expressed by the

Rule : *To express a decimal as a whole number times a power of ten, move the decimal point to the right and count the number of places to the original point. The number of places counted is the proper negative power of ten.*

Examples.

$$0.00687 = 6.87 \times 10^{-3}$$
$$0.0000482 = 4.82 \times 10^{-5}$$
$$0.346 = 34.6 \times 10^{-2}$$
$$0.08643 = 86.43 \times 10^{-3}$$

Also, it is seen that any large number may be expressed as some smaller number times the proper power of ten. This may be expressed by the

Rule : *To express a large number as a smaller number times a power of ten, move the decimal point to the left and count the number of places to the original decimal point. The number of places counted will give the proper positive power of ten.*

Examples.

$$435 = 4.35 \times 10^{2}$$
$$964,000 = 96.4 \times 10^{4}$$
$$6835.2 = 6.8352 \times 10^{3}$$
$$5723 = 5.723 \times 10^{3}$$

PROBLEMS 7-1

Express the following as numbers between 1 and 10, times the proper power of ten:

1. 643,000,000.   **2.** 4356.
3. 0.0136.   **4.** 14.
5. 0.000250.   **6.** 0.0369.
7. 48,900.   **8.** 0.000000643.
9. 0.0000000000125.   **10.** 59,300.
11. 0.259.   **12.** 1890×10^3.
13. 259×10^{-4}.   **14.** 0.000086×10^{-6}.
15. 56,500,000.   **16.** 1,684,000,000.
17. 0.367×10^{-6}.   **18.** 8420×10^{-12}.
19. 256×10^{-8}.   **20.** 0.000399×10^8.

7-7. Multiplication with Powers of Ten.   In Art. 4-3 the law of exponents in multiplication was expressed in the general form

$$a^m \cdot a^n = a^{m+n} \qquad \text{(where } a \neq 0\text{)}$$

This law is directly applicable to the powers of ten.

Example 1.   Multiply 1000 by 100,000.

Solution: $1000 = 10^3$ and $100,000 = 10^5$
Then $1000 \times 100,000 = 10^3 \times 10^5 = 10^{3+5} = 10^8$

Example 2.   Multiply 0.000001 by 0.001.

Solution: $0.000001 = 10^{-6}$ and $0.001 = 10^{-3}$
Then
     $0.000001 \times 0.001 = 10^{-6} \times 10^{-3} = 10^{-6+(-3)} = 10^{-6-3} = 10^{-9}$

Example 3.   Multiply 23,000 by 7000.

Solution: $23,000 = 2.3 \times 10^4$ and $7000 = 7 \times 10^3$
Then $23,000 \times 7000 = 2.3 \times 10^4 \times 7 \times 10^3$
                                 $= 2.3 \times 7 \times 10^7$
                                 $= 16.1 \times 10^7$, or 161,000,000

Example 4.   Multiply 0.000037 by 600.

Solution: $0.000037 \times 600 = 3.7 \times 10^{-5} \times 6 \times 10^2$
                                        $= 3.7 \times 6 \times 10^{-3}$
                                        $= 22.2 \times 10^{-3}$, or 0.0222

Example 5.   Multiply $72,000 \times 0.000025 \times 4600$.

Solution: $72,000 \times 0.000025 \times 4600$
                   $= 7.2 \times 10^4 \times 2.5 \times 10^{-5} \times 4.6 \times 10^3$
                   $= 7.2 \times 2.5 \times 4.6 \times 10^2$
                   $= 82.8 \times 10^2$, or 8280

The student will find that by expressing all numbers between 1 and 10. times the proper power of ten, the determination of the proper place for the decimal point will become a matter of inspection.

PROBLEMS 7-2

Multiply:

1. 10,000 × 0.0001 × 100,000.

2. 0.00001 × 10^5 × 1000.

3. 104,000 × 0.00025.

4. 23 × 10^8 × 45 × 10^{-3} × 0.0000002.

5. 0.0000084 × 0.0005 × 0.000017.

6. 68,000,000 × 0.00000035 × 0.000055.

7. 0.328 × 10^{-3} × 25,000 × 0.00029 × 10^5.

8. 782 × 10^{-8} × 500 × 10^4 × 0.000037 × 10^{-6}.

9. 38.6 × 10^{-3} × 0.485 × 10^6 × 4930 × 10^{-12}.

10. 0.00000000793 × 10^{-4} × 597,000 × 683 × 10^8 × 3 × 10^{-6}.

7-8. Division with Powers of Ten. The law of exponents in division (Arts. 5-2, 5-3, and 5-4) may be summed up in the following general form:

$$\frac{a^m}{a^n} = a^{m-n} \qquad \text{(where } a \neq 0)$$

Example 1. $\qquad \dfrac{10^5}{10^3} = 10^{5-3} = 10^2$

or $\qquad \dfrac{10^5}{10^3} = 10^5 \times 10^{-3} = 10^2$

Example 2. $\dfrac{72,000}{0.0008} = \dfrac{72 \times 10^3}{8 \times 10^{-4}} = \dfrac{72}{8} \times 10^{3+4} = 9 \times 10^7$

or $\dfrac{72,000}{0.0008} = \dfrac{72 \times 10^3}{8 \times 10^{-4}} = \dfrac{72}{8} \times 10^3 \times 10^4 = 9 \times 10^7$

Example 3. $\dfrac{169 \times 10^5}{13 \times 10^5} = \dfrac{169}{13} \times 10^{5-5} = 13 \times 10^0 = 13 \times 1 = 13$

or $\qquad \dfrac{169 \times \cancel{10^5}}{13 \times \cancel{10^5}} = 13$

It is apparent that like exponents in numerator and denominator may be canceled. Also, the student will note that powers of ten may be transferred at will from denominator to numerator, or vice versa, if the sign of the exponent is changed when the transfer is made (Art. 5-4).

7-9. Combined Multiplication and Division. This is most conveniently accomplished by alternately multiplying and dividing until the problem is completed.

Example.   Simplify $\dfrac{0.000644 \times 96{,}000 \times 3300}{161{,}000 \times 0.00000120}$.

Solution: First convert all numbers in the problem to numbers between 1 and 10, times their proper power of 10, thus:

$$\frac{6.44 \times 10^{-4} \times 9.6 \times 10^4 \times 3.3 \times 10^3}{1.61 \times 10^5 \times 1.2 \times 10^{-6}} = \frac{6.44 \times 9.6 \times 3.3 \times 10^4}{1.61 \times 1.2}$$

The problem as now written consists of multiplication and division of simple numbers. If the remainder of the problem is solved by slide rule, rough multiplication and division may be carried along mentally with no danger of misplacing the decimal point. If the problem is solved without the aid of a slide rule, there are no small decimals and no cumbersome large numbers to handle.

Instead of first finding the product of the numerator and dividing it by the product of the denominator, it is best to divide and multiply alternately. Thus, we divide 6.44 by 1.61 to obtain 4. Then we multiply this 4 by 9.6 to obtain 38.4. The 38.4 is then divided by 1.2 which results in a quotient of 32. Finally, 32 is multiplied by 3.3 which results in a product of 105.6. Because we still have a factor of 10^4, the answer is 105.6×10^4. If we desire to express the answer in powers of ten, it would be written 1.056×10^6; but written out, without the power of ten, it would be 1,056,000.

The method of alternately dividing and multiplying offers the slide-rule operator the advantage of working the problem straight through without the necessity of jotting down the product of the factors of the numerator before proceeding to find the product of the denominator factors.

7-10. Reciprocals. In radio and electrical problems, many formulas are used that involve reciprocals, such as $\dfrac{1}{R_t} = \dfrac{1}{R_1} + \dfrac{1}{R_2}$, $X_c = \dfrac{1}{2\pi f C}$, $F = \dfrac{1}{2\pi \sqrt{LC}}$, etc. The reciprocal of a number is 1 divided by that number. Such problems present no difficulty if the powers of ten are used properly.

Example 1.   Simplify $\dfrac{1}{40{,}000 \times 0.00025 \times 125 \times 10^{-6}}$.

Solution: First convert all numbers in the denominator to numbers between 1 and 10, times their proper power of ten, thus:

$$\frac{1}{4 \times 10^4 \times 2.5 \times 10^{-4} \times 1.25 \times 10^{-4}} = \frac{10^4}{4 \times 2.5 \times 1.25}$$

Multiplying the factors of the denominator results in

$$\frac{10^4}{12.5}$$

Instead of writing out the numerator as 10,000 and then dividing by 12.5, the numerator is written as two factors in order better to divide mentally. The problem may be written:

$$\frac{10^2 \times 10^2}{12.5}, \text{ or } \frac{100}{12.5} \times 10^2 = 8 \times 10^2$$

This method is of particular advantage to the slide-rule operator because of the ease of estimating the number of figures in the final result.

If the final result is a decimal, rewriting the numerator into two factors allows fixing the decimal point with the least effort.

Example 2. Simplify $\dfrac{1}{625 \times 10^4 \times 2000 \times 64,000}$.

Solution: First convert all numbers in the denominator to numbers between 1 and 10, times their proper power of ten, thus:

$$\frac{1}{6.25 \times 10^6 \times 2 \times 10^3 \times 6.4 \times 10^4} = \frac{10^{-13}}{6.25 \times 2 \times 6.4}$$

Multiplying the factors in the denominator results in

$$\frac{10^{-13}}{80}$$

Instead of writing out the numerator as 0.0000000000001 and dividing it by 80, the numerator is written as two factors in order better to divide mentally. The problem may be written as follows:

$$\frac{10^2 \times 10^{-15}}{80}, \text{ or } \frac{100}{80} \times 10^{-15} = 1.25 \times 10^{-15}$$

If the value of the denominator product was over 100 and less than 1000, we should break up the numerator so that one of the factors would be 10^3 or 1000, and so on. This method will always result in a final quotient of a number between 1 and 10, times the proper power of ten.

PROBLEMS 7-3

Perform the indicated operations. Round off the figures in the results, if necessary, and express answers to three significant figures.

1. $\dfrac{0.000025}{5000}$.

2. $\dfrac{1}{0.000125 \times 8000}$.

3. $\dfrac{36,000 \times 0.00042}{0.0090}$.

4. $\dfrac{1}{6.28 \times 1550 \times 10^3 \times 452 \times 10^{-7}}$.

5. $\dfrac{159 \times 10^3}{56 \times 10^{-6} \times 250 \times 10^{-12}}$.

6. $\dfrac{1}{6.28 \times 500 \times 10^{-12} \times 750}$.

7. $\dfrac{593 \times 10^4 \times 793 \times 10^5}{37 \times 10^9 \times 78 \times 10^6}$.

8. $\dfrac{0.000079 \times 0.00036}{58 \times 10^{-8}}$.

9. $\dfrac{0.0058 \times 0.000983}{0.0000071}$.

10. $\dfrac{1}{248,000 \times 563 \times 10^{-3} \times 0.0000903}$.

11. $\dfrac{14.1 \times 156,000 \times 0.0036}{72 \times 0.0624 \times 0.0353}$.

12. $\dfrac{0.015 \times 216 \times 1.78}{0.0477 \times 12.3 \times 0.0000603}$.

13. $\dfrac{1}{6.28 \times 225 \times 10^3 \times 563 \times 10^{-12}}$.

14. $\dfrac{1}{346 \times 10^6 \times 8000 \times 0.000062 \times 963 \times 10^{-5}}$.

15. $\dfrac{104,000 \times 830 \times 10^{-6} \times 0.0000213}{732 \times 10^{-4} \times 3,840,000}$.

16. $\dfrac{0.0000653 \times 50.4 \times 10^7 \times 12,700}{312,000 \times 0.00700 \times 0.682 \times 10^4}$.

17. $\dfrac{15,700 \times 944 \times 10^{-3} \times 0.000273}{84.5 \times 10^{-5} \times 382 \times 10^{-1}}$.

18. $\dfrac{0.0000413 \times 7830 \times 10^{-8} \times 524,000}{1.24 \times 10^{-7} \times 0.000000704}$.

19. $\dfrac{1}{6.28 \times 485 \times 6190 \times 10^3}$.

20. $\dfrac{159 \times 10^3}{85 \times 10^{-6} \times 350 \times 10^{-12}}$.

7-11. The Power of a Power. It becomes necessary, in order to work a variety of problems utilizing the powers of ten, to consider a few new definitions concerning the laws of exponents before we study them in algebra. This, however, should present no difficulty.

In finding the power of a power the exponents are multiplied. That is, in general,

$$(a^m)^n = a^{mn} \qquad \text{(where } a \neq 0)$$

Example 1. $(100)^3 = 100 \times 100 \times 100 = 1,000,000 = 10^6$

or $(100)^3 = 10^2 \times 10^2 \times 10^2 = 10^6$

Then $(100)^3 = (10^2)^3 = 10^{2 \times 3} = 10^6$

Numbers may be factored when raised to a power in order to reduce the labor in obtaining the correct number of significant figures, or properly fixing the decimal point.

Example 2. $(19,000)^3 = (1.9 \times 10^4)^3$
$$= (1.9)^3 \times 10^{4 \times 3}$$
$$= 6.859 \times 10^{12}$$

Example 3.
$$(0.0000075)^2 = (7.5 \times 10^{-6})^2$$
$$= (7.5)^2 \times 10^{(-6)\times 2}$$
$$= 56.25 \times 10^{-12}$$
$$= 5.625 \times 10^{-11}$$

In Example 2, 19,000 was factored into 1.9×10^4 in order to allow an easy mental check. Because 1.9 is nearly 2 and $2^3 = 8$, it is apparent that the result of cubing 1.9 must be 6.859, not 0.6859 or 68.59.

In Example 3, the 0.0000075 was factored for the same reason. We know that $7^2 = 49$; therefore the result of squaring 7.5 must be 56.25, not 0.5625 or 5.625.

7-12. The Power of a Product. The power of a product is the same as the product of the powers of the factors. That is, in general,

$$(abc)^m = a^m b^m c^m$$

Example.
$$(10^5 \times 10^3)^3 = 10^{5\times 3} \times 10^{3\times 3}$$
$$= 10^{15} \times 10^9$$
$$= 10^{24}$$

Or
$$(10^5 \times 10^3)^3 = (10^8)^3 = 10^{8\times 3} = 10^{24}$$

7-13. The Power of a Fraction. The power of a fraction equals the power of the numerator divided by the power of the denominator. That is,

$$\left(\frac{a}{b}\right)^m = \frac{a^m}{b^m}$$

Example.
$$\left(\frac{10^5}{10^3}\right)^2 = \frac{10^{5\times 2}}{10^{3\times 2}} = \frac{10^{10}}{10^6} = 10^4$$

The above may be solved by first clearing the exponents inside the parenthesis and then raising to the required power. Thus,

$$\left(\frac{10^5}{10^3}\right)^2 = (10^{5-3})^2 = (10^2)^2 = 10^4$$

7-14. The Root of a Power. The root of a power in exponents is given by

$$\sqrt[n]{a^m} = a^{m \div n} \qquad \text{(where } a \neq 0)$$

Example 1. $\sqrt{25 \times 10^8} = \sqrt{25} \times \sqrt{10^8} = 5 \times 10^{8 \div 2} = 5 \times 10^4$

Example 2. $\sqrt[3]{125 \times 10^6} = \sqrt[3]{125} \times \sqrt[3]{10^6} = 5 \times 10^{6 \div 3} = 5 \times 10^2$

In the general case where (m) is evenly divisible by (n) the process of extracting roots is comparatively simple. When (m)

is not evenly divisible by (n), the result obtained by extracting the root is a fractional power.

Example 3. $\sqrt{10^5} = 10^{5 \div 2} = 10^{\frac{5}{2}}$, or $10^{2.5}$

Such fractional exponents are encountered in various phases of engineering mathematics and are conveniently solved by the use of logarithms. However, in using the powers of ten, the fractional exponent is cumbersome for obtaining a final answer. It becomes necessary, therefore, to devise some means of extracting a root whereby an integer may be obtained as an exponent in the final result.

This is accomplished by expressing the number, the root of which is desired, as some number times the proper power of ten, the power of ten being evenly divisible by the index of the required root. As an example, suppose it is desired to extract the square root of 400,000. Though it is true that

$$\sqrt{400{,}000} = \sqrt{4 \times 10^5} = \sqrt{4} \times \sqrt{10^5} = 2 \times 10^{2.5}$$

we have a fractional exponent that is not readily reduced to actual figures. However, if we express the number differently, we obtain an integer as an exponent. Thus,

$$\sqrt{400{,}000} = \sqrt{40 \times 10^4} = \sqrt{40} \times \sqrt{10^4} = 6.32 \times 10^2$$

It will be noted that there are a number of ways of expressing the above square root, such as

$$\sqrt{400{,}000} = \sqrt{0.4 \times 10^6} \quad \text{or} \quad \sqrt{4000 \times 10^2} \quad \text{or} \quad \sqrt{0.004 \times 10^8}, \text{ etc.}$$

All are equally correct, but the student should try to write the problem in a form that will allow a rough mental approximation in order that the decimal may be properly placed with respect to the significant figures.

PROBLEMS 7-4

Perform the indicated operations. Where answers do not come out in round numbers, express to three significant figures.

1. $(10^4)^3$.

2. $(10^2 \times 10^3)^3$.

3. $(10^{-3})^4$.

4. $(3 \times 10^{-3})^2$.

5. $(5 \times 10^4)^3$.

6. $(7 \times 10^{-3})^3$.

7. $(8 \times 10^4 \times 2 \times 10^5)^2$.

8. $\left[\dfrac{8 \times 10^4}{2 \times 10^3}\right]^2$.

9. $\sqrt{0.0025 \times 0.0004}$.

10. $\sqrt{0.00081 \times 0.009}$.

11. $\sqrt{64 \times 10^{-5} \times 25 \times 10^9}$.

12. $\dfrac{1}{6.28\sqrt{4 \times 10^3 \times 7 \times 10^{-6}}}$.

13. $\dfrac{159 \times 10}{\sqrt{45 \times 10^{-6} \times 25 \times 10^{-11}}}$.

14. $\dfrac{159 \times 10^3}{\sqrt{0.000169 \times 0.000350 \times 10^{-6}}}$.

15. $\left(\dfrac{63 \times 10^3 \times 46 \times 10^{-8}}{0.0000051}\right)^2$.

CHAPTER VIII

UNITS

Before taking up the study of practical radio and electrical problems, it is necessary to define a few of the more common electrical units. Problems involving some of these units will be included in Chaps. IX and X, whereas other units will not be used for some time.

8-1. The Volt. The *volt* is the unit of electromotive force, or electric potential. It is that potential which will cause a current of 1 ampere to flow through a resistance of 1 ohm.

8-2. The Ampere. The *ampere* is the unit of electric current. It is that amount of current which will flow through a resistance of 1 ohm when a potential of 1 volt is applied across the resistance.

8-3. The Ohm. The *ohm* is the unit of resistance. It is that amount of resistance which will permit 1 ampere to flow at a potential difference of 1 volt.

8-4. The Mho. The *mho* is the unit of conductance. It is the reciprocal of resistance; that is, the relation between conductance G and resistance R is given by

$$G = \frac{1}{R}$$

If the resistance is thought of as representing the *difficulty* with which an electric current is forced through a circuit, the conductivity may be thought of as the *ease* with which an electric current may be forced through the same circuit. Note that the word "mho" is simply "ohm" spelled backward.

8-5. The Watt. The *watt* is the unit of electrical power. In direct-current circuits the power in watts is the product of the voltage times the current, or

$$P = EI$$

8-6. The Henry. The *henry* is the unit of inductance. A circuit is said to have a self-inductance of 1 henry when a counter electromotive force of 1 volt is generated by a rate of change of current of 1 ampere per second.

69

8-7. The Farad. The *farad* is the unit of capacitance. A condenser is said to have a capacitance of 1 farad when a change of 1 volt per second across it produces a current of 1 ampere.

8-8. Frequency. A current that reverses itself at regular intervals is called an *alternating current.* When this current rises from zero to maximum, returns to zero, increases to maximum in the opposite direction, and finally falls to zero again, it is said to have completed one *cycle.* The number of times this cycle is repeated in 1 second is known as the *frequency* of the alternating current. Thus the average house current is 60 cycles per second. The frequency of radio waves may be as high as many millions of cycles per second.

8-9. Ranges of Units. The fields of communication and electrical engineering embrace extremely wide ranges in values of the foregoing units. For example, at the input of a radio receiver, we deal in millionths of a volt, whereas the output circuit of a transmitter may develop hundreds of thousands of volts. An electric clock might consume a fraction of a watt, whereas the powerhouse furnishing this power probably has a capability of millions of watts.

Furthermore, two of these units, the henry and the farad, are very large units, especially the latter. The average radio receiver employs inductances ranging from a few millionths of a henry, as represented by tuning inductance, to several henrys for power filters. The farad is so large that even the largest capacitors, or condensers, are rated in millionths of a farad. Smaller capacitors used in radio circuits are often rated in terms of so many millionths of one-millionth of a farad.

The use of some power of ten is very convenient in converting to larger multiples or smaller fractions of the basic so-called *practical* units.

8-10. Milliunits. The *milliunit* is one-thousandth of a unit. Thus, 1 volt is equal to 1000 millivolts, 500 milliamperes is equal to 0.5 ampere, etc. This unit is commonly used in connection with volts, amperes, henrys, and watts. It is abbreviated m. Thus, 10 mh = 10 millihenrys.*

8-11. Microunits. The *microunit* is one-millionth of a unit. Thus, 1 ampere is equal to 1,000,000, or 10^6, microamperes:

---

* See Table III, page 501, for standard abbreviations.

2,000,000 microfarads is equal to 2 farads, etc. This unit is commonly used in connection with volts, amperes, ohms, mhos, henrys, and farads. It is represented by μ. Thus, 5 μf means 5 microfarads.

8-12. Micromicrounits. The *micromicrounit* is one-millionth of one-millionth of a unit. Thus, 1 farad is equal to 1,000,000,-000,000, or 10^{12}, micromicrofarads. This unit is seldom used for other than farads. It is represented by $\mu\mu$. Thus, 250 $\mu\mu$f means 250 micromicrofarads.

8-13. Kilounits. The *kilounit* is 1000 basic units. Thus, 1 kilovolt is equal to 1000 volts. This unit is commonly used with cycles, volts, amperes, watts, and volt-amperes. It is abbreviated k. Thus, 35 kw means 35 kilowatts; 2000 cycles = 2 kc (2 kilocycles per second).

8-14. Megunits. The *megunit* is 1,000,000, or 10^6, basic units. Thus, 1 megohm is equal to 10^6 ohms. This unit is used mainly for ohms and cycles.

8-15. Conversion Factors. Although Table IV consists of conversion factors, the following table is included here to enable the student to see the whole picture of unit conversion in simplified form:

Multiply	By	To obtain
Units....................	10^3	milliunits
Milliunits...............	10^3	microunits
Units....................	10^6	microunits
Units....................	10^{12}	micromicrounits
Microunits...............	10^6	micromicrounits
Micromicrounits..........	10^{-6}	microunits
Micromicrounits..........	10^{-12}	units
Microunits...............	10^{-6}	units
Microunits...............	10^{-3}	milliunits
Milliunits...............	10^{-3}	units
Kilounits..	10^3	units
Units....................	10^{-3}	kilounits
Megunits.................	10^6	units
Units....................	10^{-6}	megunits
Kilounits................	10^{-3}	megunits
Megunits.................	10^3	kilounits

In some electrical texts, it will be noted the term "microfarad" is written Mfd; also, some capacitors are marked in the same manner.   This is simply an abbreviation for microfarad.   The preferred abbreviation is μf.

Example 1.   Convert 8 microfarads to farads.

Solution: $8 \, \mu f = 8 \times 10^{-6} \, f$

Example 2.   Convert 250 milliamperes to amperes.

Solution: $250 \, ma = 250 \times 10^{-3} \, a$
$= 2.50 \times 10^{-1} \, a$
or $= 0.250 \, a$

Example 3.   Convert 1500 watts to kilowatts.

Solution: $1500 \, w = 1500 \times 10^{-3} \, kw$
or $= 1.5 \, kw$

Example 4.   Convert 200,000 ohms to megohms.

Solution: $200,000 \, \Omega = 200,000 \times 10^{-6} \, M\Omega$
$= 0.2 \, M\Omega$

Example 5.   Convert 2500 kilocycles to megacycles.

Solution: $2500 \, kc = 2500 \times 10^{-3} \, Mc$
$= 2.500 \, Mc$

Example 6.   Convert 0.000450 mho to micromhos.

Solution: $0.000450 \, mho = 0.000450 \times 10^{6} \, micromhos$
or $= 450 \, micromhos$

PROBLEMS 8-1

Express answers as numbers between 1 and 10, times the proper power of ten.

1. $0.02 \, a =$ (a)_____ma?   (b)_____μa?

2. $3.42 \, a =$ (a)_____μa?   (b)_____ma?

3. $0.350 \, a =$ (a)_____ma?   (b)_____μa?

4. $0.042 \, v =$ (a)_____mv?   (b)_____μv?   (c)_____kv?

5. $25 \, ma =$ (a)_____a?   (b)_____μa?

6. $0.00025 \, \mu f =$ (a)_____f?   (b)_____$\mu\mu$f?

7. $358 \, mh =$ (a)_____μh?   (b)_____h?

8. $13.5 \, kv =$ (a)_____v?   (b)_____μv?   (c)_____mv?

9. $150 \, \mu h =$ (a)_____h?   (b)_____mh?

10. $350 \, \mu\mu f =$ (a)_____f?   (b)_____μf?

11. $0.0045 \, M\Omega =$ (a)_____Ω?   (b)_____$\mu\Omega$?

12. $165,000 \, \Omega =$ (a)_____$M\Omega$?   (b)_____$\mu\Omega$?

13. 250 w =   *(a)*____kw?   *(b)*____mw?
14. 4.3 kv =   *(a)*____v?   *(b)*____mv?
15. 0.000000035 f = *(a)*____μf?   *(b)*____μμf?
16. 36.4 kw =   *(a)*____w?   *(b)*____mw?
17. 30 μμf =   *(a)*____f?   *(b)*____μf?
18. 16.2 μa =   *(a)*____ma?   *(b)*____ɩ?
19. 125 μh =   *(a)*____mh?   *(b)*____h?
20. 0.002 μf =   *(a)*____f?   *(b)*____μμf?
21. 500 μμf =   *(a)*____μf?   *(b)*____f?
22. 0.65 h =   *(a)*____mh?   *(b)*____μh?
23. 0.003 MΩ =   *(a)*____Ω?   *(b)*____μΩ?
24. 12.5 μa =   *(a)*____a?   *(b)*____ma?
25. 0.2 v =   *(a)*____μv?   *(b)*____mv?
26. 10,000 ∼ =   *(a)*____kc?   *(b)*____Mc?
27. 4.35 Mc =   *(a)*____∼?   *(b)*____kc?
28. 4135 kc =   *(a)*____Mc?   *(b)*____∼?
29. 0.0340 mho = ____micromhos?
30. 1260 micromhos = ____mhos?

8-16. Significant Figures. The subjects of accuracy and significant figures were discussed in Arts. 7-2 and 7-4. Now that we have some idea of the various units used in electrical and radio problems, two questions arise:

1. To how many significant figures should an answer be expressed?

2. How may we definitely show that an answer is correct to just so many significant figures?

The answer to the first question is comparatively easy. No answer can be more accurate than the figures, or data, used in the problem. As stated in Art. 7-2, it is safe to assume that the values of the average circuit components and calibrations of meters that we use in our everyday work are not known beyond three significant figures. Therefore, in the future we shall round off long answers and express them to three significant figures. The exception will be when it is necessary to carry figures out in order carefully to demonstrate some fact or law.

The second question brings out some interesting points. As an example, suppose we have a resistance of 500,000 ohms and we want to write this value so that it will be apparent to anyone that the figure 500,000 is correct to three significant figures.

This may be accomplished by writing

$$500 \times 10^3 \ \Omega$$
$$50.0 \times 10^4 \ \Omega$$
$$5.00 \times 10^5 \ \Omega, \text{ etc.}$$

Any of these expressions definitely shows that the resistance is correct to three significant figures. Similarly, suppose we had measured the capacitance of a condenser to be 3500 micromicrofarads. How shall we specify that the figure 3500 is correct to three significant figures? Again, this is accomplished by writing

$$350 \times 10 \ \mu\mu f$$
$$35.0 \times 10^2 \ \mu\mu f$$
$$3.50 \times 10^3 \ \mu\mu f, \text{ etc.}$$

As in the previous example, there are definitely three figures, in the first factor, that show the degree of accuracy.

CHAPTER IX

OHM'S LAW—SERIES CIRCUITS

Ohm's law for the electric circuit is the foundation of electric-circuit analysis and is, therefore, of fundamental importance. The various relations of Ohm's law are easily learned and readily applied to practical circuits. A thorough knowledge of these relations and their applications is essential to an understanding of the electric circuit.

This chapter concerns itself with the study of Ohm's law in direct-current series circuits as applied to *parts* of a circuit. For this reason, the internal resistance of a source of voltage, such as a generator or a battery, and the resistance of the wires connecting the parts of a circuit will not be discussed in this chapter.

9-1. The Electric Circuit. An electric circuit consists of a source of voltage which is connected by means of conductors to the apparatus that is to use the electrical energy.

An electric current will flow between two points in a conductor when a difference of potential exists across these points. The most generally accepted concept of an electric current is that it consists of a motion, or flow, of electrons from the negative toward a more positive point in a circuit. The force that causes the motion of electrons is called an *electromotive force*, or a *potential difference*, and the opposition to their motion is called *resistance*.

The basic theories of electrical phenomena and the methods of producing currents are not within the scope of this book. The student will find these adequately treated in the great majority of textbooks on the subject.

9-2. Ohm's Law. Ohm's law for the electric circuit, reduced to plain terms, states the relation that exists between voltage, current, and resistance. One way of stating this relation is as follows: The voltage across any *part* of a circuit is proportional to the product of the current through that *part* of the circuit and the resistance of that *part* of the circuit. Stated as a formula the foregoing is expressed as

$$E = IR \qquad (1)$$

where E = voltage, or potential difference, in volts,
  I = current in amperes,
  R = resistance in ohms.

If any two factors are known the third may be found by solving Eq. (1). Thus,

$$I = \frac{E}{R} \qquad (2)$$

and

$$R = \frac{E}{I} \qquad (3)$$

9-3. Methods of Solution. The general outline for working problems given in Art. 6-10 is applicable to the solution of circuit problems. In addition, a neat, simplified diagram of the circuit should be drawn for each problem. The diagram should be labeled with all the known values of the circuit such as voltage, current, and resistances. In this manner the circuit and problem can be visualized and understood. Solving a problem by making purely mechanical substitutions in the proper formulas is not conducive to a complete understanding of any problem.

Example 1. How much current will flow through a resistance of 20 ohms if the applied voltage across the resistance is 110 volts?

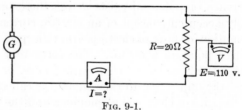

FIG. 9-1.

Solution: The circuit is represented in Fig. 9-1.

Given E = 110 v   and R = 20 Ω
          I = ?

$$I = \frac{E}{R} = \frac{110}{20} = 5.50 \text{ a}$$

Example 2. A voltmeter connected across a resistance reads 220 volts, and an ammeter connected in series with the resistance reads 2.60 amperes. What is the value of the resistance?

Solution: The circuit is represented in Fig. 9-2.

Given E = 220 v   and I = 2.60 a
          R = ?

$$R = \frac{E}{I} = \frac{220}{2.60} = 84.6 \text{ } \Omega$$

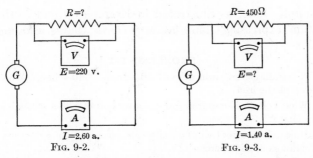

$R=?$ $R=450\Omega$

$E=220$ v. $E=?$

$I=2.60$ a. $I=1.40$ a.
Fig. 9-2.   Fig. 9-3.

Example 3.   A current of 1.40 amperes flows through a resistance of 450 ohms.   What should be the reading of a voltmeter when connected across the resistance?

Solution: The diagram of the circuit is shown in Fig. 9-3.

Given $I = 1.40$ a   and $R = 450$ Ω
                      $E = ?$
                 $E = IR = 1.40 \times 450 = 630$ v

Example 4.   A measurement shows a potential difference of 63.0 microvolts across a resistance of 300 ohms.   How much current is flowing through the resistance?

Solution: The circuit is represented in Fig. 9-4.

Given $E = 63.0$ μv $= 6.3 \times 10^{-5}$ v,   and $R = 300$ Ω
            $I = ?$

$$I = \frac{E}{R} = \frac{6.3 \times 10^{-5}}{300} = \frac{6.3 \times 10^{-7}}{3.00} = 2.1 \times 10^{-7} \text{ a}$$

or $I = 0.21$ μa

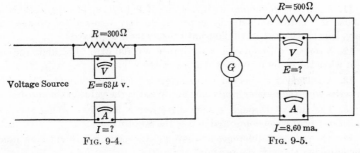

$R=500\Omega$

$R=300\Omega$

Voltage Source $E=63\mu$ v. $E=?$

$I=?$ $I=8.60$ ma.
Fig. 9-4.   Fig. 9-5.

Example 5.   A current of 8.60 milliamperes flows through a resistance of 500 ohms.   What voltage exists across the resistance?

Solution: The circuit is represented in Fig. 9-5.

Given $I = 8.60$ ma $= 8.60 \times 10^{-3}$ a,   and $R = 500$ Ω
            $E = ?$
       $E = IR = 8.60 \times 10^{-3} \times 500 = 8.60 \times 10^{-3} \times 5 \times 10^2$
                                    $= 8.60 \times 5 \times 10^{-1}$
                                    $= 4.30$ v

Carefully note, as illustrated in Examples 4 and 5, that the equations expressing Ohm's law are in *units*, that is, *volts, amperes,* and *ohms*.

PROBLEMS 9-1

1. A certain electric iron draws 3.20 a from a 110-v line. What is the resistance of the iron?

2. What voltage is required to force a current of 4.40 a through a resistance of 50.0 Ω?

3. How much current will flow through a resistance of 80.0 Ω if a potential of 440 v is applied across it?

4. A 220-v tungsten lamp has a resistance of 520 Ω when connected to a 220-v line. How much current flows through the lamp?

5. A coil is marked "Resistance = 25 Ω, maximum allowable current = 350 ma." What is the maximum voltage which should be applied to the coil?

6. The tungsten lamp in Prob. 4 has resistance of 50.0 Ω when cold. What current flows through the lamp at the instant the lamp is connected to the 220-v line?

7. A milliammeter connected in series with a resistor reads 15.0 ma, and a voltmeter connected across the resistor reads 4.50 v. What is the value of the resistance?

8. A current of 27.0 μa flows through a resistance of 3.00 MΩ. What is the voltage across the resistance?

9. How much current will 2.35 kv force through a resistance of 3000 Ω?

10. What potential in microvolts is required to force a current of 560 ma through a resistance of 0.0250 MΩ?

11. A certain ammeter, with a scale of 0 to 25 a, has a resistance of 0.0080 Ω. If this ammeter is connected directly across a 6-v storage battery, how much current will flow until the meter is destroyed?

12. A certain voltmeter has a resistance of 0.100 MΩ. Calculate the current when the meter is connected across a 440-v line.

13. A voltmeter connected across a resistor reads 108 v, and an ammeter in series with the resistor reads 2.50 a. What is the value of the resistance?

14. The current through a 2500-Ω resistor is 3.25 ma. What should a voltmeter read when connected across the resistor?

15. The potential difference across a 600-Ω resistor is 1.73 v. How much current flows through the resistor?

16. An electric lamp is designed to carry 0.750 a. Its hot resistance is 148 Ω. For what line voltage was the lamp designed?

17. The resistance of a relay coil is 150 Ω, and it requires 145 ma to operate the relay. What is the lowest voltage necessary to operate the relay?

18. The maximum resistance of a field rheostat is 3.05 Ω, and the minimum resistance is 0.750 Ω. What is the voltage across the rheostat for each condition when the current through the rheostat is 16.4 a?

19. The cold resistance of a carbon-filament lamp is 400 Ω, and the hot resistance is 380 Ω. Determine the current that flows at the instant it is connected across a 220-v line and the current when the constant operating temperature is reached.

20. What is the potential difference across a resistance of 10,000 Ω when 2.50 ma flows through it?

21. A buzzer requires 150 ma at 2.5 v for operation. How much resistance does it represent?

9-4. Power. In specifying the rating of electrical apparatus, it is customary to state not only the voltage at which it is designed to operate but also the rate at which it produces or consumes electrical energy.

The rate of producing or consuming energy is called *power*, and electrical energy is measured in watts or kilowatts. Thus, your study lamp may be rated 100 watts at 110 volts; a generator may be rated 2000 kilowatts at 440 volts, etc.

Electric motors are generally rated in terms of the mechanical horsepower they will develop. The conversion from electrical energy to equivalent mechanical energy is given by the relation

$$746 \text{ w} = 1 \text{ hp}$$

9-5. The Watt. Energy is expended at a rate of 1 watt-second every second, when 1 volt causes a current of 1 ampere to flow. In this case, we say that the power represented, when 1 volt causes 1 ampere to flow, is 1 watt. This relation is expressed as

$$P = EI \tag{4}$$

This is a useful equation when the voltage and current are known.

Because, by Ohm's law, $E = IR$, this value of E may be substituted in Eq. (4). Thus,

$$P = (IR)I$$

or $$P = I^2R \tag{5}$$

This is a useful equation when the current and resistance are known.

By substituting the value of I of Eq. (2) in Eq. (4),

$$P = E\left(\frac{E}{R}\right)$$

or $$P = \frac{E^2}{R} \tag{6}$$

This is a useful equation when the voltage and resistance are known.

Watt-hours—Kilowatt-hours. The consumer of electrical energy pays for the amount of energy used by his apparatus. This is measured by instruments known as *watt-hour* or *kilowatt-hour meters.* These meters record the amount of energy taken by the consumer.

Electrical energy is sold at so much per kilowatt-hour. One watt-hour of energy is consumed when 1 watt of power continues in action for 1 hour. Similarly, 1 kilowatt-hour is consumed when the power is 1000 watts and the action continues for 1 hour, or when a 100-watt rate persists for 10 hours, etc. Thus the amount of energy consumed is the product of the power and the time.

9-6. Losses. In physics, the study of the various forms in which energy may occur and the transformation of one kind of energy into another has led to the important principle known as the principle of the *conservation of energy.* Briefly, this states that energy can never be created or destroyed. It can be transformed from one form to another, but the total amount remains unchanged. Thus, an electric motor converts electrical energy into mechanical energy, the incandescent lamp changes electrical energy into heat energy, the loud-speaker converts electrical energy into sound energy, the generator converts mechanical energy into electrical energy, etc. In each instance the transformation from one type of energy to another is not accomplished with 100 per cent efficiency because some energy is converted into heat and does no useful work as far as that particular conversion is concerned.

Resistance in a circuit may serve a number of useful purposes; but unless it has been specifically designed for heating or dissipation purposes, the energy transformed in the resistance generally serves no useful purpose.

9-7. Efficiency. Because every electrical apparatus contains resistance, there must always be some heat developed when current flows. Unless the apparatus is to be used for producing heat, the heat due to the resistance of the apparatus represents wasted energy. No electrical apparatus or other machine is capable of converting energy received into useful work without some loss.

The power that is furnished a machine is called its *input,* and the power received from a machine is called its *output.* The efficiency of a machine is equal to the ratio of the output to the input. That is,

$$\text{Efficiency} = \frac{\text{output}}{\text{input}} \tag{7}$$

It is evident that the efficiency, as given in Eq. (7), is always a decimal, that is, a number less than 1. Naturally, in Eq. (7), the output and input must be expressed in the same units. Hence, if the output is expressed in kilowatts, then the input must be expressed in kilowatts; if the output is expressed in horsepower, then the input must be expressed in horsepower, etc.

Example 1. A voltage of 110 volts across a resistor causes a current of 5 amperes to flow through it. How much power is expended in the resistor?

Solution: The circuit is represented in Fig. 9-6.

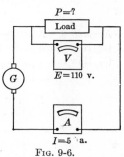

FIG. 9-6.

Given $E = 110$ v   and $I = 5$ a
         $P = ?$

Using Eq. (4),

$$P = EI = 110 \times 5 = 550 \text{ w}$$

Alternate Solution: Find the value of the resistance and use it to solve for *P*. Thus, using Eq. (3),

$$R = \frac{E}{I} = \frac{110}{5} = 22 \ \Omega$$

Using Eq. (5), $P = I^2R = 5^2 \times 22 = 5 \times 5 \times 22 = 550$ w

Alternate Solution: Using Eq. (6),

$$P = \frac{E^2}{R} = \frac{(110)^2}{22} = \frac{110 \times 110}{22} = 550 \text{ w}$$

Solving a problem by two methods serves as an excellent check on the results, for there is little chance of making the same error twice, as is too often the case when a problem is repeated using the same method of solution.

Example 2. A current of 2.5 amperes flows through a resistance of 40 ohms.

(a) How much power is expended in the resistor?

(b) What is the potential difference across the resistor?

Solution: The circuit is represented in Fig. 9-7.

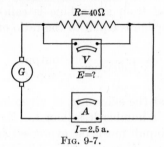

$R=40\,\Omega$

$E=?$

$I=2.5$ a.

FIG. 9-7.

Given $I = 2.5$ a   and $R = 40\ \Omega$

$P = ?$ $E = ?$

(a) $P = I^2R = (2.5)^2 \times 40 = 2.5 \times 2.5 \times 40 = 250$ w

(b) $E = IR = 2.5 \times 40 = 100$ v

Alternate Solutions: (a) Find E, as above, and use it to solve for P.

Thus, $P = \dfrac{E^2}{R} = \dfrac{(100)^2}{40} = \dfrac{100 \times 100}{40} = 250$ w

or $P = EI = 100 \times 2.5 = 250$ w

Example 3. A voltage of 1.732 volts is applied across a 500-ohm resistor.
(a) How much power is expended in the resistor?
(b) How much current flows through the resistor?

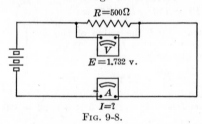

$R=500\,\Omega$

$E=1.732$ v.

$I=?$

FIG. 9-8.

Solution: A diagram of the circuit is shown in Fig. 9-8.

Given $E = 1.732$ v   and $R = 500\ \Omega$

$P = ?$ $I = ?$

(a) $P = \dfrac{E^2}{R} = \dfrac{(1.732)^2}{500} = \dfrac{(1.732)^2}{5 \times 10^2} = \dfrac{(1.732)^2}{5} \times 10^{-2} = 0.006$ w

or $P = 6$ mw

(b) $I = \dfrac{E}{R} = \dfrac{1.732}{500} = \dfrac{1.732}{5} \times 10^{-2} = 0.346 \times 10^{-2}$ a

or $I = 3.46$ ma

Check the foregoing solution for power by using an alternate method.

Example 4. (a) What is the hot resistance of a 100-watt 110-volt lamp?
(b) How much current does it take?

(c) At 4 cents per kilowatt-hour, how much does it cost to operate this lamp for 24 hours?

Solution: The circuit is represented in Fig. 9-9.

Given $P = 100$ w   and $E = 110$ v

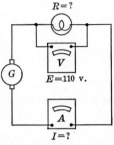

R = ?

(a) Because the power and voltage are known and the resistance is unknown, an equation that contains these three must be used.   Thus,

$$P = \frac{E^2}{R} \qquad (6)$$

Hence, $R = \dfrac{E^2}{P} = \dfrac{(110)^2}{100} = 121 \ \Omega$

(b) $I = \dfrac{E}{R} = \dfrac{110}{121} = 0.909$ a

Fig. 9-9.

(c) If the lamp is lighted for 24 hours, it will consume $100 \times 24 = 2400$ watt-hours $= 2.40$ kilowatt-hours.   At 4 cents per kilowatt-hour the cost would be

$$2.4 \times 4 = 9.6 \text{ cents}$$

Alternate Solution: The current may be found first by making use of the relation

$$P = EI \qquad (4)$$

which results in $I = \dfrac{P}{E} = \dfrac{100}{110} = 0.909$ a

The resistance may now be determined by

$$R = \frac{E}{I} = \frac{110}{0.909} = 121 \ \Omega$$

The solution may be checked by

$$P = I^2R = (0.909)^2 \times 121 = 100 \text{ w}$$

which is the power rating of the lamp as given in the example.   The cost is computed as before.

Example 5.   A motor delivering 6.50 mechanical horsepower is drawing 26.5 amperes from a 220-volt line.

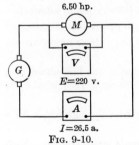

6.50 hp.

E = 220 v.

I = 26.5 a.
Fig. 9-10.

(a) How much electrical power is the motor taking from the line?

(b) What is the efficiency of the motor?

(c) If power costs 3 cents per kilowatt-hour, how much does it cost to run the motor for 8 hours?

Solution: A diagram of the circuit is shown in Fig. 9-10.

Given $E = 220$ v, $I = 26.5$ a,   and mechanical horsepower

$$P = 6.5 \text{ hp} = 6.5 \times 746 = 4850 \text{ w} = 4.85 \text{ kw}$$

(a) The power taken by the motor is

$$P = EI = 220 \times 26.5 = 5830 \text{ w}$$
$$= 5.83 \text{ kw}$$

(b) $$\text{Efficiency} = \frac{\text{output}}{\text{input}} = \frac{4.85}{5.83} = 0.832$$
$$= 83.2\%$$

(c) Because the motor consumes 5.83 kilowatts, in 8 hours it would take

$$5.83 \times 8 = 46.6 \text{ kw-hr}$$

At 3 cents per kilowatt-hour, the cost would be

$$46.6 \times 0.03 = \$1.40$$

NOTE: The cost was computed in two steps for the purpose of illustrating the solution. When the student has become familiar with the method, the cost should be computed in one step. Thus,

$$\text{Cost} = 5.83 \times 8 \times 0.03 = \$1.40$$

From the foregoing examples, it will be noted that computations involving power consist mainly in the applications of Ohm's law. Little trouble will be encountered if each problem is given careful thought and a systematic procedure followed for the solution as previously outlined.

PROBLEMS 9-2

1. 2500 w = (a) _____ kw?
            (b) _____ hp?
2. 30,000 watts = (a) _____ kw?
                  (b) _____ hp?
3. 5.25 hp = (a) _____ kw?
            (b) _____ w?
4. What is the electrical horsepower of a generator that delivers 60 a at 440 v?
5. A Diesel engine is rated at 500 hp. What is its rating in kilowatts?
6. A 110-v electric iron takes 4.5 a. How much power does it consume?
7. A certain motor takes 550 w from a 220-v line. How much current does the motor take from the line?
8. A wattmeter and an ammeter are connected in the line ahead of a motor. When the motor is running, the wattmeter reads 1250 w, and the ammeter reads 4.5 a. What is the line voltage?
9. How much power is expended in a 50-Ω resistor through which 5.4 a flows?
10. There is a potential difference of 50 v across a 500-Ω resistor. How much power is being expended in the resistor?

11. The resistance in a certain voltmeter is 150,000 Ω. Determine the power expended in the voltmeter when connected across a 110-v line.

12. The resistance of a certain ammeter is 0.00075 Ω. Determine the power lost in the ammeter when it reads 150 a.

13. A voltmeter connected across a 1500-Ω cathode-biasing resistor reads 3 v.

(a) How much power is being expended in the resistor?

(b) How much current flows through the resistor?

14. A milliammeter connected in series with a 500-Ω cathode-biasing resistor reads 12.5 ma.

(a) How much power is being expended in the resistor?

(b) What is the voltage across the resistor?

15. A motor is running across a 440-v line. A kilowatt meter that measures the power taken by the motor reads 12.6 kw.

(a) How much current is being taken by the motor?

(b) If power costs 2.5 cents per kilowatt-hour, how much will it cost to run this motor for 24 hrs?

16. A certain radio receiver consumes 120 w. At 3.5 cents per kilowatt-hour, how long could this receiver be operated for $1.00?

17. An electric percolator that consumes 175 watts is used 45 min each day. At 4 cents per kilowatt-hour, how much will it cost to use the percolator for 30 days?

18. A motor takes the equivalent of 15 hp from a 220-v line. How much current does the motor take?

19. A voltage of 50μv is applied across a 300-Ω resistor.

(a) How much power is expended in the resistor?

(b) How much current flows through the resistor?

20. A motor is delivering 10.5 hp. A kilowattmeter that measures the power taken by the motor reads 9.80 kw.

(a) What is the efficiency of the motor?

(b) At 2.7 cents per kilowatt-hour, how much would it cost to run this motor continuously for 1 week?

21. It requires 40 hp to drive a generator that delivers 54.5 a at 440 v. What is the efficiency of the generator?

HINT: In this case the input is the power required to drive the generator.

22. A 7.5-hp motor has an efficiency of 80%. How many kilowatts are required to drive it?

HINT: Solve Eq. (7) for input.

23. A 220-v 5-hp motor has an efficiency of 76%.

(a) How many kilowatts does it consume?

(b) How much current does it take from the line?

(c) How much equivalent resistance does it represent?

(d) Power costs 3.5 cents per kilowatt-hour for the first 50 kw-hr, 3 cents per kilowatt-hour for the next 50 kw-hr, and 2 cents per kilowatt-hour from then on. How much does it cost to run this motor continuously for 1 week?

24. A generator delivers 67.5 a at 440 v with an efficiency of 78%. How much power is lost in the generator?

25. A 440-v 3-hp motor with an efficiency of 73% is coupled to a 3000-v generator that has an efficiency of 79%. With the motor running fully loaded,

(a) How much power does the motor take from the line?

(b) How much current does the motor take?

(c) How much power will the generator deliver when fully loaded?

(d) How much current will the generator deliver?

(e) What is the over-all efficiency, that is, from motor input to generator output?

9-8. Resistances in Series. So far, our studies of the electric circuit have taken into consideration but one electrical apparatus in the circuit, excluding the source of voltage. This is all very well for the purpose of becoming familiar with simple Ohm's law and power relations. However, practical circuits consist of more than one piece of apparatus as far as circuit computations are concerned.

In a *series circuit* the various apparatus comprising the circuit are so connected that the current, starting from the voltage source, must flow through each circuit component, in turn, before returning to the other side of the source.

There are three important facts concerning series circuits that must be borne in mind in order thoroughly to understand the action of such circuits and to facilitate their solution.

In a series circuit,

1. The total voltage is equal to the sum of the voltages across the different parts of the circuit.

2. The current in any part of the circuit is the same.

3. The total resistance of the circuit is equal to the sum of the resistances of the different parts.

Point 1 is practically self-evident. If the sum of all the potential differences (voltage drops) around the circuit were not equal to the applied voltage, there would be some voltage left over which would cause an increase in current. This increase in current would continue until it caused enough voltage drop across some resistance just to balance the applied voltage. Hence,

$$E_t = E_1 + E_2 + E_3 \cdots \tag{8}$$

Point 2 is evident, for the apparatus is connected so that the current must flow through each part in turn and there are no other paths back to the source.

To some, point 3 might not be self-evident. However, because it is agreed that the current I in Fig. 9-11 flows through all resistors, Eq. (8) may be used to demonstrate the truth of point 3

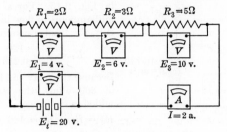

FIG. 9-11.

above.   Thus, by dividing each member of Eq. (8) by I,

$$\frac{E_t}{I} = \frac{E_1 + E_2 + E_3}{I}$$

or

$$\frac{E_t}{I} = \frac{E_1}{I} + \frac{E_2}{I} + \frac{E_3}{I}$$

Substituting R for $\frac{E}{I}$, $R_t = R_1 + R_2 + R_3$ (9)

NOTE: E_t and R_t are used to denote "total voltage" and "total resistance," respectively.

Example 1.   Three resistors $R_1 = 16.5$ ohms, $R_2 = 45.6$ ohms, and $R_3 = 67.9$ ohms are connected in series across a generator.   A voltmeter connected across R_2 reads 35 volts.   What is the voltage of the generator?

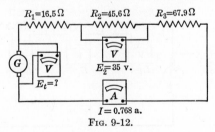

$I = 0.768$ a.
FIG. 9-12.

Solution: Figure 9-12 is a diagram of the circuit.

$$I = \frac{E_2}{R_2} = \frac{35}{45.6} = 0.768 \text{ a}$$

$$R_t = R_1 + R_2 + R_3 = 16.5 + 45.6 + 67.9 = 130 \ \Omega$$

$$E_t = IR_t = 0.768 \times 130 = 99.8 \text{ v}$$

Example 2.   A 300-ohm relay must be operated from a 120-volt line. How much resistance must be added in series with the relay coil to limit the current through it to 250 milliamperes?

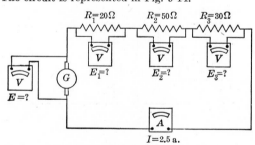

Solution: The circuit is represented in Fig. 9-13. For a current of 250 milliamperes to flow in a 120-volt circuit, the total resistance must be

$$R_t = \frac{E}{I} = \frac{120}{0.250} = 480 \ \Omega$$

Because the relay coil has a resistance of 300 ohms, the resistance to be added is

$$R_x = R_t - R_c = 480 - 300 = 180 \ \Omega$$

Alternate Solution: For 0.250 ampere to flow through the relay coil, the voltage across the coil must be

$$E_c = I R_c = 0.250 \times 300 = 75 \text{ v}$$

Because the line voltage is 120 volts, the voltage across the added resistance must be

$$E_x = E - E_c = 120 - 75 = 45 \text{ v}$$

Then the value of resistance to be added is

$$R_x = \frac{E_x}{I} = \frac{45}{0.250} = 180 \ \Omega$$

Example 3.   Three resistors $R_1 = 20$ ohms, $R_2 = 50$ ohms, and $R_3 = 30$ ohms are connected in series across a generator. The current through the circuit is 2.5 amperes.

(a) What is the generator voltage?
(b) What is the voltage across each resistor?
(c) How much power is expended in each resistor?
(d) What is the total power expended?

Solution: The circuit is represented in Fig. 9-14.

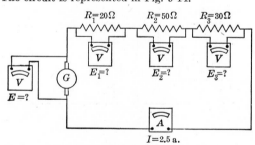

Fig. 9-14.

(a)
$$R_t = R_1 + R_2 + R_3 = 20 + 50 + 30 = 100 \ \Omega$$
$$E = I R_t = 2.5 \times 100 = 250 \text{ v}$$

(b)
$$E_1 = I R_1 = 2.5 \times 20 = 50 \text{ v}$$
$$E_2 = I R_2 = 2.5 \times 50 = 125 \text{ v}$$
$$E_3 = I R_3 = 2.5 \times 30 = 75 \text{ v}$$

Check.

$$E = E_1 + E_2 + E_3$$
$$= 50 + 125 + 75 = 250 \text{ v}$$

(c) Power in R_1, $P_1 = E_1 I = 50 \times 2.5 = 125 \text{ w}$

Check. $P_1 = I^2 R_1 = (2.5)^2 \times 20 = 125 \text{ w}$

Power in R_2, $P_2 = E_2 I = 125 \times 2.5 = 312.5 \text{ w}$

Check. $P_2 = I^2 R_2 = (2.5)^2 \times 50 = 312.5 \text{ w}$

Power in R_3, $P_3 = E_3 I = 75 \times 2.5 = 187.5 \text{ w}$

Check. $P_3 = I^2 R_3 = (2.5)^2 \times 30 = 187.5 \text{ w}$

(d) Total power, $P_t = P_1 + P_2 + P_3$
$$= 125 + 312.5 + 187.5 = 625 \text{ w}$$

Check. $P_t = I^2 R_t = (2.5)^2 \times 100 = 625 \text{ w}$

or $P_t = \dfrac{E^2}{R_t} = \dfrac{(250)^2}{100} = 625 \text{ w}$

PROBLEMS 9-3

1. Three resistors $R_1 = 7.25$ Ω, $R_2 = 4.12$ Ω, and $R_3 = 9.63$ Ω are connected in series across 110 v. How much current flows in the circuit?

2. Three resistors $R_1 = 6.87$ Ω, $R_2 = 9.13$ Ω, and $R_3 = 20.5$ Ω are connected in series across a 220-v generator. What is the voltage across each resistor?

3. A coil of 4.63 Ω, a lamp of 30.4 Ω, and a resistor of 15.6 Ω are connected in series across a generator. A voltmeter across the lamp reads 76 v. How much power is expended in the coil?

4. A 110-v soldering iron, which is rated at 300 w, is to be used on a 220-v line.

(a) How much resistance must be connected in series with the iron to limit the current to rated value?

(b) How much power will be expended in the added resistance?

5. Three lamps of equal voltage and power rating are connected in series across a 440-v line. If the current through the lamps is 680 ma, what is the resistance of each lamp?

6. Three resistors R_1, R_2, and R_3 are connected in series across a 115-v line. A voltmeter, when connected across R_1, reads 35 v; when connected across R_2, it reads 10 v. $R_3 = 45.5$ Ω.

(a) What is the value of R_1?

(b) What is the value of R_2?

(c) How much current flows through the circuit?

(d) How much power is expended in R_1?

7. An arc lamp that is designed to operate on a current of 5.7 a is to be used in a 220-v circuit. If the operating resistance of the lamp is 13.2 Ω, how much resistance must be connected in series with the lamp?

8. Four resistors of 20.5, 7.20, 63.7, and 88.6 Ω are connected in series across a 40-v generator. If 200 ma flow through the circuit, what is the resistance of the connecting wires?

9. Three resistors $R_1 = 35.5$ Ω, R_2, and R_3 are connected in series across a 115-v generator which results in a current of 1.63 a. The voltage across R_3 is 20.2 v.

(a) What is the value of R_2?

(b) How much power is expended in the circuit?

10. Four resistors $R_1 = 88.4$ Ω, $R_2 = 13.6$ Ω, $R_3 = 26.4$ Ω, and $R_4 = 46.4$ Ω are connected in series across a generator.   The voltage across R_2 is 36.3 v.

(a) What is the generator voltage?

(b) How much power is being supplied by the generator?

(c) What is the voltage across R_1?

CHAPTER X

RESISTANCE—WIRE SIZES

The effects of resistance in series circuits were discussed in the preceding chapter. However, in order to prevent confusion while the more simple relations of Ohm's law were being discussed, the nature of resistance and the resistance of wires used for connecting sources of voltage with their respective loads were not mentioned.

In the consideration of practical circuits two important features must be taken into account, the resistance of the wires between the source of power and the electrical appliances that are to be furnished with power, and the current-carrying capacity of these wires for a given temperature rise.

10-1. Resistance. There is a wide variation in the ease (conductance) of current flow through different materials. No material is a perfect conductor, and the amount of opposition (resistance) to current flow within it is governed by the specific resistance of the material, its length, cross-sectional area, and temperature. Thus, for the same material and cross-sectional area, a long conductor will have a greater resistance than a shorter one. That is, *the resistance of a conductor of uniform cross-sectional area is directly proportional to its length.* This is conveniently expressed as

$$\frac{R_1}{R_2} = \frac{L_1}{L_2} \tag{1}$$

where R_1 and R_2 are the resistances of conductors with lengths L_1 and L_2, respectively.

Example 1. The resistance of No. 8 copper wire is 0.641 ohm per 1000 feet. What is the resistance of 1 mile of the wire?

Solution: Given $R_1 = 0.641$ ohm, $L_1 = 1000$ feet, and $L_2 = 1$ mile $= 5280$ feet. $R_2 = ?$

Solving Eq. (1) for R_2, $R_2 = \dfrac{R_1 L_2}{L_1}$

$$= \frac{0.641 \times 5280}{1000} = 3.38 \ \Omega$$

For the same material and length, a conductor will have more resistance than another with a larger cross-sectional area. That is, *the resistance of a conductor is inversely proportional to its cross-sectional area.* Expressed as an equation,

$$\frac{R_1}{R_2} = \frac{A_2}{A_1} \tag{2}$$

where R_1 and R_2 are the resistances of conductors with cross-sectional areas A_1 and A_2, respectively.

Because most wires are drawn round, Eq. (2) can be rearranged into a more convenient form. For example, let A_1 and A_2 represent the cross-sectional areas of two equal lengths of round wires with diameters d_1 and d_2, respectively. Because the area A of a circle of a diameter d is given by

$$A = \frac{\pi d^2}{4}$$

then

$$A_1 = \frac{\pi d_1^2}{4}$$

and

$$A_2 = \frac{\pi d_2^2}{4}$$

Substituting in Eq. (2),

$$\frac{R_1}{R_2} = \frac{\dfrac{\pi d_2^2}{4}}{\dfrac{\pi d_1^2}{4}}$$

or

$$\frac{R_1}{R_2} = \frac{d_2^2}{d_1^2} \tag{3}$$

Hence, the resistance of a round conductor varies inversely as the square of its diameter.

Example 2. A rectangular conductor with a cross-sectional area of 0.01 square inch has a resistance of 0.075 ohm. What would be its resistance if the cross-sectional area were 0.02 square inch?

Solution: Given $R_1 = 0.075$ ohm, $A_1 = 0.01$ square inch, and $A_2 = 0.02$ square inch. $R_2 = ?$

Solving Eq. (2) for R_2,

$$R_2 = \frac{R_1 A_1}{A_2}$$

$$= \frac{0.075 \times 0.01}{0.02} = 0.0375 \ \Omega$$

Example 3.   A round conductor, with a diameter of 0.25 inch, has a resistance of 8 ohms.   What would be its resistance if the diameter were 0.5 inch?

Solution: Given $d_1 = 0.25$ inch, $R_1 = 8$ ohms, and $d_2 = 0.5$ inch. $R_2 = ?$

Solving Eq. (3) for R_2,

$$R_2 = \frac{R_1 d_1^2}{d_2^2}$$

$$= \frac{8 \times (0.25)^2}{(0.5)^2} = 2 \ \Omega$$

Hence, if the diameter is doubled, the cross-sectional area is increased four times and the resistance is reduced to one-quarter of its original value.

PROBLEMS 10-1

1. Number 10 copper wire has a resistance of 1.02 Ω per 1000 ft.   What is the resistance of 1 mile of this wire?

2. The values of Prob. 1 being used, what is the resistance of 3500 ft of No. 10 wire?

3. The values of Prob. 1 being used, what is the resistance of

(*a*) 150 ft of No. 10 wire?

(*b*) 60 ft of No. 10 wire?

4. Number 14 copper wire has a resistance of approximately 13.6 Ω per mile.   What is its resistance per 1000 ft?

5. The values of Prob. 4 being used, what is the resistance of

(*a*) 150 ft of No. 14 wire?

(*b*) 50 ft of No. 14 wire?

6. A square conductor that is 0.75 in. on a side has a resistance of 0.0084 Ω.   Another square conductor that is 0.25 in. on a side is of the same material and the same length.   What is the resistance of the second conductor?

7. Number 2 copper wire, which has a diameter of 0.258 in., has a resistance of 0.159 Ω per 1000 ft.   What is the resistance of 1000 ft of No. 6 wire, which has a diameter of 0.162 in.?

8. Number 00 copper wire, which has a diameter of 0.365 in., has a resistance of 0.420 Ω per mile.   What is the resistance of 500 ft of No. 0000 wire, which has a diameter of 0.460 in.?

9. The resistance of 90 ft of No. 18 copper wire was measured and found to be 0.586 Ω.   A coil wound of identical wire had a resistance of 2.80 Ω. Find the length of wire in the coil.

10. The resistance of 10 yd of No. 40 copper wire was found to be 32.1 Ω. ˙ A coil wound with identical wire had a resistance of 702 Ω.   Calculate the length of wire in the coil.

10-2. The Circular Mil.   In the measurement of wire cross section, it is convenient to use a small unit of measurement because the diameter of a wire is usually only a small fraction of an inch.   Accordingly, the diameter of a wire is expressed in terms of a unit called the *mil*, which is $\frac{1}{1000}$ inch. That is, there are 1000 mils in an inch. This is easily remembered because the mil is simply a milli-inch (Art. 8-10). For example, it is evident that using 64 mils as the diameter of No. 14 wire is more convenient than using 0.064 inch.

The cross-sectional areas of round conductors are measured in terms of the circular mil. The *circular mil*, abbreviated cir mil or C.M., is the area of a circle whose diameter is 1 mil.

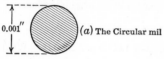
0.001″   (*a*) The Circular mil

The student should carefully note that the circular mil is a unit of *area* in its own right; except for purposes of comparison, it is seldom necessary to convert wire cross sections into any other units. The relative sizes of the circular mil and the square mil are illus-

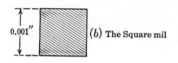
0.001″   (*b*) The Square mil

trated in Fig. 10-1.

The areas of circles vary as the squares of their diameters. For example, a circle whose diameter is 2 inches has four times the area of a circle having a diameter of 1 inch. Similarly, the area of a circle whose diameter is 0.003 inch

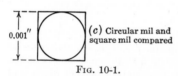
0.001″   (*c*) Circular mil and square mil compared

FIG. 10-1.

(3 mils) has nine times the area of a circle having a diameter of 0.001 inch (1 mil). Because, by definition, the circular mil is the area of a circle with a diameter of 1 mil, it is evident that a circle whose diameter is 3 mils must have an area of 9 circular mils. Hence the area of a circle can be expressed in circular mils by squaring the diameter, provided, however, that the diameter is expressed in mils. Conversely, if the area of a circle is expressed in circular mils, the diameter in mils can be found by extracting the square root of the area.

Example 1. Number 10 wire has a diameter of 0.102 inch. What is its circular-mil area?

Solution: Given d = 0.102 inch = 102 mils.

$$\text{Area} = (\text{diameter})^2 = 102^2 = 10,400 \text{ cir mils} \quad \text{(Art. 8-16)}$$

Example 2. Number 14 wire has a cross-sectional area of 4110 circular mils. What is the diameter?

Solution: Given A = 4,110 circular mils.

$$\text{Diameter} = \sqrt{\text{cir-mil area}} = \sqrt{4110} = 64 \text{ mils}$$

Because the area of a circle is

$$A = \frac{\pi d^2}{4}$$

or A = $0.7854d^2$ square units

it follows that

$$\text{Sq mils} = \text{cir mils} \times 0.7854 \tag{4}$$

From Eq. (4), $\text{Cir mils} = \dfrac{\text{sq mils}}{0.7854}$ (5)

Equations (4) and (5) are useful relations in determining the equivalence of round and rectangular conductors.

Example 3. A bus bar is 1 inch wide and $\frac{1}{4}$ inch thick. What is its circular-mil area?

Solution: Given

$$\text{Width} = 1 \text{ in.} = 1000 \text{ mils,}$$
and $\text{Thickness} = 0.25 \text{ in.} = 250 \text{ mils}$
$$\text{Area} = \text{width} \times \text{thickness} = 1000 \times 250 = 250{,}000 \text{ sq mils}$$
$$\text{Cir mils} = \frac{250{,}000}{0.7854} = 318{,}000 \text{ cir mils}$$

PROBLEMS 10-2

1. Find the circular-mil area of a wire 0.032 in. in diameter.

2. Find the circular-mil area of a wire 0.365 in. in diameter.

3. What is the cross-sectional area of a wire 20.1 mils in diameter?

4. What is the diameter in mils of a wire whose cross-sectional area is 642 cir mils?

5. Find the diameter in mils of a wire whose cross-sectional area is 168,000 cir mils.

6. Find the diameter in inches of a wire with a cross-sectional area of 202 cir mils.

7. A certain wire has a cross-sectional area of 6530 cir mils. What is its area in square mils?

8. A rectangular bus bar has a cross-sectional area of 1270 sq mils. What is its circular-mil area?

9. A wire has a cross-sectional area of 20,000 cir mils. What is the area in square inches?

10. A rectangular bus bar has a cross-sectional area of 0.25 sq in. Find its circular-mil area.

10-3. The Circular-mil-foot. For the purpose of computing the resistance of wires of various areas and lengths and for comparing the resistances of wires made of different materials, it is apparent that some standardized unit of wire size is needed. Hence, the circular-mil-foot has been taken as the unit conductor. A conductor having 1 circular mil cross-sectional area and a length of 1 foot is called a *circular-mil-foot*, or a *mil-foot*, of conductor. Such a conductor is represented in Fig. 10-2.

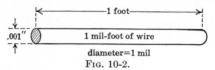

FIG. 10-2.

Since the resistance of a conductor is proportional to its length and inversely proportional to the area, the resistance of any wire may be expressed by the equation

$$R = \rho \frac{l}{d^2} \qquad (6)$$

where R = resistance of wire in ohms,
ρ = resistance in ohms per circular-mil-foot of the material composing the wire,
l = length of wire in feet,
d = diameter of wire in mils.

The factor ρ (Greek letter rho) in Eq. (6) is called the *specific resistance* or *resistivity* of the material. Thus, the specific resistance of a wire is the resistance of 1 mil-foot of that wire. The accompanying table lists the specific resistances of a few of the materials used for conductors.

SPECIFIC RESISTANCES AT 20°C. (68°F.)

Material	Ohms per circular mil-foot	Material	Ohms per circular mil-foot
Aluminum	17.0	Lead	132
Bismuth	663.	Mercury	565
Copper (drawn)	10.4	Nichrome	600 to 660
German silver	200 to 290	Nickel	47
Gold	14.7	Phosphor-bronze	23.7
Iron (cast)	448 to 588	Steel	95 to 308

Example 1.   What is the resistance at 20°C. of a copper wire 250 feet long and 5.6 mils in diameter?

Solution: Given $l = 250$ feet, $d = 5.6$ mils, and, from table, $\rho = 10.4$ ohms, $R = ?$

Substituting in Eq. (6), $R = \dfrac{10.4 \times 250}{5.6^2} = 82.9 \ \Omega$

Example 2.   The resistance of a conductor 1000 feet long and 32 mils in diameter was found to be 12 Ω at 20°C.   What is the specific resistance of the wire?

Solution: Given $l = 1000$ feet, $d = 32$ mils, and $R = 12$ ohms. $\rho = ?$

Solving Eq. (6) for ρ, $\rho = \dfrac{Rd^2}{l}$

Substituting the known values, $\rho = \dfrac{12 \times 32^2}{1000} = 12.3 \ \Omega$ per mil-foot

Example 3.   A roll of copper wire was found to have a resistance of 2.54 ohms at 20°C.   The diameter of the wire is 64 mils.   How long is the wire?

Solution: Given $R = 2.54$ ohms, $d = 64$ mils, and $\rho = 10.4$. $l = ?$

Solving Eq. (6) for l, $l = \dfrac{Rd^2}{\rho}$

Substituting the known values, $l = \dfrac{2.54 \times 64^2}{10.4} = 1000$ ft

PROBLEMS 10-3

Note: In the following problems, consider all wire temperatures as 20°C.

1. What is the resistance of a copper wire 250 ft long and 14.2 mils in diameter?

2. What is the resistance of an aluminum wire of the same dimensions as the wire in Prob. 1?

3. What is the resistance of a phosphor-bronze wire of the same dimensions as the wire in Prob. 1?

4. A German silver wire 15 ft long and 0.0031 in. in diameter has a resistance of 390 Ω.   What is the specific resistance?

5. What is the resistance per 1000 ft of copper wire with a diameter of 0.010 in.?

6. Fixture wire has a diameter of 0.064 in.   How many feet are required to make a resistance of 1 Ω?

7. A certain nichrome wire with a diameter 0.0201 in. has a specific resistance of 625 Ω per mil-foot.   How many feet are required to make a resistance of 5 Ω?

8. How many miles of copper wire 0.128 in. in diameter will it take to make 10 Ω resistance?

9. A coil of copper wire has a resistance of 0.792 Ω.   If the diameter of the wire is 81 mils, find the length of the wire.

10. What is the resistance of 2 miles of the wire in Prob. 9?

10-4. Temperature Effects. In the preceding article the specific resistance of certain materials was given at a temperature of 20°C. The reason for stating the temperature is that the resistance of all pure metals increases with a rise in temperature. The results of experiments show that over ordinary temperature ranges this variation in resistance is directly proportional to the temperature. Hence, for each degree rise in temperature, above some reference value, each ohm of resistance is increased by a constant amount α, called the *temperature coefficient of resistance*. The relation between temperature and resistance may be expressed by the equation

$$R_t = R_0(1 + \alpha t) \qquad (7)$$

where R_t = resistance at a temperature of t°C.,
R_0 = resistance at 0°C.,
α = temperature coefficient of resistance at 0°C.

The temperature coefficient for copper is 0.00427. That is, if a copper wire has a resistance of 1 ohm at 0°C., it will have a resistance of $1 + 0.00427 = 1.00427$ ohms at 1°C. The value of the temperature coefficient for copper is essentially the same as that for most of the unalloyed metals.

A more convenient relation is derived by assuming that the proportionality between resistance and temperature extends linearly to the point where copper has a resistance of 0 ohms at a temperature of -234.5°C. This results in the ratio

$$\frac{R_2}{R_1} = \frac{234.5 + t_2}{234.5 + t_1} \qquad (8)$$

where R_1 = resistance of copper in ohms at a temperature of t_1°C.,
R_2 = resistance of copper in ohms at a temperature of t_2°C.

Example 1. The resistance of a coil of copper wire is 34 ohms at 15°C. What is its resistance at 70°C.?
Solution: Given $R_1 = 34$ ohms, $t_1 = 15$°C., and $t_2 = 70$°C. $R_2 = ?$

Solving Eq. (8) for R_2, $R_2 = \left(\dfrac{234.5 + t_2}{234.5 + t_1}\right) R_1$

Substituting the known values, $R_2 = \left(\dfrac{234.5 + 70}{234.5 + 15}\right) \times 34 = 41.5\ \Omega$

The specifications for electrical machines generally include a provision that the temperature of the coils, etc., when the machines are operating under a specified load for a specified time, must not rise more than a certain number of degrees. The temperature rise may be computed by measuring the resistance of the coils at room temperature and then again at the end of the test.

Example 2. The field coils of a shunt motor have a resistance of 90 ohms at 20°C. After running the motor for 3 hours the resistance of the field coils was 146 ohms. What was the temperature of the coils?

Solution: Given $R_1 = 90$ ohms, $t_1 = 20°C.$, $R_2 = 146$ ohms. $t_2 = ?$

Solving Eq. (8) for t_2, $$t_2 = \left(\frac{234.5 + t_1}{R_1} R_2\right) - 234.5$$

Substituting the known values, $$t_2 = \left(\frac{234.5 + 20}{90} \times 146\right) - 234.5$$
$$= 413 - 234.5$$
$$= 178.5°$$

The actual temperature rise is $t_2 - t_1 = 178.5° - 20° = 158.5°$

PROBLEMS 10-4

1. If the resistance of a copper wire is 8.45 Ω at 0°C., what will be its resistance at 40°C.?

2. The resistance of the secondary of a transformer is 15.8 Ω at 20°C. What will be the resistance when the temperature has increased to 80°C?

3. What will be the resistance of the transformer secondary of Prob. 2 at a temperature of −10°C.?

4. The resistance of the primary of a transformer was 3.06 Ω at 20°C. After operating for 2 hr the resistance increased to 3.86 Ω. What was the final operating temperature?

5. The specifications for a certain generator included a provision that it was to operate continuously under full load with the temperature of the coils not exceeding 95°C. The resistance of the coils was measured and found to be 84.6 Ω at a temperature of 40°C. After a day's run at full load the machine was shut down and the resistance of the coils measured. Now the resistance was 105 Ω. Did the machine meet the specifications?

10-5. Wire Measure. Wire sizes are designated by numbers in a system known as the American wire gage (formerly Brown and Sharpe gage). These numbers, ranging from 0000, the largest size, to 40, the smallest size, are based on a constant ratio between successive gage numbers. Table V lists the wire sizes in addition to other pertinent data.

Inspection of the wire table will reveal that the progression formed by the wire diameters serves as an aid in remembering relative wire sizes and the respective resistances. For example, No. 10 wire is a convenient reference because it is nearly $\frac{1}{10}$ inch in diameter and has a cross-sectional area of approximately 10,000 circular mils. Moreover, its resistance is very nearly 1 ohm per 1000 feet. As the wire sizes become smaller, every third gage number results in one-half the area and, therefore, double the resistance. Hence, No. 13 wire (three numbers from No. 10) has an area of about 5000 circular mils and a resistance of approximately 2 ohms per 1000 feet. Similarly, by using additional approximations, No. 16 has an area of 2500 circular mils with a resistance of 4 ohms per 1000 feet, No. 19 has an area of 1250 circular mils with a resistance of 8 ohms per 1000 feet, etc. Conversely, as the wire sizes become larger, every third gage number results in twice the circular-mil area and half the resistance. For example, No. 7 has an approximate area of 20,000 circular mils, with a resistance of nearly 0.5 ohm per 1000 feet.

10-6. Factors Governing Wire Size in Practice. From an electrical viewpoint, three factors govern the selection of the size of wire to be used for transmitting current:

1. The safe current-carrying capacity of the wire.
2. The power lost in the wire.
3. The allowable voltage variation, or the voltage drop, in the wire.

It must be remembered that the length of wire, for the purpose of computing wire resistance and its effects, is always twice the distance from the source of power to the load (outgoing and return leads).

Example. A motor receives its power through No. 4 wire from a generator located at a distance of 1000 feet. The voltage across the motor is 220 volts, and the current taken by the motor is 19.8 amperes. What is the brush potential of the generator?

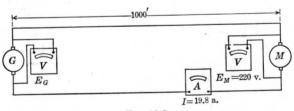

FIG. 10-3.

Solution: The circuit is represented in Fig. 10-3. The student will note that it consists of a simple series circuit which can be simplified to that of Fig. 10-4. The resistance of the 1000 feet of No. 4 wire from the generator to the motor is represented by R_o; reference to Table V shows it to be 0.253 ohm.   Similarly, the resistance from the motor back to the generator, which is represented by R_r, is also 0.253 ohm.   The voltage drop in *each* wire is

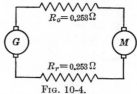

$$E = IR_o = IR_r = 19.8 \times 0.253 = 5.01 \text{ v}$$

Since the applied voltage must equal the sum of all the voltage drops around the circuit (Art. 9-8), the brush potential of the generator is

FIG. 10-4.

$$E_g = 220 + 5.01 + 5.01 = 230.02 \text{ or } 230 \text{ v}$$

Since the resistance out R_o is equal to the return resistance R_r, the foregoing solution is simplified by taking twice the actual wire distance for the length of wire that comprises the resistance of the feeders.   Therefore, the length of No. 4 wire between generator and motor is 2000 feet which results in a line resistance R_L of

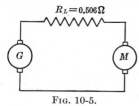

FIG. 10-5.

$$2 \times 0.253 = 0.506 \ \Omega$$

The circuit may be further simplified as shown in Fig. 10-5.

Thus, the generator brush potential is

$$E_g = 220 + IR_L = 220 + (19.8 \times 0.506) = 230 \text{ v}$$

The power lost in the line is

$$P_L = I^2R_L = 19.8^2 \times 0.506 = 198 \text{ w}$$

The power taken by the motor is

$$P_M = E_MI = 220 \times 19.8 = 4356 \text{ w}$$
$$= 4.356 \text{ kw}$$

The power delivered by the generator is

$$P_G = P_L + P_M = 198 + 4356 = 4554 \text{ w}$$

$$\text{Efficiency of transmission} = \frac{\text{power delivered to load}}{\text{power delivered by generator}} \quad (9)$$

$$= \frac{4356}{4554} = 0.956$$

$$= 95.6\%$$

The efficiency of transmission is obtainable in terms of the generator terminal voltage E_G and the voltage across the load E_L.   Because

$$\text{Power delivered to load} = E_LI$$

and $$\text{Power delivered by generator} = E_GI$$

substituting in Eq. (9), $\text{Efficiency of transmission} = \dfrac{E_LI}{E_GI} = \dfrac{E_L}{E_G}$ (10)

Substituting the voltages in Eq. (10),

$$\text{Efficiency of transmission} = \frac{220}{230} = 0.956$$

$$= 95.6\%$$

PROBLEMS 10-5

NOTE: All wires in the following problems are copper, with characteristics as listed in Table V.

1. (a) What is the resistance of 2500 ft of No. 0 wire?
   (b) What is its weight?

2. (a) What is the resistance of 1 mile of No. 8 wire?
   (b) What is its weight?

3. (a) What is the resistance of 200 ft of No. 14 wire?
   (b) What is its weight?

4. (a) What is the resistance of 60 ft of No. 18 wire?
   (b) What is its weight?

5. A solenoid is to be wound with 2000 turns of No. 22 wire. If the average diameter of a turn is 3.6 in., what will be the resistance?

6. A telephone cable, consisting of many pairs of No. 19 wire, runs between two cities 36 miles apart. If a pair is short-circuited at one end, what will be the resistance of the loop thus formed?

7. A generator with a brush potential of 240 v is feeding a motor 234 ft away. The feeders are No. 14 wire, and the motor load is 8.3 a.
   (a) What would a voltmeter read if connected across the motor brushes?
   (b) What is the efficiency of transmission?

8. A motor requiring 31.2 a at 230 v is located 250 ft from a generator that maintains a constant terminal voltage of 240 v.
   (a) What size wire must be used between generator and motor in order to supply the motor with rated current and voltage?
   (b) What will be the efficiency of transmission?

9. Twelve kilowatts of power is to be transmitted 0.5 mile from a generator that maintains a constant potential of 240 v. If 10% line drop is allowed, what size wire must be used?

10. A 10-hp 230-v motor is to be installed 300 ft from a generator that maintains a constant potential of 240 v. If the motor is 86% efficient,
   (a) What size wire should be used between motor and generator?
   (b) If the wire specified in (a) is used, what will be the motor voltage under rated-load condition?

CHAPTER XI

SPECIAL PRODUCTS AND FACTORING

In the study of arithmetic, it is necessary to memorize the multiplication tables as an aid to rapid computation. Similarly, in the study of algebra, certain forms of expressions occur so frequently that it is essential for the student to be able to multiply, divide, or factor them by inspection.

11-1. Factoring. To *factor* an algebraic expression means to find two or more expressions that when multiplied will result in the original expression.

Example 1. $2 \times 3 \times 4 = 24$. Thus, 2, 4, and 3 are some of the factors of 24.

Example 2. $b(x + y) = bx + by$. b and $(x + y)$ are the factors of $bx + by$.

Example 3. $(x + 4)(x - 3) = x^2 + x - 12$. The quantities $(x + 4)$ and $(x - 3)$ are the factors of $x^2 + x - 12$.

11-2. Prime Numbers. A number that has no factor other than itself and unity is known as a *prime number*. Thus, 3, 5, 13, x, $(a + b)$, etc., are prime numbers.

11-3. The Square of a Monomial. The student should review the law of exponents for multiplication in Art. 4-3.

Example 1. $(2ab^2)^2 = (2ab^2)(2ab^2) = 4a^2b^4$

Example 2. $(-3x^2y^3)^2 = (-3x^2y^3)(-3x^2y^3) = 9x^4y^6$

By application of the rules for the multiplication of numbers having like signs and the law of exponents, we have the following rule:

Rule: *To square a monomial, square the numerical coefficient and multiply this product by the literal factors of the monomial, multiplying the exponent of each letter by 2.*

103

11-4. The Cube of a Monomial.

Example 1. $(3a^2b)^3 = (3a^2b)(3a^2b)(3a^2b) = 27a^6b^3$

Example 2. $(-2xy^3)^3 = (-2xy^3)(-2xy^3)(-2xy^3) = -8x^3y^9$

Note that the cube of a *positive* number is always *positive* and that the cube of a *negative* number is always *negative*. Again, by application of the rules for the multiplication of positive and negative numbers and the law of exponents, we have the following rule:

Rule : *To cube a monomial, cube the numerical coefficient, and multiply this product by the literal factors of the monomial, multiplying the exponent of each letter by 3.*

PROBLEMS 11-1

Find the values of the following indicated powers:

1. $(ei)^2.$

2. $(ir)^3.$

3. $(a^2bc^3)^2.$

4. $\left(2\dfrac{e}{z}\right)^2.$

5. $(-3x^3y)^2.$

6. $(4i^2R)^2.$

7. $(-2a^2b)^3.$

8. $(3x^2y^3z)^2.$

9. $(-4I^2R)^3.$

10. $(-16s^2t^3)^2.$

11. $(11W^2x^3y^4)^2.$

12. $(-13p^2qr^3)^2.$

13. $(-5c^3de^2)^3.$

14. $(4a^2b^3c)^3.$

15. $(-12xy^3z^2)^2.$

16. $(\tfrac{1}{3}a^2)^2.$

17. $(-\tfrac{1}{2}xy^2)^3.$

18. $\left(-\dfrac{3ab^3}{4}\right)^3.$

19. $(-\tfrac{2}{5}rs^2t)^2.$

20. $\left(\dfrac{x^2yz^3}{ab^2c}\right)^2.$

21. $\left(-\dfrac{cd^3e^2}{p^2rs^3}\right)^3.$

22. $-(\tfrac{4}{5}rs^2t)^3.$

23. $-(-\tfrac{5}{8}p^2r)^2.$

24. $-(-\tfrac{1}{2}a^2bc^3)^3.$

25. $-(\tfrac{2}{3}m^2n^3)^3.$

26. $-\left(-\dfrac{a^4b^3c}{r^2s^4t^3}\right)^3.$

27. $(\tfrac{4}{5}c^3b^3e^5)^3.$

28. $(\tfrac{5}{6}x^3y^5z^6)^2.$

29. $(-\tfrac{3}{4}a^2b^4c^3)^3.$

30. $-(-\tfrac{3}{8}m^2n^5p)^2.$

31. $-(-\tfrac{2}{3}rs^3t^2u^4)^2.$

11-5. The Square Root of a Monomial.   The *square root* of an expression is one of its equal factors.

Example 1. $\sqrt{3}$ is a number such that
$$\sqrt{3} \cdot \sqrt{3} = 3$$

Example 2. $\sqrt{n}$ is a number such that
$$\sqrt{n} \cdot \sqrt{n} = n$$

Because $(+2)(+2) = +4$
and $(-2)(-2) = +4$

it is apparent that 4 has two square roots, $+2$ and -2. Similarly, 16 has two square roots, $+4$ and -4.

In general, every number has two square roots, equal in magnitude, one positive and one negative. **The** positive root is known as the *principal root;* if no sign precedes the radical, the positive root is understood. Thus, in practical numerical computations, the following is understood:

$$\sqrt{4} = +2$$
and
$$-\sqrt{4} = -2$$

In dealing with literal numbers, the values of the various factors often are unknown. Therefore, when extracting a square root we affix the double sign $\pm$ to denote "plus or minus."

Example 3. Since $a^4 \cdot a^4 = a^8$ and $(-a^4)(-a^4) = a^8$,

then $\qquad\qquad \sqrt{a^8} = \pm a^4$

Example 4. Since $x^2y^3 \cdot x^2y^3 = x^4y^6$ and $(-x^2y^3)(-x^2y^3) = x^4y^6$,

then $\qquad\qquad \sqrt{x^4y^6} = \pm x^2y^3$

From the foregoing examples, we formulate the following:

Rule: *To extract the square root of a monomial, extract the square root of the numerical coefficient, divide the exponents of the letters by 2, and affix the $\pm$ sign.*

Example 5. $\qquad \sqrt{4a^4b^2} = \pm 2a^2b$

Example 6. $\qquad \sqrt{\frac{1}{9}x^2y^6z^4} = \pm \frac{1}{3}xy^3z^2$

NOTE: A perfect monomial square is positive and has a perfect square numerical coefficient and only even numbers as exponents.

11-6. Cube Root of a Monomial. The *cube root* of a monomial is one of its three equal factors.

Because $\qquad\qquad (+2)(+2)(+2) = 8$
then $\qquad\qquad\qquad \sqrt[3]{8} = 2$
Similarly, $\qquad\quad (-2)(-2)(-2) = -8$
and $\qquad\qquad\quad \sqrt[3]{-8} = -2$

From this it is evident that the cube root of a monomial has the same sign as the monomial itself.

Because $\qquad\quad x^2y^3 \cdot x^2y^3 \cdot x^2y^3 = x^6y^9$
then $\qquad\qquad\quad \sqrt[3]{x^6y^9} = x^2y^3$

The above results may be stated as follows:

Rule : *To extract the cube root of a monomial, extract the cube root of the numerical coefficient, divide the exponents of the letters by 3, and affix the same sign as the monomial.*

Example 1. $\sqrt[3]{8x^6y^3z^{12}} = 2x^2yz^4$

Example 2. $\sqrt[3]{-27a^3b^9c^6} = -3ab^3c^2$

NOTE: A perfect cube monomial has a positive or negative perfect cube numerical coefficient and exponents that are exactly divisible by 3.

PROBLEMS 11-2

Find the value of the following:

1. $\sqrt{3^2}$.

2. $\sqrt{5^2}$.

3. $\sqrt{4^4}$.

4. $\sqrt{4^2 \cdot 3^2}$.

5. $\sqrt{16 \cdot 5^2}$.

6. $\sqrt{9a^2}$.

7. $\sqrt{4e^4}$.

8. $\sqrt{16r^4}$.

9. $\sqrt{9x^8}$.

10. $\sqrt{4e^2i^2}$.

11. $\sqrt{25c^2d^4}$.

12. $\sqrt{81r^6s^{10}}$.

13. $\sqrt{36p^2q^4}$.

14. $\sqrt[3]{-8}$.

15. $\sqrt[3]{(-2)^6}$.

16. $\sqrt{49m^2n^{14}}$.

17. $\sqrt[3]{125x^3y^9}$.

18. $\sqrt{225r^{10}s^{12}}$.

19. $\sqrt{100x^2y^{10}}$.

20. $2\sqrt{r^8}$.

21. $\sqrt[3]{-8 \cdot 27}$.

22. $\sqrt{144c^8d^{10}}$.

23. $\sqrt[3]{27a^6b^3c^{12}}$.

24. $\sqrt[3]{1000x^{12}y^6z^3}$.

25. $\sqrt{196a^6x^{18}}$.

26. $\sqrt{3^2a^2b^4}$.

27. $\sqrt[3]{8^3}$.

28. $\sqrt{121x^{18}y^{10}z^4}$.

29. $\sqrt[5]{32z^{15}}$.

30. $\sqrt{289m^2n^6p^4}$.

31. $\sqrt[5]{-243r^{20}}$.

32. $\sqrt{c^4b^{12}}$.

33. $\sqrt[5]{2^3 \cdot 4p^{10}q^5r^{15}}$.

34. $\sqrt{\frac{1}{4}n^2}$.

35. $\sqrt[3]{-216a^3z^3}$.

36. $\sqrt{\frac{25}{16}m^2n^2p^6}$.

37. $\sqrt{\frac{1}{9}x^2y^4}$.

38. $\sqrt[3]{\frac{1}{27}}$.

39. $\sqrt{\frac{9c^4d^2e^8}{25x^2}}$.

40. $\sqrt{\frac{e^2}{4}}$.

41. $\sqrt{\frac{1}{25a^4}}$.

42. $\sqrt{\frac{64h^2i^4k^{10}}{121a^8b^2c^6}}$.

43. $\sqrt{\frac{256a^8b^2x^4}{25y^4z^6}}$.

44. $\sqrt{\frac{169v^2t^2}{144a^6z^4}}$.

45. $\sqrt{\frac{196m^4n^2p^8}{225a^2b^4c^{12}}}$.

46. $\sqrt[3]{-\frac{1}{27}a^3b^6c^{15}}$.

47. $\sqrt[3]{\frac{x^6y^3z^{18}}{125}}$.

48. $\sqrt{\frac{64c^4d^6e^2}{121x^2z^6}}$.

49. $\sqrt[3]{-\frac{1}{216x^6y^{12}z^3}}$.

50. $\sqrt[3]{\frac{27a^{15}b^3c^9}{343x^3y^{12}z^6}}$.

11-7. Polynomials with a Common Monomial Factor.

Type: $a(b + c + d) = ab + ac + ad$

Rule: *To factor polynomials whose terms contain a common monomial factor,*

1. *Determine by inspection the greatest common factor of its terms.*
2. *Divide the polynomial by this factor.*
3. *Write the quotient in parentheses preceded by the monomial factor.*

Example 1. Factor $3x^2 - 9xy^2$.
Solution: The common monomial factor of both terms is $3x$.

Therefore, $3x^2 - 9xy^2 = 3x(x - 3y^2)$

Example 2. Factor $2a - 6a^2b + 4ax - 10ay^3$.
Solution: Each term contains the factor $2a$.

Therefore, $2a - 6a^2b + 4ax - 10ay^3 = 2a(1 - 3ab + 2x - 5y^3)$.

Example 3. Factor $14x^2yz^3 - 7xy^2z^2 + 35xz^5$.
Solution: Each term contains the factor $7xz^2$.

Therefore, $14x^2yz^3 - 7xy^2z^2 + 35xz^5 = 7xz^2(2xyz - y^2 + 5z^3)$

PROBLEMS 11-3

Factor:

1. $2x + 6$.
2. $\frac{1}{3}r + \frac{1}{6}R$.
3. $e^2 + 2ei + 3e$.
4. $\frac{1}{5}c^2d - \frac{1}{10}c^2d^4 + \frac{1}{20}cd^2$.
5. $3a^3 - 15a^4$.
6. $5ab^3 - 15ab^2c + 15abc^2 - 5ac^3$.
7. $30i - 12ir$.
8. $48r^2s^2 - 144r^3s^3 + 108r^2s^4$.
9. $3x^4 + 6x^3y - 3x^3$.
10. $\frac{1}{3}x^2y^2 + \frac{1}{3}x^iy - \frac{1}{6}x^4y$.
11. $e^2 + e^3 - e^4 + 2e$.
12. $\frac{1}{4}cd^3 + \frac{1}{8}c^2d - \frac{1}{12}c^4d^5$.
13. $5e^2 + 10e - 15e^3$.
14. $pq^6 - 5pq^3 + 6p$.
15. $9x^2y - 6xy - 63y$.
16. $39v^6t^3x^4 - 26v^2t^3x^4 - 52v^2t^2x$.
17. $3ab - 6abc + 3ab^2 - 3ax$.
18. $28m^2n^3 - 42mn^4 + 70m^3n^2$.
19. $\frac{1}{2}i^2r - \frac{1}{4}ir^2 - \frac{1}{8}irz$.
20. $\frac{1}{18}c^4d^2 - \frac{1}{27}c^2d^3 - \frac{1}{81}c^2d$.
21. $30a^4b^2c^3d - 225a^2bc^4d^2 + 45abc$.
22. Solve for x if $bx = b(c + d)$.
23. Solve for y if $cy = c^2 + cd$.

11-8. The Square of a Binomial.

Type: $(a \pm b)^2 = a^2 \pm 2ab + b^2$

The multiplication
$$\begin{array}{r} a + b \\ a + b \\ \hline a^2 + ab \\ + ab + b^2 \\ \hline a^2 + 2ab + b^2 \end{array}$$

results in the formula $(a + b)^2 = a^2 + 2ab + b^2$

which may be expressed by the following rule:

Rule: *To square the sum of two terms, square the first term; add twice the product of the two terms; add the square of the second term.*

Example 1.   Square $(2b + 4cd)$.

Solution: $(2b + 4cd)^2 = (2b)^2 + 2(2b)(4cd) + (4cd)^2$
$= 4b^2 + 16bcd + 16c^2d^2$

Example 2.   Let x and y be represented by lengths.   Then

$$(x + y)^2 = x^2 + 2xy + y^2$$

may be illustrated graphically as shown in Fig. 11-1.

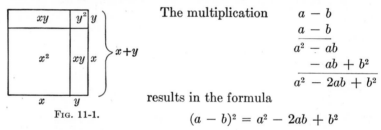

FIG. 11-1.

The multiplication

$$a - b$$
$$a - b$$
$$\overline{a^2 - ab}$$
$$ - ab + b^2$$
$$\overline{a^2 - 2ab + b^2}$$

results in the formula

$$(a - b)^2 = a^2 - 2ab + b^2$$

which may be expressed as follows:

Rule: *To square the difference of two terms, square the first term; subtract twice the product of the two terms; add the square of the second term.*

Example 3.   Square $(3a^2 - 5xy)$

Solution: $(3a^2 - 5xy)^2 = (3a^2)^2 - 2(3a^2)(5xy) + (5xy)^2$
$= 9a^4 - 30a^2xy + 25x^2y^2$

Example 4.   Let x and y be represented by lengths.   Then

$$(x - y)^2 = x^2 - 2xy + y^2$$

may be illustrated graphically as shown in Fig. 11-2. x^2 is the large square.   The figure shows that the two rectangles taken from x^2 leave $(x - y)^2$.   Since an amount y^2 is a part of one xy that has been subtracted from x^2 and is outside x^2, we must add it. Hence, we obtain

$$(x - y)^2 = x^2 - 2xy + y^2$$

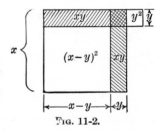

FIG. 11-2.

The student should practice squaring sums and differences of binomials mentally by following the foregoing rules. Proficiency in these and later methods will greatly reduce the labor in performing multiplications.

PROBLEMS 11-4

Square the following by inspection:

1. $e + 3$.
2. $2r - R$.
3. $3i - 2I$.
4. $p + 2$.
5. $i^2 - 3$.
6. $i^2 + 3$.
7. $b - 4$.
8. $z + 6$.
9. $t^3 - 7$.
10. $\lambda - 2$.
11. $3x - y$.
12. $2ir + 6$.
13. $6 + b$.
14. $R + r$.
15. $F - f$.
16. $9 - \alpha$.
17. $\alpha - \beta$.
18. $c - a$.
19. $11 - m$.
20. $5x - y$.
21. $7m + p$.
22. $3a - 2b$.
23. $12r - s$.
24. $a + 1$.
25. $\mu + 10$.
26. $m^3 + n^2$.
27. $x - 1$.
28. $6ab - 3cd$.
29. $5 - 3x^2$.
30. $9v^2 - 6t^2$.
31. $4s^2 + 10r$.
32. $9c^2 + 6d^2$.
33. $4a^2 - 3b$.
34. $5p - 11q$.
35. $3c + 8d^2e^3$.
36. $1 + e^4$.
37. $1 - a^2b^3$.
38. $5p - 6qr^2$.
39. $x^2 - 4z$.
40. $3a^2b^2 - c^2d^2$.

Expand:

41. $(R + \frac{1}{2})^2$.
42. $(e - \frac{1}{3})^2$.
43. $(r - \frac{1}{4})^2$.
44. $(d + \frac{3}{8})^2$.
45. $(Z - \frac{2}{3})^2$.
46. $(B - \frac{3}{4})^2$.
47. $(r - \frac{1}{5})^2$.
48. $(E + \frac{1}{6})^2$.
49. $(\mu + \frac{1}{6})^2$.
50. $(R - \frac{2}{7})^2$.
51. $(y^2 + \frac{2}{5})^2$.
52. $(c^2 + \frac{5}{6})^2$.
53. $(a^2 - \frac{3}{8})^2$.
54. $(b - \frac{4}{5})^2$.
55. $(x^3 - \frac{5}{8})^2$.

56. Square 38 mentally.

Solution: $38^2 = (40 - 2)^2 = 1600 - 160 + 4 = 1604 - 160$
$$= 1444$$

57. Square 52 mentally.

Solution: $52^2 = (50 + 2)^2 = 2500 + 200 + 4 = 2704$.

Square mentally:

58. 21.
59. 19.
60. 36.
61. 43.
62. 53.
63 33.
64. 22.
65. 39.
66. 29.
67. 18.
68. 28.
69. 61.
70. 59.

71. Formulate a general rule for squaring by inspection any number ending in 5.

Solution:

$$25 = 2 \times 10 + 5$$
$$35 = 3 \times 10 + 5$$
$$65 = 6 \times 10 + 5, \text{ etc.}$$

Likewise, any number ending in 5 may be written

$$10x + 5$$

Thus, for 85, $x = 8$, since $8 \times 10 + 5 = 85$.

Now, $(10x + 5)^2 = 100x^2 + 100x + 25$
Factoring, $= 100x(x + 1) + 25$
     $= x(x + 1) \text{ hundreds} + 25$

Then the square of 85, where $x = 8$, is

$$8(8 + 1) \text{ hundreds} + 25 = 7225$$

Rule: *To square a number ending in 5 drop the 5, multiply the balance of the number by the next higher number, and affix 25 to the result.*

Example. $75^2 = 7 \times 8 = 56$
Affixing 25, $= 5625$

Example. $35^2 = 3 \times 4 = 12$
Affixing 25, $= 1225$

Square mentally:

72. 65.   **73.** 55.   **74.** 85.
75. 75.   **76.** 105.   **77.** 125.
78. 95.   **79.** 115.   **80.** 45.

11-9. The Square Root of a Trinomial.

In the preceding article, it was shown that

$$(a + b)^2 = a^2 + 2ab + b^2$$
and $$(a - b)^2 = a^2 - 2ab + b^2$$

From these and other binomials that have been squared, it is evident that a trinomial is a perfect square if

1. *Two terms are squares of monomials and positive.*
2. *The other term is twice the product of these monomials and has affixed either a plus or a minus sign.*

Example 1. $x^2 + 2xy + y^2$ is a perfect trinomial square because x^2 and y^2 are the squares of the monomials x and y, respectively, and $2xy$ is twice the product of the monomials. Therefore,

$$x^2 + 2xy + y^2 = (x + y)^2$$

Example 2. $4a^2 - 12ab + 9b^2$ is a perfect trinomial square because $4a^2$ and $9b^2$ are the squares of $2a$ and $3b$, respectively, and the other term is

$-2(2a)(3b)$. Therefore,

$$4a^2 - 12ab + 9b^2 = (2a - 3b)^2$$

Rule : *To extract the square root of a perfect trinomial square, extract the square roots of the two perfect square monomials, and connect them with the sign of the remaining term.*

Example 3. Supply the missing term in $x^4 + (?) + 16$ so that the three will form a perfect trinomial square.

Solution: The missing term is twice the product of the monomials whose squares result in the two known terms; that is, $2(x^2)(4) = 8x^2$. Hence,

$$x^4 + 8x^2 + 16 = (x^2 + 4)^2$$

Example 4. Supply the missing term in $25a^2 + 30ab + (?)$ so that the three will form a perfect trinomial square.

Solution: The square root of the first term is $5a$. The missing term is the square of some number N such that $2(5a)(N) = 30ab$. Multiplying, we obtain $10aN = 30ab$, or $N = 3b$. Therefore,

$$25a^2 + 30ab + 9b^2 = (5a + 3b)^2$$

PROBLEMS 11-5

Supply the missing terms in the following so that the three form a perfect trinomial square:

1. $e^2 + (?) + i^2$.

2. $r^2 - (?) + S^2$.

3. $E^2 + (?) + 36I^2$.

4. $m^4 - (?) + 9n^2$.

5. $16x^4 - (?) + 49y^2$.

6. $100p^2 + (?) + 16q^2$.

7. $25m^4 - (?) + 81n^6$.

8. $4a^2 + (?) + 9b^2$.

9. $\frac{1}{9}X^2 - (?) + \frac{1}{4}Y^2$.

10. $\frac{1}{16}C^4 - (?) + \frac{1}{4}d^2$.

11. $\frac{4}{25}e^6 + (?) + 25$.

12. $9 - (?) + \frac{1}{36}a^2$.

13. $x^2 + 4x + (?)$.

14. $a^4 - 10a^2 + (?)$.

15. $c^2 - 6cd + (?)$.

16. $9p^2 - (?) + 64$.

17. $4m^2 + (?) + 1$.

18. $4r^2 + 16r + (?)$.

19. $(?) - \frac{2}{15}x + \frac{1}{25}x^2$.

20. $(?) + \frac{1}{14}y + \frac{1}{16}y^2$.

Extract the square roots of the following:

21. $x^2 - 10xy + 25y^2$.

22. $Z^2 + Z + \frac{1}{4}$.

23. $a^2b^2 + 18ab + 81$.

24. $r^2 + \frac{x^2}{9} - \frac{2rx}{3}$.

25. $64m^2n^2 + 16mnpq + p^2q^2$.

26. $\frac{4v \cdot t^2}{5} + \frac{9t^4}{25} + \frac{4v^4}{9}$.

27. $49a^2 - 70ab + 25b^2$.

28. $\frac{12pq}{5} + 9p^2 + \frac{4q^2}{25}$.

29. $\frac{4}{5}cd + d^2 + \frac{4c^2}{25}$.

30. $\frac{10xy}{21} + \frac{25y^2}{36} + \frac{4x^2}{49}$.

11-10. Prime Factors of an Expression.   In factoring a number, all its prime factors should be obtained.   After factoring an expression once, it may be possible to factor it again.

Example.   Find the prime factors of $12i^2r + 12iIr + 3I^2r$.

Solution:

$$12i^2r + 12iIr + 3I^2r$$
$$= 3r(4i^2 + 4iI + I^2)$$
$$= 3r(2i + I)(2i + I)$$
$$= 3r(2i + I)^2$$

PROBLEMS 11-6

Find the prime factors of the following:

1. $3ax^2 + 6axy + 3ay^2$.

2. $4x^4 + 48x^2y + 144y^2$.

3. $6ie^2 - 60ieE + 150iE^2$.

4. $18r - 12ir + 2i^2r$.

5. $5a^2b^2c + 70abc + 245c$.

6. $\dfrac{27E^2}{R} - \dfrac{36Ee}{R} + \dfrac{12e^2}{R}$.

7. $3cd^2 - 6cde + 3ce^2$.

8. $75mn^2 + 48mp^2 - 120mnp$.

9. $\dfrac{45eE^2}{Z} - \dfrac{150eE}{Z} + \dfrac{125e}{Z}$.

10. $11ab^2c^2 + 44abc + 44a$.

11-11. The Product of the Sum and Difference of Two Numbers.

Type: $(a + b)(a - b) = a^2 - b^2$

The multiplication of the sum and difference of two general numbers, such as

$$a + b$$
$$a - b$$
$$\overline{a^2 + ab}$$
$$- ab - b^2$$
$$\overline{a^2- b^2}$$

results in the formula

$$(a + b)(a - b) = a^2 - b^2$$

which may be expressed by the following:

Rule: *The product of the sum and difference of two numbers is equal to the difference of their squares.*

Example 1. $(3x + 4y)(3x - 4y) = 9x^2 - 16y^2$

Example 2. $(6ab^2 + 7c^3d)(6ab^2 - 7c^3d) = 36a^2b^4 - 49c^6d^2$

PROBLEMS 11-7

Multiply by inspection:

1. $(e + 2)(e - 2)$.

2. $(r - 4)(r + 4)$.

3. $(E + e)(E - e)$.

4. $(3Z - 2R)(3Z + 2R)$.

5. $\left(\dfrac{2i}{3} + \dfrac{1}{s}\right)\left(\dfrac{2i}{3} - \dfrac{1}{s}\right)$.

6. $\left(\dfrac{7P}{8} - \dfrac{3}{5}\right)\left(\dfrac{7P}{8} + \dfrac{3}{5}\right)$.

7. $\left(\dfrac{4}{9}\alpha + \dfrac{5\beta}{11}\right)\left(\dfrac{4}{9}\alpha - \dfrac{5\beta}{11}\right)$.

8. $\left(\dfrac{3\theta^2}{4} - \dfrac{2\phi}{5}\right)\left(\dfrac{3\theta^2}{4} + \dfrac{2\phi}{5}\right)$.

9. $\left(\dfrac{R^2}{6} + \dfrac{3Z^2}{10}\right)\left(\dfrac{R^2}{6} - \dfrac{3Z^2}{10}\right)$.

10. $\left(\dfrac{E^2}{R} + I^2R\right)\left(\dfrac{E^2}{R} - I^2R\right)$.

11-12. Factoring the Difference of Two Squares.

Rule : *To factor the difference of two squares, extract the square root of the two squares, add the roots for one factor, and subtract the second from the first for the other factor.*

Example 1. $\qquad x^2 - y^2 = (x + y)(x - y)$

Example 2. $\quad 9a^2c^4 - 36d^6 = (3ac^2 + 6d^3)(3ac^2 - 6d^3)$

PROBLEMS 11-8

Factor:

1. $Z^2 - R^2$.

2. $4E^2 - 16e^2$.

3. $36 - 9b^4$.

4. $1 - 36r^2$.

5. $Z^2 - \frac{1}{4}$.

6. $c^2d^4 - e^2$.

7. $4F^2 - f_0^2$.

8. $25a^2 - 16B^2$.

9. $64v^2t^2 - 1$.

10. $1 - 225\theta^2$.

11. $\dfrac{25}{\phi^2} - \dfrac{\alpha^2}{36}$.

12. $\dfrac{1}{R^2} - \dfrac{1}{r^2}$.

13. $\dfrac{E^2}{I^2} - \dfrac{81}{i^2}$.

14. $\frac{4}{25}Z^2 - \frac{1}{49}R^2$.

15. $\dfrac{1}{c^2} - \dfrac{V^2}{Q^2}$.

16. $9c^2 - a^2 + 2ab - b^2$.

Solution: $9c^2 - a^2 + 2ab - b^2 = 9c^2 - (a^2 - 2ab + b^2)$
$$= [3c + (a - b)][3c - (a - b)]$$
$$= (3c + a - b)(3c - a + b)$$

17. $(a^2 + 4ab + 4b^2) - x^2$.

18. $16x^2 - y^2 + 14yz - 49z^2$.

19. $36e^2 - 81x^2y^2 + 9c^2d^2 - 36cde$.

20. $100abcd - 144c^2 + 25a^2b^2 + 100c^2d^2$.

11-13. The Product of Two Binomials Having a Common Term.

Type: $\quad (x + a)(x + b) = x^2 + (a + b)x + ab$

The multiplication

$$x + a$$
$$x + b$$
$$\overline{x^2 + ax}$$
$$ + bx + ab$$
$$\overline{x^2 + ax + bx + ab}$$

when factored, results in $x^2 + (a + b)x + ab$.
This type of formula may be expressed as follows:

Rule : *To obtain the product of two binominals having a common term, square the common term, multiply the common term by the algebraic sum of the second terms of the binominals, find the product of the second terms, and add the results.*

Example 1.   Find the product of $x - 7$ and $x + 5$.

Solution: $(x - 7)(x + 5) = x^2 + (-7 + 5)x + (-7)(+5)$
$$= x^2 - 2x - 35$$

Example 2. $(ir + 3)(ir - 6) = i^2r^2 + (+3 - 6)ir + (+3)(-6)$
$$= i^2r^2 - 3ir - 18$$

Although the above examples have been written out in order to illustrate the method, the actual multiplication should be mental. In Example 2 above, the i^2r^2 term is written first. Then one glances at the $+3$ and -6, notes their sum is -3 and the product is -18, and writes down the complete product.

PROBLEMS 11-9

Multiply the following mentally:

1. $(e + 1)(e + 2)$.
2. $(r + 3)(r + 5)$.
3. $(i + 5)(i + 3)$.
4. $(x + 4)(x + 6)$.
5. $(\alpha - 3)(\alpha - 7)$.
6. $(R - 6)(R - 8)$.
7. $(E + 10)(E - 3)$.
8. $(\beta + 6)(\beta - 12)$.
9. $(Z - 2)(Z + 10)$.
10. $(t + 11)(t - 3)$.
11. $(vt - 4)(vt - 9)$.
12. $(\theta^2 - 6)(\theta^2 + 10)$.
13. $(\alpha t^2 - 5)(\alpha t^2 - 3)$.
14. $(a - 12b)(a - 4b)$.
15. $\left(I + \dfrac{2E}{R}\right)\left(I - \dfrac{6E}{R}\right)$.
16. $(\theta - \frac{1}{5})(\theta + 15)$.
17. $(\alpha^2 - \frac{1}{2})(\alpha^2 + \frac{1}{4})$.
18. $(\beta^2 + 3)(\beta^2 + \frac{1}{3})$.
19. $(te + 3i^2R)(te - 4i^2R)$.
20. $(\phi^2 + \frac{1}{10})(\phi^2 + \frac{1}{4})$.

11-14. Factoring Trinomials of the Form $a^2 + ba + c$. A trinomial of this form can be factored if it is the product of two binomials having a common term.

Rule : *To factor a trimonial of the form* $a^2 + ba + c$, *find two numbers whose sum is* b *and whose product is* c. *Add each of them to the square root of the first term for the factors.*

Example 1. Factor $a^2 + 7a + 12$.
Solution: It is necessary to find the two numbers whose product is $+12$ and whose sum is $+7$.
The factors of 12 are

$$1 \times 12$$
$$2 \times 6$$
$$3 \times 4$$

The first two pairs will not do because their sums are not 7. The third pair gives the correct sum.

$$\therefore a^2 + 7a + 12 = (a + 3)(a + 4)$$

Example 2. Factor $x^2 - 15x + 36$.
Solution: Since the 36 is positive, its factors must bear the same sign; also, since -15 is negative, it follows that both factors must be negative.
The factors of 36 are

$$1 \times 36$$
$$2 \times 18$$
$$3 \times 12$$
$$4 \times 9$$
$$6 \times 6$$

Inspection of these factors shows that 3 and 12 are the required numbers.

$$\therefore x^2 - 15x + 36 = (x - 3)(x - 12)$$

Example 3. Factor $e^2 - e - 56$.
Solution: Since we have -56, the two factors must have unlike signs. The sum of the factors must equal -1; therefore the negative factor of -56 must have the greater absolute value.
The factors of 56 are

$$1 \times 56$$
$$2 \times 28$$
$$4 \times 14$$
$$7 \times 8$$

Since the factors 7 and 8 differ in value by 1, we have

$$e^2 - e - 56 = (e + 7)(e - 8)$$

PROBLEMS 11-10

Factor:

1. $e^2 + 5e + 6.$
2. $r^2 - 8r + 12.$
3. $i^2 + 7i + 12.$
4. $E^2 - 9E + 14.$
5. $P^2 - 11P + 24.$
6. $Z^2 - 2Z - 35.$
7. $R^2 - 4R - 45.$
8. $X^2 - 15X + 54.$
9. $\alpha^2 + \alpha - 2.$
10. $V^2 + 15Vt + 36t^2.$
11. $\theta^2 + 2\theta - 63.$
12. $B^2 - 7B - 44.$
13. $I^2 - 6IR - 55R^2.$
14. $\phi^6 - 18\phi^3 + 72.$
15. $X^2 + 150 - 25X.$
16. $a^2 + 50 - 27a.$
17. $Q^2 - 10Q - 24.$
18. $j^2 - 7jx - 120x^2.$
19. $a^2b^2 - 96 - 10ab.$
20. $e^2 - 21ej + 110j^2.$
21. $j^2 + 7j - 60.$
22. $x^2y^2 - 16xyZ + 28Z^2.$
23. $E^2 + EI - 72I^2.$
24. $R^2 + 160 - 26R.$
25. $\alpha^2 + 4\alpha - 96.$
26. $I^2 + 84 + 20I.$
27. $B^2 - 3B - 70.$
28. $\theta^2 - 27\theta + 50.$
29. $x^2y^2 - xy - 6.$
30. $\phi^2 + 9 + 10\phi.$

11-15. The Product of Any Two Binomials.

Type: $(ax + b)(cx + d)$

Up to the present, if it was desired to multiply $(5x - 2)$ by $(3x + 6)$, we multiplied in the following manner:

$$
\begin{array}{r}
5x - 2 \\
3x + 6 \\
\hline
15x^2 - 6x \\
+ 30x - 12 \\
\hline
15x^2 + 24x - 12
\end{array}
$$

Note that $15x^2$ is the product of the first terms of the binomials, and the last term is the product of the last terms of the binomials. Also, the middle term is the sum of the products of the first term of each binomial by the second term of the other binomial.

The above example may be written in the following manner:

$$
\begin{array}{c}
5x - 2 \\
\nwarrow \nearrow \\
\swarrow \searrow \\
3x + 6 \\
\hline
15x^2 + 24x - 12
\end{array}
$$

The middle term $(+24x)$ is the sum of the *cross products* $(5x)(+6)$ and $(3x)(-2)$, which is obtained by multiplying the first term of each binomial by the second term of the other. The usual method of obtaining this product is indicated by the following solution:

$$(5x - 2)(3x + 6) = 15x^2 + 24x - 12$$

Rule : *For finding the product of any two binomials,*

1. *The first term of the product is the product of the first terms of the binomials.*

2. *The second term is the algebraic sum of the product of the two outer terms and the product of the two inner terms.*

3. *The third term is the product of the last terms of the binomials.*

Example 1.   Find the product of $(4e + 7j)(2e - 3j)$.
Solution: The only difficulty encountered in obtaining such products mentally is that of finding the second term.

$(4e)(-3j) = -12ej$, $(7j)(2e) = 14ej$,   and $(-12ej) + (14ej) = +2ej$
$\therefore (4e + 7j)(2e - 3j) = 8e^2 + 2ej - 21j^2$

Example 2.   Find the product $(7r^2 + 8Z)(8r^2 - 9Z)$.
Solution: 1. The first term of the product is $(7r^2)(8r^2) = 56r^4$.
2. Since $(7r^2)(-9Z) = -63r^2Z$ and $(8Z)(8r^2) = 64r^2Z$, the second term is $(-63r^2Z) + (64r^2Z) = +r^2Z$.
3. The third term is $(8Z)(-9Z) = -72Z^2$.

$$\therefore (7r^2 + 8Z)(8r^2 - 9Z) = 56r^4 + r^2Z - 72Z^2$$

By repeated drills the student should acquire enough skill so that he may readily obtain such products mentally. This type oi product is frequently encountered in algebra, and the ability to multiply rapidly will save much time.

PROBLEMS 11-11

1. $(2e - 3)(4e + 5)$.   **2.** $(3Z + 4)(3Z + 2)$.
3. $(3j - 2)(4j + 1)$.   **4.** $(E - 4)(4E + 3)$.
5. $(5r - 3)(2r - 5)$.   **6.** $(3R + 1)(2R + 3)$.
7. $(2I + 3)(3I + 2)$.   **8.** $(7P + 6)(3P - 2)$.
9. $(10a - 7)(4a + 1)$.   **10.** $(15x - 20)(3x + 2)$.
11. $(7ei - 4)(6ei - 3)$.   **12.** $(5\theta - 3)(4\theta + 3)$.

13. $(r - 8)(4r + 1)$.

14. $(5E - 1)(E - 1)$.

15. $(6j + b)(j - b)$.

16. $(4I^2 - 3)(I^2 + 3)$.

17. $(x + 3y)(3x - y)$.

18. $(c - j)(4c - 5j)$.

19. $(6\phi - 5)(\phi + 1)$.

20. $(6r + 5R)(7r - 4R)$.

21. $(8v - 3t)(9v - t)$.

22. $(2\alpha - 3\beta)(2\alpha - 3\beta)$.

23. $(9ei - w)(3ei + 5w)$.

24. $(6ab - 7y)(5ab + 6y)$.

25. $(9xy^2 + 4)(6xy^2 - 3)$.

26. $(6r - \frac{1}{3})(9r + \frac{2}{3})$.

27. $(2 + 9E)(3 + 2E)$.

28. $(7i + 0.3)(2i + 0.6)$.

29. $(5 - 7Z^2)(6 + 9Z^2)$.

30. $(\frac{1}{8}R + \frac{1}{5})(5R - 8)$.

31. $(8 + 3\theta)(10 - 4\theta)$.

32. $(\alpha^2 + 0.9)(3\alpha^2 - 0.9)$.

33. $(R - 11i)(4R - i)$.

34. $\left(\dfrac{a}{4} - \dfrac{1}{3}\right)(3a + 8)$.

35. $(10x^2y - 6Z)(9x^2y - 2Z)$.

36. $(6 - 3E)(7 + 8E)$.

37. $(12\alpha^2 + 7)(5\alpha^2 - 4)$.

38. $(2v - t)(5v + 2t)$.

39. $(9E^2 - 5e^2)(7E^2 + 5e^2)$.

40. $(\theta + \frac{1}{2})(\theta + \frac{1}{4})$.

41. $(8\alpha^2 - 9)(4\alpha^2 + 5)$.

42. $\left(12R + \dfrac{2}{3i}\right)\left(10R - \dfrac{2}{3i}\right)$.

43. $(a + b)(c + d)$.

44. $\left(8a - \dfrac{2}{3b}\right)\left(9a - \dfrac{1}{2b}\right)$.

45. $(5\theta + \frac{1}{5})(10\theta - \frac{1}{10})$.

46. $\left(6I + \dfrac{1}{2r}\right)\left(4I + \dfrac{1}{3r}\right)$.

47. $(7e^2 + 3E^2)(5e^2 - 2E^2)$.

48. $(8Z^2 - 9R^2)(4Z^2 + 5R^2)$.

49. $(20x - 7y)(8x + 3y)$.

50. $(7ei - 6I^2R)(5ei + 6I^2R)$.

11-16. Factoring Trinomials of the Type $ax^2 + bx + c$.   This is best illustrated by examples.

Example 1.   Factor $3a^2 + 5a + 2$.

Solution: It is apparent that the two factors are binomials and the product of the end terms must be $3a^2$ and 2.   Therefore the binomials to choose from are

$$(3a + 1)(a + 2)$$

and
$$(3a + 2)(a + 1)$$

However, the first factors when multiplied result in a product of $7a$ for the middle term.   The second pair of factors when multiplied give a middle term of $5a$.   Therefore,

$$3a^2 + 5a + 2 = (3a + 2)(a + 1)$$

Example 2.   Factor $6e^2 + 7e + 2$.

Solution: Again, the end terms of the binomial factors must be chosen so that their products result in $6e^2$ and 2.   Both the last terms of the factors are of like signs, for the last term of the trinomial is positive.   Also, both last terms of the factors must be positive, for the second term of the trinomial

is positive.   One of the several methods of arranging the work is as shown
below.   The tentative factors are arranged as if for multiplication:

Trial Factors		Products	
$(6e + 1)(e + 2)$	$=$	$6e^2 + 13e + 2$	Wrong
$(6e + 2)(e + 1)$	$=$	$6e^2 + 8e + 2$	Wrong
$(3e + 1)(2e + 2)$	$=$	$6e^2 + 8e + 2$	Wrong
$(3e + 2)(2e + 1)$	$=$	$6e^2 + 7e + 2$	Right

It is seen that any combination of the trial factors when multiplied results
in the correct first and last term.

$$\therefore\ 6e^2 + 7e + 2 = (3e + 2)(2e + 1)$$

Note: This may seem to be a long process; but, with practice, most of the
factor trials can be tested mentally.

Example 3.   Factor $12i^2 - 17i + 6$.
Solution: The third term of this trinomial is $+6$; therefore, its factors
must have like signs.   Since the second term is negative, the cross products
must be negative.   Then it follows that both factors of 6 must be negative.
Some of the combinations are as follows:

Trial Factors		Products	
$(2i - 3)(6i - 2)$	$=$	$12i^2 - 22i + 6$	Wrong
$(2i - 2)(6i - 3)$	$=$	$12i^2 - 18i + 6$	Wrong
$(3i - 3)(4i - 2)$	$=$	$12i^2 - 18i + 6$	Wrong
$(3i - 2)(4i - 3)$	$=$	$12i^2 - 17i + 6$	Right

$$\therefore\ 12i^2 - 17i + 6 = (3i - 2)(4i - 3)$$

Example 4.   Factor $8r^2 - 14r - 15$.
Solution: The factors of -15 must have unlike signs.   The signs of these
factors must be arranged so that the cross product of greater absolute value
is minus, because the middle term of the trinomial is negative.

Trial Factors		Products	
$(8r + 3)(r - 5)$	$=$	$8r^2 - 37r - 15$	Wrong
$(4r + 5)(2r - 3)$	$=$	$8r^2 - 2r - 15$	Wrong
$(4r + 3)(2r - 5)$	$=$	$8r^2 - 14r - 15$	Right

Example 5.   Factor $6R^2 - 7R - 20$.
Note: Many students prefer the following method to that of the foregoing
examples in which trial-and-error methods were used.
Solution: Multiply and divide the entire expression by the coefficient of R^2.
The result is

$$\frac{36R^2 - 42R - 120}{6}$$

Take the square root of the first term, which is $6R$, and let that be some other
letter such as x.

Then, if $$6R = x$$

by substituting the value of $6R$ in the above expression, we obtain

$$\frac{x^2 - 7x - 120}{6}$$

This results in an expression with a numerator easy to factor. Thus,

$$\frac{x^2 - 7x - 120}{6} = \frac{(x + 8)(x - 15)}{6}$$

Substituting $6R$ for x in the last expression, we obtain

$$\frac{(6R + 8)(6R - 15)}{6}$$

Factoring the numerator, $\dfrac{2(3R + 4)3(2R - 5)}{6}$

Canceling, $6R^2 - 7R - 20 = (3R + 4)(2R - 5)$

Example 6.   Factor $4E^2 - 8EI - 21I^2$.
Solution: Multiplying and dividing by the coefficient of E^2,

$$\frac{16E^2 - 32EI - 84I^2}{4}$$

Let $4E$ (the square root of the first term) $= x$.

Then $\dfrac{x^2 - 8Ix - 84I^2}{4} = \dfrac{(x + 6I)(x - 14I)}{4}$

Substituting for x, $= \dfrac{(4E + 6I)(4E - 14I)}{4}$

Factoring, $= \dfrac{2(2E + 3I)2(2E - 7I)}{4}$

Canceling, $4E^2 - 8EI - 21I^2 = (2E + 3I)(2E - 7I)$

PROBLEMS 11-12

Factor:

1. $9a^2 + 9a + 2$.
2. $2e^2 - 7e + 3$.
3. $9b^2 + 36b + 32$.
4. $5r^2 - 16r + 3$.
5. $6I^2 - 18I - 60$.
6. $3Z^2 - 56Z - 19$.
7. $2a^2 - 21ab - 11b^2$.
8. $28x^2 - 19x + 3$.
9. $10\theta^2 + 7\theta - 3$.
10. $12e^2 + 13ei - 35i^2$.
11. $8R^2 + 18R - 35$.
12. $12a^2 + 17a + 6$.
13. $9E^2 - 6E - 35$.
14. $2i^2 - 3ir - 20r^2$.
15. $6v^2 - 25vt + 25t^2$.
16. $15x^2 + 19x + 6$.
17. $21r^2 - 29ri - 10i^2$.
18. $4x^2y^2 + 4xy - 15$.
19. $15\theta^2 + 29\theta + 12$.
20. $10e^2 + 19e - 15$.
21. $7a^2 - 26ab - 8b^2$.
22. $24\theta^2 - 18\theta - 15$.
23. $15x^2 - 26xy - 21y^2$.
24. $6p^2 + 31pq + 35q^2$.
25. $3R^2 + 22R + 7$.
26. $14B^2 - 31B - 10$.

27. $a^4 + \dfrac{a^2}{4} - \dfrac{1}{8}.$

28. $4c^2 - 24cd + 35d^2.$

29. $12t^2 + 13t - 35.$

30. $e^2 - \tfrac{2}{3}e + \tfrac{1}{9}.$

31. $a^2 + 0.2a - 0.15.$

32. $x^2 - x + \tfrac{1}{4}.$

33. $5v^2 + 35vt - 150t^2.$

34. $9c^2 + 3cd - 56d^2.$

35. $18B^2 + 17B - 15.$

36. $2\theta^2 - 0.9\theta - 0.05.$

37. $m^2 + 0.1m - 0.9.$

38. $r^2 + 0.5r - 0.14.$

39. $10x^2 + 9xy - 9y^2.$

40. $10a^2 - 13ab - 30b^2.$

11-17. Factoring the Sum and Difference of Two Cubes.

Type: $a^3 + b^3 = (a + b)(a^2 - ab + b^2)$

Type: $a^3 - b^3 = (a - b)(a^2 + ab + b^2)$

Rule : *To factor the sum or difference of two cubes,*

1. *The sum of the cubes of two numbers is always divisible by the sum of the numbers. The quotient is the sum of the squares of the numbers minus their product.*

2. *The difference of two cubes is always divisible by the difference of the numbers. The quotient is the sum of the squares of the numbers plus their product.*

Example 1.   Factor $8x^3 - 27y^3$.

Solution: $8x^3 - 27y^3 = (2x)^3 - (3y)^3$

This is the difference of the cubes of $2x$ and $3y$ and can be divided by $(2x - 3y)$.

$$\therefore 8x^3 - 27y^3 = (2x - 3y)(4x^2 + 6xy + 9y^2)$$

Example 2.   Factor $64a^3 + 125b^3x^3$.

Solution: $64a^3 + 125b^3x^3 = (4a)^3 + (5bx)^3$

This is the sum of the cubes of $4a$ and $5bx$ and can be divided by $(4a + 5bx)$.

$$\therefore 64a^3 + 125b^3x^3 = (4a + 5bx)(16a^2 - 20abx + 25b^2x^2)$$

PROBLEMS 11-13

Factor:

1. $a^3 + 1.$

2. $x^3 - 125.$

3. $x^3 - 1.$

4. $m^3 - 8n^3.$

5. $27e^3 - 1.$

6. $64x^3 - 1.$

7. $8a^3 + x^3.$

8. $a^3 + \tfrac{1}{8}.$

9. $64 - b^3.$

10. $x^3 + \dfrac{8}{27y^3}.$

11. $27r^3 + 1$.   **12.** $e^3 - \dfrac{i^3}{125}$.

13. $1 - e^3$.   **14.** $\theta^3 - 27$.

15. $(a + b)^3 + (c + d)^3$.   **16.** $(x + y)^3 + 1$.

17. $8a^3 - 64B^3$.   **18.** $1 + R^3$.

19. $\frac{8}{27}x^3 - \frac{1}{8}$.   **20.** $125\theta^3 - \frac{1}{125}$.

11-18. Summary. In this chapter, various cases of products and factoring have been treated separately in the different articles. Frequently, however, it becomes necessary to apply the principles underlying two or more cases to a single problem. It is essential, therefore, that the student recognize the standard type of forms in order that he may apply them as needed. These are summarized as follows:

General type	Factors	Article
$ab + ac + ad$	$a(b + c + d)$	11-7
$a^2 + 2ab + b^2$	$(a + b)^2$	11-8
$a^2 - 2ab + b^2$	$(a - b)^2$	11-8
$a^2 - b^2$	$(a + b)(a - b)$	11-12
$a^2 + (b + c)a + bc$	$(a + b)(a + c)$	11-13
$acx^2 + (bc + ad)x + bd$	$(ax + b)(cx + d)$	11-15
$a^3 + b^3$	$(a + b)(a^2 - ab + b^2)$	11-17
$a^3 - b^3$	$(a - b)(a^2 + ab + b^2)$	11-17

Problems 11-14 are included as a review of the entire chapter. If the student can work all of them, he thoroughly understands the contents of this chapter. If not, a review of the doubtful parts is suggested, for a good working knowledge of special products and factoring makes it possible

1. To perform quickly many multiplications and divisions mentally.

2. To solve many problems that might appear impossible of solution unless factoring is used.

PROBLEMS 11-14

Find the value of:

1. $\left(-3\dfrac{e^2}{Z}\right)^3$.   **2.** $(-2a^2bx^5y^3)^4$.   **3.** $\left(\dfrac{4d^2ef^3}{9x^2y^4z}\right)^3$.

4. $\sqrt{25x^4y^2z^6}$.   **5.** $-\sqrt{81a^8b^{10}c^2}$.   **6.** $\sqrt{\dfrac{49e^4i^2r^6}{625x^2y^8z^6}}$.

7. $\sqrt[3]{27a^3b^6c^{12}}$.   **8.** $\sqrt[3]{-\frac{8}{27}x^6y^3z^9}$.   **9.** $-\sqrt[3]{-\dfrac{125c^3d^9e^6}{216x^6y^{12}z^3}}$.

Factor:

10. $\pi R^2 - \pi r^2$.

11. $\frac{1}{3}ir - \frac{4}{5}er + \frac{2}{3}i^2r$.

12. $p + prt$.

13. $\frac{1}{2}IR - 0.5I - \frac{3}{2}EI$.

14. $\dfrac{E}{R} + \dfrac{e}{R}$.

15. $0.15wt - 0.45wn + 0.6w$.

Expand mentally:

16. $(e + 10)^2$.

17. $(7R^2 - 2r)^2$.

18. $(12\theta - \frac{3}{4})^2$.

19. $(\frac{2}{3} + 12i)^2$.

20. $(0.5\alpha + 0.3\beta)^2$.

21. $(\frac{1}{2} - 6E^3)^2$.

Supply the missing terms so that the three form a perfect trinomial square:

22. $e^2 - (?) + 100$.

23. $(?) - 20R + 25$.

24. $4I^2 + 4I + (?)$.

25. $36 + 12E + (?)$.

26. $(?) - 18\alpha + \alpha^2$.

27. $9 - 6B + (?)$.

Extract the square roots of the following:

28. $9 - 30x + 25x^2$.

29. $a^2 + 8a + 16$.

30. $i^2 + i + \frac{1}{4}$.

31. $1 - \phi + \dfrac{\phi^2}{4}$.

32. $R^2 + \dfrac{4R}{3} + \dfrac{4}{9}$.

33. $\dfrac{100}{9} - \dfrac{100E}{3} + 25E^2$.

Find the products:

34. $(3e - 4i)(3e + 4i)$.

35. $(x^2 + 3y)(x^2 - 3y)$.

36. $\left(\dfrac{3Z}{5} - 7\right)\left(\dfrac{3Z}{5} + 7\right)$.

37. $(5E + 9e)(5E - 9e)$.

Find the quotients:

38. $\dfrac{x^2 - y^2}{x - y}$.

39. $\dfrac{36 - Z^2}{6 + Z}$.

40. $\dfrac{4I^2 - 9i^2}{2I - 3i}$.

41. $\dfrac{e^2 - \frac{1}{4}}{e + \frac{1}{2}}$.

42. $\dfrac{\frac{1}{4} - 0.09a^2}{\frac{1}{2} + 0.3a}$.

43. $\dfrac{(x^2 + 2xy + y^2) - 25}{(x + y) - 5}$.

44. $\dfrac{\frac{4}{81} - \frac{16w^2}{100}}{\frac{2}{9} - 0.4w}$.

45. $\dfrac{(a + b)^2 - 1}{(a + b) - 1}$.

Factor:

46. $81 - V^2$.

47. $4\alpha^2 - 49\beta^2$.

48. $x^2y^2 - a^2b^6c^4$.

49. $e^2 - 0.16$.

50. $0.09i^2 - \dfrac{49I^2}{4}$.

51. $0.16R^2 - 0.0025Z^2$.

52. $\dfrac{\theta^2}{81} - \dfrac{\phi^2}{25}$.

Find the products:

53. $(6 - 3\alpha)(4 + 3\alpha)$.

55. $(e^2 - 0.2)(e^2 + 0.5)$.

57. $(3E + 8)\left(\dfrac{E}{4} - \dfrac{1}{3}\right)$.

59. $(Z + 0.5)(0.8Z - 0.3)$.

54. $(5R - 3)(3R + 8)$

56. $(i + \frac{1}{4})(i - \frac{1}{2})$.

58. $(10I - \frac{1}{10})(5I + \frac{1}{5})$.

60. $(5\theta - 8)\left(\dfrac{\theta}{8} + \dfrac{1}{5}\right)$.

Factor:

61. $R^2 - 11R + 10$.

63. $i^2 + 14i + 49$.

65. $e^2 - 0.1e - 0.06$.

62. $a^2 + 3a - 10$.

64. $x^2 - 2x - 35$.

66. $I^2 + \dfrac{I}{12} - \dfrac{1}{12}$.

Find the products:

67. $(3x - 4)(x - 3)$.

69. $(10a^2 - 11b)(11a^2 + 12b)$.

68. $(4R - 5)(2R - 5)$.

70. $(0.1e + 0.2)(0.1e + 0.4)$.

Factor:

71. $10a^2 - 31a + 15$.

73. $9i^2 - 9i - 70$.

75. $15x^2 + 2xy - 8y^2$.

77. $E^2 - 0.9EI + 0.18I^2$.

79. $56\theta^2 + 9\theta - 35$.

81. $x^2 + \dfrac{2x}{y} + \dfrac{1}{y^2}$.

83. $7i^3 - 7$.

85. $x^5 + 4x^3 - 5x$.

87. $x^4y - xy^4$.

89. $1 + I^3$.

91. $300x^4 - 243y^2$.

93. $x^4 - 18x^2 + 77$.

95. $b^3 - bc^2$.

97. $3E^2 + 33E + 72$.

99. $169m^2 + 78mn + 9n^2$.

72. $\alpha^2 + \frac{5}{6}\alpha + \frac{1}{6}$.

74. $15r^2 - 1 + 2r$.

76. $3w^2 + 0.4w - 0.15$.

78. $27y^2 + 4x^2 - 21xy$.

80. $\alpha^2 + 0.1\alpha\beta - 0.20\beta^2$.

82. $e^3 + 27E^3$.

84. $3b^4 - 3b^2 - 36$.

86. $250e - 2e^4$.

88. $R^3 - Rr^2$.

90. $a^2 + \frac{2}{9}a + \frac{1}{81}$.

92. $\frac{25}{169}e^2 - 196E^2$.

94. $\alpha^3 - 64\beta^3$.

96. $3x^3 - 108x$.

98. $C^6 + 14C^3 + 49$.

100. $3a^3 + 24b^3$.

CHAPTER XII

FRACTIONS

Algebraic fractions play an important role in mathematics, especially in equations for electrical and radio circuits. At this time, if the student feels he has not thoroughly mastered arithmetical fractions, he is urged to review them. A good foundation in arithmetical fractions is essential, for every rule and operation pertaining to them are applicable to algebraic fractions. It is a fact that the student who really knows arithmetical fractions rarely has much trouble with algebraic fractions.

12-1. The Degree of a Monomial. The degree of a monomial is determined by the number of literal factors it has.

Thus, $6ab^2$ is a monomial of the third degree because $ab^2 = a \cdot b \cdot b$; $3mn$ is a monomial of the second degree. From these examples, it is seen that the degree of a monomial is the sum of the exponents of the letters.

In such an expression as $5X^2Y^2Z$ we speak of the whole term as being of the fifth degree, X and Y as being of the second degree, and Z as being of the first degree.

The above definition for the degree of a monomial does not apply to letters in a denominator. Such degrees will be considered later.

12-2. The Degree of a Polynomial. The degree of a polynomial is taken as the degree of its term of highest degree. Thus, $3ab^2 - 4cd - d$ is of the *third* degree; $6x^2y + 5xy^2 + y^4$ is a polynomial of the *fourth* degree.

12-3. Highest Common Factor. A factor of each of two or more expressions is a *common factor* of those expressions. For example, 2 is a common factor of 4 and 6; a^2 is a common factor of a^3, $(a^2 - a^2b)$, and $(a^2x^2 - a^2y)$.

The product of all the factors common to two or more numbers, or expressions, is called their *highest common factor*. That is, the highest common factor is the expression of highest degree that will divide each of them without a remainder. It is commonly abbreviated H.C.F.

125

Example 1.   Find the highest common factor of

$$6a^2b^3(c + 1)(c + 3)^2 \quad \text{and} \quad 30a^3b^2(c - 2)(c + 3)$$

Solution: 6 is the greatest integer that will divide both expressions.
The highest power of a that will divide both is a^2.
The highest power of b that will divide both is b^2.
The highest power of $(c + 3)$ that will divide both is $(c + 3)$.
$(c + 1)$ and $(c - 2)$ will not divide both expressions.

$$\therefore 6a^2b^2(c + 3) = \text{H.C.F.}$$

Rule : *To determine the highest common factor,*
1. *Determine all the prime factors of each expression.*
2. *Take the common factors of all the expressions, giving to each the lowest exponent it has in any of the expressions.*
3. *The highest common factor is the product of all the common factors as obtained in step 2.*

Example 2.   Find the highest common factor of

$$50a^2b^3c(x + y)^3(x - y)^4 \quad \text{and} \quad 75a^2bc^2(x + y)^2(x - y)$$

Solution: $50a^2b^3c(x + y)^3(x - y)^4 = 2 \cdot 5 \cdot 5a^2b^3c(x + y)^3(x - y)^4$
$75a^2bc^2(x + y)^2(x - y) = 3 \cdot 5 \cdot 5a^2bc^2(x + y)^2(x - y)$
$\therefore \text{H.C.F.} = 5^2a^2bc(x + y)^2(x - y) = 25a^2bc(x + y)^2(x - y)$

Example 3.   Find the highest common factor of

$$a^3 + b^3, \quad a^2 + 2ab + b^2, \quad \text{and} \quad a^2 - b^2$$

Solution: $a^3 + b^3 = (a + b)(a^2 - ab + b^2)$
$a^2 + 2ab + b^2 = (a + b)^2$
$a^2 - b^2 = (a + b)(a - b)$
$\therefore \text{H.C.F.} = a + b$

PROBLEMS 12-1

Find the H.C.F. of:

1. 48, 60.

2. 32, 80.

3. $21xy,\ 33xy^2,\ 42x^2y^2$.

4. $25ab^2,\ 15a^3b^3,\ 60a^4b^2$.

5. $12e^2i^2,\ 48ei^3,\ 18e^5i^2$.

6. $88x^2y^4,\ 56x^3y^2,\ 16x^4y^2$.

7. $27vt^2,\ 18v^2t,\ 27v^2t^2$.

8. $x^2 - y^2,\ x^2 - 2xy + y^2,\ x^3 - y^3$.

9. $3m^2 - 3n^2,\ a(m - n),\ 3m^3 - 3n^3$.

10. $2c^2d^2 - 2c^2e^2,\ 4cd^2 - 12cde + 8ce^2,\ 10cd - 10ce$.

11. $18x^4 - 2x^2y^2,\ 12x^6 - 8x^5y - 4x^4y^2,\ 30x^4y^2 + 10x^3y^3$.

12. $a^5 - 3a^4b + 2a^3b^2,\ a^7 - 5a^5b^2 + 4a^3b^4,\ a^4 - 3a^3b + 2a^2b^2$.

13. $a^3(x - y)^2,\ a^4(x^4 - y^4),\ a^2(x - y)$.

14. $m^2n^2(x^3 + y^3),\ mn^2(x^5 + y^5),\ mn(x^2 - y^2)$.

15. $27x^3 + 8y^3,\ 9x^2 - 4y^2,\ 9x^2 + 12xy + 4y^2$.

12-4. Multiple. A number is a *multiple* of any one of its factors. For example, some of the multiples of 4 are 8, 16, 20, and 24. Similarly, some of the multiples of $(a + b)$ are $3(a + b)$, $a^2 + 2ab + b^2$, and $a^2 - b^2$. A *common multiple* of two or more numbers is a multiple of each of them. Thus, 45 is a common multiple of 1, 3, 5, 9, and 15.

12-5. Lowest Common Multiple. The smallest number that will contain each one of a set of factors is called their *lowest common multiple*. Thus, 48, 60, and 72 are all common multiples of 4 and 6; but the lowest common multiple of 4 and 6 is 12.

The lowest common multiple is abbreviated L.C.M.

Example 1. Find the lowest common multiple of $6x^2y$, $9xy^2z$, and $30x^3y^3$.

Solution:
$$6x^2y = 2 \cdot 3 \cdot x^2y$$
$$9xy^2z = 3^2xy^2z$$
$$30x^3y^3 = 2 \cdot 3 \cdot 5x^3y^3$$

Because the lowest common multiple must contain *each* of the expressions, it must have 2, 3^2, and 5 as factors. Also, it must contain the literal factors of highest degree, or x^3y^3z.

$$\therefore \text{L.C.M.} = 2 \cdot 3^2 \cdot 5 \cdot x^3y^3z = 90x^3y^3z$$

Rule: *To determine the lowest common multiple of two or more expressions,*

Determine all the prime factors of each expression. Find the product of all the different prime factors, taking each factor the greatest number of times it occurs in any one expression.

Example 2. Find the lowest common multiple of

$$3a^3 + 6a^2b + 3ab^2, \qquad 6a^4 - 12a^3b + 6a^2b^2, \qquad \text{and} \qquad 9a^3b - 9ab^3$$

Solution:
$$3a^3 + 6a^2b + 3ab^2 = 3a(a + b)^2$$
$$6a^4 - 12a^3b + 6a^2b^2 = 2 \cdot 3 \cdot a^2(a - b)^2$$
$$9a^3b - 9ab^3 = 3^2 \cdot ab(a + b)(a - b)$$
$$\therefore \text{L.C.M.} = 2 \cdot 3^2 \cdot a^2b(a + b)^2(a - b)^2$$

PROBLEMS 12-2

Find the L.C.M. of the following:

1. 5, 20, 25. **2.** 24, 30, 90. **3.** 45, 105, 175.

4. a^2b, ab^3, a^2b^2.

5. $2x$, $3y$, $4b$.

6. $7x^2$, $2xy$, $3y^2$.

7. $24m^3n^4$, $16m^2n^5$.

8. $32xy$, $16x^3y^2$, $64y^4$.

9. $7r^2s$, $4rt^2$, $6rt^3$, $21st$.

10. a^2, $a^2 - 3a$.

11. $21r^3$, $7r^2(r + 1)$.

12. $(x + y)(x - y)$, $x^2 + y^2$. **13.** $(a + 3)(a - 2)$, $(a - 2)(a - 3)$.
14. $e^2 + 2e - 35$, $e^2 + e - 42$, $e^2 - 11e + 30$.
15. $a^2 - b^2$, $(a - b)^2$, $a^3 - b^3$. **16.** $1 - 5i - 24i^2$, $1 + 27i^3$.
17. $x^3 - x$, $x^3 - 9x^2 - 10x$. **18.** $1 + a^2$, $(1 + a)^2$, $1 + a^3$.
19. $r^2 - 9$, $2r^3 + 6r^2 + 18r$, $2r^4 - 54r$.
20. $b^2 - 4b$, $4b^2 + 2b$, $2b^2 + 4b$, $2b^2 - 3b - 2$.

12-6. Definitions. A fraction is an indicated division. Thus, we indicate 4 divided by 5 as $\frac{4}{5}$ (read four-fifths). Similarly, X divided by Y is written $\frac{X}{Y}$ (read X divided by Y or X over Y).

The quantity above the horizontal line is called the *numerator* and that below the line is called the *denominator* of the fraction. The numerator and denominator are often called the *terms* of the fraction.

12-7. Operations on Numerator and Denominator. As in arithmetic, when fractions are to be simplified or affected by one of the four fundamental operations, we find it necessary to make frequent use of the following important principles.

1. *The numerator and the denominator of a fraction may be multiplied by the same number or expression, except zero, without changing the value of the fraction.*

2. *The numerator and the denominator may be divided by the same number or expression, except zero, without changing the value of the fraction.*

Example 1. $\dfrac{2}{3} = \dfrac{2 \times 3}{3 \times 3} = \dfrac{6}{9} = \dfrac{2}{3}$

Also, $\dfrac{6}{9} = \dfrac{6 \div 3}{9 \div 3} = \dfrac{2}{3} = \dfrac{6}{9}$

Example 2. $\dfrac{x}{y} = \dfrac{x \cdot a}{y \cdot a} = \dfrac{ax}{ay} = \dfrac{x}{y}$

Also, $\dfrac{ax \div a}{ay \div a} = \dfrac{x}{y}$ (where $a \neq 0$)

No new principles are involved in performing these operations; for multiplying or dividing both numerator and denominator by the same number, except zero, is equivalent to multiplying or dividing the fraction by 1.

It will be noted that, in the foregoing principles, multiplication and division of numerator and denominator by zero are excluded. When any expression is multiplied by zero, the product is zero.

For example, $6 \times 0 = 0$. Therefore, if we multiplied both numerator and denominator of some fraction by zero, the result would be meaningless. Thus,

$$\frac{5}{6} \neq \frac{5 \times 0}{6 \times 0} \qquad \text{because} \qquad \frac{5 \times 0}{6 \times 0} = \frac{0}{0}$$

Division by zero is meaningless. Some mathematicians say that any number divided by zero gives a quotient of infinity, denoted by ∞. If this is accepted, we immediately impose a severe restriction on operations with even simple equations. For example, let us assume for the moment that any number divided by zero *does* result in infinity. Then if

$$\frac{4}{0} = \infty$$

by following Axiom 3 we should be able to multiply both sides of this equation by 0. If so, we obtain

$$4 = \infty \cdot 0$$

which we know is not sensible. Obviously, there is a fallacy existing here; therefore, we shall simply say that *division by zero is not a permissible operation.*

12-8. Equivalent Fractions. Examples 1 and 2 in the preceding article show that when a numerator and a denominator are multiplied or divided by the same number, except zero, we change the *form* of the given fraction but *not* its value. Therefore, two fractions having the same value but not the same form are called *equivalent fractions.*

PROBLEMS 12-3

Supply the missing terms:

1. $\dfrac{3}{4} = \dfrac{?}{12}$.

2. $\dfrac{16}{60} = \dfrac{?}{30}$.

3. $\dfrac{1}{b} = \dfrac{?}{bx}$.

4. $\dfrac{4e}{9e} = \dfrac{?}{9ei}$.

5. $\dfrac{r + 4}{r + 3} = \dfrac{?}{(r + 3)(r - 4)}$.

6. $\dfrac{6}{x + 2y} = \dfrac{?}{x^2 + 4xy + 4y^2}$.

7. $\dfrac{E - 8}{E - 4} = \dfrac{?}{4E - E^2}$.

8. $\dfrac{x + 3}{1} = \dfrac{?}{x - 2}$.

9. $\dfrac{1}{i - 2e} = \dfrac{?}{i^2 - 5ie + 6e^2}$.

10. $\dfrac{6}{3x + 9} = \dfrac{?}{6x^2 + 18x}$.

11. Change the fraction $\frac{12}{20}$ into an equivalent fraction whose denominator is 5.

12. Change the fraction $\frac{2}{3}$ into an equivalent fraction whose denominator is 42.

13. Change the fraction $\dfrac{8E^2}{R}$ into an equivalent fraction whose denominator is $3I^2R$.

14. Change the fraction $\dfrac{1}{2\pi fC}$ into an equivalent fraction whose denominator is $4\pi f^2 C$.

15. Change the fraction $\dfrac{1}{2\pi \sqrt{LC}}$ into an equivalent fraction whose denominator is $2\pi LC$.

12-9. Reduction of Fractions to Their Lowest Terms.   If the numerator and denominator of a fraction have no common factor other than 1, then the fraction is said to be in its lowest terms. Thus, the fractions $\frac{2}{3}$, $\frac{3}{5}$, $\dfrac{x}{y}$ and $\dfrac{x+y}{x-y}$ are in their lowest terms, for the numerator and denominator of each fraction have no common factor except 1.

The fractions $\frac{4}{6}$ and $\dfrac{3x}{9x^2}$ are not in their lowest terms, for $\frac{4}{6}$ can be reduced to $\frac{2}{3}$ if both numerator and denominator are divided by 2. Similarly, $\dfrac{3x}{9x^2}$ can be reduced to $\dfrac{1}{3x}$ by dividing both numerator and denominator by $3x$.

> **Rule:** *To reduce a fraction to its lowest terms,*
> *Factor the numerator and denominator into prime factors, and cancel the factors common to both.*

Cancellation as used in the rule really means that we actually *divide* both terms of the fraction by the *common factors*.   Then, to reduce a fraction to its lowest terms, it is only necessary to divide both numerator and denominator by the highest common factor, which leaves an equivalent fraction.

Example 1.   Reduce $\frac{27}{108}$ to lowest terms.

Solution: $\dfrac{27}{108} = \dfrac{3 \cdot 3 \cdot 3}{2 \cdot 2 \cdot 3 \cdot 3 \cdot 3} = \dfrac{1}{4}$

Example 2.   Reduce $\dfrac{24x^2yz^3}{42x^2yz^2}$ to lowest terms.

Solution: $\dfrac{24x^2yz^3}{42x^2yz^2} = \dfrac{\cancel{2} \cdot 2 \cdot 2 \cdot \cancel{3} \cdot x^2yz^3}{\cancel{2} \cdot \cancel{3} \cdot 7 \cdot x^2yz^2} = \dfrac{4z}{7}$

Actually, the above solution need not have been written out, for it can be seen by inspection that the highest common factor of both terms of the fraction is $6x^2yz^2$ which we divide into both terms to obtain the equivalent fraction $\dfrac{4z}{7}$.

Also, in reducing fractions, we may resort to direct cancellation as in arithmetic.

Example 3. Reduce $\dfrac{x^2 - y^2}{x^3 - y^3}$ to lowest terms.

Solution: $\dfrac{x^2 - y^2}{x^3 - y^3} = \dfrac{(x + y)\cancel{(x - y)}}{\cancel{(x - y)}(x^2 + xy + y^2)} = \dfrac{x + y}{x^2 + xy + y^2}$

PROBLEMS 12-4

Reduce to lowest terms:

1. $\dfrac{34}{85}$.

2. $\dfrac{51}{153}$.

3. $\dfrac{49}{63}$.

4. $\dfrac{x^2}{x(x + y)}$.

5. $\dfrac{2(a - 1)}{(a - 1)^2(3a + 1)}$.

6. $\dfrac{a^2 - b^2}{(a + b)^2}$.

7. $\dfrac{10a^2b^2 - 5ab^3}{15ab^3}$.

8. $\dfrac{r^2 - 10r + 21}{r^2 + r - 12}$.

9. $\dfrac{4i^2 - 25}{4i^2 - 20i + 25}$.

10. $\dfrac{(a + b)^2 - c^2}{(a + c)^2 - b^2}$.

11. $\dfrac{e^4 + e^2 + 1}{e^3 + e^2 + e}$.

12. $\dfrac{a^2x^2 - 16a^2}{ax^2 + 9ax + 20a}$.

13. $\dfrac{r^2 + rs - 2s^2}{r^3 - s^3}$.

14. $\dfrac{a^2 - 5a}{a^2 - 4a - 5}$.

15. $\dfrac{3m^4 - 3n^4}{m^4 + 2m^2n^2 + n^4}$.

16. $\dfrac{c^3d - 8d}{(c^2 - 4)(c - 1)}$.

17. $\dfrac{E^4 - 14E^2 - 51}{E^4 - 2E^2 - 15}$.

18. $\dfrac{x^4 - y^4}{x^4 + 3x^2y^2 + 2y^4}$.

19. $\dfrac{I^3 - 49I}{42I^2 - 27I^3 + 3I^4}$.

20. $\dfrac{x^6 - 1}{x^2 - 1}$.

12-10. Signs of Fractions. As stated in Art. 12-6, a fraction is an indicated division or an indicated quotient. Heretofore, all our fractions have been positive, but now there must be taken into account three signs in working with an algebraic fraction: the sign of the numerator, the sign of the denominator, and the sign preceding the fraction.

By the law of signs in division, we have

$$+ \frac{+12}{+6} = + \frac{-12}{-6} = - \frac{+12}{-6} = - \frac{-12}{+6} = +2$$

or, in general,

$$+ \frac{+a}{+b} = + \frac{-a}{-b} = - \frac{+a}{-b} = - \frac{-a}{+b}$$

Careful study of the above examples will show the truths of the following important principles:

1. *The sign before either term of a fraction may be changed if the sign before the fraction is changed.*

2. *If the signs of both terms are changed, the sign before the fraction must not be changed.*

That is, we may change *any two* of the three signs of a fraction without changing its value.

It must be remembered that, when a term of a fraction is a polynomial, changing the sign of the term involves changing the sign of *each term* of the polynomial.

Changing the signs of both numerator and denominator, as mentioned in the second principle above, may be explained by considering both terms as multiplied or divided by -1 which, as previously explained, does not change the value of the fraction.

Multiplying (or dividing) a quantity by -1 twice does not change the value of the quantity. Hence, multiplying each of the two factors of a product by -1 does not change the value of the product.

Thus, $(a - 4)(a - 8) = (-a + 4)(-a + 8) = (4 - a)(8 - a)$
Also, $(a - b)(c - d)(e - f) = (b - a)(d - c)(e - f)$

The validity of these illustrations should be checked by multiplication.

Example 1.   Change $- \frac{a}{b}$ to three equivalent fractions having different signs.

Solution: $- \frac{a}{b} = \frac{-a}{b} = \frac{a}{-b} = - \frac{-a}{-b}$

Example 2.   Change $\frac{a - b}{c - d}$ to three equivalent fractions having different signs.

Solution: $\dfrac{a-b}{c-d} = \dfrac{-a+b}{-c+d} = -\dfrac{-a+b}{c-d} = -\dfrac{a-b}{-c+d}$

Example 3. Change $\dfrac{a-b}{c-d}$ to a fraction whose denominator is $d-c$.

Solution: $\dfrac{a-b}{c-d} = \dfrac{-a+b}{-c+d} = \dfrac{b-a}{d-c}$

PROBLEMS 12-5

Express as a positive fraction (with a positive numerator):

1. $\dfrac{-6}{a^2-b^2}.$

2. $-\dfrac{-8E^2}{R-r}.$

3. $\dfrac{-E}{R_1-R_2}.$

4. $\dfrac{-a-b}{x^2-y^2}.$

5. $\dfrac{-(c+d)}{e-f}.$

Express as a positive fraction (with a positive denominator):

6. $\dfrac{a-b}{-23}.$

7. $\dfrac{E-e}{-r}.$

8. $-\dfrac{E^2+e^2}{-3r}.$

Reduce to lowest terms:

9. $\dfrac{x-y}{y-x}.$

10. $\dfrac{x-y}{y^2-x^2}.$

11. $-\dfrac{rs-2rt}{4t^2-s^2}.$

12. $\dfrac{m^2-2m+1}{1-m^2}.$

13. $\dfrac{2a^2+2a}{2a^3+12a^2+10a}.$

14. $\dfrac{x^2-2xy+y^2-z^2}{3x-3y+3z}.$

12-11. Common Errors in Working with Fractions.

It has been demonstrated that a fraction may be reduced to lower terms by dividing both numerator and denominator by the same number (Art. 12-9). Mistakes are often made by canceling parts of numerator and denominator that *are not* factors. Take, for example,

$$\frac{5+2}{7+2} = \frac{7}{9}$$

Here is a case where both terms of the fraction are polynomials and the terms, even if alike, can never be canceled. Thus,

$$\frac{5+\cancel{2}}{7+\cancel{2}} \neq \frac{5}{7}$$

because, by canceling terms, the value of the fraction has been changed.

Similarly, it would be incorrect to cancel the x's in the fraction $\dfrac{3a - x}{5c - x}$, for the x's *are not factors*. Hence, it is apparent that $\dfrac{3a - x}{5c - x}$ cannot be reduced to lower terms, for neither term of the fraction can be factored. It is permissible to cancel x's in the fraction $\dfrac{6x}{ax + 5x}$ because *each term* of the denominator contains x. Or the denominator may be factored to give $\dfrac{6x}{x(a + 5)}$, the result being that the x's are a factor in both terms of the fraction. Thus, *we cannot remove, or cancel, like* **terms** *from the numerator and denominator of a fraction. Only like* **factors** *can be removed, or canceled.*

Another important fact to be remembered is that adding the same number to or subtracting the same number from both numerator and denominator changes the value of the fraction. That is,

$$\frac{3}{4} \neq \frac{3 + 2}{4 + 2} \text{ because the latter equals } \frac{5}{6}$$

Likewise, $\dfrac{3}{4} \neq \dfrac{3 - 2}{4 - 2}$ because the latter equals $\dfrac{1}{2}$

Similarly, squaring or extracting the same root of numerator and denominator results in a different value.

For example, $\dfrac{3}{4} \neq \dfrac{3^2}{4^2}$ because the latter equals $\dfrac{9}{16}$

Likewise, $\dfrac{16}{25} \neq \dfrac{\sqrt{16}}{\sqrt{25}}$ because the latter equals $\dfrac{4}{5}$

Students sometimes thoughtlessly make the error of writing 0 as the result of the cancellation of all factors. For example,

$$\frac{4x^2 y(a + b)}{4x^2 y(a + b)} = 1, \text{ not } 0$$

12-12. Changing Mixed Expressions to Fractions. In arithmetic, an expression such as $3\frac{1}{3}$ is called a *mixed number*. $3\frac{1}{3}$ means $3 + \frac{1}{3}$. Likewise, in algebra, an expression such as $x + \dfrac{y}{z}$ is called a *mixed expression*.

Because $4\frac{2}{3} = 4 + \frac{2}{3} = \frac{4}{1} + \frac{2}{3} = \frac{12}{3} + \frac{2}{3} = \frac{14}{3}$

then, $x + \frac{y}{z} = \frac{x}{1} + \frac{y}{z} = \frac{xz}{z} + \frac{y}{z} = \frac{xz + y}{z}$

Also, $3x^2 - 4x + \dfrac{3}{x^2 - 1} = \dfrac{3x^2}{1} - \dfrac{4x}{1} + \dfrac{3}{x^2 - 1}$

$$= \frac{3x^2(x^2 - 1)}{x^2 - 1} - \frac{4x(x^2 - 1)}{x^2 - 1} + \frac{3}{x^2 - 1}$$

$$= \frac{3x^4 - 3x^2 - 4x^3 + 4x + 3}{x^2 - 1}$$

12-13. Reduction of a Fraction to a Mixed Expression.

As would be expected, reducing a fraction to a mixed expression is the reverse of changing a mixed expression to a fraction. That is, a fraction may be changed to a mixed expression by dividing the numerator by the denominator and adding to the quotient thus obtained the remainder which is written as a fraction.

Example 1.   Change $\dfrac{12x^3 + 16x^2 - 8x - 3}{4x}$ to a mixed expression.

Solution: Divide each term of the numerator by the denominator.

Thus, $\dfrac{12x^3 + 16x^2 - 8x - 3}{4x} = 3x^2 + 4x - 2 - \dfrac{3}{4x}$

Example 2.   Change $\dfrac{a^2 + 1}{a - 2}$ to a mixed expression.

Solution: By division,

$$
\begin{array}{r}
a + 2 \\
a - 2 \overline{\smash{\big)}\, a^2 \quad + 1} \\
\underline{a^2 - 2a} \\
2a + 1 \\
\underline{2a - 4} \\
5
\end{array}
$$

$$\therefore \frac{a^2 + 1}{a - 2} = a + 2 + \frac{5}{a - 2}$$

PROBLEMS 12-6

Change the following mixed expressions to fractions:

1. $3\frac{2}{3}$.   2. $6\frac{3}{7}$.   3. $5 + \frac{2}{3}$.

4. $1 + \dfrac{x}{y}$.   5. $c - \dfrac{d}{e}$.   6. $I - \dfrac{e}{r}$.

7. $I^2R - \dfrac{e^2}{r}$.   8. $R^2 - \dfrac{R^2}{4}$.   9. $V^2 - \left(\dfrac{V}{3}\right)^2$.

10. $EI + \dfrac{e^2}{R}$.   **11.** $\left(\dfrac{w}{2}\right)^2 - w^2$.   **12.** $\left(\dfrac{f}{3}\right)^2 - \dfrac{f^2}{3}$.

13. $3 + \dfrac{5}{x+1}$.   **14.** $I - \dfrac{e}{R+r}$.

15. $\alpha + \beta - \dfrac{1}{\alpha - \beta}$.   **16.** $2e - 3E - \dfrac{4e}{5e + E}$.

17. $i - 3 - \dfrac{i+3}{i-3}$.   **18.** $6 - \dfrac{16}{3P} + 2P$.

19. $x^2 + y^2 - \dfrac{(x+y)^2}{2}$.   **20.** $a^2 - ab - \dfrac{a^3 - b^3}{a + b} + b^2$.

Reduce the following to mixed expressions:

21. $1\frac{27}{25}$.   **22.** $1\frac{48}{12}$.   **23.** $1\frac{96}{13}$.

24. $\dfrac{9x^3 - 27x^2 - 18x + 3}{3x}$.   **25.** $\dfrac{12I^2 - 16I - 9}{4I}$.

26. $\dfrac{18R^2 + 6R - 3}{6R}$.   **27.** $\dfrac{9a^2 + 6}{3a + 1}$.

28. $\dfrac{x^3 + 8y^3}{x - 2y}$.   **29.** $\dfrac{a^3 + a^2b + 6b^3}{a - 2b}$.

30. $\dfrac{3m^3 + 8m^2 - 7}{m^2 - 2m - 3}$.

12-14. Reduction to the Lowest Common Denominator.

The *lowest common denominator* of two or more fractions is the lowest common multiple of their denominators.

Example 1.   Reduce $\frac{1}{3}$ and $\frac{3}{5}$ to their lowest common denominator.

Solution: The lowest common multiple of 3 and 5 is 15.   To change the denominator of $\frac{1}{3}$ to 15, we must multiply the 3 by 5, $(15 \div 3)$.   In order not to change the value of the fraction, the numerator must also be multiplied by 5.

Hence, $\frac{1}{3} = \frac{1}{3} \times \frac{5}{5} = \frac{5}{15}$

For the second fraction, we must multiply the denominator by 3 in order to obtain a new denominator of 15, $(15 \div 5)$.   Again we must also multiply the numerator by 3 to maintain the original value of the fraction.

Hence, $\frac{3}{5} = \frac{3}{5} \times \frac{3}{3} = \frac{9}{15}$

Example 2.   Reduce $\dfrac{4a^2b}{3x^2y}$ and $\dfrac{6cd^2}{4xy^2}$ to their lowest common denominator.

Solution: The lowest common multiple of the two denominators is $12x^2y^2$. This is the lowest common denominator.

For the first fraction the lowest common denominator is divided by the denominator.

That is, $12x^2y^2 \div 3x^2y = 4y$

Multiplying both numerator and denominator by $4y$,

$$\frac{4a^2b}{3x^2y} = \frac{4a^2b}{3x^2y} \cdot \frac{4y}{4y} = \frac{16a^2by}{12x^2y^2}$$

For the second fraction the same procedure is followed.

$$12x^2y^2 \div 4xy^2 = 3x$$

Multiplying both numerator and denominator by $3x$,

$$\frac{6cd^2}{4xy^2} = \frac{6cd^2}{4xy^2} \cdot \frac{3x}{3x} = \frac{18cd^2x}{12x^2y^2}$$

Rule : *To reduce fractions to their lowest common denominator,*

1. *Factor each denominator into its prime factors, and find the lowest common multiple of the denominators. This is the lowest common denominator.*

2. *For each fraction, divide the lowest common denominator by the denominator, and multiply both numerator and denominator by the quotient thus obtained.*

Example 3. Reduce $\dfrac{3x}{x^2 - y^2}$ and $\dfrac{4y}{x^2 - xy - 2y^2}$ to their lowest common denominator.

Solution:

$$\frac{3x}{x^2 - y^2} = \frac{3x}{(x + y)(x - y)}$$

$$\frac{4y}{x^2 - xy - 2y^2} = \frac{4y}{(x + y)(x - 2y)}$$

The lowest common multiple of the two denominators, and therefore the lowest common denominator, is $(x + y)(x - y)(x - 2y)$.

For the first fraction, the lowest common denominator divided by the denominator is $(x + y)(x - y)(x - 2y) \div (x + y)(x - y) = x - 2y$.

$$\therefore \frac{3x}{(x + y)(x - y)} = \frac{3x(x - 2y)}{(x + y)(x - y)(x - 2y)}$$

For the second fraction, the lowest common denominator divided by the denominator is $(x + y)(x - y)(x - 2y) \div (x + y)(x - 2y) = x - y$.

$$\therefore \frac{4y}{(x + y)(x - 2y)} = \frac{4y(x - y)}{(x + y)(x - 2y)(x - y)}$$

To check the solution, the fractions having the lowest common denominator may be changed into the original fractions by cancellation.

PROBLEMS 12-7

Reduce to equivalent fractions having their lowest common denominator:

1. $\frac{1}{2}$, $\frac{2}{3}$, $\frac{3}{5}$.

2. $\frac{5}{6}$, $\frac{3}{4}$, $\frac{7}{10}$.

3. $\frac{3}{4}$, $\frac{6}{7}$, $\frac{5}{8}$.

4. $\frac{1}{a}$, $\frac{1}{b}$.

5. $\frac{a}{x}$, $\frac{b}{y}$.

6. $\frac{1}{R}$, $\frac{1}{r}$, $\frac{1}{r}$.

7. $\dfrac{1}{E}, \dfrac{3}{E^2}, \dfrac{8}{e}.$

8. $\dfrac{1}{x+1}, \dfrac{b}{x-1}.$

9. $\dfrac{x}{a^2-b^2}, \dfrac{y}{(a+b)^2}.$

10. $\dfrac{V^2}{2x^2y}, \dfrac{Vt^2}{3xy^2}, \dfrac{Vt^2}{5x^3y^4}.$

11. $\dfrac{3a}{5a-10}, \dfrac{5}{2a-4}.$

12. $\dfrac{e}{e^2-6e+8}, \dfrac{e^2}{e^2-16}.$

13. $\dfrac{e-r}{a^2+2ab+b^2}, \dfrac{a+b}{e^2-er-12r^2}.$

14. $\dfrac{c^2-c-12}{i^2+12i+36}, \dfrac{c^2-36}{i^2+2i-24}.$

15. $\dfrac{x+2}{x^2+2x-3}, \dfrac{x-3}{x^2-3x+2}, \dfrac{x+1}{x^2+x-6}.$

12-15. Addition and Subtraction of Fractions.   The sum of two or more fractions having the same denominator is obtained by adding the numerators and writing the result over the common denominator.

Example 1. $\dfrac{2}{7}+\dfrac{1}{7}+\dfrac{5}{7}=\dfrac{2+1+5}{7}=\dfrac{8}{7}$

Example 2. $\dfrac{3e}{R+r}+\dfrac{e}{R+r}+\dfrac{5e}{R+r}=\dfrac{3e+e+5e}{R+r}=\dfrac{9e}{R+r}$

To subtract two fractions having the same denominator, subtract the numerator of the subtrahend from the numerator of the minuend and write the result over their common denominator.

Example 3. $\dfrac{4}{5}-\dfrac{3}{5}=\dfrac{4-3}{5}=\dfrac{1}{5}$

Example 4. $\dfrac{a}{x}-\dfrac{b}{x}=\dfrac{a-b}{x}$

Example 5. $\dfrac{a}{x}-\dfrac{b-c}{x}=\dfrac{a-b+c}{x}$

Note that the vinculum is a sign of grouping and that, when a minus sign precedes a fraction having a polynomial numerator, all the signs in the numerator must be changed in order to complete the process of subtraction.

We have thus the following:

Rule: *To add or subtract fractions having unlike denominators,*

1. *Reduce them to equivalent fractions having their lowest common denominator.*

2. *Combine the numerators of these equivalent fractions, in parentheses, giving each the sign of the fraction.   This is the numerator of the result.*

3. *The denominator of the result is the lowest common denominator.*

4. *Simplify the numerator by removing parentheses and combining terms.*

5. *Reduce the fraction to the lowest terms.*

Example 6.   Simplify $\dfrac{a-5}{6x} - \dfrac{2a-5}{16x}$.

Solution: $\dfrac{a-5}{6x} - \dfrac{2a-5}{16x} = \dfrac{8(a-5)}{48x} - \dfrac{3(2a-5)}{48x}$

$$= \frac{8(a-5) - 3(2a-5)}{48x}$$

$$= \frac{8a - 40 - 6a + 15}{48x}$$

$$= \frac{2a - 25}{48x}$$

Check.   Let $a = 6$, $x = 1$.

$$\frac{a-5}{6x} = \frac{1}{6}, \qquad \frac{2a-5}{16} = \frac{7}{16}$$

$$\frac{1}{6} - \frac{7}{16} = \frac{8-21}{48} = -\frac{13}{48}$$

Also, $\dfrac{2a-25}{48} = \dfrac{12-25}{48} = -\dfrac{13}{48}$

Solution is correct.

Example 7.   Simplify $x^2 - xy + y^2 - \dfrac{2y^3}{x+y}$.

Solution: $x^2 - xy + y^2 - \dfrac{2y^3}{x+y}$

$$= \frac{(x+y)x^2}{x+y} - \frac{(x+y)xy}{x+y} + \frac{(x+y)y^2}{x+y} - \frac{2y^3}{x+y}$$

$$= \frac{x^3 + x^2y - x^2y - xy^2 + xy^2 + y^3 - 2y^3}{x+y}$$

$$= \frac{x^3 - y^3}{x+y}$$

PROBLEMS 12-8

Perform the following indicated additions and subtractions:

1. $\dfrac{2}{3} - \dfrac{5}{8} + \dfrac{1}{4}$.

2. $\dfrac{1}{6} + \dfrac{7}{24} - \dfrac{3}{8}$.

3. $\dfrac{2}{21} - \dfrac{5}{84} + \dfrac{3}{14}$.

4. $\dfrac{5x}{7} - \dfrac{x}{5} + \dfrac{12x}{35}$.

5. $\dfrac{7r}{8} + \dfrac{2r}{3} - \dfrac{3r}{16}$.

6. $\dfrac{3a}{2} - \dfrac{7a}{4} + \dfrac{15a}{8}$.

7. $\dfrac{3}{e} - \dfrac{5}{4e}$.

8. $\dfrac{xy}{2} + \dfrac{yz}{4} - \dfrac{az}{6}$.

9. $\dfrac{1}{ei} - \dfrac{5}{i}$.

10. $\dfrac{16}{25c^2r} + \dfrac{4}{5r}$.

11. $\dfrac{9}{\theta} - \dfrac{8}{\theta^2} + \dfrac{4}{\theta^3}$.

12. $\dfrac{x}{a} - \dfrac{y}{b} - \dfrac{z}{c}$.

13. $\dfrac{2x-8}{7} + \dfrac{3x+5}{14}$.

14. $\dfrac{4r-r}{9} - \dfrac{3r-8}{12}$.

15. $\dfrac{1}{e-4} + \dfrac{1}{e+4}$.

16. $\dfrac{5}{r-2} - \dfrac{2}{r-6}$.

17. $\dfrac{7}{3x+6} + \dfrac{12}{x^2-4}$.

18. $\dfrac{x}{xy+y^2} - \dfrac{y}{x^2+xy}$.

19. $\dfrac{3a+b}{a-b} + \dfrac{a}{b}$.

20. $\dfrac{12}{b^2-9} - \dfrac{2}{b^2-5b+6}$.

21. $\dfrac{5}{4a^2-1} - \dfrac{3a}{8a^3-1}$.

22. $\dfrac{2i+7}{3+i} - \dfrac{2i^2-35}{i^2-11i-42}$.

23. $\dfrac{2}{r^2+7r} - \dfrac{3}{r} + \dfrac{3}{r-7}$.

24. $\dfrac{5E+1}{2E^2-2} + \dfrac{7}{6E+6}$.

25. $\dfrac{10a+3b}{2a^2b} - \dfrac{3a+5b}{ab^2}$.

26. $\dfrac{2x-y}{xy} + \dfrac{2y-z}{yz} + \dfrac{2z-x}{xz}$.

27. $\dfrac{1}{a-b} - \dfrac{3b}{a^2-b^2} + \dfrac{ab}{a^3-b^3}$.

28. $\dfrac{a+b}{a-b} - \dfrac{a-b}{a+b} - \dfrac{4ab}{a^2-b^2}$.

29. $\dfrac{1}{R+r} - \dfrac{1}{R-r} + \dfrac{2R}{R^2-r^2}$.

30. $\dfrac{2x}{2x+3y} + \dfrac{3y}{2x-3y} - \dfrac{8y^2}{4x^2-9y^2}$.

31. $\dfrac{2x}{2x+3y} - \dfrac{3y}{2x-3y} + \dfrac{8y^2}{4x^2-9y^2}$.

32. $\dfrac{1}{\theta^2-9\theta+20} + \dfrac{1}{\theta^2-11\theta+30}$.

33. $\dfrac{x}{x+y} - \dfrac{y}{x-y} - \dfrac{2y^2}{b^2-a^2}$.

34. $\dfrac{1}{2r^2-r-1} - \dfrac{1}{2r^2+r-3}$.

35. $\dfrac{1}{\alpha+1} - \dfrac{1}{(\alpha+1)(\alpha+2)} + \dfrac{1}{(\alpha+1)(\alpha+2)(\alpha+3)}$.

36. $\dfrac{1}{e+1} - \dfrac{e}{e^2-e+1} + \dfrac{e^2-4}{e^3+1}$.

37. $\dfrac{R}{R^2+5R+6} + \dfrac{15}{R^2+9R+14} - \dfrac{12}{R^2+10R+21}$.

38. $\dfrac{6w}{w^2+8w+15} - \dfrac{2w+1}{w^2+5w} + \dfrac{5w-1}{w^2+3w}$.

39. $3I + 2 - \dfrac{5}{3I-2}$.

40. $\dfrac{i^2+5}{i-4} + i + 4$.

41. $x + y - \dfrac{x^2-y^2}{x-y} + 1$.

42. $\left(\dfrac{e}{2}\right)^2 - 5e - \left(\dfrac{1}{4}\right)^2$.

43. $\dfrac{(\theta-1)^2}{\theta+1} - \dfrac{5}{6} + 6$.

44. $\dfrac{d^2+3d+9}{d^2-3d+9} - \dfrac{d-3}{d+3} - \dfrac{54}{d^3+27}$.

45. $\dfrac{ab^2}{a^2-b^2} - \dfrac{2ab}{a^2-ab} - \dfrac{ab^2(a-2)}{a^3-a b^2}$.

46. $\dfrac{a-b}{a+b} + 1$.

47. $3R + 4 - \dfrac{9R^2+16}{3R-4}$.

48. $\dfrac{1}{8 - 8a} - \dfrac{1}{8 + 8a} + \dfrac{a}{4 + 4a^2} - \dfrac{a}{2 + 2a^2}.$

49. $\dfrac{r - 3}{r + 2} - \dfrac{r - 2}{r + 2} + \dfrac{1}{r - 1}.$

50. $\dfrac{x + 3y}{4(x + y)(x + 2y)} + \dfrac{x + 2y}{(x + y)(x + 3y)} - \dfrac{x + y}{4(x + 2y)(x + 3y)}.$

12-16. Multiplication of Fractions. The methods of multiplication of fractions in algebra are identical with those in arithmetic. The product of two or more fractions is the product of their numerators divided by the product of their denominators.

Example 1. $\qquad\qquad \frac{2}{3} \times \frac{3}{5} = \frac{6}{15}$

Example 2. $\qquad\qquad \dfrac{a}{b} \cdot \dfrac{x}{y} = \dfrac{ax}{by}$

Where a factor occurs one or more times in *any* numerator and in *any* denominator of the product of two or more fractions, it may be canceled the same number of times from both, this process resulting in the product of the given fractions in lower terms.

Example 3. Multiply $\dfrac{6x^2y}{7b}$ by $\dfrac{21b^2c}{24xy^2}.$

Solution: $\qquad\qquad \dfrac{6x^2y}{7b} \cdot \dfrac{21b^2c}{24xy^2} = \dfrac{3bcx}{4y}$

Example 4. Simplify $\dfrac{2a^2 - ab - b^2}{a^2 + 2ab + b^2} \cdot \dfrac{a^2 - b^2}{4a^2 + 4ab + b^2}.$

Solution:
$$\dfrac{2a^2 - ab - b^2}{a^2 + 2ab + b^2} \cdot \dfrac{a^2 - b^2}{4a^2 + 4ab + b^2}$$
$$= \dfrac{(2a + b)(a - b)}{(a + b)(a + b)} \cdot \dfrac{(a + b)(a - b)}{(2a + b)(2a + b)}$$
$$= \dfrac{(a - b)(a - b)}{(a + b)(2a + b)}$$
$$= \dfrac{a^2 - 2ab + b^2}{2a^2 + 3ab + b^2}$$

It is very important that the student understand clearly what we are allowed to cancel in the numerators and the denominators. The *whole* of an expression is always canceled, *never one term.* For example, in the expression $\dfrac{8a}{a - 5}$, it is not permissible to cancel the a's and obtain $\dfrac{8}{-5}.$ It must be remembered that the denominator $a - 5$ denotes *one quantity.* We should not cancel the a's if the expression were written $\dfrac{8a}{(a-5)}$ because of the parentheses. However, the parentheses are not needed; for the *vinculum, which is also a sign of grouping, serves the same purpose.* We shall consider this again in the next chapter.

12-17. Division of Fractions. As with multiplication, the methods of division of fractions in algebra are identical with those of arithmetic. Therefore, to divide by a fraction, invert the divisor fraction and proceed as in the multiplication of fractions.

Example 1. $\qquad \frac{5}{2} \div \frac{2}{3} = \frac{5}{2} \cdot \frac{3}{2} = \frac{15}{4}$

Example 2. $\qquad \dfrac{ab^2}{xy} \div \dfrac{a^2b}{xy^2} = \dfrac{ab^2}{xy} \cdot \dfrac{xy^2}{a^2b} = \dfrac{by}{a}$

Example 3. $\quad \dfrac{x}{y} \div \left(a + \dfrac{b}{c}\right) = \dfrac{x}{y} \div \dfrac{ac + b}{c}$

$$= \dfrac{x}{y} \cdot \dfrac{c}{ac + b} = \dfrac{cx}{y(ac + b)}$$

$$= \dfrac{cx}{acy + by}$$

Students often ask why we must invert the divisor and multiply by the dividend in dividing fractions. As an example, suppose we have $\dfrac{a}{b} \div \dfrac{x}{y}$. The dividend is $\dfrac{a}{b}$, and the divisor is $\dfrac{x}{y}$.

Now, $\qquad$ Quotient $\times$ divisor $=$ dividend

Therefore, the quotient must be such a number that when multiplied by $\dfrac{x}{y}$ it will give $\dfrac{a}{b}$ as a product. Then,

$$\left(\dfrac{a}{b} \cdot \dfrac{y}{x}\right) \cdot \dfrac{x}{y} = \dfrac{a}{b}$$

Hence, the quotient is $\dfrac{a}{b} \cdot \dfrac{y}{x}$, which is the dividend, multiplied by the inverted divisor.

PROBLEMS 12-9

Simplify:

1. $\frac{5}{9} \times \frac{4}{5} \times \frac{15}{18}$.

2. $\frac{12}{35} \times \frac{5}{18} \times 42$.

3. $\frac{2}{3} \div \frac{5}{8}$.

4. $\frac{12}{15} \div \left(-\frac{4}{5}\right)$.

5. $\dfrac{5r^2s}{2rt^2} \cdot \dfrac{s^2t}{3r^2s} \cdot \dfrac{6rt^2}{5r^2t}$.

6. $\dfrac{4x^6}{9y^3} \cdot \dfrac{15y^4}{7z^4} \cdot \dfrac{21z^5}{10x^5}$.

7. $\dfrac{2a^2b}{3bc} \cdot \dfrac{5ac^2}{7ab^2} \div \dfrac{21a^2b^3c^2}{40ab^2c}.$

8. $\dfrac{e^2}{r^2} \cdot \dfrac{3r}{10e} \cdot 10r^2.$

9. $\dfrac{7R^2}{6r^2} \cdot \dfrac{8r^3}{21R} \cdot 2r.$

10. $\dfrac{\pi r^2}{3} \div 2\pi r.$

11. $\dfrac{\pi r^2 h}{3} \div \dfrac{1}{6}.$

12. $(x^2 - 2xy) \div \dfrac{x}{y}.$

13. $\dfrac{14E^2 - 7E}{12E^3 + 24E^2} \div \dfrac{2E - 1}{E^2 + 2E}.$

14. $\dfrac{4w^2 - 1}{w^3 - 16w} \cdot \dfrac{w^2 + 4w}{2w + 1}.$

15. $\dfrac{\theta^4 - \phi^4}{(\theta - \phi)^2} \div \dfrac{\theta^2 + \phi^2}{\theta + \phi}.$

16. $\dfrac{x^2 - y^2}{x^2 + 2xy + y^2} \div \dfrac{(x - y)^2}{4x + 4y}.$

17. $\dfrac{Z^2 - 121}{Z^2 - 4} \div \dfrac{Z + 2}{Z + 11}.$

18. $\dfrac{E^2 - 4e^2}{Ee + 2e^2} \cdot \dfrac{2e}{E - 2e}.$

19. $\dfrac{a^2 + 3a + 2}{a^2 + 9a + 20} \cdot \dfrac{a^2 + 7a + 12}{a^2 + 5a + 6}.$

20. $\dfrac{2I^2 + 13I + 15}{4I^2 - 9} \div \dfrac{2I^2 + 11I + 5}{4I^2 - 1}.$

21. $\dfrac{1 - R^2}{1 - R^3} \cdot \dfrac{1 - 3R^2 + 2R^3}{(1 - R)^3}.$

22. $\dfrac{1 - b^2}{2b - 4} \cdot \dfrac{b^2 - 4}{b^2 - b - 2} \cdot \dfrac{3b - 6}{b^2 + b - 2}.$

23. $\dfrac{x^3 + y^3}{x^3 - y^3} \cdot \dfrac{y - x}{y + x} \cdot \dfrac{(x + y)^2 - xy}{(x - y)^2 + xy}.$

24. $\dfrac{c^2 - 5cd - 14d^2}{c^2 + 5cd - 24d^2} \div \dfrac{c^2 - 3cd - 28d^2}{c^2 - 8cd + 15d^2}.$

25. $\dfrac{\theta^2 - \theta - 20}{\theta^2 - 25} \cdot \dfrac{\theta^2 - \theta - 2}{\theta^2 + 2\theta - 8} \div \dfrac{\theta + 1}{\theta^2 + 5\theta}.$

26. $\dfrac{m^2 - n^2}{m^2 - 3mn + 2n^2} \cdot \dfrac{mn - 2n^2}{n^2 + mn} \div \dfrac{(m - n)^2}{m(m - n)}.$

27. $\dfrac{ax^4 - ay^4}{bx^3 - by^3} \div \left(\dfrac{x^2 + y^2}{x^2 - y^2} \cdot \dfrac{bx^2 + bxy + by^2}{ax^2 + 2axy + ay^2}\right).$

28. $\dfrac{r^2 - 5r - 14}{(r - 2)^2} \cdot \dfrac{r^2 - 11r + 18}{r^2 - 4} \div \dfrac{r^2 - 16r + 63}{ar^3 - 4ar^2 + 4ar}.$

29. $\left(1 - \dfrac{a}{b}\right) \cdot \dfrac{b}{b^2 - a^2}.$

30. $\left(\dfrac{2}{x} - \dfrac{3}{y}\right) \div \left(\dfrac{2}{x} + \dfrac{3}{y}\right).$

31. $\left(2 - \dfrac{b}{a + b}\right) \div \left(2 - \dfrac{a}{a + b}\right).$

32. $\left(1 - \dfrac{2xy}{x^2 + xy + y^2}\right) \cdot \left(1 - \dfrac{2y^3}{x^3 + y^3}\right).$

33. $\left(a + b + \dfrac{b^2}{a}\right) \cdot \left(2 + \dfrac{2b^2}{a^3 - b^3}\right).$

34. $\left(\dfrac{R^2}{r^2} - 1\right) \div \left(1 + \dfrac{R^2 + r^2}{2Rr}\right).$

35. $\left(\dfrac{3y^2 - 2xy}{x^2 - y^2} + \dfrac{x - y}{x + y}\right) \div \dfrac{x^2 - xy - 2y^2}{x - y}.$

36. $\left(\dfrac{a + b}{a^2 + b^2} - \dfrac{1}{a + b}\right) \div \left(\dfrac{1}{a + b} - \dfrac{a}{a^2 + b^2}\right).$

37. $\left(\dfrac{m^2}{n^2} - 4\right)\left(\dfrac{2m + 4n}{m^3 - 8n^3}\right)\left(\dfrac{m^2 + 2mn + 4n^2}{m^2 + 4mn + 4n^2}\right).$

38. $\left(3a - 4 + \dfrac{21}{4 + a}\right)\left(\dfrac{1}{a + 1}\right)^2 \left(a + \dfrac{a - 3}{3a + 5} + 3\right).$

39. $\left(2E + \dfrac{e^2}{2E} - 2e\right)\left(e + \dfrac{12E^2}{e - 2E} + 4E\right)\left(\dfrac{2E^2}{e^3 - 8E^3}\right).$

40. $\left(\dfrac{4}{a^2} - \dfrac{5}{a} + 1\right)\left(\dfrac{5a^4 + 5a^3}{a^2 - 11a + 28}\right)\left(1 - \dfrac{7a - 1}{a^2 - 1}\right).$

12-18. Complex Fractions. A *complex fraction* is one whose numerator or denominator, or both, are themselves fractions. The name is an unfortunate one. There is nothing complex or intricate about such compounded fractions, as we shall see.

Rule: *To simplify a complex fraction, reduce both numerator and denominator to simple fractions; then perform the indicated division.*

Example 1.   Simplify $\dfrac{\frac{1}{3} + \frac{1}{5}}{4 - \frac{1}{5}}$.

Solution:
$$\dfrac{\dfrac{1}{3} + \dfrac{1}{5}}{4 - \dfrac{1}{5}} = \dfrac{\dfrac{5 + 3}{15}}{\dfrac{20 - 1}{5}} = \dfrac{\dfrac{8}{15}}{\dfrac{19}{5}} = \dfrac{8}{15} \times \dfrac{5}{19} = \dfrac{8}{57}$$

Example 2.   Simplify $\dfrac{5 - \dfrac{1}{a + 1}}{3 + \dfrac{2}{a + 1}}$.

Solution:
$$\dfrac{5 - \dfrac{1}{a + 1}}{3 + \dfrac{2}{a + 1}} = \dfrac{\dfrac{5(a + 1) - 1}{a + 1}}{\dfrac{3(a + 1) + 2}{a + 1}} = \dfrac{\dfrac{5a + 4}{a + 1}}{\dfrac{3a + 5}{a + 1}}$$
$$= \dfrac{5a + 4}{a + 1} \cdot \dfrac{a + 1}{3a + 5}$$
$$= \dfrac{5a + 4}{3a + 5}$$

NOTE: It is evident that if the same factor occurs in both numerators of a complex fraction the factors may be canceled. Also, if a factor occurs in both denominators, it may be canceled. Thus, $(a + 1)$ could have been canceled in Example 2 after reducing the numerators and denominators from mixed expressions to simple fractions.

Example 3.   Simplify $\dfrac{\dfrac{a}{b} + \dfrac{a+b}{a-b}}{\dfrac{a}{b} - \dfrac{a-b}{a+b}}$.

Solution: $\dfrac{\dfrac{a}{b} + \dfrac{a+b}{a-b}}{\dfrac{a}{b} - \dfrac{a-b}{a+b}} = \dfrac{\dfrac{a(a-b) + b(a+b)}{b(a-b)}}{\dfrac{a(a+b) - b(a-b)}{b(a+b)}} = \dfrac{\dfrac{a^2 - ab + ab + b^2}{b(a-b)}}{\dfrac{a^2 + ab - ab + b^2}{b(a+b)}}$

$= \dfrac{\dfrac{a^2 + b^2}{b(a-b)}}{\dfrac{a^2 + b^2}{b(a+b)}} = \dfrac{a+b}{a-b}$

PROBLEMS 12-10

Simplify:

1. $\dfrac{\frac{6}{7} - 2}{1 - \frac{3}{7}}$.

2. $\dfrac{(\frac{3}{2})^2 - 16}{\frac{3}{2} + 4}$.

3. $\dfrac{4}{6 - \frac{2}{3}}$.

4. $\dfrac{\dfrac{3ab}{c}}{\dfrac{6a^2b}{c^2}}$.

5. $\dfrac{2 + \dfrac{1}{a}}{\dfrac{1}{a} - 3}$.

6. $\dfrac{x}{\dfrac{1}{a} + \dfrac{1}{b}}$.

7. $\dfrac{\dfrac{e^2}{5} - 5}{1 + \dfrac{e}{5}}$.

8. $\dfrac{\dfrac{1}{R} - R}{R + 2 + \dfrac{1}{R}}$.

9. $\dfrac{\dfrac{a}{b} + \dfrac{b}{a}}{\dfrac{a}{b} - \dfrac{b}{a}}$.

10. $\dfrac{Z_1 - \dfrac{Z_1 Z_2}{Z_1 + Z_2}}{\dfrac{Z_1 Z_2}{Z_1 - Z_2} + Z_1}$.

11. $\dfrac{1 + \dfrac{1}{r} - \dfrac{2}{r^2}}{1 - \dfrac{1}{r}}$.

12. $\dfrac{\dfrac{x}{x+y}}{1 + \dfrac{y}{x-y}}$.

13. $\dfrac{a - \dfrac{a-b}{1+ab}}{1 + \dfrac{a^2 - ab}{1+ab}}$.

14. $\dfrac{1}{i - \dfrac{i^2 - 1}{i + \dfrac{1}{i-1}}}$.

15. $\dfrac{1}{R - \dfrac{1}{R + \dfrac{1}{R}}} - \dfrac{1}{R + \dfrac{1}{R - \dfrac{1}{R}}}$.

16. $\dfrac{\dfrac{x}{x-y} - \dfrac{x}{x+y}}{\dfrac{y}{x-y} + \dfrac{x}{x+y}}$.

17. $\dfrac{1}{1 + \dfrac{y - 1}{1 - \dfrac{y}{3} - \dfrac{1}{y}}}$.

18. $\dfrac{\dfrac{x + 1}{x} - \dfrac{y + 1}{y}}{\dfrac{1}{x} + \dfrac{1}{y}}$.

19. $\dfrac{\dfrac{E + e}{E - e} + \dfrac{E - e}{E + e}}{\dfrac{E + e}{E - e} - \dfrac{E - e}{E + e}}$.

20. $\dfrac{a - \dfrac{b^2}{a}}{1 + \dfrac{b}{a}}$.

CHAPTER XIII

FRACTIONAL EQUATIONS

An equation containing a fraction in which the unknown occurs in the denominator is called a *fractional equation*. Equations of this type are encountered in many problems involving electrical and radio circuits. Simple fractional equations, wherein the unknown appeared only as a factor, were studied in earlier chapters.

13-1. Fractional Coefficients. A number of problems lead to equations containing *fractional coefficients*. This type of equation is included in this chapter because the methods of solution apply also to fractional equations.

Example 1. $$\frac{3x}{4} + \frac{3}{2} = \frac{5x}{8} \quad \text{and} \quad \frac{x}{2} + \frac{x}{3} = 5$$

are equations having fractional coefficients.

Example 2. $$\frac{60}{x} - 3 = \frac{60}{4x} \quad \text{and} \quad \frac{x-2}{x} = \frac{4}{5}$$

are fractional equations.

The student is familiar with the methods of solving simple equations that do not contain fractions. An equation involving fractions may be changed to an equation containing no denominators and then solved as heretofore. To accomplish this we have the following rule:

Rule: *To solve an equation containing fractions,*

1. *First clear of fractions by multiplying every term of the equation by the lowest common denominator.* (*This will permit canceling all denominators.*)

2. *Solve the resulting equation.*

Example 3. Given $\frac{5x}{12} - 13 = \frac{x}{18}$. Solve for x.

Solution: Given $$\frac{5x}{12} - 13 = \frac{x}{18}$$

M : 36, the L.C.D., $\dfrac{36 \cdot 5x}{12} - 36 \cdot 13 = \dfrac{36x}{18}$

Canceling, $\dfrac{\overset{3}{\cancel{36}} \cdot 5x}{\cancel{12}} - 36 \cdot 13 = \dfrac{\overset{2}{\cancel{36}}x}{\cancel{18}}$

Simplifying, $15x - 468 = 2x$
Collecting terms, $13x = 468$
D : 13, $x = 36$

Check.   Substitute 36 for x in the original equation.

$$\frac{5 \cdot 36}{12} - 13 = \frac{36}{18}$$

Clearing fractions, $15 - 13 = 2$
$$2 = 2$$

Example 4.   Given $\dfrac{e - 4}{9} = \dfrac{e}{10}$.   Solve for e.

Solution: Given $\dfrac{e - 4}{9} = \dfrac{e}{10}$

M : 90, the L.C.D., $\dfrac{90(e - 4)}{9} = \dfrac{90e}{10}$

Canceling, $\dfrac{\overset{10}{\cancel{90}}(e - 4)}{\cancel{9}} = \dfrac{\overset{9}{\cancel{90}}e}{\cancel{10}}$

Simplifying, $10(e - 4) = 9e$
or $10e - 40 = 9e$
Collecting terms, $10e - 9e = 40$
or $e = 40$

Check.   Substituting 40 for e in the original equation,

$$\frac{40 - 4}{9} = \frac{40}{10}$$

Clearing fractions, $4 = 4$

Note that when the fractions were cleared and the equation written in simplified form in the above solution, the resulting equation was

$$10(e - 4) = 9e$$

which is equivalent to multiplying each member by the denominator of the other member and expressing the resulting equation with no denominators.   This is called *cross multiplication*.   The student will see the justification of this if each member is expressed as a fraction having the lowest common denominator.   Although the method is convenient, it must be remembered that *cross multiplication is permissible only when each term of a member of an equation has the same denominator.*

Solve the following:

1. $\dfrac{e}{2} - \dfrac{e}{3} = 2.$

2. $x = \dfrac{x}{7} - 3.$

3. $i - \dfrac{3i}{5} = 2.$

4. $\dfrac{4R}{9} = \dfrac{2R}{3} - 4.$

5. $Z - \dfrac{4Z}{7} = 8.$

6. $\dfrac{E}{3} - \dfrac{E}{5} = \dfrac{1}{3}.$

7. $\dfrac{12I + 5}{8} = \dfrac{17 - 8I}{10} - \dfrac{1}{2}.$

8. $\dfrac{2t - 3}{3} + \dfrac{t + 1}{2} = 3.$

9. $4r - 10 = \dfrac{5r - 4}{18} + \dfrac{9r + 8}{6}.$

10. $\dfrac{R}{3} + \dfrac{R - 5}{10} = \dfrac{4R + 3}{5}.$

NOTE: If a fraction is negative, the sign of each term of the numerator must be changed after removing the denominator. Remember that *the vinculum is a sign of grouping.*

11. $\dfrac{2a + 3}{6} - \dfrac{a - 9}{4} = 5.$

12. $\dfrac{e - 1}{3} - \dfrac{2e + 2}{5} = 0.$

13. $\dfrac{I + 1}{5} - \dfrac{I - 1}{2} = \dfrac{3 - I}{3}.$

14. $\dfrac{Z + 2}{2} - \dfrac{Z - 3}{3} = 0.$

15. $\dfrac{2r}{3} - \dfrac{2r + 5}{4} = 0.$

16. $\dfrac{2i - 5}{10} - \dfrac{i - 4}{15} = \dfrac{4i + 7}{6} - i.$

17. $\dfrac{1}{9}(2m - 1) - \dfrac{2}{15}(2m + 3) + \dfrac{m - 3}{5} = 2.$

NOTE: $\dfrac{1}{9}(2m - 1) = \dfrac{2m - 1}{9}.$

18. $\dfrac{2\alpha - 1}{6} + \dfrac{8\alpha}{15} = \dfrac{20 - 4\alpha}{5} - \dfrac{11}{3}.$

19. $\frac{1}{3}(5E - 1) + 5 - \frac{1}{2}(7E + 2) = 0.$

20. $\frac{2}{3}(R + 1) - \frac{1}{6}(R + 1) = \frac{3}{4}(R + 2).$

13-2. Equations Containing Decimals.
Equations containing decimals are readily solved by first clearing the equation of the decimals. This is accomplished by multiplying both members by a power of ten that corresponds to the largest number of decimal places appearing in any term.

Example 1.   Solve $0.75 - 0.7a = 0.26.$
Solution: Given $0.75 - 0.7a = 0.26.$

M : 100, $75 - 70a = 26$
Collecting terms, $70a = 49$
D : 70, $a = 0.7$

Check. Substituting 0.7 for a in the original equation,

$$0.75 - 0.7 \cdot 0.7 = 0.26$$
$$0.75 - 0.49 = 0.26$$
$$0.26 = 0.26$$

If decimals occur in any denominator, multiply both numerator and denominator of the fraction by a power of ten that will reduce the decimals to integers.

Example 2. Solve $\dfrac{5m - 1.33}{0.02} - \dfrac{m}{0.05} = 1083.5$.

Solution: Given $\dfrac{5m - 1.33}{0.02} - \dfrac{m}{0.05} = 1083.5$.

Multiplying numerator and denominator of each fraction by 100,

$$\frac{500m - 133}{2} - \frac{100m}{5} = 1083.5$$

The equation is then solved and checked by the usual methods.

PROBLEMS 13-2

Solve the following:

1. $0.4R = 6$.

2. $0.2r = 4$.

3. $0.3i + 4 = 0.25$.

4. $0.17e + 0.15e - 3 = 0.14e + 2.4$.

5. $\dfrac{1.8I - 2}{1.7} = \dfrac{5.7 - 0.7I}{1.8}$.

6. $0.3E + 0.16 = 0.58$.

7. $3.75 = 2.15 - 0.5Z$.

8. $0.7(3R - 5) - 0.2(5R - 1.5) = -4.3$.

9. $\dfrac{0.3R - 6.2}{4} - \dfrac{6.75 - 0.4R}{5} = \dfrac{3.5}{2}$.

10. $0.3(1.5 - 0.9E) - 0.5(1.7E - 1.3) = 0.14E + 2.36$.

11. $0.04(100 - x) - 0.02x = 1.9$.

12. $\dfrac{10I - 0.75}{12} - \dfrac{2.5I}{3} = \dfrac{5I}{8}$.

13. $\dfrac{0.3(5 - R)}{6.25} = \dfrac{1.5 - 10R}{14} + 0.56R$.

14. $0.92 + 0.9(e - 0.3) = 2e - 5.95$.

15. $0.25r + 0.35(1000 - r) = 280$.

13-3. Fractional Equations. Fractional equations are solved in the same manner as equations containing fractional coefficients (Art. 13-1). That is, every term of the equation must be multiplied by the lowest common denominator.

Example 1. Solve $\dfrac{x + 2}{3x} - \dfrac{2x^2 + 3}{6x^2} = \dfrac{1}{2x}$.

Solution: Given $\dfrac{x + 2}{3x} - \dfrac{2x^2 + 3}{6x^2} = \dfrac{1}{2x}$.

M : $6x^2$, the L.C.D., $\dfrac{6x^2(x+2)}{3x} - \dfrac{6x^2(2x^2+3)}{6x^2} = \dfrac{6x^2}{2x}$

Canceling, $\dfrac{\overset{2x}{\cancel{6x^2}}(x+2)}{\cancel{3x}} - \dfrac{\overset{}{\cancel{6x^2}}(2x^2+3)}{\cancel{6x^2}} = \dfrac{\overset{3x}{\cancel{6x^2}}}{\cancel{2x}}$

Rewriting, $2x(x+2) - (2x^2+3) = 3x$

Simplifying, $2x^2 + 4x - 2x^2 - 3 = 3x$

Collecting terms, $4x - 3x = 3$

or $x = 3$

Check. Substituting 3 for x in the original equation,

$$\frac{3+2}{9} - \frac{18+3}{54} = \frac{1}{6}$$

That is, $\dfrac{30}{54} - \dfrac{21}{54} = \dfrac{9}{54}$

Example 2. Solve $\dfrac{8a+2}{a-2} - \dfrac{2a-1}{3a-6} + \dfrac{3a+2}{5a-10} + 5 = 15.$

Solution: Given $\dfrac{8a+2}{a-2} - \dfrac{2a-1}{3a-6} + \dfrac{3a+2}{5a-10} + 5 = 15.$

Factoring denominators, $\dfrac{8a+2}{a-2} - \dfrac{2a-1}{3(a-2)} + \dfrac{3a+2}{5(a-2)} + 5 = 15$

M : $15(a-2)$, the L.C.D.,

$\dfrac{15(a-2)(8a+2)}{a-2} - \dfrac{15(a-2)(2a-1)}{3(a-2)} + \dfrac{15(a-2)(3a+2)}{5(a-2)}$
$$+ \; 15(a-2)(5) = 15(a-2)(15)$$

Canceling,

$\dfrac{15(\cancel{a-2})(8a+2)}{\cancel{a-2}} - \dfrac{\overset{5}{\cancel{15}}(\cancel{a-2})(2a-1)}{\cancel{3}(\cancel{a-2})} + \dfrac{\overset{3}{\cancel{15}}(\cancel{a-2})(3a+2)}{\cancel{5}(\cancel{a-2})}$
$$+ \; 15(a-2)(5) = 15(a-2)(15)$$

Rewriting,

$15(8a+2) - 5(2a-1) + 3(3a+2) + 15(a-2)(5) = 15(a-2)(15)$

Simplifying, $120a + 30 - 10a + 5 + 9a + 6 + 75a - 150 = 225a - 450$

Collecting terms,

$$120a - 10a + 9a + 75a - 225a = -30 - 5 - 6 + 150 - 450$$
$$-31a = -341$$
$$a = 11$$

Check the solution by the usual method.

PROBLEMS 13-3

1. $\dfrac{11}{x} + \dfrac{17}{x} = 4.$ 2. $\dfrac{1}{r} + \dfrac{1}{12} = \dfrac{1}{6}.$

3. $\dfrac{1}{e} = 3 + \dfrac{16}{e}.$ 4. $\dfrac{1}{r} + \dfrac{2}{3r} = \dfrac{7}{6} + \dfrac{4}{r}.$

5. $\dfrac{8}{I} - \dfrac{1}{2I} = \dfrac{5}{2}.$

6. $\dfrac{E - 2}{E} - \dfrac{4}{5} = 0.$

7. $\dfrac{Z + 5}{Z} - \dfrac{5}{6} = \dfrac{Z - 5}{3Z}.$

8. $\dfrac{2 - \theta}{\theta} - \dfrac{\theta + 2}{4\theta} + \dfrac{11}{12} = 0.$

9. $\dfrac{6 + 2y}{5y} - \dfrac{1}{y} = \dfrac{2y + 1}{8y}.$

10. $\dfrac{\alpha - 4}{2\alpha} = \dfrac{5}{2} - \dfrac{\alpha + 4}{\alpha}.$

11. $\dfrac{x + 4}{x + 1} = \dfrac{2}{5}.$

12. $\dfrac{9}{r + 3} - \dfrac{8r - 20}{r^2 - 9} = 0.$

13. $\dfrac{3e - 2}{5e - 10} - \dfrac{2}{5} = 0.$

14. $\dfrac{4i - 3}{i - 6} = \dfrac{4i + 2}{i - 10}.$

15. $\dfrac{1}{5 + 7a} - \dfrac{9 - 11a}{5 - 7a} + \dfrac{3a}{5 + 7a} = \dfrac{14(2a - 3)^2}{25 - 49a^2}.$

16. $\dfrac{3r - 17}{3r - 6} - \dfrac{r - 5}{r + 6} = 0.$

17. $\dfrac{1}{e + 1} + \dfrac{1}{e - 1} = 1 - \dfrac{e^2}{e^2 - 1}.$

18. $\dfrac{1}{Z + 1} + \dfrac{2}{Z - 1} - \dfrac{4}{Z + 1} = 0.$

19. $\dfrac{2a}{2a - 1} - \dfrac{2a - 1}{2a + 1} - \dfrac{1}{1 - 2a} = \dfrac{8}{4a^2 - 1}.$

HINT: Change signs in the third term.

20. $\dfrac{2}{b - 1} + \dfrac{5}{2(1 - b)} - \dfrac{8}{3(b - 1)} - \dfrac{5}{18} = \dfrac{b}{1 - b}.$

21. $\dfrac{1}{9} - \dfrac{10}{8e - 2} - \dfrac{6}{1 - 4e} = 0.$

22. $\dfrac{27 - c}{(c + 1)^2} + \dfrac{c}{c + 1} = 1.$

23. $\dfrac{r + 3}{r - 8} - \dfrac{2r^2 - 2}{r^2 - 7r - 8} = \dfrac{5 - r}{r + 1}.$

24. $\dfrac{2x + 7}{6x - 4} - \dfrac{3x - 5}{9x + 6} = \dfrac{17x + 7}{9x^2 - 4}.$

25. $\dfrac{2R + 1}{2R - 16} - \dfrac{2R - 1}{2R + 12} - \dfrac{9R + 17}{R^2 - 2R - 48} = 0.$

PROBLEMS 13-4

1. A can do a piece of work in 8 hr, and B can do it in 6 hr; how long will it take them to do it together?

Solution: Let n = number of hours it will take them to do it together.

Now A does $\frac{1}{8}$ of the job in 1 hr; therefore, he will do $\dfrac{n}{8}$ in n hr.

Also, B does $\frac{1}{6}$ of the job in 1 hr; therefore, he will do $\dfrac{n}{6}$ in n hr.

Then they will do $\dfrac{n}{8} + \dfrac{n}{6}$ in n hr.

The entire job will be completed in n hr, which we may represent by $\frac{8}{8}$ or $\frac{8}{8}$ of itself, which is 1.

$$\therefore \frac{n}{8} + \frac{n}{6} = 1$$

M : 24, the L.C.D., $3n + 4n = 24$

$$7n = 24$$

$$n = 3\tfrac{3}{7} \text{ hr}$$

2. An electrician can run a conduit in 9 hr, and his helper can do it in 16 hr. In how many hours can they do it if they work together?

3. A cooling tank can be filled in 30 min if one pipe is used. If a different pipe is used, it takes 35 min to fill the tank. How long will it take to fill the tank if both pipes are used?

4. A can do a piece of work in a days, and B can do it in b days. Derive a general formula for the number of days it would take both together to do the work.

Solution: Let x = number of days it will take both together.

Now A will do $\dfrac{x}{a}$ of the job in x days.

Also, B will do $\dfrac{x}{b}$ of the job in x days.

Then $\dfrac{x}{a} + \dfrac{x}{b} = 1$

M : ab, $bx + ax = ab$

Factoring, $x(a + b) = ab$

D : $(a + b)$, $x = \dfrac{ab}{a + b}$

Alternate Solution: Let x = number of days it will take both together.

Then $\dfrac{1}{x}$ = part that both together can do in 1 day.

$\dfrac{1}{a}$ = part that A alone can do in 1 day.

$\dfrac{1}{b}$ = part that B alone can do in 1 day.

Now, $\dfrac{1}{a} + \dfrac{1}{b} = \dfrac{1}{x}$

M : abx, $bx + ax = ab$

Factoring, $x(b + a) = ab$

D : $(a + b)$, $x = \dfrac{ab}{a + b}$

5. A can do a piece of work in a days, B in b days, and C in c days. Derive a general formula for the number of days it would take them to do it together.

6. A tank can be filled by two pipes in 3 hr and 5 hr, respectively. It can be emptied by the drain pipe in 6 hr. If all three pipes are open, how long will it take to fill the tank?

7. Three circuits may be connected to a storage battery. Circuit 1 completely discharges the battery in 20 hr, circuit 2 in 15 hr, and circuit 3 in 12 hr. All circuits are connected to the battery in parallel. In how many hours will the battery be discharged?

8. A tank can be filled by two pipes in x and y hr, respectively, and emptied by a drain pipe in z hr. Derive a general formula for the number of hours required to fill the tank with all pipes open.

9. A bottle contains 1 gal of a mixture of equal parts of acid and water. How much water must be added to make a mixture that will be one-tenth acid?

Solution: Let n = number of quarts of water to be added.

   4 qt = amount of original mixture.

Then,   2 qt = amount of acid.

Hence, $n + 4$ = amount of new one-tenth acid mixture.

Now, $\dfrac{1}{10} = \dfrac{\text{amount of acid}}{\text{total mixture}}$

Then, $\dfrac{1}{10} = \dfrac{2}{n+4}$

or $n = 16$ qt of water to be added

10. An engine radiator contains 6 gal of a 30% alcohol solution. How much alcohol must be added to obtain a 45% mixture?

11. One-third of a certain number plus one-half the number is 80. Find the number.

12. The sum of two numbers is 300. When the larger is divided by the smaller, the quotient is 24. Find the numbers.

13. The sum of two numbers is 433. When the larger is divided by the smaller, the quotient is 32 and there is a remainder of 4. Find the numbers.

14. The denominator of a certain fraction exceeds the numerator by 27; if 9 be subtracted from both terms of the fraction, the value of the fraction becomes $\frac{1}{4}$. Find the fraction.

15. Separate 108 into two parts such that their quotient is $\frac{2}{7}$.

16. A rectangle is four times as long as it is wide. If it were 4 ft shorter and 1.5 ft wider, its area would be 11 sq ft more. Find its dimensions.

17. The perimeter of a triangle is 41 in. The second side is 9 in. longer than one-third the first, and the third side is 1 in. shorter than one-half the first. Find the length of each side.

18. The width of a room is two-thirds its length. If the width had been 3 ft more and the length 3 ft less, the room would have been square. Find its dimensions.

19. There are two consecutive numbers such that one-fourth of the smaller exceeds one-fifth of the greater by 1. Find the numbers.

20. What number subtracted from each term of the fraction $\frac{17}{29}$ makes it equal to $\frac{1}{2}$?

21. In a certain fraction the numerator is 4 less than the denominator. If 1 is added to the numerator and 21 is added to the denominator, the value of the fraction is $\frac{1}{3}$. Find the fraction.

13-4. Literal Equations. Equations in which some or all of the numbers are replaced by letters are called *literal equations.* These were studied in Chap. VI. Having attained more knowledge of algebra, such as factoring, fractions, etc., we are now ready to proceed with the solution of more difficult literal equations, or formulas. No new methods are involved in the actual solutions—we are prepared to solve a more complicated equation simply because we have available more tools with which to work. Again, it is desired to point out that the ability to solve formulas is of utmost importance.

Example 1.   Given $I = \dfrac{E}{R + r}$, solve for r.

Solution: Given $\qquad\qquad\qquad I = \dfrac{E}{R + r}.$

M : $(R + r)$,$\qquad\qquad I(R + r) = E$

Remove parentheses.$\qquad IR + Ir = E$

S : IR,$\qquad\qquad\qquad\quad Ir = E - IR$

D : I,$\qquad\qquad\qquad\qquad r = \dfrac{E - IR}{I}$

Example 2.   Given $S = \dfrac{RL - a}{R - 1}$, solve for L.

Solution: Given $\qquad \dfrac{RL - a}{R - 1} = S$

M : $(R - 1)$,$\qquad RL - a = S(R - 1)$

A : a,$\qquad\qquad\qquad RL = S(R - 1) + a$

D : R,$\qquad\qquad\qquad L = \dfrac{S(R - 1) + a}{R}$

Example 3.   Given $\dfrac{a}{x - b} = \dfrac{2a}{x + b}$, solve for x.

Solution: Given $\qquad\qquad \dfrac{a}{x - b} = \dfrac{2a}{x + b}.$

M : $(x^2 - b^2)$, the L.C.D., $\quad \dfrac{(x^2 - b^2)a}{x - b} = \dfrac{(x^2 - b^2)2a}{x + b}$

Canceling, $\qquad\qquad \dfrac{\overset{x + b}{(\cancel{x^2 - b^2})a}}{\cancel{x - b}} = \dfrac{\overset{x - b}{(\cancel{x^2 - b^2})2a}}{\cancel{x + b}}$

Rewriting, $\qquad\qquad (x + b)a = (x - b)2a$

Removing parentheses, $\quad ax + ab = 2ax - 2ab$

Collecting terms, $\qquad ax - 2ax = -2ab - ab$

or $\qquad\qquad\qquad\qquad -ax = -3ab$

M : -1,$\qquad\qquad\qquad ax = 3ab$

D : a,$\qquad\qquad\qquad\qquad x = 3b$

NOTE: The last two steps may be combined into one step by dividing $-ax = -3ab$ by $-a$ to obtain $x = 3b$.

Check.   Substitute $3b$ for x in the given equation.

$$\frac{a}{3b - b} = \frac{2a}{3b + b}$$

Simplifying,

$$\frac{a}{2b} = \frac{2a}{4b}$$

or

$$\frac{a}{2b} = \frac{a}{2b}$$

PROBLEMS 13-5

Given: Solve for·

1. $a^2 = b^2 + c^2 + 2bx.$ $x.$

2. $\dfrac{E}{e} = \dfrac{R + r}{r}.$ $e, r.$

3. $E_t = E_g - IR.$ $I.$

4. $I = \dfrac{E_b - E_c}{R}.$ $E_b.$

5. $N = \dfrac{2s}{a + L}.$ $s, a.$

6. $P = \dfrac{ad^2 + d}{t}.$ $t.$

7. $a = p + prt.$ $p.$

8. $p = \dfrac{r(R + EI)}{s} - e.$ $s.$

9. $F = \dfrac{m_1 m_2}{r^2}.$ $m_2.$

10. $C = \frac{5}{9}(F - 32).$ $F.$

11. $I_p = \dfrac{E_p + \mu E_g + m}{R_p}.$ $E_g.$

12. $\dfrac{1}{R_t} = \dfrac{1}{R_1} + \dfrac{1}{R_2}.$ $R_t, R_1, R_2.$

13. $L = \dfrac{Mt - g}{t}.$ $g, M, t.$

14. $T = \dfrac{1}{a} + t.$ $a, t.$

15. $C = \dfrac{kab}{b - a}.$ $a, b.$

16. $\mu = \left(\dfrac{M}{M + m}\right) v.$ $M, m.$

17. $\dfrac{1}{f} = \dfrac{1}{p} + \dfrac{1}{q}.$ $q.$

18. $s = V_0 t + \frac{1}{2}gt^2.$ $V_0.$

19. $F_t = \dfrac{w}{g}(V_1 - V_0).$ $V_1.$

Given:

Solve for:

20. $h = k(1 + 2\frac{1}{7}\frac{3}{8}t)$. k, t.

21. $s = \dfrac{rL - a}{r - 1}$. a, L.

22. $Y_c = \dfrac{C - 2m}{p}$. C, m.

23. $D = \dfrac{c - AL}{12}$. L.

24. $p = \dfrac{m}{d - L} - \dfrac{m}{d + L}$. m.

25. $MH\alpha = C\left(\dfrac{\pi}{2} - \alpha\right)$. α.

26. $E_b = k\left(\dfrac{E_p}{\mu} + E_g\right)$. μ, E_g.

27. $\dfrac{a}{x} - c = \dfrac{bd}{x}$. x.

28. $\dfrac{b + 2}{n} = \dfrac{2}{n} + \dfrac{1}{x}$. x.

29. $ax - a^2 = x - 1$. x.

30. $p = \dfrac{WL_1 + VL + W_g}{AL}$. L.

31. $A = \frac{1}{2}h(b_1 + b_2)$. b_1.

32. $\mu = \dfrac{E_p' - E_p}{E_g - E_g'}$. E_g'.

33. $Z = \dfrac{R + \omega^2 L^2}{R}$. R.

34. $p = \dfrac{I^2_{\max}R_b}{2}$. R_b.

35. $P_{ac} = \dfrac{E_b - E_p}{\sqrt{2}}$. E_b.

36. $\dfrac{r_1}{r_1 + r_2} = \dfrac{r_3}{r_3 + r_4}$. r_1, r_4

37. $\dfrac{i_g}{i} = \dfrac{r - r_1}{r_g + r_1}$. r_1.

38. $I_2 = \dfrac{ER_0}{R_1R_0 + R_2R_0 + R_1R_1}$. R_1.

39. $ax - b = 0$. x.

40. $\dfrac{a}{x} = C(a - b) + \dfrac{b}{x}$. x.

41. $e_2 = \dfrac{\mu e}{\omega C\left(r_p + Z_e + \dfrac{r_p Z_e}{Z_c}\right)}$. Z_c.

Given: Solve for:

42. $\dfrac{Q}{p} = \dfrac{L_2 + \alpha}{100 - L_2 + \beta}$. L_2.

43. $E_2 = \left(\dfrac{3k}{k_2 + 2k_1}\right) E$. k_1.

44. $\dfrac{x}{a} + \dfrac{x}{b} + \dfrac{x}{c} = 1$. x.

45. $L_t = L_0 + L_0\alpha t$. L_0.

46. $i_p = \dfrac{\mu e_g}{r_p + R_b + \omega L_b}$. L_b.

47. $F' = \left(\dfrac{2M}{x^3} - \dfrac{6M}{x^4}\right) m'$. M.

48. $I_s = \dfrac{E}{\dfrac{1}{a} Z_2 + aZ_1}$. Z_1.

49. $e_1 = \mu e_g \left(\dfrac{R_p}{R_p + Z_1}\right)$. R_p.

50. $C_g = C_{gf} + C_{gp}\left(1 + \dfrac{\mu R_b}{r_p + r_b}\right)$. $C_{gp},\ R_b$.

51. $E_c + E_s\left(\dfrac{R_p}{R_1 + R_p}\right) = \dfrac{E_b - E_c}{\mu}$. R_1.

52. $I_{\max} = \dfrac{E\omega M}{R_1 R_2 + \omega^2 M^2}$. $E,\ R_1$.

53. $MH' = \dfrac{4\pi r^2}{T^2\left(1 + \dfrac{\alpha}{\dfrac{\pi}{2} - \alpha}\right)}$. α.

54. $R = R_{gl} + \dfrac{R_c}{1 + \dfrac{R_c}{R_p}}$. $R_c,\ R_p$.

55. $\dfrac{x + a}{x - b} - \dfrac{3}{4} = 0$. x.

56. $L = \dfrac{0.8 r^2 N^2}{6r + 9d + 10t}$. d.

57. $e_2 = \dfrac{\mu e_g Z_2}{r_p\left(1 + \dfrac{R_2}{Z_1}\right) + R_2}$. $R_2,\ Z_1$.

58. $\mu = G_m\left(\dfrac{\omega L Q}{1 + \dfrac{\omega L Q}{R_p} + \dfrac{\omega L Q}{R_{gl}}}\right)$. $L,\ R_p$.

59. $\dfrac{a - \dfrac{x}{a - b}}{a + \dfrac{x}{a - b}} - 1 = \dfrac{a}{b}$. x.

60. A source of voltage consists of n cells in parallel, each having an e.m.f of E volts and an internal resistance of r ohms. The current I that flows through a load of R ohms is given by the relation

$$I = \frac{E}{R + \dfrac{r}{n}}$$

Solve for n and R.

61. A source of voltage of E volts consists of n cells in series, each with an e.m.f. of E volts and an internal resistance of r ohms. The current flowing through a load of R ohms is given by the relation

$$I = \frac{nE}{R + nr}$$

Solve for n and r.

62. The joint conductance $\dfrac{1}{R_t}$ mhos of three resistances R_1, R_2, and R_3 in parallel is expressed

$$\frac{1}{R_t} = \frac{1}{R_1} + \frac{1}{R_2} + \frac{1}{R_3}$$

Solve for R_t.

63. The incremental plate resistance R_b of a vacuum tube is equal to the quotient obtained by dividing the plate-voltage swing by the plate-current swing. That is,

$$R_b = \frac{E_{max} - E_{min}}{I_{max} - I_{min}}$$

Solve for E_{max} and I_{min}.

64. The joint impedance Z_t of two paralleled impedances Z_1 and Z_2 is

$$Z_t = \frac{Z_1 Z_2}{Z_1 + Z_2}$$

Solve for Z_1.

65. When a signal voltage e_g is impressed upon the grid of a vacuum tube, which has an amplification of μ, the resulting plate current i_p flowing in the output circuit, which consists of the plate resistance r_p in series with the load resistance r_b, is

$$i_p = \frac{\mu e_g}{r_p + r_b}$$

Solve for e_g and r_p.

66. Using the formula $I = \dfrac{E}{R}$,

  (a) How is the value of I changed when E is replaced by $2E$?
  (b) How is the value of I changed if R is doubled, that is, when R is replaced by $2R$?

67. In the formula $I = \dfrac{E}{R + r}$, what is the value of r if $E = 220$ v, $R = 40\ \Omega$, and $I = 5$ a?

68. A lens formula is $\dfrac{1}{f} = \dfrac{1}{p} + \dfrac{1}{q}$. How much is p when $f = 50$ and $q = 80$?

69. A pulley formula is $P = \dfrac{W(R - r)}{2R}$. Find R if $W = 60$, $r = 4$, and $P = 10$.

70. $V = \frac{1}{3}\pi r^2 h$ is the formula for the volume of a circular cone, where r = radius and h = height. A certain cone has twice the volume of another. Their radii are equal. How much more height has the first cone?

71. Does $\dfrac{IR + E}{R} = I + E$? Explain your answer.

72. Given $I = \dfrac{E}{R_1 + R_2 + R_3}$. Is $R_3 = \dfrac{E}{R_1 + R_2 + I}$ correct? Explain your answer.

73. In the temperature formula $C = \frac{5}{9}(F - 32)$, find the temperature at which the Fahrenheit and centigrade temperatures are equal, that is, at which $F = C$.

74. $\dfrac{1}{f} = \dfrac{1}{p} + \dfrac{1}{q}$. If the focal length f is -40 and the object distance p is 40, find the image distance q.

75. $I_p = \dfrac{E_p + \mu E_g + m}{R_p}$. Find m when $I_p = 0.050$ a, $E_g = 50$ v, $E_p = 250$ v, $R_p = 50,000$ Ω, and $\mu = 50$.

76. $I = \dfrac{E}{R + \dfrac{r}{n}}$. Find n in terms of I and E, when $R = 25$ and $r = 4$.

77. $\mu = \left(\dfrac{M}{M + m}\right) v$. Find m when $M = 75$, $v = 48$, and $\mu = 500$.

78. $A = \dfrac{h(b_1 + b_2)}{2}$. Find b_2 when $b_1 = 50$, $A = 300$, and $h = 4$.

79. $S = V_0 t + \frac{1}{2}gt^2$. Find S when the initial velocity V_0 is 10 ft per second, $g = 32.2$, and $t = 10$ sec.

80. $\dfrac{a - \dfrac{x}{a - b}}{a + \dfrac{x}{a - b}} - 1 = \dfrac{a}{b}$. Find b when $a = 3$ and $x = 11$.

81. $\dfrac{x}{a} + \dfrac{x}{b} + \dfrac{x}{c} = 1$. Find b if $x = 25$, $a = 36$, and $c = 30$.

82. $i_p = \dfrac{\mu e_g}{r_p + r_b}$. $i_p = 500$ ma, when $e_g = 20$ v, $r_p = 10,000$ Ω, and $r_b = r_p$. If r_p remains constant, what will be the value of i_p when r_b is raised to 40,000 Ω?

83. $\dfrac{r_1}{r_1 + r_2} = \dfrac{r_3}{r_3 + r_4}$. If $r_1 = 20$, what is the value of r_3 in terms of r_2 and r_4?

84. $F_t = \dfrac{W}{g}(V_1 - V_0)$. Find the initial velocity V_0 when $F_t = 155.3$, $W = 100$ lb, $g = 32.2$, and $V_1 = 10$ ft per second.

85. $F = K\dfrac{W_1 W_2}{D}$. If the force of attraction between two bodies $W_1 = 50$ kg and $W_2 = 150$ kg is $F = 0.01$ dyne, find the distance D in centimeters between the two bodies. K, the constant of gravitation, is 6.67×10^{-8}.

86. $E = L \left(\dfrac{I_1 - I_2}{t} \right).$ $L = 5$ h and $I_2 = 2$ a. The induced voltage E is 1000 v in $t = 0.5$ sec. What was the initial current I_1?

87. $I = C \left(\dfrac{E_1 - E_2}{t} \right).$ A current I of 0.05 a flows in a condenser circuit C of 15 µf $(C = 15 \times 10^{-6})$ when the voltage changes from $E_1 = 100$ v. to $E_2 = 2v$. What was the time t of discharge?

88. $\dfrac{1}{C} = \dfrac{1}{C_1} + \dfrac{1}{C_2}.$ $C_1 = 4$ µf, $C_2 = 5$ µf, $C = ?$

89. $P = \dfrac{LI^2}{2}.$ The coefficient of self-induction $L = 80$ h, and the energy P stored in the circuit is 100 joules. Find the current I.

90. $F = \dfrac{S_1 S_2}{l^2}.$ The strength of two magnetic poles is $S_1 = 60$ units and $S_2 = 90$ units. If a force $F = 1.5$ dynes exists between them, what is the distance l?

91. $H = 0.4\pi NI.$ A solenoid has a magnetic field of $H = 300$ oersteds when the current $I = 2$ a. Find the number of turns N.

92. $R_t = R_0(1 + 0.0042t).$ The resistance of a copper wire is $R_0 = 27$ Ω at 0°C. What is the temperature t when the resistance has increased to $R_t = 35$ Ω?

93. $\dfrac{R_1}{R_2} = \dfrac{V_1}{V_2}.$ $R_2 = 100$ Ω, $V_1 = 16.2$ v, and $V_2 = 34$ v. $R_1 = ?$

94. $I = \dfrac{nE}{R + nr}.$ The voltage E per cell of a battery of n cells is 2.1 v. If the current $I = 2$ a when the load $R = 4.5$ Ω, how many cells are connected in series? The internal resistance r of each cell is 0.6 Ω.

95. $I = \dfrac{E}{R + \dfrac{r}{n}}.$ $E = 2.1$ v, $r = 0.6$ Ω, $R = 0.9$ Ω, and $I = 2$ a. $n = ?$

96. $\dfrac{E_p}{E_s} = \dfrac{N_p}{N_s}.$ $E_p = 100$, $E_s = 20$, and $N_p = 400$. $N_s = ?$

97. $Z_t = \dfrac{Z_1 Z_2}{Z_1 + Z_2}.$ $Z_t = 3$ Ω, and $Z_1 = 6$ Ω. $Z_2 = ?$

98. $L_t = L_0 + L_0 \alpha t.$ $L_0 = 10$, $L_t = 15$, $t = 6$. $\alpha = ?$

99. $F = \tfrac{9}{5}C + 32.$ $C = 20°$. $F = ?$

100. $R_a = \dfrac{R_1 R_3}{R_1 + R_2 + R_3}.$ Three resistances $R_1 = 2$ Ω, $R_2 = 3$ Ω, and $R_3 = ?$ are connected in a delta circuit. One branch of the equivalent Y circuit is $R_a = 0.6$ Ω. Find R_3.

CHAPTER XIV

OHM'S LAW—PARALLEL CIRCUITS

Most of the systems employed for the distribution of electrical energy consist of parallel circuits; that is, a source of electromotive force is connected to a pair of conductors, known as "feeders." Various types of load such as motors, lighting circuits, and other appliances are connected across the feeders. Figure 14-1 represents a simple distribution circuit consisting of a motor and a bank of five lamps. The motor and lamps are said to be in *parallel*, and it is evident that the current supplied by the generator divides between the motor and the lamps.

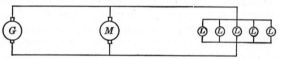

FIG. 14-1.

In this chapter the student will analyze parallel circuits and solve parallel-circuit problems. The solution of a parallel circuit generally consists in reducing the circuit to an equivalent single resistance that would replace the original circuit, without change in voltage or current.

14-1. Two Resistances in Parallel. Figure 14-2 represents two resistors R_1 and R_2 connected in parallel across a source of voltage E. An examination of this circuit brings out two important facts:

1. The same voltage exists across the two resistors.

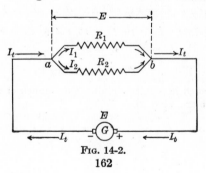

FIG. 14-2.

162

2. The total current I_t delivered by the generator enters the paralleled resistors at junction a, divides between the resistors, and leaves the parallel circuit at junction b.   Thus, the sum of the currents I_1 and I_2, which flow through R_1 and R_2 respectively, is equal to the total current I_t.

By making use of these facts and applying Ohm's law, it is easy to derive equations that show how paralleled resistances combine.

From 1 above, $I_1 = \dfrac{E}{R_1},$ $I_2 = \dfrac{E}{R_2},$ and $I_t = \dfrac{E}{R_t}$

where R_t is the joint resistance of R_1 and R_2, or the total resistance of the parallel combination.

From 2 above, $I_t = I_1 + I_2$ (1)

Substituting in Eq. (1) the value of the currents,

$$\frac{E}{R_t} = \frac{E}{R_1} + \frac{E}{R_2}$$

D : E, $\dfrac{1}{R_t} = \dfrac{1}{R_1} + \dfrac{1}{R_2}$ (2)

Equation (2) states that the total conductance (Art. 8-4) of the circuit is equal to the sum of the parallel conductances of R_1 and R_2; that is,

$$G_t = G_1 + G_2 \qquad\qquad (3)$$

It is evident, therefore, that, when resistances are connected in parallel, each additional resistance represents another path (conductance) through which current will flow.   Hence, increasing the number of resistances in parallel increases the total conductance of the circuit, thus decreasing the equivalent resistance of the circuit.

Example 1.   What is the joint resistance of the circuit of Fig. 14-2 if $R_1 = 6$ ohms and $R_2 = 12$ ohms?

Solution: Given $R_1 = 6$ ohms and $R_2 = 12$ ohms. $R_t = ?$
Substituting the known values in Eq. (2),

$$\frac{1}{R_t} = \frac{1}{6} + \frac{1}{12}$$
$$= 0.1667 + 0.0833$$

or $\dfrac{1}{R_t} = 0.250$

Solving for R_t, $R_t = \dfrac{1}{0.250} = 4.0\ \Omega$

Alternate Solution: A more convenient formula for the joint resistance of two parallel resistances is obtained by solving Eq. (2) for R_t. Thus,

$$R_t = \frac{R_1 R_2}{R_1 + R_2} \tag{4}$$

Hence, *the joint resistance of two resistances in parallel is equal to their product divided by their sum.* Substituting the values of R_1 and R_2 in Eq. (4),

$$R_t = \frac{6 \times 12}{6 + 12} = \frac{72}{18} = 4.0 \ \Omega$$

Thus, the paralleled resistors R_1 and R_2 are equivalent to a single resistance of 4.0 ohms. Note that the joint resistance is *less* than either of the resistances in parallel.

Example 2. (a) What is the joint resistance of the circuit of Fig. 14-2 if $R_1 = 21$ ohms and $R_2 = 15$ ohms?

(b) If the generator supplies 120 volts across points a and b, what is the generator (line) current?

Solution:

(a) $$R_t = \frac{R_1 R_2}{R_1 + R_2} = \frac{21 \times 15}{21 + 15} = 8.75 \ \Omega$$

(b) $$I_t = \frac{E}{R_t} = \frac{120}{8.75} = 13.71 \ a$$

Alternate Solution: Since 120 volts exist across both resistors, the current through each may be found and added to obtain the total current. Thus,

Current through R_1, $\quad I_1 = \dfrac{E}{R_1} = \dfrac{120}{21} = 5.71 \ a$

Current through R_2, $\quad I_2 = \dfrac{E}{R_2} = \dfrac{120}{15} = 8.0 \ a$

Total current, $\qquad\quad I_t = I_1 + I_2 = 5.71 + 8.0 = 13.71 \ a$

Hence, $\qquad\qquad\quad R_t = \dfrac{E}{I_t} = \dfrac{120}{13.71} = 8.75 \ \Omega$

From the foregoing, it is evident that R_1 and R_2 could be replaced by a single resistance of 8.75 ohms, connected between a and b, and the generator would be working under the same load conditions. Also, it is apparent that when a current enters a junction of resistances connected in parallel the current divides between the branches in inverse proportion to their resistances; that is, the greatest current flows through the least resistance.

Example 3. In the circuit of Fig. 14-2, $R_1 = 25$ ohms, $E = 220$ volts, and $I_t = 14.3$ amperes. What is the resistance of R_2?

Solution: Current through R_1, $\quad I_1 = \dfrac{E}{R_1} = \dfrac{220}{25} = 8.8 \ a$

Since $\qquad\qquad\qquad\qquad I_t = I_1 + I_2$

the current through R_2 is

$$I_2 = I_t - I_1$$
$$= 14.3 - 8.8 = 5.5 \text{ a}$$

Then

$$R_2 = \frac{E}{I_2} = \frac{220}{5.5} = 40 \ \Omega$$

Alternate Solution:

$$R_t = \frac{E}{I_t} = \frac{220}{14.3} = 15.4 \ \Omega$$

Solving Eq. (2) or Eq. (4) for R_2,

$$R_2 = \frac{R_1 R_t}{R_1 - R_t}$$
$$= \frac{25 \times 15.4}{25 - 15.4} = 40 \ \Omega$$

PROBLEMS 14-1

1. Two resistances of 5 Ω and 10 Ω are connected in parallel. Find the equivalent resistance of the combination.

2. A resistance of 25 Ω is connected in parallel with a resistance of 100 Ω. What is their joint resistance?

3. Find the joint resistance of 500 Ω and 250 Ω connected in parallel.

4. What is the joint resistance of 10 Ω and 15 Ω connected in parallel?

5. Find the total resistance of:

    (*a*) Two 100-Ω resistors connected in parallel.
    (*b*) Two 80-Ω resistors connected in parallel.

6. State a general formula for the total resistance R_t of two equal resistances of R Ω connected in parallel.

7. In the circuit of Fig. 14-2, how many volts would be required to force a total current of 12 a through a parallel combination of 22 Ω and 15.7 Ω?

8. How much power would be expended in the 22-Ω resistor of Prob. 7?

9. In the circuit of Fig. 14-2, $R_2 = 9.14$ Ω, $E = 32$ v, and $I_t = 10$ a. Find the resistance of R_1.

10. How much power is expended in R_2 of Prob. 9?

11. In the circuit of Fig. 14-2, a total current $I_t = 5$ a flows through the combination. $R_1 = 48.6$ Ω, and the current through R_2 is 2.53 a. What is the resistance of R_2?

12. How much power is expended in R_2 in Prob. 11?

13. What is the joint resistance of 10 Ω and 10,000 Ω connected in parallel?

14. A resistance of 500 Ω is connected across a generator that maintains a constant potential of 230 v. How much resistance must be connected in parallel with the 500-Ω resistor to raise the generator current to 1 a?

15. How much power is expended in the added resistance of Prob. 14?

14-2. Three or More Resistances in Parallel.

The procedure for deriving a general equation for the joint resistance of three or more resistances in parallel is the same as that of the preceding article. For example, Fig. 14-3 represents three resistances R_1,

R_2, and R_3 connected in parallel across a source of voltage E. The total line current I_t splits at junction a into currents I_1, I_2, and I_3 which flow through R_1, R_2, and R_3 respectively. Then

$$I_1 = \frac{E}{R_1}, \qquad I_2 = \frac{E}{R_2}, \qquad I_3 = \frac{E}{R_3}, \qquad \text{and} \qquad I_t = \frac{E}{R_t}$$

where R_t is the joint resistance of the parallel combination.

Since $\qquad\qquad I_t = I_1 + I_2 + I_3$

by substituting, $\qquad \dfrac{E}{R_t} = \dfrac{E}{R_1} + \dfrac{E}{R_2} + \dfrac{E}{R_3}$

D : E, $\qquad\qquad \dfrac{1}{R_t} = \dfrac{1}{R_1} + \dfrac{1}{R_2} + \dfrac{1}{R_3}$ (5)

From Eq. (5), it is evident that the total conductance of the

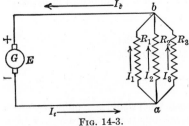

FIG. 14-3.

circuit is equal to the sum of the paralleled conductances of R_1, R_2, and R_3; that is,

$$G_t = G_1 + G_2 + G_3$$

In like manner, it can be demonstrated that the joint resistance R_t of any number of resistances connected in parallel is

$$\frac{1}{R_t} = \frac{1}{R_1} + \frac{1}{R_2} + \frac{1}{R_3} + \frac{1}{R_4} + \frac{1}{R_5} \cdots$$

Or, in terms of conductances,

$$G_t = G_1 + G_2 + G_3 + G_4 + G_5 \cdots$$

Example 1. What is the joint resistance of the circuit of Fig. 14-3 if $R_1 = 5$ ohms, $R_2 = 10$ ohms, and $R_3 = 12.5$ ohms?

Solution: Substituting the known values in Eq. (5),

$$\frac{1}{R_t} = \frac{1}{5} + \frac{1}{10} + \frac{1}{12.5}$$
$$= 0.2 + 0.1 + 0.08$$

or $\qquad\qquad \dfrac{1}{R_t} = 0.38$

Solving for R_t, $\qquad\qquad R_t = \dfrac{1}{0.38} = 2.63 \ \Omega$

If Eq. (5) is solved for R_t, the result is

$$R_t = \frac{R_1 R_2 R_3}{R_1 R_2 + R_1 R_3 + R_2 R_3} \tag{6}$$

It is seen that Eq. (6) is somewhat cumbersome for computing the joint resistance of three resistances connected in parallel. However, the student should recognize such expressions for three or more resistances in parallel, for they will be encountered in the analysis of networks.

Finding the joint resistance of any number of resistances in parallel is facilitated by arbitrarily assuming a voltage to exist across the parallel combination. The currents through the individual branches that *would* flow if the assumed voltage were actually impressed are added to obtain the total line current. The assumed voltage divided by this total current results in the joint resistance of the combination.

The assumed voltage should always be a power of ten in order that the slide-rule operator may make full use of the reciprocal scales. In order to avoid decimal quantities, that is, currents of less than 1 ampere, the assumed voltage should be numerically greater than the highest resistance of any parallel branch.

Example 2. Three resistances $R_1 = 10$ ohms, $R_2 = 15$ ohms, and $R_3 = 45$ ohms are connected in parallel. Find their joint resistance.

Solution: Assume $E_a = 100$ volts to exist across the combination.

Current through R_1, $I_1 = \dfrac{E_a}{R_1} = \dfrac{100}{10} = 10$ a

Current through R_2, $I_2 = \dfrac{E_a}{R_2} = \dfrac{100}{15} = 6.67$ a

Current through R_3, $I_3 = \dfrac{E_a}{R_3} = \dfrac{100}{45} = 2.22$ a

Total current, $I_t = 18.89$ a

Joint resistance, $R_t = \dfrac{E_a}{I_t} = \dfrac{100}{18.89} = 5.3$ Ω

PROBLEMS 14-2

1. Three resistances of 10, 15, and 30 Ω are connected in parallel. Find the equivalent resistance of the combination.

2. Find the total resistance of 5, 8, and 10 Ω connected in parallel.

3. Find the resistance of 250, 100, and 500 Ω connected in parallel.

4. Find the resistance of 42.4, 21.6, and 33.2 Ω connected in parallel.

5. What is the joint resistance of 5, 10, 20, and 15 Ω connected in parallel?

6. What is the equivalent resistance of 125, 300, 500, and 1000 Ω connected in parallel?

7. What is the total resistance of 15.6, 14.2, 18.2, and 95.2 Ω connected in parallel?

8. What is the joint resistance of

(*a*) Three 10-Ω resistors connected in parallel?
(*b*) Four 10-Ω resistors connected in parallel?

9. What is the joint resistance of

(*a*) Three 50-Ω resistors connected in parallel?
(*b*) Four 50-Ω resistors connected in parallel?
(*c*) Five 50-Ω resistors connected in parallel?

10. State a general formula for the total resistance R_t of n equal resistances of R Ω connected in parallel.

11. In the circuit of Fig. 14-3, $R_2 = 30$ Ω, $R_3 = 60$ Ω, $I_t = 12$ a, and $E = 120$ v. Find the resistance of R_1.

12. The values of Prob. 11 being used, what power will be expended in the circuit if an additional resistance of 5 Ω is connected across junctions a and b?

13. In the circuit of Fig. 14-3, $E = 100$ v, $R_1 = 80$ Ω, $R_3 = 50$ Ω, and $I_2 = 7.5$ a. Find

(*a*) I_t. (*b*) I_1. (*c*) I_3. (*d*) R_2.

14. In the circuit of Fig. 14-3, $I_t = 16$ a, $I_1 = 2.5$ a, $R_2 = 17$ Ω, and $R_3 = 41$ Ω. Find
(*a*) E. (*b*) I_2. (*c*) I_3. (*d*) R_1.

15. In the circuit of Fig. 14-3, $E = 200$ v, $I_t = 32$ a, $R_1 = 16$ Ω, and $R_2 = 22$ Ω. Find

(*a*) I_1. (*b*) I_2. (*c*) I_3. (*d*) R_3.

14-3. Compound Circuits. The solution of circuits containing combinations of series and parallel branches generally consists in reducing the parallel branches to equivalent series circuits and combining these with the series branches. No set rules can be formulated for the solution of all types of such circuits, but from the examples that follow the student will be able to build up his own methods of attack.

Example 1. Find the total resistance of the circuit represented in Fig. 14-4.

Solution: Note that the parallel branch of Fig. 14-4 is the circuit of Example 1 in Art. 14-1. Since the equivalent series resistance of the parallel

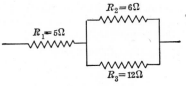

FIG. 14-4.

branch is

$$\frac{R_2 R_3}{R_2 + R_3}$$

the circuit reduces to two resistances in series, the total resistance of which is

$$R_t = R_1 + \frac{R_2 R_3}{R_2 + R_3}$$

$$= 5 + \frac{6 \times 12}{6 + 12} = 9.0 \ \Omega$$

Example 2. Find the total resistance of the circuit represented in Fig 14-5.

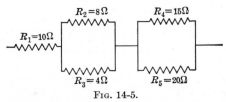

FIG. 14-5.

Solution: This circuit is similar to that shown in Fig. 14-4, with an additional parallel branch. By utilizing the expression for the joint resistance of two resistances in parallel, the entire circuit reduces to three resistances in series, the total resistance of which is

$$R_t = R_1 + \frac{R_2 R_3}{R_2 + R_3} + \frac{R_4 R_5}{R_4 + R_5}$$

$$= 10 + \frac{8 \times 4}{8 + 4} + \frac{15 \times 20}{15 + 20} = 21.2 \ \Omega$$

Example 3. Find the total resistance between points a and b in Fig. 14-6.
Solution: Since R_2 and R_L are in series, they must be added before being

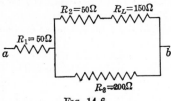

FIG. 14-6.

combined with R_3. Again, by utilizing the expression for the joint resistance of two resistances in parallel, the entire circuit reduces to two resistances in series. Thus, the total resistance is

$$R_t = R_1 + \frac{R_3(R_2 + R_L)}{R_3 + (R_2 + R_L)}$$

$$= 50 + \frac{200(50 + 150)}{200 + 50 + 150} = 150 \ \Omega$$

Note that the circuit of Fig. 14-6 is identical to that of Fig. 14-7. The latter is the customary method for representing

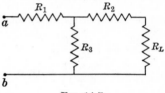

Fig. 14-7.

T networks, often encountered in communication circuits, where R_L is the load or receiving resistance.

Example 4. Find the resistance between points a and b in Fig. 14-8.

Solution: In many instances a circuit diagram that *appears* to be complicated can be better understood and analyzed by redrawing it in a more simplified form. For example, Fig. 14-9 represents the circuit of Fig. 14-8.

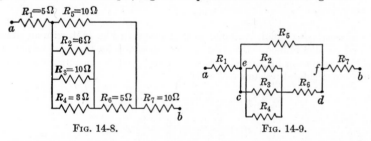

Fig. 14-8.   Fig. 14-9.

First find the equivalent series resistance of the parallel group formed by R_2, R_3, and R_4; add this resistance to R_6 which will result in the resistance R_{cd} between points c and d. R_{cd} is now combined with R_5, which is in parallel, to give an equivalent series resistance R_{ef} between points e and f. The circuit is now reduced to an equivalence of R_1, R_{ef}, and R_7 in series, which are added to obtain the total resistance R_{ab} between points a and b.

The joint resistance of R_2, R_3, and R_4 is 1.67 ohms which, when added to R_6, results in a resistance $R_{cd} = 6.67$ ohms between c and d. The equivalent series resistance R_{ef} between points e and f, formed by R_{cd} and R_5 in parallel, is 4.0 ohms. Therefore the resistance R_{ab} between points a and b is

$$R_{ab} = R_1 + R_{ef} + R_7 = 19 \ \Omega$$

PROBLEMS 14-3

1. In the circuit of Fig. 14-10, $R_1 = 50$ Ω, $R_2 = 60$ Ω, and $R_3 = 40$ Ω. What is the total resistance R_t of the circuit?

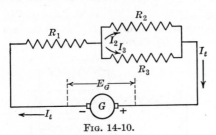

Fig. 14-10.

2. In the circuit of Fig. 14-10, $I_t = 19$ a, $R_1 = 7.1$ Ω, $R_2 = 11.2$ Ω, and the voltage E across R_3 is 40 v.   Find

(a) I_2 (b) I_3. (c) R_3. (d) R_t. (e) E_G.

3. In Prob. 2, if R_1 is short-circuited, how much power will be expended in R_3?

4. In the circuit of Fig. 14-10, $I_2 = 14$ a, $R_1 = 4.75$ Ω, $R_t = 10.8$ Ω, and $E_G = 214$ v.   Find

(a) Total current I_t. (b) Current through R_3.
(c) Resistance of R_2. (d) Resistance of R_3.
(e) Voltage across R_1. (f) Voltage across R_2.

5. In Prob. 4, if R_1 is short-circuited, how much power will be expended in R_2?

6. In the circuit of Fig. 14-7, $R_1 = 15$ Ω, $R_2 = 20$ Ω, $R_3 = 300$ Ω, and $R_L = 600$ Ω.   Find the resistance between points a and b.

7. In the circuit of Fig. 14-11, $R_1 = 100$ Ω, $R_3 = 800$ Ω, $R_2 = 200$ Ω, $E_G = 100$ v, and $I_t = 0.2$ a.   What is the resistance of R_L?

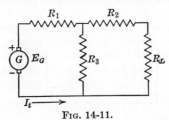

Fig. 14-11.

8. In the circuit of Fig. 14-11, $R_1 = 350$ Ω, $R_2 = 300$ Ω, $R_3 = 500$ Ω, and $R_L = 600$ Ω.   If a voltage of 60 v exists across R_L, what is the generator voltage?

9. How much power is being taken from the generator of Prob. 8?

10. If, in Prob. 8, the load resistance R_L is short-circuited, how much current will flow through R_3?

11. In the circuit of Fig. 14-12, the voltage E_{ab} across points a and b is 25 v, $I_t = 5.74$ a, $R_2 = 10\ \Omega$, $I_2 = 1.35$ a, and $R_3 = 8\ \Omega$.   Find

(*a*) Resistance of R_1.   (*b*) Resistance of R_4.
(*c*) Total resistance of circuit.   (*d*) Current through R_3.
(*e*) Current through R_4.

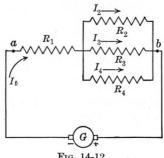

Fig. 14-12.

12. How much current I_t will flow in the circuit represented by Fig. 14-13?

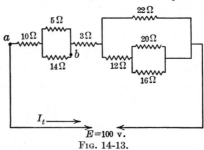

Fig. 14-13.

13. How much power will be expended in the circuit of Fig. 14-13 if points a and b are short-circuited?

14. How much current I_t will flow in the circuit represented by Fig. 14-14?

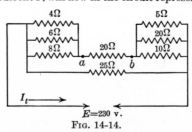

Fig. 14-14.

15. How much power will be expended in the circuit of Fig. 14-14 if points a and b are short-circuited?

14-4. Distribution Circuits.   Computations involving voltages and currents of two-wire distribution circuits are simply applications of Ohm's law to series and parallel circuits.

Previous consideration of power transmission (Art. 10-6) has been limited to cases where the line wires have carried current to one location only, this resulting in the same current throughout the system.   In practice, however, multiple circuits result in different currents flowing in different parts of the distribution circuit.

Example 1.   Figure 14-15 represents a generator, with a constant brush potential of 120 volts, delivering current to a motor and a group of lamps. The motor draws 10 amperes, and each lamp takes 1 ampere.   Determine the voltage across the motor, the voltage across the lamps, and the power lost in the lines.

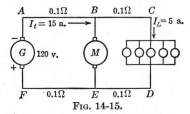

Fig. 14-15.

Solution: It is evident that all the current supplied by the generator must flow through wires AB and EF and that voltage will be lost in forcing this current through the resistance of the wires.   Such a loss is called a *line drop* or a *voltage drop*.   Also, there will be a voltage drop in wires BC and DE due to the current drawn by the lamps.   Listing the current distribution,

$$\text{Current in } AB = I_t = I_M + I_L = 15 \text{ a}$$
$$\text{Current in } BC = I_L = 5 \text{ a}$$
$$\text{Current in } DE = I_L = 5 \text{ a}$$
$$\text{Current in } EF = I_t = 15 \text{ a}$$

The line drops are

$$\text{Voltage drop in } AB = I_t R_{AB} = 15 \times 0.1 = 1.5 \text{ v}$$
$$\text{Voltage drop in } BC = I_L R_{BC} = 5 \times 0.1 = 0.5 \text{ v}$$
$$\text{Voltage drop in } DE = I_L R_{DE} = 5 \times 0.1 = 0.5 \text{ v}$$
$$\text{Voltage drop in } EF = I_t R_{EF} = 15 \times 0.1 = \underline{1.5 \text{ v}}$$
$$\text{Total line drop} = 4.0 \text{ v}$$

The voltage across the motor will be the generator voltage minus the line drops in AB and EF, or

$$E_M = 120 - 1.5 - 1.5 = 117 \text{ v}$$

The voltage across the lamps is the generator voltage minus the total line drop, or

$$E_L = 120 - 4 = 116 \text{ v}$$

Figure 14-16 is a diagram of the circuit showing the voltage distribution.

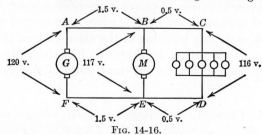

FIG. 14-16.

The line power loss may be computed as follows:

Power lost in $AB = I_t^2 R_{AB} = 15^2 \times 0.1 = 22.5$ w
Power lost in $BC = I_L^2 R_{BC} = 5^2 \times 0.1 = 2.5$ w
Power lost in $DE = I_L^2 R_{DE} = 5^2 \times 0.1 = 2.5$ w
Power lost in $EF = I_t^2 R_{EF} = 15^2 \times 0.1 = 22.5$ w

Total line loss = 50.0 w

By what other method could the line losses be computed?

Example 2. In Fig. 14-17, motor M_2 draws 55 amperes, M_2 draws 20 amperes, M_3 draws 5 amperes, and a lamp load represented by L draws 10 amperes. The generator maintains a constant brush potential of 240 volts. Find the line drop in each part of the line, the line voltage across each motor, the voltage across the lamps, and the total power lost in the line.

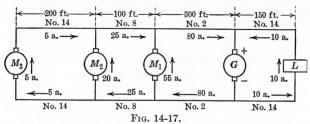

FIG. 14-17.

Solution: Total line resistances,

Between M_2 and M_3 = 400 ft of No. 14 wire = 1.03 Ω
Between M_1 and M_2 = 200 ft of No. 8 wire = 0.128 Ω
Between G and M_1 = 600 ft of No. 2 wire = 0.0954 Ω
Between G and L = 300 ft of No. 14 wire = 0.774 Ω

The line currents are

Between M_2 and M_3 = 5 a
Between M_1 and M_2 = 25 a
Between G and M_1 = 80 a
Between G and L = 10 a

Then the line drops are

Between M_2 and $M_3 = 5 \times 1.03 = 5.15$ v
Between M_1 and $M_2 = 25 \times 0.128 = 3.20$ v
Between G and $M_1 = 80 \times 0.0954 = 7.63$ v
Between G and $L = 10 \times 0.774 = 7.74$ v

The voltage across any load is equal to the generator voltage minus the line drop between the generator and the load.

Voltage across $M_3 = 240 - (7.63 + 3.20 + 5.15) \cong 224$ v
Voltage across $M_2 = 240 - (7.63 + 3.2) \cong 229.2$ v
Voltage across $M_1 = 240 - 7.63 \cong 232.4$ v
Voltage across $L = 240 - 7.74 \cong 232.3$ v

Figure 14-18 shows the distribution of voltages in the circuit.

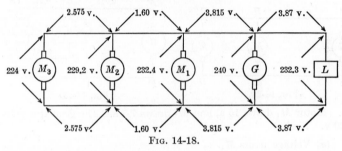

Fig. 14-18.

Power losses,

Between M_2 and $M_3 = 5^2 \times 1.03 = 25.8$ w
Between M_1 and $M_2 = 25^2 \times 0.128 = 80$ w
Between G and $M_1 = 80^2 \times 0.0954 = 610$ w
Between G and $L = 10^2 \times 0.774 = \underline{77.4}$ w
Total power lost in line $= \overline{793.2}$ w

PROBLEMS 14-4

1. In the circuit represented by Fig. 14-19, the motor draws 25 a and each lamp draws 1 a. The generator brush potential is 115 v. Find

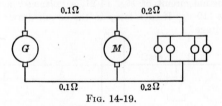

Fig. 14-19.

(a) Voltage across motor.
(b) Voltage across lamps.
(c) Power lost in lines.

2. On the assumption that the resistances of the lamps in Prob. 1 remain constant, how much voltage will exist across them if the motor is disconnected from the line?

3. In Fig. 14-20, the distance from A to B is 200 ft, and that from B to C is 150 ft. AB and EF are No. 6 wire, and BC and DE are No. 14 wire. Motor M_1 draws 35 a, and M_2 draws 10 a. The generator brush potential is 230 v. Find

    (*a*) Voltage across M_1.
    (*b*) Voltage across M_2.
    (*c*) Power lost in lines.

4. In Fig. 14-20, the distance from A to B is 100 ft, and that from B to C is 300 ft. AB and EF are No. 10 wire, and BC and DE are No. 14

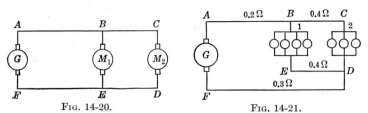

FIG. 14-20.   FIG. 14-21.

wire. Motor M_1 draws 15 a, and M_2 draws 7.5 a. The generator voltage is 120 v. Find

    (*a*) Voltage across M_1.
    (*b*) Voltage across M_2.
    (*c*) Power lost in lines.

5. The generator supplies 115 v across points A and F in Fig. 14-21. If each lamp draws 0.5 a, find

    (*a*) Voltage across group 1.
    (*b*) Voltage across group 2.

6. Repeat Prob. 5, with each lamp drawing 1 a.

7. Using the values of Prob. 5, repeat the problem, but the wire FD disconnected from D and connected to the point E.

8. In the original circuit of Fig. 14-21, a voltmeter across the lamps of group 2 reads 110 v. If each lamp in the circuit draws 0.75 a, what is the generator voltage?

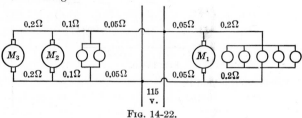

FIG. 14-22.

9. In the circuit of Fig. 14-22, motor M_1 draws 50 a, M_2 draws 12 a, M_3 draws 15 a, and each lamp draws 1 a. Find

    (*a*) Voltage across M_1.
    (*b*) Voltage across M_2.
    (*c*) Voltage across M_3.
    (*d*) Power lost in lines.

10. *A*, *B*, *C*, *D*, and *E* represent loads in Fig. 14-23. *A* draws 5 a, *B* draws 6.5 a, *C* draws 12 a, *D* draws 7.5 a, and *E* draws 4 a at 100 v. Find

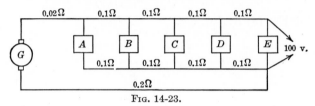

Fig. 14-23.

    (*a*) Voltage across each load.
    (*b*) Generator voltage.

14-5. Bridge Circuits.

The accuracy of resistance measurements by the voltmeter-ammeter method is limited, mainly because of errors in the meters and the difficulty of reading the meters precisely. Probably the most widely used device for precise resistance measurement is the Wheatstone bridge, the circuit diagram of which is shown in Fig. 14-24.

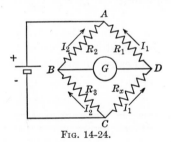

Fig. 14-24.

Resistors R_1, R_2, and R_3 are known values, and R_x is the resistance to be measured. In most bridges, R_1 and R_2 are adjustable in ratios of 1 to 1, 10 to 1, 100 to 1, etc., and R_3 is adjustable in small steps. In measuring a resistance, R_3 is adjusted until the galvanometer reads zero, and in this condition the bridge is said to be "balanced." Since the galvanometer reads zero, it is evident that the points *B* and *D* are exactly at the same potential;

that is, the voltage drop from A to B is the same as from A to D. Expressed as an equation,

$$E_{AD} = E_{AB}$$

or
$$I_1R_1 = I_2R_2 \tag{7}$$

Similarly, the voltage drop across R_x must be equal to that across R_3. Hence

$$I_1R_x = I_2R_3 \tag{8}$$

Dividing Eq. (8) by Eq. (7),

$$\frac{I_1R_x}{I_1R_1} = \frac{I_2R_3}{I_2R_2}$$

$$\therefore \frac{R_x}{R_1} = \frac{R_3}{R_2} \tag{9}$$

Equation (9) is the fundamental equation of the Wheatstone bridge, and by solving for the only unknown R_x the value of the resistance under measurement can be computed.

Example 1. In the circuit of Fig. 14-24, $R_1 = 10$ ohms, $R_2 = 100$ ohms, and $R_3 = 13.9$ ohms. If the bridge is balanced, what is the value of the unknown resistance?

Solution: Solving Eq. (9) for R_x, $R_x = \dfrac{R_1R_3}{R_2}$

Substituting the known values, $R_x = \dfrac{10 \times 13.9}{100} = 1.39\ \Omega$

Locating the point at which a telephone cable or a long control line is grounded is simplified by the use of two circuits that are modifications of the Wheatstone bridge. These are the Murray loop and the Varley loop.

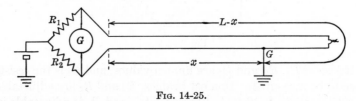

Fig. 14-25.

Figure 14-25 represents the method of locating the grounded point in a cable using a Murray loop. A spare ungrounded cable is connected to the grounded cable at a convenient location **beyond** the grounded point G. This forms a loop of length L, one part of which is the distance x from the point of measurement to the grounded point G. The other part of the loop is then $L - x$. These two parts of the loop form a bridge with R_1 and R_2 which are adjusted until the galvanometer shows no deflection. Because this results in a balanced bridge circuit,

$$\frac{R_2}{R_1} = \frac{x}{L - x} \tag{10}$$

Solving for x,

$$x = \left(\frac{R_2}{R_1 + R_2}\right) L \tag{11}$$

Example 2. A Murray loop is connected as in Fig. 14-25 to locate a ground in a cable between two cities 40 miles apart. The lines forming the loop are identical. With the bridge balanced, $R_1 = 645$ ohms, and $R_2 = 476$ ohms. How far is the grounded point from the test end?

Solution: Substituting the known values in Eq. (11),

$$x = \left(\frac{476}{645 + 476}\right) 80 = 33.97 \text{ miles}$$

If the two cables forming the loop are not the same size, the relations of Eq. (11) may be used to compute the resistance R_x of the grounded cable from the point of measurement to the grounded point. Then if R_L be the resistance of the entire loop,

$$R_x = \left(\frac{R_2}{R_1 + R_2}\right) R_L \tag{12}$$

Example 3. A Murray loop is connected as in Fig. 14-25. The grounded cable is No. 19 wire, and a different sized wire is used to complete the loop. The resistance of the entire loop is 126 ohms; and when the bridge is balanced, $R_1 = 342$ ohms, and $R_2 = 217$ ohms. How far is the ground from the test end?

Solution: Substituting the known values in Eq. (12),

$$R_x = \left(\frac{217}{342 + 217}\right) 126 = 48.9 \ \Omega$$

Since No. 19 wire has a resistance of 8.21 ohms per 1000 feet, 48.9 ohms represents 5960 feet of wire between the test end and the grounded point.

PROBLEMS 14-5

1. In a Wheatstone bridge, $R_1 = 0.001 \ \Omega$, $R_2 = 1 \ \Omega$, and $R_3 = 28.7 \ \Omega$. What is the value of the unknown resistance?

2. In a Wheatstone bridge, if $\dfrac{R_1}{R_2} = 1000$ and $R_x = 9.43$ Ω, what is the value of R_3?

3. A ground exists in one conductor of a lead-covered No. 14 pair. A Murray loop is used to locate the fault by connecting the pair together at the far end. When the bridge circuit is balanced, $R_1 = 18.7$ Ω and $R_2 = 13.2$ Ω. If the cable is 4500 ft long, how far from the test end is the grounded point?

4. Several No. 8 wires run between two cities located 35 miles apart. One wire becomes grounded, and a Murray loop is used in one city to locate the fault by connecting two wires in the other city. When the bridge is balanced, $R_1 = 716$ Ω, and $R_2 = 273$ Ω. How far from the test end is the cable grounded?

5. A No. 6 wire, which is known to be grounded, is made into a loop by connecting a wire of different size at its far end. The resistance of the loop thus formed is 5.62 Ω. When a Murray loop is connected and balanced, the value of R_1 is 16.8 Ω, and that of R_2 is 36.2 Ω. How far from the test end does the ground exist?

CHAPTER XV

SIMULTANEOUS LINEAR EQUATIONS

A graph is a pictorial representation of the relation existing between two or more quantities. Everyone is familiar with various types of graph or graphic chart. They are used extensively in magazines, newspapers, and trade journals and by engineers, manufacturers, and others concerned with relative values. It is difficult to conceive how the electrical engineer or radio engineer could dispense with them.

The study of simultaneous linear equations provides the student an excellent opportunity to begin the study of graphs. Therefore, in this chapter we shall pave the way for some very important and interesting topics which will follow in later chapters.

15-1. Solving Problems by Means of Graphs. In many instances, problems arise involving relationships that, though readily solved by usual arithmetical or algebraic methods, are more clearly understood when solved graphically. It is also true that there are many problems which may be solved graphically with less labor than is required for the purely mathematical solutions. The following illustrative examples will show how some problems may be worked graphically:

Example 1. Steamship A sailed from New York at 6 A.M., steaming at an average speed of 10 knots. (A knot is a measure of speed and is 1 nautical mile per hour). The same day, at 9 A.M., steamship B sailed from New York, steering the same course as A but steaming at 15 knots.

(*a*) How long will it take B to overtake A?

(*b*) What will be the distance from New York at that time?

Solution: Choose convenient scales on graph paper, and plot the distance in nautical miles covered by each vessel against the time in hours, as shown in Fig. 15-2. This is conveniently accomplished by making such a table as that shown in Fig. 15-1.

It will be noted that the graphs of the two distances intersect at 90 miles, or at 3 P.M. This means the two ships will be 90 miles from New York at 3 P.M. Because they steered the same course, B overtakes A at this time and distance.

181

Time, hours	Distance covered by A	Distance covered by B
2	20	30
4	40	60
6	60	90
8	80	120
10	100	150

Fig. 15-1.

The graphic solution furnishes us with other information. For example, by measuring the vertical distance between the graphs, we may determine how far apart the ships were at any time. Thus, at 11 A.M. the ships were 20 miles apart, at 1 P.M. they were 10 miles apart, etc.

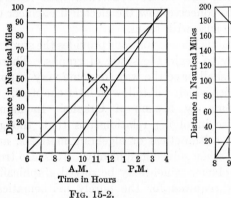

Fig. 15-2.

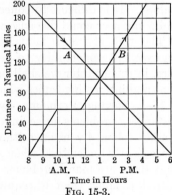

Fig. 15-3.

Example 2.   Ship A is 200 miles at sea, and ship B is in port. At 8 A.M., A starts toward this port, making a speed of 20 knots. At the same time, B left port at a speed of 30 knots to intercept A. After traveling 2 hours, B was delayed for 1 hour and 40 minutes at the lightship. B then continued on his course to intercept A.

(a) At what time did the two ships meet?

(b) How far were they from port at this time?

Solution: Figure 15-3 is a graph showing the conditions of the problem. The graph is constructed as in Example 1. A table of distances against time is made up, a convenient scale is chosen, and the points are plotted and joined with a straight line.

The intersection of the graphs shows that the two ships will meet 100 miles from port at 1 P.M. Why is there a horizontal portion in the graph of B's distance from port? If A and B continue their speeds and courses, at what time will A reach port? At what time will B arrive at A's 10 A.M. position? What will be the distance between ships at this time?

PROBLEMS 15-1
Solve graphically:

1. The owner of a radio store decides to pay his salesmen according to either of two plans. The first plan provides for a fixed salary of $25.00 per week, plus a commission of $3.00 for each radio sold. According to the second plan, a salesman may take a straight commission of $4.00 for each radio set. Determine at which point the second plan becomes more profitable for the salesmen.

2. A owns a motor that consumes 10 kw-hr per day, and B owns a motor that takes 30 kw-hr per day. Beginning the first day of the month, A lets his motor run continuously. B's motor runs for 1 day, is idle for 4 days, then runs for 2 days, is idle for 6 days, and then runs the rest of the month. On what days of the month will A's and B's power bill be the same?

3. Two men start from two places 75 miles apart and travel toward each other, the first at the rate of 5 m.p.h. and the second at the rate of 10 m.p.h.

(a) How long will it be before they meet?
(b) How far will each have traveled?
(c) How far are they apart 2 hr after starting? 7 hr?

4. A man started a savings account with a deposit of $25.00 and thereafter deposited $5.00 per week. Two weeks later, his brother started an account with $10.00 per week.

(a) In how many weeks after the brother made his deposit will their accounts be equal?
(b) During what weeks will their accounts differ by $10.00?
(c) When will the brother's account be $100.00 greater?

5. A circuit consists of a resistance of 5 Ω connected across a source of variable potential. Plot the current through the resistance against the voltage across the resistance, as the voltage is varied in 10-v steps from 0 to 120 v. What conclusions do you draw from this graph?

6. Train A starts from a town and travels at the rate of 30 m.p.h. Six hours later, another train B starts from the same town, on the same track, traveling at the rate of 45 m.p.h.

(a) In how many hours will the train B overtake A?
(b) How far will they be from the starting point at this time?
(c) How far apart are the trains 1 hr after the second starts?

7. A variable resistance is connected across a generator that maintains a potential of 120 v. Plot the current through the resistance as the resistance is varied in 2-Ω steps from 2 to 20 Ω. What conclusions do you draw from this graph?

15-2. Coordinate Notation.
Let us suppose you are standing on a street corner and a stranger asks you to direct him to some

prominent building. You tell him to go four blocks east and five blocks north. By these directions, you have automatically made the street intersection a *point of reference,* or *origin,* from which distances are measured. From this point, you could count distances to any point in the city, using the blocks as a unit of distance, and pairs of directions (east, north, west, or south) for locating the various points.

To draw a graph, we had to use two lines of reference, or *axes.* These correspond to the streets meeting at right angles. Also, in fixing a point on a graph, it was necessary to locate that point by pairs of numbers. For example, when we plot distance against time, we need one number to represent the time and another number to represent the distance covered in that time.

So far, only positive numbers have been used for graphs. To restrict graphs to positive values would impose just as severe a handicap as if we were to restrict algebra to positive numbers. Accordingly, a system must be established for plotting pairs of numbers, either or both of which may be positive or negative. In so doing a sheet of squared paper is divided into four sections, or quadrants, by drawing two intersecting axes at right angles to each other. The point O, at the intersection of the axes, is called the *origin.* The horizontal axis is generally known as the X *axis* and the vertical axis is called the Y *axis.*

There is nothing new about measuring distances along the X axis; it is the same as the basic system described in Art. 3-4 and shown in Fig. 3-2. That is, we agree to regard distances along the X axis, to the *right* of the origin, as *positive,* and those to the *left* as *negative.* Also, distances along the Y axis are considered as *positive* if *above* the origin and *negative* if *below* the origin. In effect, we have simply added to our method of graphical representation as originally outlined in Fig. 3-2.

With this system of representation, which is called a system of *rectangular coordinates,* we are able to locate any pair of numbers regardless of the signs.

Example: Referring to Fig. 15-4,
Point A is in the first quadrant. Its x value is $+3$, and its y value is $+4$.
Point B is in the second quadrant. Its x value is -4, and its y value is $+5$.
Point C is in the third quadrant. Its x value is -5, and its y value is -2.
Point D is in the fourth quadrant. Its x value is $+5$, and its y value is -3.

Thus, every point on the surface of the paper corresponds to a pair of coordinate numbers that completely describe the point.

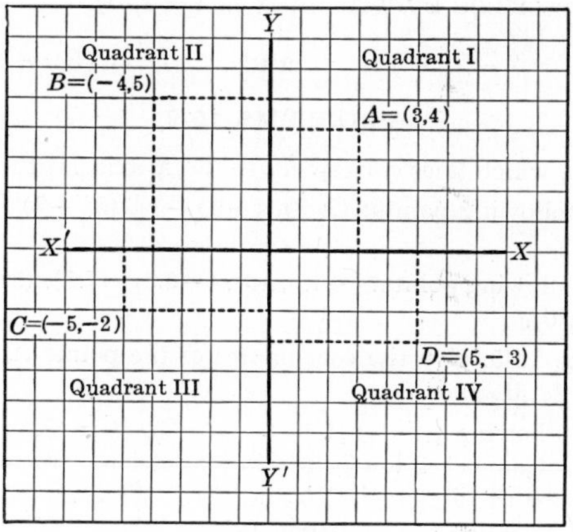

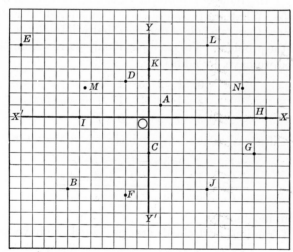

FIG. 15-4.

The two signed numbers that locate a point are called the *coordinates* of that point.   The x value is called the *abscissa* of the point, and the y value is the *ordinate* of the point.

FIG. 15-5.

In describing a point in terms of its coordinates, the abscissa is always stated first.   Thus, to locate the point A in Fig. 15-4, we write $A = (3, 4)$, meaning that, to locate the point A, we count three divisions to the right of the origin along the X axis and up four divisions along the Y axis. In like manner, the point B is completely described by writing $B = (-4, 5)$. Also,

$$C = (-5, -2), \quad \text{and} \quad D = (5, -3).$$

PROBLEMS 15-2

1. On a map, which lines correspond to the X axis, latitude or longitude?

2. Plot the following points: $(2, 3)$, $(-6, -1)$, $(3, -7)$, $(0, -6)$, $(0, 0)$, $(-8, 0)$.

3. Plot the following points: $(-1.5, 10)$, $(-6.5, -7.5)$, $(3.6, -4)$, $(0, 2.5)$, $(6.5, 8.5)$, $(3.5, 0)$.

4. Using Fig. 15-5, give the coordinates of the points A, B, C, D, E, F, G, H, I, J, K, L, M, and N.

5. Plot the following points: $A = (-1, -2)$, $B = (5, -2)$, $C = (5, 4)$, $D = (-1, 4)$. Connect these points in succession. What kind of figure is $ABCD$? Draw the diagonals DB and CA. What are the coordinates of the point of intersection of the diagonals?

15-3. Graphs of Linear Equations. A relation between a pair of numbers, not necessarily connected with physical quantities such as those in foregoing exercises, can be expressed by a graph.

Consider the following problem: The sum of two numbers is equal to 5. What are the numbers? Immediately it is evident there is more than one pair of numbers that will fulfill the requirements of the problem. For example, if only positive numbers are considered we have, by addition,

$$
\begin{array}{cccccc}
0 & 1 & 2 & 3 & 4 & 5 \\
5 & 4 & 3 & 2 & 1 & 0 \\
\hline
5 & 5 & 5 & 5 & 5 & 5
\end{array}
$$

Similarly, if negative numbers are included we may write

$$
\begin{array}{cccccc}
-1 & -2 & -3 & -4 & -5 & -6 \\
+6 & +7 & +8 & +9 & +10 & +11 \\
\hline
5 & 5 & 5 & 5 & 5 & 5
\end{array}
$$

and so on, indefinitely.

Also, if fractions or decimals are considered, we have

$$
\begin{array}{cccc}
1.5 & -3.75 & -1.63 & -8.36 \\
3.5 & +8.75 & +6.63 & +13.36 \\
\hline
5 & 5 & 5 & 5
\end{array}
$$

and so on, indefinitely.

It follows that there are an infinite number of pairs of numbers whose sum is 5.

Let x represent any possible value of one of these numbers, and let y represent the corresponding value of the second number. Then

$$x + y = 5$$

For any value assigned to x, we may solve for the corresponding value of y. Thus, if $x = 1$, $y = 4$. Also, if $x = 2$, $y = 3$. Likewise, if $x = -4$, $y = 9$, because, by substituting -4 for x in the equation, we obtain

$$-4 + y = 5$$
or
$$y = 9$$

In this manner, there may be obtained an unlimited number of values for x and y that satisfy the equations, some of which are listed below:

If $x =$	-6	-4	-2	0	2	4	6	8	10
Then $y =$	11	9	7	5	3	1	-1	-3	-5
Coordinates of	A	B	C	D	E	F	G	H	I

With the above pairs of numbers as coordinates the points are plotted and connected in succession as shown in Fig. 15-6. The line drawn through these points is called the *graph of the equation* $x + y = 5$.

Regardless of what pairs of numbers (coordinates) are chosen from the graph, it will be found that each pair satisfies the equation. For example, the point P has coordinates $(15, -10)$; that is, $x = 15$, and $y = -10$. These numbers satisfy the equation because $15 - 10 = 5$. Likewise, the point P_1 has coordinates $(-9, 14)$ that also satisfy the equation because $-9 + 14 = 5$. The point P_3 has coordinates $(3, 7)$. This point is not on the line; nor do its coordinates satisfy the equation, for $3 + 7 \neq 5$. The straight line, or graph, may be extended in either direction, always passing through points whose coordinates satisfy the conditions of the equation. This is as would be expected; for there are an infinite number of pairs of numbers called *solutions* that, when added, are equal to 5.

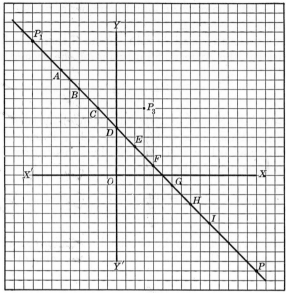

Fig. 15-6.

PROBLEMS 15-3

1. Graph the equation $x - y = 8$ by tabulating and plotting five pairs of values for x and y that satisfy the equation. Can a straight line be drawn through these points? Plot the point (4, 4). Is it on the graph of the equation? Do the coordinates of this point satisfy the equation? From the graph, when $x = 0$, what is the value of y? When $y = 0$, what is the value of x? Do these pairs of values satisfy the equation?

2. Graph the equation $2x + 3y = 6$ by tabulating and plotting at least five pairs of values for x and y that satisfy the equation. Can a straight line be drawn through these points? Plot the point $(-15, 12)$. Is this point on the graph of the equation? Do the coordinates satisfy the equation? Plot the point (10, -5). Is this point on the graph of the equation? Do the coordinates satisfy the equation? From the graph, when $x = 0$, what is the value of y? When $y = 0$, what is the value of x? Do these pairs of values satisfy the equation?

15-4. Each of the equations that have been plotted, is of the *first degree* (Art. 12-1) and contain *two unknowns*. From their graphs the following important facts are obtained:

1. *The graph of an equation of the first degree is a straight line.*

2. *The coordinates of every point on the graph satisfy the conditions of the equation.*

3. *The coordinates of every point not on the graph do not satisfy the conditions of the equation.*

Because the graph of every equation of the first degree results in a straight line, as stated under 1 above, first degree equations are called *linear equations*. Also, because such equations have an infinite number of solutions, they are called *indeterminate* equations.

As *x* changes in value in such an equation, the value of *y* also changes. Hence, *x* and *y* are called *variables*.

15-5. Methods of Plotting.   To graph a linear equation of two variables,

1. *Choose a convenient value for one variable, substitute it in the equation, and solve for the corresponding value of the other variable. This results in one solution, or one set of coordinates.*

2. *Choose another value and find a solution as in step 1.*

3. *Plot the two points whose coordinates were found in steps 1 and 2. Connect them with a straight line.*

4. *Check the resulting graph by solving for and plotting a third point. This third point should lie on the plotted line or its extension.*

Example.   Graph the equation $2x - 5y = 10$.

Solution: Step 1.   It is convenient in plotting such an equation to first let $x = 0$, for in so doing the resulting solution will fall on the Y axis.

Then, if
$$x = 0,$$
$$0 - 5y = 10$$
and
$$y = -2.$$

This results in a point, which we shall call A, whose coordinates are $(0, -2)$.

Step 2.   If we now let $y = 0$, the resulting solution will fall on the X axis for, if

$$y = 0,$$
$$2x - 0 = 10$$
and
$$x = 5.$$

This results in another point, which we shall call B, whose coordinates are $(5, 0)$.

Step 3.   Plot points A and B, and connect them with a straight line as shown in Fig. 15-7.

Step 4.   Check.   Choose another value for x in order to solve for a third point.

Let
$$x = -10$$
Then
$$-20 - 5y = 10$$
and
$$y = -6$$

This results in point C with coordinates $(-10, -6)$ which, when plotted falls on the graph of the equation as shown in Fig. 15-7.

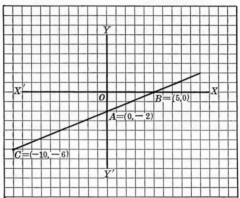

FIG. 15-7.

When x was set equal to zero, the resulting point A had coordinates that located the point where the graph crossed the Y axis. This point is called the Y *intercept*. Likewise, when y was set equal to zero, the resulting point B had coordinates that located the point where the graph crossed the X axis. This point is called the X *intercept*. Not only are these easy methods of locating two points with which to graph the equation, but also these two points give us the exact location of the intercepts. These are important, as will be shown later.

PROBLEMS 15-4

Graph the following equations and determine the X and Y intercepts:

1. $5x + 4y = 12$.   2. $2x - y = 8$.

3. $x - 3y = 3$.   4. $2x + y = 9$.

5. Plot the following equations on the same sheet of graph paper (same axes), and carefully study the results:

(a) $x - y = -8$.   (b) $x - y = -5$.

(c) $x - y = 0$.   (d) $x - y = 4$.

(e) $x - y = 8$.

Are the graphs parallel? Note that all left members of the given equations are identical. Solve each of these equations for y and write them in a column, thus:

(a) $y = x + 8$.
(b) $y = x + 5$.
(c) $y = x + 0$.
(d) $y = x - 4$.
(e) $y = x - 8$.

In each equation, does the last term of the right member represent the Y intercept?

When the equations are solved for y, as above, each coefficient of x is $+1$. The graphs all slant to the right because the coefficient of each x is positive. Each time an x increases one unit, note that the corresponding y increases one unit. This is because the coefficient of x in each equation is 1.

6. Plot the following equations on the same sheet of graph paper (same axes), and carefully study the results.

(*a*) $4x - 2y = -30$.   (*b*) $4x - 2y = -16$.
(*c*) $4x - 2y = 0$.   (*d*) $4x - 2y = 12$.
(*e*) $4x - 2y = 30$.   (*f*) $8x - 4y = 60$.

Are all the graphs parallel? Again note that all left members are identical. Does the graph of Eq. (*f*) fall on that of Eq. (*e*)? Note that (*e*) and (*f*) are *identical equations*. Why?

Solve each of these equations, except (*f*), for y, and write them in a column, thus:

(*a*) $y = 2x + 15$.
(*b*) $y = 2x + 8$.
(*c*) $y = 2x + 0$.
(*d*) $y = 2x - 6$.
(*e*) $y = 2x - 15$.

In each equation, does the last term of the right member represent the Y intercept? When linear equations are written in this form, this last term is known as the *constant* term.

Are all the coefficients of the x's positive? This is why all the graphs slant to the right. Lines slanting in this manner are said to have *positive slopes*.

Each time an x increases or decreases one unit, note that y increases or decreases, respectively, two units. This is because the coefficient of each x is 2. If a graph has a *positive slope*, an increase or decrease in x always results in a corresponding increase or decrease in y. In these equations, each line has a slope of $+2$, the coefficient of each x.

7. Plot the following equations on the same set of axes:

(*a*) $x + 2y = 18$.   (*b*) $x + 2y = 10$.
(*c*) $x + 2y = 0$.   (*d*) $x + 2y = -14$.
(*e*) $x + 2y = -22$.   (*f*) $3x + 6y = -66$.

Are all the graphs parallel? How should you have known they would be parallel without plotting them?

Does the graph of (*f*) fall on that of (*e*)? How should you have known (*e*) and (*f*) would plot the same graph without actually plotting them?

Solve each equation for y as in Probs. 5 and 6. Does the constant term denote the Y intercept in each case? Is the coefficient of each x equal to $-\frac{1}{2}$? The minus sign means that each graph has a *negative slope;* that is, the lines slant toward the left. Thus, when x increases, y decreases, and vice versa. The $\frac{1}{2}$ slope means that, when x varies one unit, y is changed $\frac{1}{2}$ unit. Therefore, the variations of x and y are completely described by saying the slope is $-\frac{1}{2}$.

8. Plot the following equations on the same set of axes:

(a) $x - 4y = 0$.	(b) $x - 2y = 0$.	(c) $x - y = 0$.
(d) $2x - y = 0$.	(e) $4x - y = 0$.	(f) $4x + y = 0$.
(g) $2x + y = 0$.	(h) $x + y = 0$.	(i) $x + 2y = 0$.
(j) $x + 4y = 0$.		

Solve the equations for y, as before, and carefully analyze your results.

15-6. Variables. When two variables, such as x and y in the foregoing problems, are so related that a change in x causes a change in y, then y is said to be a *function* of x. By assigning values to x and then solving for the value of y, we make x the *independent variable* and y the *dependent variable*.

The above definitions are applicable to all types of equations and physical relations. For example, in Fig. 15-2, distance is plotted against time. The distance covered by a body moving at a constant velocity is given by

$$s = vt$$

where
$$s = \text{distance},$$
$$v = \text{velocity},$$
$$t = \text{time}.$$

In this equation, and therefore in the resulting graph, the distance is the dependent variable because it depends upon the amount of time. The time is the independent variable, and the velocity is a constant.

Similarly, in 5 of Probs. 15-1, the formula $I = \dfrac{E}{R}$ was used to obtain values for plotting the graph. Here the resistance R is the constant, the voltage E is the independent variable, and the current I is the dependent variable.

In 7 of Probs. 15-1, the same formula $I = \dfrac{E}{R}$ was used to obtain coordinates for the graph. Here the voltage E is a constant, the resistance R is the independent variable, and the current I is the dependent variable.

From these and other examples, it is evident, as stated in Art. 15-4, that the graph of an equation having variables of the first degree is a straight line. This fact does not apply to variables in the denominator of a fraction as in the case above where R is a variable. However, $I = \dfrac{E}{R}$ is not an equation of the first degree as far as R is concerned because, by applying the law of exponents, $I = ER^{-1}$.

It is general practice to plot the independent variable along the horizontal, or X axis, and the dependent variable along the vertical, or Y axis.

In plotting the graph of an equation, it is convenient to solve the equation for the dependent variable first. Values are then assigned to the independent variable in order to find the corresponding values of the dependent variable.

If an equation or formula contains more than two variables, after choosing the dependent variable, we must decide which one is to be the independent variable for each separate investigation, or graphing. For example, consider the formula

$$X_L = 2\pi f L$$

where

X_L = inductive reactance of an inductance,
f = frequency in cycles per second,
L = inductance,
2π = a constant.

In this case, we may vary either the frequency f or the inductance L in order to determine the effect upon the inductive reactance X_L; but both must not be varied at the same time. Either f must be fixed at some constant value and L varied, or L must be fixed. A little thought will show the difficulty of plotting, on a plane, the variations of X_L if f and L are varied simultaneously.

15-7. Graphical Solution of Simultaneous Linear Equations. The graphs of the equations

$$x + 2y = 12$$

and

$$3x - y = 1$$

are shown in Fig. 15-8. The point of intersection of the lines has the coordinates $(2, 5)$; that is, the x value is 2, and the y value is 5. Now this point is on both of the graphs; it follows, therefore, that the x and y values should satisfy both equations. Substituting 2 for x and 5 for y in each equation results in the identities

$$2 + 10 = 12$$
and $$6 - 5 = 1$$

From this it is observed that, if the graphs of two linear equations intersect, they have one common set of values for the variables, or one common solution. These are called *simultaneous linear equations*.

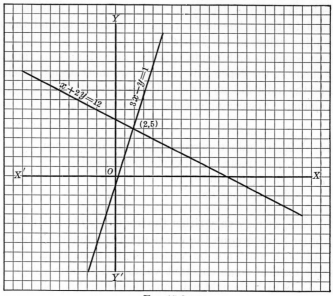

Fig. 15-8.

Because two straight lines can intersect in only one point, there can be only one common set of values, or one common solution that satisfies both equations.

Two equations, each with two variables, are called *inconsistent equations* when their plotted lines are parallel to each other. Because parallel lines do not intersect, there is no common solution for two or more inconsistent equations.

Considerable care must be used in graphing equations, for a deviation in the graph of either equation will cause the intersection to be in the wrong place and hence will lead to an incorrect solution.

PROBLEMS 15-5

Solve the following pairs of equations graphically, and check by substituting the x and y values thus obtained in each pair of equations:

1. $3x + 2y = 5.$
   $2x - y = 8.$

2. $x - 2y = 8.$
   $5x + 4y = 12.$

3. $2x + 3y = 12.$
   $2x - y = 4.$

4. $3x + y = 6.$
   $x - 3y = -8.$

5. $3I - 2E = 10.$
   $I + 2E = 6.$

6. $4I - R = 6.$
   $2I + R = 9.$

7. $2f - 2F = 6.$
   $f - 4F = 9.$

8. $3a - 2b = -12.$
   $4a + 2b = -2.$

9. $4a + 3b = 10.$
   $2b - a = 3.$

10. $3x + 7y = 8.$
    $x + y = 0.$

15-8. Solution of Simultaneous Linear Equations by Addition and Subtraction. It has been shown in previous articles that an unlimited number of pairs of values of variables satisfy one linear equation. Also, it can be determined graphically whether there is one pair of values, or solution, that will satisfy two given linear equations. The solution of two simultaneous linear equations can also be found by algebraic methods, as illustrated in the following examples:

Example 1. Solve the equations $x + y = 6$ (1)

$x - y = 2$ (2)

Solution: Given $x + y = 6$ (1)

$x - y = 2$ (2)

Add (1) and (2), $2x = 8$ (3)

D:2 in (3), $x = 4$ (4)

Substitute this value of x in (1), $4 + y = 6$ (5)

Collecting terms, $y = 2$ (6)

The common solution for (1) and (2) is

$$x = 4, \qquad y = 2$$

Check.   Substitute in (1), $4 + 2 = 6$

Substitute in (2), $4 - 2 = 2$

In the above example the coefficients of y in Eqs. (1) and (2) are the same except for signs. This being the case, y may be *eliminated* by adding these equations, which sum results in an equation in one unknown. This method of solution is called *elimination by addition.*

Because the coefficients of x are the same in Eqs. (1) and (2), x could have been eliminated by subtracting either equation from the other, an equation containing only y as a variable being the result. This method of solution is called *elimination by subtraction*. The remaining variable x would have been solved for in the usual manner by substituting the value of y in either equation.

Example 2.   Solve the equations

	$3x - 4y = 13$	(1)
	$5x + 6y = 9$	(2)
Solution: Given	$3x - 4y = 13$	(1)
	$5x + 6y = 9$	(2)
M:3 in (1),	$9x - 12y = 39$	(3)
M:2 in (2),	$10x + 12y = 18$	(4)
Add (3) and (4),	$19x = 57$	(5)
D:19 in (5),	$x = 3$	(6)
Substitute this value of x in (1),	$9 - 4y = 13$	(7)
Collecting terms,	$-4y = 4$	(8)
D: -4 in (8),	$y = -1$	

The common solution for (1) and (2) is

$$x = 3, \quad y = -1$$

Check.   Substitute in (1), $9 + 4 = 13$
        Substitute in (2) $15 - 6 = 9$

In the above example the coefficients of x and y in Eqs. (1) and (2) are not the same. The coefficients of y were made the same absolute value in Eqs. (3) and (4) in order to eliminate y by the method of addition.

Example 3.   Solve the equations

	$4a - 3b = 27$	(1)
	$7a - 2b = 31$	(2)
Solution: Given	$4a - 3b = 27$	(1)
	$7a - 2b = 31$	(2)
M:7 in (1),	$28a - 21b = 189$	(3)
M:4 in (2),	$28a - 8b = 124$	(4)
Subtract (4) from (3),	$-13b = 65$	(5)
D: -13 in (5),	$b = -5$	(6)
Substitute this value of b in (1),	$4a + 15 = 27$	(7)
Collecting terms,	$4a = 12$	(8)
D:4 in (8),	$a = 3$	(9)

The common solution for (1) and (2) is

$$a = 3, \quad b = -5$$

Check.   Substitute the values of the variables in (1) and (2) as usual.

In the above example the coefficients of a and b in Eqs. (1) and (2) are not the same. The coefficients of a were made the same absolute value in Eqs. (3) and (4) in order to eliminate a by the method of subtraction.

Rule : *To solve two simultaneous linear equations having two variables by the method of elimination by addition or subtraction,*

1. *If necessary, multiply each equation by a number that will make the coefficients of one of the variables of equal absolute value.*

2. *If these coefficients of equal absolute value have like signs, subtract one equation from the other; if they have unlike signs, add the equations.*

3. *Solve the resulting equation.*

4. *Substitute the value of the variable found in step 3 in one of the original equations, and then solve this resulting equation for the remaining variable.*

5. *Check the solution by substituting in both the original equations.*

PROBLEMS 15-6

Solve for the unknowns by addition or subtraction:

1. $3x + 2y = 8.$
$5x + y = 11.$

2. $5x + y = 7.$
$4x + 3y = -1.$

3. $5x + 4y = 22.$
$3x + y = 9.$

4. $3x - 4y = -17.$
$5x + 3y = - 9.$

5. $a + 3b = - 3.$
$3a - 4b = 17.$

6. $3R - r = 3.$
$5R + 2r = 16.$

7. $15E + 12e = 75.$
$5E - 3e = 0.$

8. $9\alpha - 8\beta = 0.$
$4\alpha - 3\beta = 5.$

9. $5I - 3i = 70.$
$6I + 8i = 26.$

10. $3E - 3R = 10.$
$12E + 5R = 6.$

11. $0.2x + 0.3y = 0.8.$
$0.4x - 0.1y = 0.2.$

12. $0.2a - 2.4b = 0.$
$0.3a - 2b = 1.6.$

13. $0.5r + 0.3s = -1.9.$
$0.3r + 0.2s = -0.9.$

14. $0.9k - 0.6p = 1.6.$
$0.3k + 0.3p = 0.7.$

15. $0.9s - 0.4t = 1.6.$
$0.7s - 0.6t = -0.2.$

16. $0.9P + 0.04R = 9.4.$
$0.05P - 0.3R = -2.5.$

17. $0.02M + 0.3k = 1.3.$
$0.3 M + 0.04k = 1.66$

18. $9p - 2q = 2.$
$15p - 4q = 3.$

19. $9e = 13 - 2i.$
$7e - 6i - 63 = 0.$

20. $15r = 14R - 15.$
$6R = 5 + 10r.$

15-9. Solution by Substitution. Another common method of solution is called *elimination by substitution.*

Example. Solve the equations

$$16x - 3y = 10 \qquad (1)$$
$$8x + 5y = 18 \qquad (2)$$

Solution: Given

$$16x - 3y = 10 \qquad (1)$$
$$8x + 5y = 18 \qquad (2)$$

Solve (1) for x in terms of y,

$$x = \frac{10 + 3y}{16} \qquad (3)$$

Substitute this value of x in (2),

$$8\left(\frac{10 + 3y}{16}\right) + 5y = 18 \qquad (4)$$

$\mathbf{M}:16$ in (4),

$$8(10 + 3y) + 80y = 288 \qquad (5)$$

Expanding (5),

$$80 + 24y + 80y = 288 \qquad (6)$$

Collecting terms in (6),

$$104y = 208 \qquad (7)$$

$\mathbf{D}:104$ in (7),

$$y = 2 \qquad (8)$$

Substitute the value of y in (1),

$$16x - 6 = 10 \qquad (9)$$

Collecting terms in (9),

$$16x = 16 \qquad (10)$$

$\mathbf{D}:16$ in (10),

$$x = 1 \qquad (11)$$

Check the solution by the usual method.

Not only is the method of substitution a very useful one, but also it serves to emphasize the fact that the values of the variables are the same in both equations.

The method of solving by substitution may be stated as follows:

Rule: *To solve by substitution,*

1. *Solve one of the equations for one of the variables in terms of the other variable.*

2. *Substitute the resultant value of the variable, found in step 1, in the remaining equation.*

3. *Solve the equation obtained in step 2 for the second variable.*

4. *In the simplest of the original equations, substitute the value of the variable found in step 3 and solve the resulting equation for the remaining unknown variable.*

PROBLEMS 15-7

Solve by the method of substitution:

1. $x - y = 2.$
    $x + y = 8.$

2. $a - 4b = -2.$
    $a + 4b = 14.$

3. $2r + 5s = 21.$
    $6r - s = 15.$

4. $4E - 3e = 9.$
    $2E + 6e = 7.$

5. $\alpha + \beta = 45.$
    $\alpha = 8\beta.$

6. $6\theta + 5\phi = -14.$
    $9\theta + 2\phi = 34.$

7. $3E - 2R = 9.$
    $4E - 3R = 11.$

8. $4I + 3i = 20.$
    $2I - i = 5.$

9. $4s - t = 32.$
    $s + 2t = 26.$

10. $7Z_1 - 6Z_2 = -2.$
    $9Z_1 - 4Z_2 = 16.$

11. $R_1 + 4R_2 = 52.$
$3R_1 - 2R_2 = 16.$

12. $3E + 4e = 14.$
$8e - E = 0.$

13. $3I - 2r = 68.$
$2I - 5r = 82.$

14. $3e_1 + 8e_2 = 44.$
$3e_2 - 8e_1 = -20.$

15. $5r_1 + 4r_2 = -23.$
$7r_2 + 3r_1 = -23.$

16. $5\alpha - 2\beta = 15.$
$3\alpha + 7\beta = 50.$

17. $7E + 3E_1 = 15.$
$5E_1 + 3E = -1.$

18. $0.05x + 0.03y = 186.$
$0.06x + 0.02y = 204.$

19. $0.06a - 0.04b = 90.$
$b + a = 4 \times 10^3.$

20. $0.03R_1 + 0.02R_2 = 0.54.$
$R_2 + R_1 = 21.$

15-10. Solution by Comparison. In this method, we solve for the value of the same variable in each equation in terms of the other variable and place these values equal to each other. This forms an equation having only one unknown.

Example. Solve the equations

$$x - 4y = 14 \tag{1}$$
$$4x + y = 5 \tag{2}$$

Solution: Given

$$x - 4y = 14 \tag{1}$$
$$4x + y = 5 \tag{2}$$

Solve (1) for x in terms of y.

$$x = 14 + 4y \tag{3}$$

Solve (2) for x in terms of y.

$$x = \frac{5 - y}{4} \tag{4}$$

Equating the values of x in (3) and (4),

$$14 + 4y = \frac{5 - y}{4} \tag{5}$$

M:4 in (5),

$$56 + 16y = 5 - y \tag{6}$$

Collecting terms in (6),

$$17y = -51 \tag{7}$$

D:17 in (7),

$$y = -3$$

Substitute the value of y in (1),

$$x + 12 = 14$$

Collecting terms,

$$x = 2$$

Check the solution by the usual method.

PROBLEMS 15-8

Solve by the comparison method:

1. $2x + y = 14.$
$4x - 3y = 8.$

2. $3a - b = 8.$
$7a + b = 42.$

3. $7R + 3r = 20.$
$5R + 9r = 28.$

4. $4E - 5I = 47.$
$5E - 2I = 1.$

5. $15\alpha + 12\beta = 39.$
$5\alpha - 3\beta = 34.$

6. $3Z - 2Z_1 = -20.$
$5Z_1 + 2Z = 69.$

7. $I + 5i = 39.$
$6i - 2I = 34.$

8. $e_1 + 4e_2 - 1 = 0.$
$2e_1 - 2e_2 - 1 = 0.$

9. $0 = 25 - 3R_1 - R_t.$
$0 = R_t + 4R_1 - 31.$

10. $0 = E + 3E_1.$
$0 = 7 - 5E + 8E_1.$

15-11. Fractional Form. Simultaneous linear equations having fractions with numerical denominators are readily solved by first clearing the fractions from the equations and then solving by any method the student considers most convenient.

Example. Solve the equations

$$\frac{x}{4} + \frac{y}{3} = \frac{7}{12} \tag{1}$$

$$\frac{x}{2} - \frac{y}{4} = \frac{1}{4} \tag{2}$$

Solution: Given

$$\frac{x}{4} + \frac{y}{3} = \frac{7}{12} \tag{1}$$

$$\frac{x}{2} - \frac{y}{4} = \frac{1}{4} \tag{2}$$

M: 12, the L.C.D., in (1), $3x + 4y = 7$ $\qquad$ (3)
M: 4, the L.C.D., in (2), $2x - y = 1$ $\qquad$ (4)

This results in equations containing no fractions. Inspection of these show that solution by addition is most convenient. The solution is

$$x = 1, \quad y = 1$$

PROBLEMS 15-9

Solve the following equations:

1. $\dfrac{x}{2} - \dfrac{y}{10} = 3.$

$\quad \dfrac{x}{4} + \dfrac{y}{5} = 4.$

2. $\dfrac{a}{6} + \dfrac{b}{4} = 2.$

$\quad \dfrac{a}{3} - \dfrac{b}{2} = 0.$

3. $\dfrac{5x}{3} - \dfrac{3y}{2} = -2.$

$\quad \dfrac{x}{2} - \dfrac{y}{4} = 1.$

4. $\frac{1}{2}a + \frac{1}{5}b = \frac{11}{10}.$

$\quad \frac{1}{5}a + \frac{1}{3}b = \frac{2}{5}.$

5. $\dfrac{R}{2} - \dfrac{5r}{7} = \dfrac{19}{14}.$

$\quad \dfrac{3R}{8} + r = \dfrac{1}{4}.$

6. $\dfrac{E}{4} + \dfrac{e}{5} - 1 = 0.$

$\quad \dfrac{2E}{9} - \dfrac{e}{9} + 2 = 0.$

7. $Z - \dfrac{Z_1}{2} = \dfrac{1}{2}.$

$\quad 0.4Z + 0.9Z_1 = 5.7.$

8. $\dfrac{a - 2}{5} - \dfrac{b - 10}{4} = \dfrac{10 - a}{3}.$

$\quad \dfrac{a + b - 9}{2} + \dfrac{a - b + 6}{3} = 0.$

9. $\dfrac{I + i}{2} - 8 = \dfrac{I - i}{3}.$

$\quad \dfrac{7I + 1}{3} - \dfrac{11i - 4}{7} = 4.$

10. $\dfrac{E + 2}{6} - \dfrac{2E_1 + E}{32} - \dfrac{E_1 + 13}{16} = 0.$

$\quad \dfrac{E_1 - 2}{5} - \dfrac{10 - E_1}{3} - \dfrac{E - 10}{4} = 0.$

15-12. Fractional Equations. Where variables occur in denominators, it is sometimes easier to solve without clearing the equations of fractions.

Example. Solve the equations

$$\frac{5}{x} - \frac{6}{y} = -\frac{1}{2} \tag{1}$$

$$\frac{2}{x} - \frac{3}{y} = -1 \tag{2}$$

Solution: Given

$$\frac{5}{x} - \frac{6}{y} = -\frac{1}{2} \tag{1}$$

$$\frac{2}{x} - \frac{3}{y} = -1 \tag{2}$$

M : 2 in (1),

$$\frac{10}{x} - \frac{12}{y} = -1 \tag{3}$$

M : 5 in (2),

$$\frac{10}{x} - \frac{15}{y} = -5 \tag{4}$$

Subtract (4) from (3),

$$\frac{3}{y} = 4 \tag{5}$$

$$y = \tfrac{3}{4} \tag{6}$$

Substitute $\tfrac{3}{4}$ for y in (2).

$$\frac{2}{x} - 4 = -1 \tag{7}$$

Collecting terms,

$$\frac{2}{x} = 3 \tag{8}$$

$$\therefore x = \tfrac{2}{3}$$

Check by the usual method.

PROBLEMS 15-10

Solve the following equations:

1. $\dfrac{1}{x} - \dfrac{1}{y} = \dfrac{1}{6}.$

$\dfrac{1}{x} + \dfrac{1}{y} = \dfrac{5}{6}.$

2. $\dfrac{3}{a} + \dfrac{2}{b} = \dfrac{19}{15}.$

$\dfrac{1}{a} + \dfrac{1}{b} = \dfrac{4}{15}.$

3. $\dfrac{2}{e} - 3e_1 = 0.$

$\dfrac{5}{e} - 5 = 0.$

4. $\dfrac{5}{2r - 5} - \dfrac{7}{2R - 39} = 0.$

$\dfrac{4}{R - 1} - \dfrac{3}{1 - r} = 0.$

5. $\dfrac{e + i - 5}{e - i + 1} - 3 = 0.$

$\dfrac{e - 3}{i + 1} - \dfrac{e - 6}{i - 2} = 0.$

6. $\dfrac{a}{4} - \dfrac{a - 2b}{6} = \dfrac{1}{6}.$

$\dfrac{a + 3b}{b - a} - \dfrac{1}{3} = 0.$

7. $\dfrac{2e}{5} - (e_1 - 1) - 1 = 0.$

$\dfrac{e - e_1}{3} = e - (e_1 + 2).$

8. $\dfrac{3r - 2r_1}{3} = \dfrac{r_1}{5} - 2.$

$\dfrac{r}{6} + \dfrac{r_1}{4} = \dfrac{3}{4}.$

9. $\dfrac{1 - 0.1I_1 + 2.5I}{I + I_1 - 10} - \dfrac{5}{2} = 0.$

$\dfrac{0.5}{0.4I - 1.1} - \dfrac{4}{1.1I_1 - 7} = 0.$

10. $\dfrac{E + E_1 - 2}{E - E_1} + \dfrac{1}{3} = 0.$

$\dfrac{3E + E_1 - 3}{2E_1 - E} + \dfrac{1}{11} = 0.$

15-13. Literal Equations in Two Unknowns.

The solution of literal simultaneous equations involves no new methods of solution.   In general, it will be found that the addition or subtraction method will suffice for most cases.

Example 1.   Solve the equations

$$ax + by = c \tag{1}$$
$$mx + ny = d \tag{2}$$

Solution: Given

$$ax + by = c \tag{1}$$
$$mx + ny = d \tag{2}$$

First eliminate x.

M:m in (1), $amx + bmy = cm$ (3)

M:a in (2), $amx + any = ad$ (4)

Subtract (4) from (3). $bmy - any = cm - ad$ (5)

Factoring (5), $y(bm - an) = cm - ad$ (6)

D:$(bm - an)$ in (6), $$y = \frac{cm - ad}{bm - an}$$

Now go back to (1) and (2), and eliminate y.

M:n in (1), $anx + bny = cn$ (7)

M:b in (2), $bmx + bny = bd$ (8)

Subtract (8) from (7). $anx - bmx = cn - bd$ (9)

Factoring (9), $x(an - bm) = cn - bd$ (10)

D:$(an - bm)$ in (10), $$x = \frac{cn - bd}{an - bm} = \frac{bd - cn}{bm - an}$$

Example 2.   Solve the equations

$$\frac{a}{x} + \frac{b}{y} = \frac{1}{xy} \tag{1}$$
$$\frac{c}{x} + \frac{d}{y} = \frac{1}{xy} \tag{2}$$

Solution: Given

$$\frac{a}{x} + \frac{b}{y} = \frac{1}{xy} \tag{1}$$
$$\frac{c}{x} + \frac{d}{y} = \frac{1}{xy} \tag{2}$$

First eliminate y, although it makes no difference which variable is eliminated first.

M:xy, the L.C.D., in (1), $ay + bx = 1$ (3)

M:xy, the L.C.D., in (2), $cy + dx = 1$ (4)

M:c in (3), $acy + bcx = c$ (5)

M:a in (4), $acy + adx = a$ (6)

Subtract (6) from (5). $bcx - adx = c - a$ (7)

Factoring (7), $x(bc - ad) = c - a$ (8)

D:$(bc - ad)$ in (8), $$x = \frac{c - a}{bc - ad}$$

Now go back to (1) and (2) to eliminate x, and find

$$y = \frac{b - d}{bc - ad}$$

PROBLEMS 15-11

Solve for x and y:

1. $x + y = b.$
  $x - y = 5B.$

2. $2x - y = a.$
  $x + 3y = a.$

3. $cx - dy = -2cd.$
  $x + y = c - d.$

4. $ry + Rx = R.$
  $rx + Ry = r.$

5. $\dfrac{5a}{x} + \dfrac{7b}{y} = 12.$
  $\dfrac{2a}{x} + \dfrac{3b}{y} = 5.$

6. $\dfrac{5r}{y} = rs - \dfrac{3s}{x}.$
  $0 = rs - \dfrac{3r}{x} - \dfrac{5s}{y}.$

7. $\dfrac{x + y}{m} - m - n = 0.$
  $\dfrac{x}{n} + \dfrac{y}{m} = mn.$

8. $ax + by = a + b.$
  $ax - by = a - b.$

Solve for E and e:

9. $EI = r + e.$
  $Ei + Ie = R.$

10. $E + e = e_1.$
  $IE - ie = e_2.$

11. $EI - ei = 0.$
  $E - I - i - e = 0.$

12. $I_2E + I_1e = I_2r + I_1R.$
  $I_1E + I_2e = I_1r + I_2R.$

15-14. Equations Containing Three Unknowns. In the preceding examples and problems, two equations were necessary to solve for two unknown variables. For problems involving three variables, three equations are necessary. The same methods of solution apply.

Example. Solve the equations

$$2x + 3y + 5z = 0 \tag{1}$$
$$6x - 2y - 3z = 3 \tag{2}$$
$$8x - 5y - 6z = 1 \tag{3}$$

Solution: Choose a variable to be eliminated. Let it be x.

M:3 in (1),
$$6x + 9y + 15z = 0 \tag{4}$$
$$6x - 2y - 3z = 3 \tag{2}$$

Subtract (2) from (4).
$$11y + 18z = -3 \tag{5}$$

M:4 in (1),
$$8x + 12y + 20z = 0 \tag{6}$$
$$8x - 5y - 6z = 1 \tag{3}$$

Subtract (3) from (6).
$$17y + 26z = -1 \tag{7}$$

This gives Eqs. (5) and (7) in two variables y and z. Solving them, we obtain $y = 3$, $z = -2$.

Substitute these values into (1).
$$2x + 9 - 10 = 0 \tag{8}$$

Collecting terms,
$$2x = 1 \tag{9}$$

D:2 in (9),
$$x = \tfrac{1}{2}$$

Check by substituting the values of the variables in the equations.

PROBLEMS 15-12

Solve:

1. $a + b - c = 0.$
$a + b + c = 6.$
$a - b + c = 2.$

2. $x - y + 2z = -11.$
$2x - y + z = -9.$
$x - 2y + z = 0.$

3. $3x + 6y - 2z = 9.$
$10x - 4y + z = 5.$
$4x - y + 3z = 11.$

4. $6E - 5E_1 - 3E_2 = 8.$
$-E + 2E_1 + 3E_2 = 12.$
$E - E_1 + 4E_2 = 14.$

5. $2R - 5r + 2r_1 = 25.$
$R + r - r_1 = 14.$
$3R + 2r - 5r_1 = 3.$

6. $I - 3i + 2\alpha = 1.$
$3I + i + \alpha = 33.$
$2I + 2i - 5\alpha = 6.$

7. $\dfrac{1}{a} - \dfrac{1}{b} - \dfrac{1}{c} = \dfrac{-5}{3}.$
$\dfrac{1}{b} - \dfrac{1}{c} - \dfrac{1}{a} = \dfrac{25}{3}.$
$\dfrac{1}{a} + \dfrac{1}{b} + \dfrac{1}{c} = \dfrac{1}{3}.$

8. $\dfrac{2}{b} + \dfrac{3}{c} = 1.$
$\dfrac{.5}{a} + \dfrac{9}{c} = 4.$
$\dfrac{8}{a} + \dfrac{4}{b} = 5.$

9. $2R_1 - R_2 + R_3 = \alpha.$
$R_1 - 2R_2 + R_3 = \beta.$
$R_1 + R_2 + 2R_3 = \gamma.$

10. $\dfrac{1}{R_2} - \dfrac{1}{R_3} - \dfrac{1}{R_1} = \beta.$
$\dfrac{1}{R_1} - \dfrac{1}{R_2} - \dfrac{1}{R_3} = \alpha.$
$\dfrac{1}{R_3} - \dfrac{1}{R_1} - \dfrac{1}{R_2} = \gamma.$

15-15. In working a problem involving more than one unknown, it is convenient to solve it by setting up a system of simultaneous equations according to the statements of the problem.

Example 1. When a certain number is increased by one third of another number, the result is 23. When the second number is increased by one half of the first number, the result is 29. What are the numbers?
Solution: Let x = first number,
y = second number.

Then $\qquad\qquad\qquad x + \frac{1}{3}y = 23 \qquad\qquad\qquad (1)$
Also, $\qquad\qquad\qquad y + \frac{1}{2}x = 29 \qquad\qquad\qquad (2)$

Solving the equations, we obtain $x = 16$, $y = 21$.
Check. When 16, the first number, is increased by $\frac{1}{3}$ of 21, we have

$$16 + 7 = 23.$$

When 21, the second number, is increased by $\frac{1}{2}$ of 16, we have

$$21 + 8 = 29.$$

Example 2. Two airplanes start from Omaha at the same time. The plane traveling west has a speed of 80 miles per hour faster than the one traveling east. At the end of 4 hours they are 1600 miles apart. What is the speed of each plane?

> *Solution:* Let x = rate of plane flying west,
> y = rate of plane flying east.

Then $\qquad\qquad x - y = 80$ (1)

Since $\qquad$ Rate $\times$ time = distance

then $\qquad\qquad 4x$ = distance traveled by plane flying west

and $\qquad\qquad 4y$ = distance traveled by plane flying east

Hence, $\qquad 4x + 4y = 1600$ (2)

Solving Eqs. (1) and (2), we obtain

$$x = 240 \text{ m.p.h.}$$
$$y = 160 \text{ m.p.h.}$$

Check the solution by substituting these values into the statements of the example.

Example 3.   Given $P = EI$ and $P = I^2R$. Solve for E in terms of I and R.

Solution: It is evident that P must be eliminated. Because both equations are equal to P, we can equate them (Axiom 5, page 45) and obtain

$$EI = I^2R$$
D: I, $\qquad\qquad\qquad E = IR$

Example 4.   Given $\qquad E = 0.707E_m$ (1)

and $\qquad\qquad\qquad E_{av} = 0.637E_m$ (2)

Show that $\qquad\qquad E = 1.11E_{av}$ (3)

Solution: Because E_m does not appear in Eq. (3), it must be eliminated.

Solving Eq. (1) for E_m, $\qquad E_m = \dfrac{E}{0.707}$ (4)

Solving Eq. (2) for E_m, $\qquad E_m = \dfrac{E_{av}}{0.637}$ (5)

Equating Eqs. (4) and (5), $\qquad \dfrac{E}{0.707} = \dfrac{E_{av}}{0.637}$ (6)

Solving Eq. (6) for E, $\qquad E = 1.11E_{av}$

Example 5.   Given $C = \dfrac{Q}{E}$, $C_a = \dfrac{Q}{E_a}$, and $C_b = \dfrac{Q}{E_b}$. The total voltage across condensers C_a and C_b in series is $E = E_a + E_b$. Find C in terms of C_a and C_b.

Solution: Solve for E, E_a, and E_b. Thus, $E = \dfrac{Q}{C}$, $E_a = \dfrac{Q}{C_a}$, and $E_b = \dfrac{Q}{C_b}$.

Then, since $\qquad\qquad E = E_a + E_b$

by substitution, $\qquad\qquad \dfrac{Q}{C} = \dfrac{Q}{C_a} + \dfrac{Q}{C_b}$

D:Q, $$\frac{1}{C} = \frac{1}{C_a} + \frac{1}{C_b}$$

M:CC_aC_b, the L.C.D., $C_aC_b = CC_b + CC_a$

Transposing, $CC_a + CC_b = C_aC_b$

Factoring, $C(C_a + C_b) = C_aC_b$

D:$(C_a + C_b)$, $$C = \frac{C_aC_b}{C_a + C_b}$$

This is the formula for the resultant capacity C of two condensers C_a and C_b in series.

PROBLEMS 15-13

1. Divide 75 into two parts such that $\frac{2}{3}$ of the larger shall be greater by 18 than $\frac{3}{4}$ of the smaller.

2. The sum of two numbers is a, and their difference is b. Find the numbers.

3. If 5 is added to both terms of a fraction, its value becomes $\frac{2}{3}$; and if 1 is subtracted from both terms of the fraction, its value becomes $\frac{1}{3}$. Find the fraction.

4. In a right triangle the acute angles are complementary. (Two angles whose sum is one right angle, or 90°, are said to be complementary angles.) Find the angles, if their difference is 35°.

5. The difference between the two acute angles of a right triangle is $n°$. Find the angles.

6. The sum of the three angles of any triangle is 180°. Find the three angles of a triangle if the sum of the first and second is 30° more than the third and the sum of the first and third is 50° more than the second.

7. A takes 5 hr longer than B to walk 36 miles; but if he doubles his pace, he takes 1 hr less than B. Find their rates of walking.

8. In 13 hr, B walks 7 miles more than A does in 9 hr; in 8 hr, A walks 12 miles more than B does in 7 hr. Find their rates of walking.

9. Given $fs = \dfrac{mv^2}{2}$ and $v = \dfrac{s}{t}$. Solve for t in terms of m, v, and f.

10. Given $s = \frac{1}{2}gt^2$ and $v = gt$. Solve for v in terms of s and t.

11. Given $h = \dfrac{s}{2}\sqrt{3}$ and $A = \frac{1}{2}sh$. Solve for A in terms of s.

12. Given $I = \dfrac{CE}{t}$ amperes and $Q = It$ coulombs. Solve for Q in terms of C and E.

13. Given $W = \dfrac{QV}{2}$ and $C = \dfrac{Q}{V}$. Solve for W in terms of C and Q.

14. Given $I_a = \dfrac{E}{R + R_a}$ and $I = \dfrac{E}{R}$. Solve for R in terms of R_a, I, and I_a.

15. $I = \dfrac{E}{R}$ and $P = I^2R$. $P = 2.42$ kw, and $E = 110$ v. Find the current I and the resistance R.

16. $H = 0.24I^2Rt$ calories, $P = EI$, and $I = \dfrac{E}{R}$. Solve for H in terms of P and t.

17. Find the voltage E necessary to produce $H = 480$ calories in a time $t = 10$ sec, when the heater resistance $R = 200\ \Omega$.

18. Given
$$aR_1 + bR_2 = c$$
and
$$dR_1 + fR_2 = g$$
Solve for R_1 and R_2.

19. Given
$$I_aR_a = I_bR_b$$
and
$$I_aR_c = I_bR_x$$
Solve for R_x in terms of R_a, R_b, and R_c.

20. Given $I = \dfrac{CE}{t}$ amperes and $Q = It$ coulombs. How many coulombs of electricity will a capacity C of 4 μf hold when the applied voltage
$$E = 2000\text{ v?}$$

21. Given $I_aR_a = I_bR_b$, $\quad \dfrac{Q_a}{C_a} = \dfrac{Q_b}{C_b}, \quad I_a = \dfrac{Q_a}{t}, \quad$ and $\quad I_b = \dfrac{Q_b}{t}$

Prove
$$\frac{R_a}{R_b} = \frac{C_b}{C_a}$$

22. Given $I_p = \dfrac{\mu E_g}{R_p + R}$ and $E_p = I_pR$.

Solve for E_p by eliminating I_p.

23. Given
$$E = I_x(R_x + R)$$
$$E = I_a(R_a + R)$$
and
$$E = IR$$

Prove
$$R_x = R_a \cdot \frac{\dfrac{I - I_x}{I_x}}{\dfrac{I - I_a}{I_a}}$$

24. Given
$$I = \frac{E}{\sqrt{R^2 + \left(\omega L - \dfrac{1}{\omega C}\right)^2}}$$

At resonance, $I_r = \dfrac{E}{R}$ and $\omega L = \dfrac{1}{\omega C_r}$

Prove
$$\frac{\omega L}{R} = \frac{\sqrt{\dfrac{I_r^2 - I^2}{I^2}}}{\dfrac{C_r - C}{C}}$$

25. Given three star-delta transformation equations
$$R_a = \frac{R_1R_3}{R_1 + R_2 + R_3}, \qquad R_b = \frac{R_1R_2}{R_1 + R_2 + R_3},$$
$$\text{and} \qquad R_c = \frac{R_2R_3}{R_1 + R_2 + R_3}$$

Solve for R_1, R_2, and R_3 in terms of R_a, R_b, and R_c.

CHAPTER XVI

GENERATOR, MOTOR, AND BATTERY CIRCUITS

In order to avoid confusion in our previous discussions of electric circuits, all sources of electromotive force have been considered as sources of constant potential, and nothing has been said regarding their internal resistances. However, electrical appliances which produce electrical energy, as well as those which consume energy, have a certain amount of internal resistance which materially affects their operation. The application of Ohm's law to a few of the fundamental cases is dealt with in this chapter.

16-1. Electromotive Force of a Generator. A *generator* is a machine that converts mechanical energy into electrical energy. Essentially, it consists of a large number of conductors, which are carried on an armature, rotating in a magnetic field. *The electromotive force of a generator*, which is induced in the rotating conductors, is the total voltage developed by the generator armature. However, this total voltage is not all available for doing useful work in a circuit external to the generator, for some of it is used in overcoming the resistance of the armature. The voltage actually supplied to the external circuit is known as the terminal voltage; that is,

Terminal voltage = e.m.f. − internal voltage drop

16-2. Types of Generator. Generators are divided into three types: *series*, *shunt*, and *compound*.

A *series* generator is one in which the armature, field, and load are in series as illustrated in Fig. 16-1. The field consists of a few turns of heavy wire and must be capable of carrying the load current. The voltage of a series generator is usually controlled by a rheostat connected across the field.

A *shunt* generator consists of a field, wound with a large number of turns of small wire, connected in shunt (parallel) with the armature as illustrated in Fig. 16-2. The voltage of a shunt generator is usually controlled by a rheostat connected in series with the field.

A *compound* generator has both a series field and a shunt field. Two methods of field connections are used in compound gener-

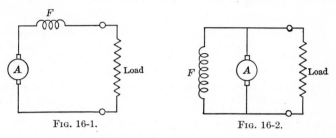

FIG. 16-1.   FIG. 16-2.

ators. Figure 16-3 represents a *short-shunt* generator, and Fig. 16-4 represents a *long-shunt* generator.

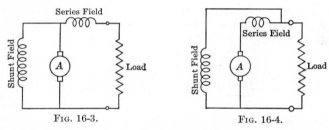

FIG. 16-3.   FIG. 16-4.

Example 1. A series generator is delivering 85 amperes to a load. The armature resistance is 0.06 ohm, and the field resistance is 0.04 ohm. A voltmeter connected across the generator terminals reads 230 volts.

(a) What is the e.m.f. of the generator?

(b) How much power is expended in the generator?

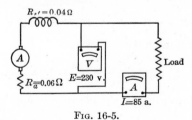

FIG. 16-5.

Solution: Figure 16-5 is a diagram of the circuit. The armature resistance is denoted by R_a.

The voltage drop across the series field is

$$E_f = IR_{sf} = 85 \times 0.04 = 3.4 \text{ v}$$

The voltage drop due to the resistance of the armature is

$$E_a = IR_a = 85 \times 0.06 = 5.1 \text{ v}$$

Since the electromotive force of the generator is the total voltage developed,

$$E.m.f. = 230 + 3.4 + 5.1 = 238.5 \text{ v}$$

Power expended in series field $= I^2 R_{sf} = 85^2 \times 0.04 = 289$ w
Power expended in armature $= I^2 R_a = 85^2 \times 0.06 = 433.5$ w
Total power expended in the generator $= \overline{722.5}$ w

Example 2. A short-shunt compound generator is delivering 60 amperes to a load. The armature resistance is 0.08 ohm, the resistance of the series field is 0.05 ohm, and the resistance of the shunt field is 118 ohms. A volt-meter connected across the generator terminals reads 115 volts.

(a) What is the shunt-field current?
(b) What is the electromotive force of the generator?
(c) How much power is expended in the generator?

Solution: Figure 16-6 is a diagram of the circuit.

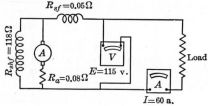

FIG. 16-6.

The voltage drop across the series field is

$$E_{sf} = IR_{sf} = 60 \times 0.05 = 3.0 \text{ v}$$

The same voltage exists across the armature and shunt field and is equal to the voltage across the generator terminals plus the voltage drop across the series field, or

$$E_{shf} = E + E_{sf} = 115 + 3 = 118 \text{ v}$$

Then the current through the shunt field is

$$I_{shf} = \frac{E_{shf}}{R_{shf}} = \frac{118}{118} = 1.0 \text{ a}$$

Since the armature must supply the current for the shunt field, the armature current is

$$I_a = I + I_{shf} = 60 + 1 = 61 \text{ a}$$

Then the voltage drop across the armature resistance is

$$E_a = I_a R_a = 61 \times 0.08 = 4.88 \text{ v}$$

Since the electromotive force is the total voltage developed,

$$E.m.f. = E + E_{sf} + E_a = 115 + 3.0 + 4.88 = 122.88 \text{ v}$$

Power expended in shunt field $= I_{shf}^2 R_{shf} = 1.0^2 \times 118 = 118$ w
Power expended in series field $= I^2 R_{sf} = 60^2 \times 0.05 = 180$ w
Power expended in armature $= I_a^2 R_a = 61^2 \times 0.08 = 298$ w
Total power expended in generator $= \overline{596}$ w

Example 3. A 50-kilowatt long-shunt compound generator maintains a voltage of 220 volts across its output terminals. The armature resistance is 0.02 ohm, the shunt-field resistance is 200 ohms, and the series-field resistance is 0.04 ohm. At rated output,

(a) What is the electromotive force of the generator?
(b) How much power is lost in the machine?
(c) How much power does the generator develop?

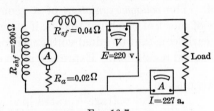

FIG. 16-7.

Solution: Figure 16-7 is a diagram of the circuit.

Load current, $\qquad I = \dfrac{P}{E} = \dfrac{50,000}{220} = 227$ a

Shunt-field current,
$$I_{shf} = \frac{E}{R_{shf}} = \frac{220}{200} = 1.1 \text{ a}$$
Armature current,
$$I_a = I + I_{shf} = 227 + 1.1 = 228.1 \text{ a}$$
Drop across series field,
$$E_{sf} = I_a R_{sf} = 228.1 \times 0.04 = 9.124 \text{ v}$$
Drop across armature resistance,
$$E_a = I_a R_a = 228.1 \times 0.02 = 4.562 \text{ v}$$
Generator electromotive force,
$$\text{E.m.f.} = E + E_{sf} + E_a$$
$$= 220 + 9.124 + 4.562 = 233.7 \text{ v}$$
Power lost in shunt field,
$$P_{shf} = I_{shf}^2 R_{shf} = 1.1^2 \times 200 = 242 \text{ w}$$
Power lost in series field,
$$P_{sf} = I_a^2 R_{sf} = 228^2 \times 0.04 = 2080 \text{ w}$$
Power lost in armature,
$$P_a = I_a^2 R_a = 228^2 \times 0.02 = 1040 \text{ w}$$
Total power lost in generator,
$$P_G = 242 + 2080 + 1040 = 3362 \text{ w}$$
Total power developed,
$$P_t = 50,000 + 3362 = 53,362 \text{ w}$$

As a check, the total power can be found by multiplying the electromotive force by the armature current.

In the foregoing examples, some of the significant figures have been carried beyond the customary three, for the purposes of illustration.

16-3. Voltage Regulation. From the preceding examples, it is apparent that the amount of current drawn by the load will affect the generator terminal voltage. Whether the terminal voltage is increased or decreased by an increase in load current depends upon the type of generator and the method employed for voltage control. The *voltage regulation* of a generator is often used as a figure of merit of machine; that is, if a generator is able to maintain a nearly constant terminal voltage within its capacity, it is said to have good regulation. Expressed as an equation,

Percentage of regulation

$$= \frac{\text{no-load voltage} - \text{rated-load voltage}}{\text{rated-load voltage}} \times 100$$

Example. A generator, while delivering full load, has a terminal voltage of 230 volts and a no-load terminal voltage of 240 volts. What is the percentage of regulation?

Solution: Regulation $= \dfrac{240 - 230}{230} = 4.35\%$

PROBLEMS 16-1

1. A series generator has an armature resistance of 0.04 Ω and a field resistance of 0.02 Ω. The load current is 100 a, and a voltmeter connected across the generator terminals reads 115 v.

(a) What is the e.m.f. of the generator?
(b) How much power is lost in the armature?

2. A series generator with an armature resistance of 0.03 Ω and a field resistance of 0.02 Ω is delivering 27.5 a to a load resistance of 8 Ω. If the total resistance of the feeder wires is 0.5 Ω, find

(a) E.m.f. of the generator.
(b) Total power developed by the generator.
(c) Voltage across generator terminals.

3. A shunt generator with a field resistance of 100 Ω and an armature resistance of 0.02 Ω is delivering 125 a to a load at a brush potential (terminal voltage) of 230 v.

(*a*) What is the e.m.f. of the generator?

(*b*) What is the total power developed by the generator?

4. A shunt generator with a field resistance of 80 Ω and an armature resistance of 0.05 Ω is delivering 75 a to a load resistance of 1.6 Ω. The feeders are 500 ft long and consist of No. 0 wire.

(*a*) What is the e.m.f. of the generator?

(*b*) What is the generator terminal voltage?

(*c*) What is the total power developed by the generator?

5. A compound short-shunt generator delivers its full load of 125 a. The armature resistance is 0.02 Ω, the shunt-field resistance is 125 Ω, and the series-field resistance is 0.015 Ω. A voltmeter connected across the generator terminals reads 120 v. Find the e.m.f. of the generator.

6. A compound long-shunt generator delivers 100 kw at a terminal voltage of 115 v. The armature resistance is 0.02 Ω, the shunt-field resistance is 80 Ω, and the series-field resistance is 0.012 Ω. What is the e.m.f. of the generator?

7. A compound short-shunt generator is connected to a load consisting of 200 lamps in parallel, each having a hot resistance of 240 Ω. The lamps require 110 v. The armature resistance is 0.03 Ω, the shunt-field resistance is 60 Ω, the series-field resistance is 0.025 Ω, and the feeders consist of 250 ft of No. 0 wire. Find

(*a*) E.m.f. of the generator.

(*b*) Power lost in feeders.

(*c*) Generator terminal voltage.

8. All other conditions remaining the same, what would be the e.m.f. of the generator of Prob. 7 if it were connected as a compound long-shunt generator?

9. At full load the terminal voltage of a generator is 115 v. When the load is disconnected, the terminal voltage is 120 v. What is the percentage regulation?

10. The no-load terminal voltage of a generator is 230 v. When the generator is delivering full load, the terminal voltage is 228 v. What is the percentage regulation?

16-4. Motors. A *motor* is a machine that converts electrical energy into mechanical energy. Direct-current motors, like generators, are classified with respect to their field and armature connections and are divided into the same three types, series, shunt, and compound. When connected to a suitable source of voltage, direct-current generators will run as motors; when driven by mechanical means, direct-current motors will function as generators.

Since the armature resistance of most motors is a small fraction of an ohm, it is evident that something other than the ohmic resistance of the armature limits the current when the motor is in operation. The conductors of a rotating motor armature cut the lines of force of the field in the same manner as the armature of a generator. This results in an electromotive force being induced in the motor armature that is of opposite polarity to the voltage applied to the motor. Hence, the motor electromotive force is known as the counter electromotive force of the motor. Then the net voltage acting on the armature of a shunt motor is equal to the difference between the applied voltage and the counter electromotive force. The counter electromotive force of a motor can be found by running it as a generator at rated speed and measuring the electromotive force developed with a voltmeter.

Example 1. The armature resistance of a shunt motor is 0.05 ohm, the armature current is 25 amperes, and the voltage is 230 volts. Find the counter electromotive force of the motor.

Solution: The voltage drop across the armature resistance is

$$E_a = I_a R_a = 25 \times 0.05 = 1.25 \text{ v}$$

Since   Counter e.m.f. = line voltage − drop across armature resistance
Counter e.m.f. = 230 − 1.25 = 228.75 v

Example 2. If full line voltage were applied to the motor of Example 1 at standstill, how much current would flow through the armature?

Solution: $$I_a = \frac{E}{R_a} = \frac{230}{0.05} = 4600 \text{ a}$$

(This illustrates the necessity of starting resistances.)

Example 3. A shunt motor is taking a total of 21.4 kilowatts from a 230-volt line. 454 watts are lost in the armature. If the resistance of the field is 100 ohms, find

(a) Line current.
(b) Field current.
(c) Armature resistance.
(d) Counter electromotive force of motor.

Solution: (a) Since $P = EI$

the line current is $$I_L = \frac{P_t}{E_L} = \frac{21,400}{230} = 93.0 \text{ a}$$

(b) The field current is $$I_f = \frac{E_L}{R_f} = \frac{230}{100} = 2.3 \text{ a}$$

(c) The armature current is $I_a = I_L - I_f$
$$= 93.0 - 2.3 = 90.7 \text{ a}$$

Since $P = I^2R$

the armature resistance is $R_a = \dfrac{P_a}{I_a{}^2} = \dfrac{454}{90.7^2} = 0.0552 \ \Omega$

(d) Counter e.m.f. $= E_L - I_a R_a$
$$= 230 - (90.7 \times 0.0552)$$
$$= 225 \text{ v}$$

PROBLEMS 16-2

1. A shunt motor with an armature resistance of 0.08 Ω is running across a 115-v line. If the armature current is 35 a, find the counter e.m.f. of the motor.

2. A 1-hp shunt motor is drawing 38 a from a 230-v line. The armature resistance is 0.05 Ω, and the shunt-field resistance is 120 Ω. Find the counter e.m.f. of the motor.

3. How much resistance must be connected in series with the armature of Prob. 2 to limit the total starting current to 57 a?

4. The counter e.m.f. of a shunt motor is 227 v. Two amperes flow through the shunt field which has a resistance of 115 Ω. If the armature resistance is 0.06 Ω, what is the armature current?

5. How much resistance must be connected in series with the armature of Prob. 4 to limit the total starting current to 75 a?

6. A shunt motor with a counter e.m.f. of 225 v takes 19.8 a from the line. A current of 1.84 a flows through the field which has a resistance of 125 Ω. What is the resistance of the armature?

7. How much resistance must be connected in series with the armature of Prob. 6 to limit the total starting current to 30 a?

8. A shunt motor is drawing 8.72 kw from the line. Three hundred and fifty-three watts are lost in the shunt field, which has a resistance of 150 Ω. The armature loss is 200 watts. Find

    (a) Field current.
    (b) Armature resistance.
    (c) Counter e.m.f. of motor.

9. A shunt motor is taking 5.25 kw from the line. Two hundred and ninety-four watts are lost in the shunt field which has a resistance of 180 Ω. The armature loss is 93 watts. Find

    (a) Field current.
    (b) Armature resistance.
    (c) Counter e.m.f. of motor.

10. A shunt motor, which is taking 7.5 kw from the line, has a field current of 1.31 a. The power loss in the armature is 129 w, and the field loss is 288 w. Find

(a) Resistance of field.
(b) Current taken by motor.
(c) Resistance of armature.

16-5. Batteries. A *battery* is a device for converting chemical energy into electrical energy. The word "battery" is taken to mean two or more *cells* connected to each other, although a single cell is often referred to as a battery.

Figure 16-8 represents a circuit by which the voltage existing across the cell can be read with the resistance connected across the

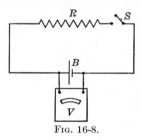

Fig. 16-8.

battery or with the resistance disconnected from the circuit.

The electromotive force of a cell is the total amount of voltage developed by the cell. For all practical purposes the electromotive force of a cell may be read with a high-resistance voltmeter connected across the cell when it is not supplying current to any other circuit, as is the case with the switch S open, in Fig. 16-8.

When a cell supplies current to an external circuit, as with the switch closed, in Fig. 16-8, it will be found that the voltmeter no longer reads the open-circuit voltage (electromotive force) of the cell. The reason for this is that part of the electromotive force is used in forcing current through the resistance of the cell, and the remainder is used in forcing current through the external circuit. Expressed as an equation,

$$E = E_t + Ir \tag{1}$$

where E is the electromotive force of the cell, or group of cells, and E_t is the voltage measured across the terminals while forcing a current I through the internal resistance r. Since I also flows through the external circuit of resistance R, Eq. (1) may be written

$$E = IR + Ir$$
or
$$E = I(R + r) \tag{2}$$

Example 1. A cell whose internal resistance is 0.15 ohm delivers 0.50 ampere to a resistance of 2.85 ohms. What is the electromotive force of the cell?

Solution: Given $r = 0.15$ ohm, $R = 2.85$ ohms, and $I = 0.50$ ampere.

From Eq. (2), $E = 0.50(2.85 + 0.15) = 1.5$ v

Example 2.   Figure 16-9 represents a cell with an electromotive force of 1.2 volts and an internal resistance r of 0.2 ohm connected to a resistance R of 5.8 ohms.   How much current flows in the circuit?

Solution: Solving Eq. (2) for the current,

$$I = \frac{E}{R + r} = \frac{1.2}{5.8 + 0.2} = 0.2 \text{ a}$$

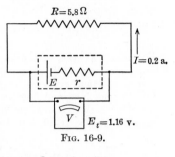

$R = 5.8\,\Omega$

$I = 0.2$ a.

$E_t = 1.16$ v.

Fig. 16-9.

Note the significance of the above equation.   It says that the current which flows in a circuit is proportional to the electromotive force of the circuit and inversely proportional to the total resistance of the circuit.   This is Ohm's law for the *complete circuit.*

Example 3.   A cell with an electromotive force of 1.6 volts delivers a current of 2 amperes to a circuit with a resistance of 0.62 ohm.   What is the internal resistance of the cell?

Solution: Solving Eq. (2) for the internal resistance,

$$r = \frac{E - IR}{I} = \frac{1.6 - (2 \times 0.62)}{2} = 0.18 \; \Omega$$

Note the significance of the above equation.   It says that a voltage equal to $E - IR$ is being used to send the current I through the internal resistance r.   Also, by rewriting the equation,

$$r = \frac{E}{I} - R$$

Now the electromotive force of the battery, denoted by E, is forcing the current I through the entire circuit.   That is,

$$\frac{E}{I} = R_t$$

Hence, $r = R_t - R$

or $R_t = R + r$

The latter equation simply states that the resistance of the entire circuit is equal to the resistance of the external circuit plus the internal resistance of the source of electromotive force.

16-6. Cells in Series.   If n identical cells are connected in series, the electromotive force of the combination will be n times the electromotive force of each cell.   Similarly, the total internal resistance of the circuit will be n times the internal resistance of each cell. By modifying Eq. (2), the expression for the current through an external resistance of R ohms is

$$I = \frac{nE}{R + nr} \tag{3}$$

Example. Six cells, each with an electromotive force of 2.1 volts and an internal resistance of 0.1 ohm, are connected in series; and a resistance of 3.6 ohms is connected across the combination.

(a) How much current flows in the circuit?

(b) What is the terminal voltage of the group?

Solution: Figure 16-10 is a diagram of the circuit. The resistance nr represents the total internal resistance of all cells in series.

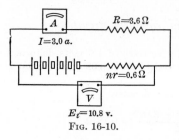

$R = 3.6\ \Omega$

$I = 3.0\ a.$

$nr = 0.6\ \Omega$

$E_t = 10.8$ v.

Fig. 16-10.

(a) $I = \dfrac{nE}{R + nr} =$

$$\frac{6 \times 2.1}{3.6 + (6 \times 0.1)} = 3.0\ \text{a}$$

(b) The terminal voltage of the group is equal to the total electromotive force minus the voltage drop across the internal resistance. From Eq. (1),

$$E_t = nE - Inr = (6 \times 2.1) - (3 \times 6 \times 0.1)$$
$$= 10.8\ \text{v}$$

Since the terminal voltage exists across the external circuit, a more simple relation is

$$E_t = IR = 3 \times 3.6 = 10.8\ \text{v}$$

16-7. Cells in Parallel. If n identical cells are connected in parallel, the electromotive force of the group will be the same as the electromotive force of one cell and the internal resistance of the group will be equal to the internal resistance of one cell divided by the number of cells in parallel, that is, to $\dfrac{r}{n}$. By modifying Eq. (2), the expression for the current through an external resistance of R ohms is

$$I = \frac{E}{R + \dfrac{r}{n}} \tag{4}$$

Example. Three cells, each with an electromotive force of 1.4 volts and an internal resistance of 0.15 ohm, are connected in parallel; and a resistance of 1.35 ohms is connected across the group.

(*a*) How much current flows in the circuit?

(*b*) What is the terminal voltage of the group?

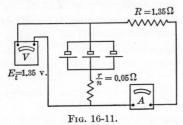

FIG. 16-11.

Solution: Figure 16-11 is a diagram of the circuit. The resistance $\frac{r}{n}$ represents the internal resistance of the group.

(*a*)
$$I = \frac{E}{R + \dfrac{r}{n}} = \frac{1.4}{1.35 + \dfrac{0.15}{3}} = 1.0 \text{ a}$$

(*b*)
$$E_t = IR = 1.0 \times 1.35 = 1.35 \text{ v}$$

PROBLEMS 16-3

1. The e.m.f. of a cell is 1.4 v. In supplying current to a circuit, the voltage drop across the internal resistance of the cell is 0.3 v. What is the terminal voltage?

2. If the internal resistance of the cell of Prob. 1 is 0.2 Ω, how much current flows in the circuit?

3. A cell whose e.m.f. is 1.6 v and internal resistance is 0.5 Ω is supplying 0.25 a to a circuit. What is the resistance of the external circuit?

4. How much power is lost in the cell of Prob. 3?

5. A cell that is delivering 5 a has an internal resistance of 0.18 Ω. If the e.m.f. of the cell is 2.0 v, what is the terminal voltage?

6. (*a*) What is the resistance of the external circuit of Prob. 5?

(*b*) How much power is lost in the cell of Prob. 5?

7. A cell that is delivering 3.5 a has an internal resistance of 0.13 Ω If the resistance of the external circuit is 0.413 Ω, what is the e.m.f. of the cell?

8. A high-resistance voltmeter reads 2.0 v when placed across a cell that is connected to no other circuit. When the cell was delivering 6 a to a circuit, the voltmeter read a terminal voltage of 1.8 v. What is the internal resistance of the cell?

9. (*a*) What is the resistance of the external circuit of Prob. 8?

(*b*) What is the total power developed in Prob. 8?

10. A cell with an e.m.f. of 2.0 v and an internal resistance of 0.1 Ω is connected to a load consisting of a variable resistance. Plot the power delivered to the load as the load resistance is varied in 0.01-Ω steps from 0.05 Ω to 0.15 Ω. What conclusion do you draw from this graph?

11. Twelve cells are connected in series. The e.m.f. of each cell is 1.2 v, and the internal resistance of each cell is 0.2 Ω. What current will this group send through an external resistance of 12 Ω?

12. If the cells of Prob. 11 are connected in parallel, how much power will be dissipated in the load resistance of 12 Ω?

13. Eighteen cells are connected in series. The e.m.f. of each cell is 1.4 v, and the internal resistance per cell is 0.75 Ω. How much power will be expended in a resistance of 1.05 Ω connected across the group of cells?

14. If the cells in Prob. 13 are connected in parallel, how much current will flow through the load resistance of 1.05 Ω?

15. Twelve identical cells are connected so that there are four series groups, each with three cells, connected in parallel as illustrated in Fig. 16-12.

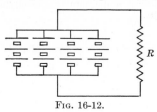

Fɪɢ. 16-12.

The e.m.f. of each cell is 1.2 v, with an internal resistance of 0.4 Ω. If $R = 0.6$ Ω, what current will flow through the external circuit?

16. How much power is dissipated in each cell of Prob. 15?

17. Eighteen cells are connected in series parallel so that there are six cells per series group. The e.m.f. of each cell is 1.8 v, and the internal resistance per cell is 0.1 Ω. How much current will flow through an external resistance of 3.8 Ω?

18. How much power is dissipated in each cell of Prob. 17?

19. The cells of Prob. 17 are arranged so that there are three cells per series group (six groups in parallel). How much current flows in the external circuit?

20. Each cell of a six-cell storage battery has an e.m.f. of 2.0 v and an internal resistance of 0.01 Ω. If the battery is to be charged from a 14-v line, how much resistance must be connected in series with the battery to limit the charging current to 15 a?

21. Sixteen storage batteries of three cells each are to be charged in series from a 115-v line. Each cell has an e.m.f. of 2.1 v and an internal resistance of 0.02 Ω. How much resistance must be connected in series with the batteries in order to limit the charging current to 10 a?

22. In Prob. 21,

(a) How much power is required for the entire circuit?

(b) How much power is lost in the series resistance?

Example. Six identical cells connected in series deliver 4 a to a circuit of 2.7 Ω. When two of the same cells are connected in parallel, they deliver

5 a to an external resistance of 0.375 Ω. What are the e.m.f. and internal resistance of each cell?

Solution: Let

E = e.m.f. of each cell,
r = internal resistance of each cell,
I = current in external circuit,
R = resistance of external circuit.

For the series connection, $6E$ = e.m.f. of six cells in series

and $6r$ = internal resistance of six cells in series

Substituting in Eq. (2), $6E = 4(2.7 + 6r)$

or $6E = 10.8 + 24r$ $\qquad$ (a)

For the parallel connection, E = e.m.f. of cells in parallel

and $\dfrac{r}{2}$ = internal resistance of two cells in parallel

Substituting in Eq. (2), $E = 5\left(0.375 + \dfrac{r}{2}\right)$

or $2E = 3.75 + 5r$ $\qquad$ (b)

Solve Eqs. (a) and (b) simultaneously to obtain

$$E = 2.0 \text{ v}$$

and $$r = 0.05 \ \Omega$$

23. Five identical cells when connected in series deliver a current of 5 a to a circuit of 0.4 Ω resistance. When four of the cells are connected in parallel, they deliver a current of 1 a to a circuit whose resistance is 1.35 Ω. What are the e.m.f. and internal resistance of each cell?

24. Ten cells connected in series force a current of 3 a through a circuit with a resistance of 1 Ω. When three of these cells are connected in parallel, they deliver a current of 6 a through an external resistance of 0.1 Ω. What are the e.m.f. and internal resistance of each cell?

25. Eight cells in parallel cause a current of 2 a to flow through a circuit of 1.05 Ω. When six of the cells are connected in series, they deliver a current of 10 a to a resistance of 0.3 Ω. What are the e.m.f. and internal resistance of each cell?

26. Twelve cells in series, each with an e.m.f. of 2.0 v, cause a certain current to flow through an external circuit of 2.4 Ω resistance. The same current flows through a circuit of 0.24 Ω resistance when five of these cells are connected in parallel. What are the values of the current and the internal resistance of each cell?

27. A cell sends a current of 20 a through an external circuit of 0.04 Ω. When the resistance of the external circuit is increased to 3.96 Ω, the current is 0.4 a. What are the e.m.f. and the internal resistance of the cell?

28. A cell with an internal resistance of 0.035 Ω sends a current of 3 a through an external circuit. Another cell, with the same e.m.f. but with an internal resistance of 0.385 Ω, causes a current of 2 a to flow through the external circuit when substituted for the first cell. What are the e.m.f. of the cells and the resistance of the external circuit?

CHAPTER XVII

EXPONENTS AND RADICALS

In earlier chapters, examples and problems have been limited to those containing exponents and roots that consisted of integers. In this chapter the study of exponents and radicals is extended to include new operations that will enable the student to solve electrical formulas and equations of a type hitherto omitted. In addition, new ideas are introduced that will be of fundamental importance in the study of alternating currents.

17-1. Fundamental Laws of Exponents. As previously explained, if n is a positive integer, a^n means that a is to be taken as a factor n times. Thus, a^4 is defined as being a shortened form of notation for the product $a \cdot a \cdot a \cdot a$. The number a is called the *base*, and the number n is called the *exponent*.

For the purpose of review, the fundamental laws for the use of *positive-integer exponents* are listed below:

(1) $$a^m \cdot a^n = a^{m+n}$$ (Art. 4-3)

(2) $$a^m \div a^n = a^{m-n} \quad \text{(when } n < m\text{)}$$ (Art. 5-2)

$$= \frac{1}{a^{n-m}} \quad \text{(when } n > m\text{)}$$

(3) $$(a^m)^n = a^{mn}$$ (Art. 7-11)

(4) $$(ab)^m = a^m b^m$$ (Art. 7-12)

(5) $$\left(\frac{a}{b}\right)^m = \frac{a^m}{b^m} \quad (b \neq 0)$$

17-2. Zero Exponent. If a^0 is to obey the law of exponents for multiplication as stated under (1) of the preceding article, then

$$a^m \cdot a^0 = a^{m+0}$$
$$= a^m$$

Also, if a^0 is to obey the law of exponents for division, then

$$\frac{a^m}{a^0} = a^{m-0}$$
$$= a^m$$

222

Therefore, the zero power of any number, except zero, is defined as being equal to 1; for 1 is the only number that, when used to multiply another number, does not change the value of the multiplicand.

17-3. Negative Exponents. If a^{-n} is to obey the multiplication law, then

$$\frac{a^n}{a^n} = a^{n-n}$$
$$= a^0$$
$$= 1$$

In Art. 5-4, it was shown that a *factor* may be transferred from one term of a fraction to the other if the sign of its exponent is changed.

PROBLEMS 17-1

Making use of the five fundamental laws of exponents, write the results of the indicated operations:

1. $a^3 \cdot a^5$.

2. $x^4 \cdot x^2$.

3. $e^6 \cdot e^4$.

4. $\theta^4 \cdot \theta^{-2}$.

5. $x^a \cdot x^b$.

6. $x^{3a} \cdot x^{2a}$.

7. $u^{x+1} \cdot u^{x-1}$.

8. $b^{x-y+z} \cdot b^{x+y-z}$.

9. $x^{10} \div x^5$.

10. $a^{3x} \div a^x$.

11. $e^{m+5} \div e^4$.

12. $v^{r+6} \div v^{r-3}$.

13. $y^{a+b} \div y^{a-b}$.

14. $(x^3)^3$.

15. $(e^4)^5$.

16. $(a^2b^3c)^3$.

17. $(xy^2z^4)^4$.

18. $(x^m)^3$.

19. $(x^3)^m$.

20. $(a^m b^n c^{2p})^3$.

21. $(-d^w e^m f^n)^3$.

22. $(-x^{2a}y^b)^4$.

23. $\left(\dfrac{a^2}{b^2}\right)^3$.

24. $\left(\dfrac{x^2}{y^3}\right)^m$.

25. $\left(\dfrac{e^3}{E^4}\right)^p$.

26. $\left(\dfrac{-a^n}{b^m}\right)^3$.

27. $\left(\dfrac{x^{2p}}{y^{4q}}\right)^2$.

28. $\left(\dfrac{a^{2m}}{a^{2m}}\right)^3$.

29. $\left(\dfrac{c^{2r}}{d^{2s}}\right)^{3t}$.

30. $-\left(\dfrac{a^{3m}}{b^{4n}}\right)^3$.

Express with positive exponents:

31. $a^{-b}b^{-2}$.

32. $x^{-3}b^{-4}$.

33. $I^{-2}R^{-1}$.

34. $3x^{-4}$.

35. $(4a)^{-2b}$.

36. $2^{-3}x^2y^{-3}$.

37. $\dfrac{a^{-3}b}{c^2}$.

38. $\dfrac{x^2}{2y^{-2}}$.

39. $\dfrac{3Ei^{-2}r^{-1}}{4}$.

40. $\dfrac{a^3}{6 \cdot (3b)^{-4}}$.

17-4. Fractional Exponents.   The meaning of a base affected by a fractional exponent is established by methods similar to those employed in determining meanings for zero or negative exponents.   If we assume that (1) of Art. 17-1 holds for fractional exponents, we should obtain, for example,

$$a^{\frac{1}{2}} \cdot a^{\frac{1}{2}} = a^{\frac{1}{2}+\frac{1}{2}} = a^1 = a$$

Also, $$a^{\frac{1}{3}} \cdot a^{\frac{1}{3}} \cdot a^{\frac{1}{3}} = a^{\frac{1}{3}+\frac{1}{3}+\frac{1}{3}} = a^1 = a$$

That is, $a^{\frac{1}{2}}$ is one of two equal factors of a, and $a^{\frac{1}{3}}$ is one of three equal factors of a.   Therefore, $a^{\frac{1}{2}}$ is the square root of a, and $a^{\frac{1}{3}}$ is the cube root of a.   Hence,

$$a^{\frac{1}{2}} = \sqrt{a}$$

and $$a^{\frac{1}{3}} = \sqrt[3]{a}$$

Likewise, $$a^{\frac{2}{3}} \cdot a^{\frac{2}{3}} \cdot a^{\frac{2}{3}} = a^{\frac{2}{3}+\frac{2}{3}+\frac{2}{3}} = a^{\frac{6}{3}} = a^2$$

Hence, $$(a^{\frac{2}{3}})^3 = a^2$$

or $$a^{\frac{2}{3}} = \sqrt[3]{a^2}$$

From the foregoing considerations, we obtain the following definition: *In a fractional exponent, the denominator denotes the root and the numerator denotes the power of the base.*   Or, in general,

$$a^{\frac{m}{n}} = \sqrt[n]{a^m}$$

Example 1. $$a^{\frac{3}{5}} = \sqrt[5]{a^3}$$

Example 2. $$-8^{\frac{1}{3}} = \sqrt[3]{-8} = -2$$

PROBLEMS 17-2

Find the values of:

1. $4^{\frac{1}{2}}$.

2. $(-27)^{\frac{1}{3}}$.

3. $-(-8)^{\frac{1}{3}}$.

4. $32^{\frac{1}{5}}$.

5. $125^{\frac{1}{3}}$.

6. $(-64i^3z^6)^{\frac{1}{3}}$.

7. $(a^{10}b^5)^{\frac{1}{5}}$.

8. $\left(\dfrac{64e^6}{r^3}\right)^{\frac{1}{3}}$.

9. $(x^9y^3)^{\frac{2}{3}}$.

10. $(a^6b^4)^{\frac{3}{2}}$.

Express with radical signs:

11. $2^{\frac{2}{3}}$.

12. $5^{\frac{3}{4}}$.

13. $3a^{\frac{1}{2}}$.

14. $x^{\frac{3}{2}}y^{\frac{2}{3}}$.

15. $(4e)^{\frac{1}{2}}$.

16. $a^{\frac{1}{2}}b^{1.5}$.

Express with fractional exponents:

17. $\sqrt[4]{x^3}$.

18. $\sqrt[5]{b^2}$.

19. $6\sqrt[3]{3x}$.

20. $\sqrt[3]{4x^2}$.

21. $\sqrt[4]{6a^3b^5}$.

22. $6\sqrt[5]{y^4}$.

23. $5x\sqrt[3]{b^2}$.

24. $a^3\sqrt[4]{b^3}$.

25. $2b\sqrt[6]{cd^2}$.

17-5. Radicand. The meaning of the radical sign was explained in Art. 2-9. The number under the radical sign is called the *radicand*.

17-6. Simplification of Radicals. The form in which a radical expression is written may be changed without altering its numerical value. Such changes are desirable for many reasons. For example, addition of several fractions containing different radicals in the denominators would be more difficult than addition with the radicals removed from the denominators. Similarly, it will be shown later that

$$\frac{1}{\sqrt{3}} = \frac{\sqrt{3}}{3}$$

It is apparent that the value to several decimal places could be computed more easily from the second fraction than from the first.

Because we are chiefly concerned with radicals involving a square root, only this type will be considered.

17-7. Removing a Factor from the Radical. Since, in general, $\sqrt{ab} = \sqrt{a} \cdot \sqrt{b}$, the following is evident:

Rule: *A radicand may be separated into two factors, one of which is the greatest perfect square it contains. The square root of this factor may then be written as the coefficient of a radical of which the other factor is the radicand.*

Example 1. $\sqrt{27} = \sqrt{9 \cdot 3} = \sqrt{9} \cdot \sqrt{3} = 3\sqrt{3}$

Example 2. $\sqrt{8} = \sqrt{4 \cdot 2} = \sqrt{4} \cdot \sqrt{2} = 2\sqrt{2}$

Example 3. $\sqrt{75} = \sqrt{25 \cdot 3} = \sqrt{25} \cdot \sqrt{3} = 5\sqrt{3}$

Example 4. $\sqrt{200a^5b^3c^2d} = \sqrt{100a^4b^2c^2} \cdot \sqrt{2abd} = 10a^2bc\sqrt{2abd}$

PROBLEMS 17-3

Simplify by removing factors from the radicand:

1. $\sqrt{18}$.
2. $\sqrt{32}$.
3. $\sqrt{48}$.
4. $\sqrt{12}$.
5. $\sqrt{20}$.
6. $\sqrt{96}$.
7. $\sqrt{63}$.
8. $\sqrt{54}$.
9. $\sqrt{99}$.
10. $\sqrt{63a^2}$.
11. $\sqrt{60e^2i^2}$.
12. $3\sqrt{40}$.
13. $2\sqrt{72x^2y^4}$.
14. $3\sqrt{8I^2z}$.
15. $5x\sqrt{81x^2y}$.
16. $6\sqrt{108m^5n^2}$.
17. $3\sqrt{63\alpha^3\beta^2}$.
18. $4\sqrt{8x^5y^2z^3}$.
19. $16a^2b\sqrt{98a^4b^3c^2d}$.
20. $2xy^2\sqrt{108xy^4z^3}$.

17-8. Simplifying Radicals Containing Fractions. Since

$$\sqrt{\frac{4}{9}} = \frac{2}{3} \quad \text{and} \quad \frac{\sqrt{4}}{\sqrt{9}} = \frac{2}{3}$$

then

$$\sqrt{\frac{4}{9}} = \frac{\sqrt{4}}{\sqrt{9}}$$

Also,

$$\sqrt{\frac{16}{25}} = \frac{4}{5} \quad \text{and} \quad \frac{\sqrt{16}}{\sqrt{25}} = \frac{4}{5}$$

then

$$\sqrt{\frac{16}{25}} = \frac{\sqrt{16}}{\sqrt{25}}.$$

Or, in general terms,

$$\sqrt{\frac{a}{b}} = \frac{\sqrt{a}}{\sqrt{b}}$$

The above relation permits simplification of radicals containing fractions by removing the radical from the denominator. This process, by which the denominator is made a rational number, is called *rationalizing the denominator*.

Rule: *To rationalize the denominator,*

1. *Multiply both numerator and denominator by a number that will make the resulting denominator a perfect square.*

2. *Simplify the resulting radical by removing factors from the radicands.*

Example 1.
$$\sqrt{\frac{2}{5}} = \sqrt{\frac{2}{5} \cdot \frac{5}{5}} = \sqrt{\frac{10}{25}} = \frac{\sqrt{10}}{\sqrt{25}} = \frac{\sqrt{10}}{5}$$

Example 2.
$$\sqrt{\frac{1}{2}} = \sqrt{\frac{1}{2} \cdot \frac{2}{2}} = \sqrt{\frac{2}{4}} = \frac{\sqrt{2}}{\sqrt{4}} = \frac{\sqrt{2}}{2}$$

Example 3.
$$\frac{3}{\sqrt{6}} = \frac{3}{\sqrt{6}} \cdot \frac{\sqrt{6}}{\sqrt{6}} = \frac{3\sqrt{6}}{6} = \frac{1}{2}\sqrt{6}$$

Example 4.
$$\sqrt{\frac{3a}{5x}} = \sqrt{\frac{3a}{5x} \cdot \frac{5x}{5x}} = \sqrt{\frac{15ax}{25x^2}} = \frac{\sqrt{15ax}}{\sqrt{25x^2}} = \frac{1}{5x}\sqrt{15ax}$$

PROBLEMS 17-4

Simplify the following:

1. $\sqrt{\frac{5}{6}}$.

2. $\sqrt{\frac{2}{3}}$.

3. $\sqrt{\frac{5}{8}}$.

4. $\frac{1}{\sqrt{5}}$.

5. $\sqrt{\frac{7}{8}}$.

6. $\frac{16}{\sqrt{5}}$.

7. $\dfrac{4\sqrt{6}}{\sqrt{2}}$.

8. $\sqrt{\dfrac{5}{12x}}$.

9. $\sqrt{\dfrac{13x^3}{20y^2}}$.

10. $\dfrac{1}{\sqrt{a}}$.

11. $\sqrt{\dfrac{a}{b}}$.

12. $y\sqrt{\dfrac{x}{y}}$.

13. $\sqrt{\dfrac{z^2}{5}}$.

14. $\dfrac{a}{b}\sqrt{\dfrac{b}{a}}$.

15. $\theta\sqrt{\dfrac{1}{\theta}}$.

16. $\dfrac{x}{y}\sqrt{\dfrac{2y}{3x}}$.

17. $\sqrt{\dfrac{x+y}{x-y}}$.

18. $\sqrt{1-(\tfrac{1}{3})^2}$.

19. $\sqrt{I^2-\left(\dfrac{I}{2}\right)^2}$.

20. $\sqrt{E^2-\left(\dfrac{E}{3}\right)^2}$.

17-9. Addition and Subtraction of Radicals. Terms that are the same except in respect to their coefficients are called *similar terms*. Likewise, *similar radicals* are defined as those having the same index and the same radicand and differing only in their coefficients. For example, $-2\sqrt{5}$, $3\sqrt{5}$, and $\sqrt{5}$ are similar radicals.

Similar radicals may be added or subtracted in the same way that similar terms are added or subtracted.

Example 1. $3\sqrt{6}-4\sqrt{6}-\sqrt{6}+8\sqrt{6}=6\sqrt{6}$

Example 2. $\sqrt{12}+\sqrt{27}=2\sqrt{3}+3\sqrt{3}=5\sqrt{3}$

Example 3.

$$\sqrt{48x}+\sqrt{\dfrac{x}{3}}+\sqrt{3x}=4\sqrt{3x}+\dfrac{1}{3}\sqrt{3x}+\sqrt{3x}=\dfrac{16}{3}\sqrt{3x}$$

If the radicands are not alike and cannot be reduced to a common radicand, then the radicals are dissimilar terms, and addition or subtraction can only be indicated. Thus the following statement may be made:

Rule: *To add or subtract radicals,*
1. *Reduce them to their simplest form.*
2. *Combine similar radicals and indicate the addition or subtraction of those which are dissimilar.*

PROBLEMS 17-5

Simplify:

1. $6\sqrt{2}-3\sqrt{2}+\sqrt{2}$.

2. $2\sqrt{63}-\sqrt{28}$.

3. $\sqrt{75}-\sqrt{12}$.

4. $\sqrt{18}-3\sqrt{6}-2\sqrt{8}$.

5. $6\sqrt{45} - 2\sqrt{20}$.

6. $2\sqrt{96} - 3\sqrt{54}$.

7. $3\sqrt{\frac{3}{2}} + \sqrt{24}$.

8. $2\sqrt{\frac{1}{2}} - 6\sqrt{\frac{1}{8}} + 8\sqrt{2}$.

9. $2\sqrt{\frac{8}{3}} - 3\sqrt{\frac{2}{27}}$.

10. $4\sqrt{10} - 2\sqrt{\frac{9}{10}} + \sqrt{\frac{2}{5}}$.

11. $\frac{E}{2} + \sqrt{\frac{9E^2}{2}}$.

12. $I - \sqrt{\frac{3I^2}{4}}$.

13. $4\sqrt{\frac{3}{5}} - \sqrt{\frac{4}{15}} + 3\sqrt{\frac{1}{15}}$.

14. $x\sqrt{xyz} + xz\sqrt{\frac{y}{xz}}$.

15. $\sqrt{\frac{a+b}{a-b}} - \sqrt{\frac{a-b}{a+b}}$.

17-10. Multiplication of Radicals. Obtaining the product of radicals is the inverse of removing a factor, as will be shown in the following examples:

Example 1. $3\sqrt{3} \cdot 5\sqrt{4} = 15\sqrt{3 \cdot 4} = 15 \cdot 2\sqrt{3} = 30\sqrt{3}$

Example 2.
$$4\sqrt{3a} \cdot 2\sqrt{6a} = 8\sqrt{3a \cdot 6a} = 8\sqrt{18a^2} = 8\sqrt{9 \cdot 2a^2} = 24a\sqrt{2}$$

Example 3.   Multiply $3\sqrt{2} + 2\sqrt{3}$ by $4\sqrt{2} - 3\sqrt{3}$.

Solution:

$$
\begin{array}{r}
3\sqrt{2} + 2\sqrt{3} \\
4\sqrt{2} - 3\sqrt{3} \\
\hline
24 + 8\sqrt{6} \\
- 9\sqrt{6} - 18 \\
\hline
24 - \sqrt{6} - 18 = 6 - \sqrt{6}
\end{array}
$$

PROBLEMS 17-6

Find the indicated products:

1. $\sqrt{15} \cdot \sqrt{5}$.

2. $\sqrt{10} \cdot \sqrt{2}$.

3. $3\sqrt{5} \cdot 4\sqrt{8}$.

4. $3\sqrt{2} \cdot 2\sqrt{3}$.

5. $3\sqrt{ab} \cdot 4\sqrt{a^3b^3c^2}$.

6. $3\sqrt{i} \cdot \sqrt{4i^3}$.

7. $(\sqrt{3x})^2$.

8. $\sqrt{\frac{27}{8}} \cdot \sqrt{\frac{2}{3}}$.

9. $(\sqrt{E - IR})^2$.

10. $(2\sqrt{e - IX_L})^2$.

11. $(5 + \sqrt{2})(5 - \sqrt{2})$.

12. $(2R - \sqrt{z})(2R + 3\sqrt{z})$.

13. $(4 + \sqrt{6})^2$.

14. $(3\sqrt{5} + 2\sqrt{2})(2\sqrt{5} - 3\sqrt{2})$.

15. $(\sqrt{a+1} + 1)^2$.

16. $(\sqrt{b} - \sqrt{b-3})^2$.

17. $(\sqrt{x+1} - \sqrt{x-1})^2$.

18. $\left(\frac{E}{3} - \frac{E\sqrt{3}}{6}\right)^2$.

19. $\frac{\theta}{2}(\sqrt{2} - 1)^2$.

20. $\sqrt{E^2 - \left(\frac{E\sqrt{3} - 2E}{3}\right)^2}$.

17-11. Division. An indicated root whose value is irrational but whose radicand is rational is called a *surd*. Thus, $\sqrt[3]{3}$, $\sqrt{2}$, $\sqrt[4]{5}$, $\sqrt{3}$, etc., are surds. If the indicated root is the square root, then the surd is called a *quadratic surd*. For example, $\sqrt{2}$, $\sqrt{5}$, $\sqrt{6}$, $\sqrt{15}$ are quadratic surds. Then, by extending the definition, such expressions as $3 + \sqrt{2}$ and $\sqrt{3} - 6$ are called *binomial quadratic surds*.

It is very important that the student become proficient in the multiplication and division of binomial quadratic surds. One method of solving alternating-current circuits, which will be discussed later, makes wide use of these particular operations. Multiplication of such expressions was covered in the preceding article. However, a new method is necessary for division.

Consider the two expressions $a - \sqrt{b}$ and $a + \sqrt{b}$. They differ only in the sign between the terms. These expressions are *conjugates;* that is, $a - \sqrt{b}$ is called the conjugate of $a + \sqrt{b}$, and $a + \sqrt{b}$ is called the conjugate of $a - \sqrt{b}$. Remember this meaning of "conjugate," for it has the same meaning with reference to certain circuit components.

To divide a number by a binomial quadratic surd, rationalize the divisor (denominator) by multiplying both dividend (numerator) and divisor by the conjugate of the divisor.

Example 1.　　$\dfrac{1}{3 + \sqrt{2}} = \dfrac{3 - \sqrt{2}}{(3 + \sqrt{2})(3 - \sqrt{2})} = \dfrac{3 - \sqrt{2}}{7}$

Example 2.　　$\dfrac{1}{3\sqrt{3} - 1} = \dfrac{3\sqrt{3} + 1}{(3\sqrt{3} - 1)(3\sqrt{3} + 1)} = \dfrac{3\sqrt{3} + 1}{26}$

Example 3.　　$\dfrac{3 - \sqrt{2}}{4 + \sqrt{2}} = \dfrac{(3 - \sqrt{2})(4 - \sqrt{2})}{(4 + \sqrt{2})(4 - \sqrt{2})} = \dfrac{14 - 7\sqrt{2}}{14} = \dfrac{2 - \sqrt{2}}{2}$

NOTE: In each of the foregoing examples the resulting denominator is a rational number. In general, the product of two conjugate surd expressions is a rational number. This important fact is widely used in the solution of alternating-current problems.

PROBLEMS 17-7

Perform the indicated divisions:

1. $\dfrac{5}{3 - \sqrt{2}}$.　　　　2. $\dfrac{4}{4 + \sqrt{3}}$.　　　　3. $\dfrac{8}{\sqrt{7} + 3}$.

4. $\dfrac{8}{4 - 3\sqrt{5}}.$ **5.** $\dfrac{7}{5\sqrt{3} - 2}.$ **6.** $\dfrac{3\sqrt{2} + 3}{2\sqrt{3} + 2}.$

7. $\dfrac{4 - \sqrt{3}}{2 + \sqrt{3}}.$ **8.** $\dfrac{a + \sqrt{b}}{a - \sqrt{b}}.$ **9.** $\dfrac{\sqrt{R} - \sqrt{r}}{\sqrt{R} + \sqrt{r}}.$

10. $\dfrac{\sqrt{x} - y + \sqrt{x}}{\sqrt{x} - y - \sqrt{x}}.$

17-12. Indicated Square Roots of Negative Numbers. So far, in the removal of factors from radicands, all the radicands have been positive numbers. Also, we have extracted the square roots of positive numbers only. How shall we proceed to factor negative radicands, and what is the meaning of the square root of a negative number?

According to our laws for multiplication, no number multiplied by itself, or raised to any even power, will produce a negative result. For example, what does $\sqrt{-25}$ mean when we know of no number that, when multiplied by itself will produce -25?

For years, mathematicians have been calling an indicated square root of a negative number an *imaginary number*. It is probable that this name was assigned before mathematicians could visualize such a number. It is even more probable that the word "imaginary" was originally used to distinguish such numbers from the so-called "real numbers" previously studied. In any event, calling such a number imaginary is unfortunate, for to electricians and radiomen such numbers are very real in the physical sense. For example, if you get across a large condenser that is highly charged, you are likely to be killed by some of these "imaginary" volts. This will be discussed later.

However, to avoid the difficulty of operations with the indicated square roots of negative numbers, or imaginary numbers, it becomes necessary to introduce a new type of number. That is, we agree that every imaginary number can be expressed as the product of a positive number and $\sqrt{-1}$.

Example 1. $\sqrt{-25} = \sqrt{(-1)25} = \sqrt{-1}\sqrt{25} = \sqrt{-1} \cdot 5$

As a convenient form of notation, mathematicians indicate $\sqrt{-1}$ by the letter i. In electrical formulas, however, this letter is used to denote current. Therefore, in order to avoid confusion we indicate $\sqrt{-1}$ by the letter j, commonly called *the operator j*

Example 2. $\sqrt{-16} = \sqrt{(-1)16} = \sqrt{-1}\sqrt{16} = \sqrt{-1}\cdot 4 = j4$

Example 3. $\sqrt{-X^2} = \sqrt{(-1)X^2} = \sqrt{-1}\sqrt{X^2} = \sqrt{-1}\cdot X = jX$

Example 4. $-\sqrt{-4X^2} = -\sqrt{(-1)4X^2} = -\sqrt{-1}\sqrt{4X^2}$
$$= -\sqrt{-1}\cdot 2X = -j2X$$

PROBLEMS 17-8

Express the following, utilizing the operator j:

1. $\sqrt{-9}$.

2. $\sqrt{-36}$.

3. $\sqrt{-64}$.

4. $-\sqrt{-49}$.

5. $\sqrt{-144b^2}$.

6. $-\sqrt{-2}$.

7. $\sqrt{-32}$.

8. $6\sqrt{-72}$.

9. $4\sqrt{-27}$.

10. $-6\sqrt{-28}$.

11. $\sqrt{\dfrac{-16}{25}}$.

12. $-\sqrt{\dfrac{-9}{36}}$.

13. $\sqrt{\dfrac{-27}{4}}$.

14. $\sqrt{\dfrac{-75}{4}}$.

15. $\sqrt{\dfrac{-32}{25}}$.

17-13. Representation of Numbers Affected by j. So far in our studies, we have represented numbers graphically whenever possible. This method is an advantageous one; because if we can visualize a diagram or graph every time we come in contact with certain types of numbers and equations, we will have a better understanding of the manner in which quantities vary. How shall we represent numbers affected by the operator j?

Since, in general, $\sqrt{a}$ is such a number that $\sqrt{a}\cdot\sqrt{a} = a$, it follows that the square root of any number, when multiplied by itself, will result in the given number (radicand). If we are to accept this definition, then $\sqrt{-1}\sqrt{-1} = -1$. This result brings us back to familiar ground, for in Fig. 3-2 we established a basis for representing positive and negative numbers. Also, in Art. 4-2 and in Figs. 4-2 and 4-3, it was pointed out that multiplication or division by -1 caused a directed number to rotate $180°$. Then, if we multiply some number by -1 twice, we get full $360°$ rotation of the number, or back to where it started from. This, of course, is equivalent to multiplying the number by $+1$.

With the above in mind, it is reasonable to assume that multiplying some number by $\sqrt{-1}$, or j, would cause rotation only halfway to $180°$, or to $90°$, because, if we multiplied by j twice, we should expect to end up $180°$ from the initial line, for, as previously shown,

$$\sqrt{-1} \cdot \sqrt{-1} = -1$$

That is, $$j \cdot j = -1$$
or $$j^2 = -1$$

Therefore, we agree to represent all directed numbers affected by the operator j as lying along a line drawn 90° from the line that we use to represent positive and negative numbers. This is illustrated in Fig. 17-1.

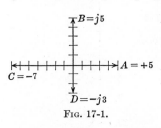

Fig. 17-1.

The horizontal line on which we plot positive and negative numbers is called the axis of *reals*. The vertical line on which we plot numbers having $+j$ or $-j$ as a coefficient is called the axis of *imaginaries*.

It is customary to think of numbers affected by $+j$ as having been rotated in a counterclockwise direction as shown in Fig.

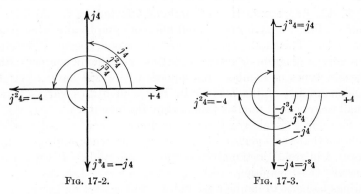

Fig. 17-2.   Fig. 17-3.

17-2. Also, we think of numbers having $-j$ as a coefficient as having been rotated in a clockwise direction as shown in Fig. 17-3.

Actually, the direction we consider the number to have been rotated in makes no difference, for the final position will be the same. The truth of this statement may be justified by the following considerations:

$$\sqrt{-1} \cdot \sqrt{-1} = -1$$

That is, $$j \cdot j = -1$$
$$\therefore j^2 = -1$$

Also, $$\sqrt{-1} \cdot \sqrt{-1} \cdot \sqrt{-1} = -1 \cdot \sqrt{-1} = -j$$

That is,
$$j \cdot j \cdot j = j^3$$
$$\therefore j^3 = -j$$

Also,
$$\sqrt{-1} \cdot \sqrt{-1} \cdot \sqrt{-1} \cdot \sqrt{-1}$$
$$= (\sqrt{-1} \cdot \sqrt{-1})(\sqrt{-1} \cdot \sqrt{-1}) = (-1)(-1) = 1$$

That is,
$$j \cdot j \cdot j \cdot j = j^4$$
$$\therefore j^4 = 1$$

Similarly, it may be shown that successive multiplication by each $+j$ rotates the number 90° in a counterclockwise direction. If we consider successive multiplication by $-j$, we have

$$(-\sqrt{-1})(-\sqrt{-1}) = -1$$

That is,
$$(-j)(-j) = j^2$$
$$\therefore (-j)^2 = -1$$

Also,

$$(-\sqrt{-1})(-\sqrt{-1})(-\sqrt{-1}) = (-1)(-\sqrt{-1}) = \sqrt{-1}$$

That is,
$$(-j)(-j)(-j) = (j^2)(-j) = (-1)(-j) = j$$
$$\therefore (-j)^3 = j$$

To demonstrate that $(-j)^4 = 1$ and $\dfrac{1}{j} = -j$ is left as a problem for the student.

To summarize, it is seen that j is simply an operator for the purpose of rotating a directed number 90°, regardless of the value of that number. A $+j$ is considered as denoting counterclockwise rotation, and $-j$ denotes clockwise rotation. j is commonly referred to as the "complex operator." Actually, there is nothing complex about it.

17-14. Complex Numbers. If a "real" number is united to an "imaginary" number by a plus or a minus sign, the expression thus obtained is called a *complex number*. Thus, $3 - j4$, $a + jb$, $R + jX$, etc., are complex numbers. Again, it is unfortunate that such expressions should be called complex numbers, for there is absolutely nothing complex about them, as we shall see in a later chapter. At this time, we shall consider, not their graphical representation, but simply how to perform the four fundamental operations algebraically.

17-15. Addition and Subtraction of Complex Numbers. Combining a real number with an imaginary number cannot be accomplished by the usual methods of addition and subtraction.

These processes can only be expressed. For example, if we have the complex number $5 + j6$, this is as far as we can simplify it at this time. We should not attempt to add 5 and $j6$ arithmetically; for these two numbers are at right angles to each other, and such an operation would be meaningless. However, we *can* add and subtract complex numbers by treating them as ordinary binomials.

Example 1. Add $3 + j7$ and $4 - j5$.
Solution:
$$3 + j7$$
$$4 - j5$$
$$\overline{7 + j2}$$

Example 2. Subtract $-15 - j6$ from $-5 + j8$.
Solution:
$$- 5 + j\ 8$$
$$-15 - j\ 6$$
$$\overline{10 + j14}$$

PROBLEMS 17-9

Find the indicated sums:

1. $3 + j8$
  $5 - j2$

2. $20 - j16$
  $13 + j27$

3. $- 7 - j11$
  $36 + j42$

4. $- 3 + j10$
  $-47 - j34$

5. $87 - j125$
  $-142 - j\ 73$

6. $j67$
  $13 - j23$

7 to 12. Subtract the lower complex number from the upper in each of the above problems.

17-16. Multiplication of Complex Numbers. As in addition and subtraction, complex numbers are treated as ordinary binomials when multiplied. However, when writing the result, we must not forget that $j^2 = -1$.

Example 1. Multiply $4 - j7$ by $8 + j2$.

Solution:
$$4 - j\ 7$$
$$8 + j\ 2$$
$$\overline{32 - j56}$$
$$+ j\ 8 - j^2 14$$
$$\overline{32 - j48 - j^2 14}$$
Since $j^2 = -1$, the product is $32 - j48 - (-1)(14) = 32 - j48 + 14$
$$= 46 - j48$$

Example 2. Multiply $7 + j3$ by $6 + j2$.

Solution:

$$
\begin{array}{r}
7 + j\,3 \\
6 + j\,2 \\
\hline
42 + j18 \\
+\,j14 + j^2 6 \\
\hline
42 + j32 + j^2 6 = 36 + j32
\end{array}
$$

17-17. Division of Complex Numbers. As in the division of binomial quadratic surds, we simplify an indicated division by rationalizing the denominator in order to obtain a "real" number as divisor (Art. 17-11). This is accomplished by multiplying by the conjugate in the usual manner.

Example 1.

$$\frac{10}{1 + j2} = \frac{10(1 - j2)}{(1 + j2)(1 - j2)} = \frac{10(1 - j2)}{1 - j^2 4} = \frac{10(1 - j2)}{5} = 2(1 - j2)$$

Example 2.

$$\frac{5 + j6}{3 - j4} = \frac{(5 + j6)(3 + j4)}{(3 - j4)(3 + j4)} = \frac{15 + j38 + j^2 24}{9 - j^2 16} = \frac{-9 + j38}{25}$$

Example 3.

$$\frac{a + jb}{a - jb} = \frac{(a + jb)(a + jb)}{(a - jb)(a + jb)} = \frac{a^2 + j2ab + j^2 b^2}{a^2 - j^2 b^2} = \frac{a^2 + j2ab - b^2}{a^2 + b^2}$$

PROBLEMS 17-10

Find the indicated products:

1. $(6 + j2)(4 + j3)$.

2. $(8 - j13)(11 - j12)$.

3. $(5 + j4)(7 - j9)$.

4. $(1 + j1)(1 - j1)$.

5. $(c + jd)(c + jd)$.

6. $(R + jX)(R - jX)$.

Find the quotients:

7. $\dfrac{2}{1 - j2}$.

8. $\dfrac{3}{1 - j1}$.

9. $\dfrac{5 - j4}{5 + j4}$.

10. $\dfrac{1 + j1}{1 - j1}$.

11. $\dfrac{3 + j5}{4 - j2}$.

12. $\dfrac{6 - j2}{4 - j7}$.

13. $\dfrac{2}{2 - jb}$.

14. $\dfrac{a - jb}{a + jb}$.

15. $\dfrac{R + jX}{R - jX}$.

17-18. Radical Equations. An equation in which the unknown occurs in a radicand is called an *irrational* or *radical equation.* To solve such an equation, arrange it in such a manner that the radical is the only term in one member of the equation. Then eliminate the radical by squaring each member of the equation.

Example 1.   Given $\sqrt{3x} = 6$; solve for x.

Solution:	$\sqrt{3x} = 6$
Squaring,	$3x = 36$
D:3,	$x = 12$

Check.   Substituting 12 for x in the given equation,

$$\sqrt{3 \cdot 12} = 6$$
$$\sqrt{36} = 6$$
$$6 = 6$$

Example 2.   Given $\sqrt{2x + 3} = 7$; solve for x.

Solution:	$\sqrt{2x + 3} = 7$
Squaring,	$2x + 3 = 49$
S:3,	$2x = 46$
D:2,	$x = 23$
Check	$\sqrt{2 \cdot 23 + 3} = 7$
	$\sqrt{49} = 7$
	$7 = 7$

Example 3.   The time for one complete swing of a simple pendulum is given by $t = 2\pi \sqrt{\dfrac{L}{g}}$, where t is the time in seconds, L is the length of the pendulum, and g is the force due to gravity.   Solve the equation for g and for L.

Solution: Given	$t = 2\pi \sqrt{\dfrac{L}{g}}$	(1)
Squaring (1),	$t^2 = 4\pi^2 \dfrac{L}{g}.$	(2)
M: g in (2),	$gt^2 = 4\pi^2 L$	(3)
D: t^2 in (3),	$g = \dfrac{4\pi^2 L}{t^2}$	(4)
Rewrite (3),	$4\pi^2 L = gt^2$	(5)
D: $4\pi^2$ in (5),	$L = \dfrac{gt^2}{4\pi^2}$	

PROBLEMS 17-11

Solve the following equations:

1. $\sqrt{x} = 2.$ 2. $\sqrt{e} = 4.$ 3. $\sqrt{I} = 9.$

4. $\sqrt{x} + 3 = 5.$ 5. $\sqrt{r} - 2 = 4.$ 6. $\sqrt{i + 3} = 4.$

7. $\sqrt{E - 1} = 7.$ 8. $5\sqrt{I - 3} - 4 = 6.$ 9. $\sqrt{\dfrac{\theta}{3}} = 4.$

10. $\sqrt{\dfrac{2z + 1}{7}} = 1.$ 11. $3\sqrt{x - 2} = \sqrt{2x + 3}.$

12. At an altitude of h ft above the sea or level ground, the distance in miles (d) that a person can see an object is given by $d = \sqrt{\dfrac{3h}{2}}$. How high must one be to see an object 15 miles away?

13. The circumference of a circle is given by the formula $c = 2\sqrt{\pi A}$, where A is the area. With $\pi = 3.14$, what is the area of a circle whose circumference is 12.56 in.?

14. Given $V = \sqrt{2gh}$. Find the value of h, when V is 600 and $g = 32.2$.

15. $V = \sqrt{\dfrac{2K}{m}}$. Solve for K and m.

16. $r = \sqrt{\dfrac{mm'}{F}}$. Solve for F.

17. $R_t = \dfrac{r}{\sqrt{\dfrac{d_o}{d_1}} - 1}$. Solve for $\dfrac{d_o}{d_1}$.

18. The relation between the resonant frequency f, the inductance L, and capacitance C of a circuit is given by the formula $f = \dfrac{1}{2\pi\sqrt{LC}}$. Find the value of L when $f = 1.40 \times 10^6$ and $C = 2.50 \times 10^{-10}$.

19. Using the formula for f as given in Prob. 18, find the value of C when $f = 6.00 \times 10^6$ and $L = 1.50 \times 10^{-8}$.

20. $f = \dfrac{1}{2\pi\sqrt{\dfrac{LC_aC_b}{C_a + C_b}}}$. Solve for C_a.

21. Using the formula in Prob. 20, find the value of C_b if $f = 2.00 \times 10^6$, $L = 3.50 \times 10^{-7}$, and $C_a = 3.50 \times 10^{-8}$.

22. Show that $KE_p^{\frac{3}{2}} = KE_p\sqrt{E_p}$. This is a convenient relation for the slide-rule operator.

23. In a line through which a current I flows, the power P_m existing in the magnetic field around the line is $\dfrac{LI^2}{2}$ w, where L is the inductance per unit length. An equal power P_e exists in the electrostatic field of the line equal to $\dfrac{CE^2}{2}$ w, where C is capacitance of the line per unit length. If the surge impedance Z_0 of the line is $\dfrac{E}{I}$ ohms, show that $Z_0 = \sqrt{\dfrac{L}{C}}$.

24. Given $E = I_pZ_p + j\omega MI_s$ and $I_sZ_s = -j\omega MI_p$. Show that

$$E = I_p\left(Z_p + \frac{(\omega M)^2}{Z_s}\right).$$

Solution: Since I_s does not appear in the final equation, it must be eliminated. Solving the given equations for I_s,

$$I_s = \frac{E - I_p Z_p}{j\omega M} \tag{1}$$

$$I_s = \frac{-j\omega M I_p}{Z_s} \tag{2}$$

Equating the right members of (1) and (2),

$$\frac{E - I_p Z_p}{j\omega M} = \frac{-j\omega M I_p}{Z_s}$$

$\mathbf{M}: j\omega M \qquad\qquad E - I_p Z_p = \dfrac{-j^2 \omega^2 M^2 I_p}{Z_s}$

Substituting -1 for j^2 in the right member,

$$E - I_p Z_p = \frac{\omega^2 M^2 I_p}{Z_s}$$

$\mathbf{A}: I_p Z_p, \qquad\qquad E = I_p Z_p + \dfrac{(\omega M)^2 I_p}{Z_s}$

Factoring the right member, $E = I_p \left(Z_p + \dfrac{(\omega M)^2}{Z_s} \right)$

CHAPTER XVIII

QUADRATIC EQUATIONS

In previous chapters the study of equations has been limited to those which contained the unknown quantity in the first degree. This chapter concerns itself with equations of the second degree which are called quadratic equations.

18-1. Definitions. In common with polynomials (Art. 12-2), the degree of an equation is defined as the degree of the term of highest degree in it. Thus, if an equation contains the square of the unknown quantity, and no higher degree, it is an equation of the second degree, or a *quadratic equation*.

A quadratic equation that contains terms of the second degree only of the unknown is called a *pure quadratic equation*. For example,

$$x^2 = 25, \qquad R^2 - 49 = 0, \qquad 3x^2 = 12, \qquad ax^2 + c = 0,$$
$$5x^2 + 2y^2 = 20, \text{ etc.}$$

are pure quadratic equations.

A quadratic equation that contains terms of *both* the first and the second degree of the unknown, is called an *affected* or a *complete quadratic equation*. Thus, $x^2 + 3x + 2 = 0$, $3x^2 + 11x = -2$, $ax^2 + bx + c = 0$, etc., are affected, or complete, quadratic equations.

When a quadratic equation is solved, values of the unknown are found that will satisfy the conditions of the equation.

A value of the unknown that will satisfy the equation is called a *solution* or a *root* of the equation.

18-2. Solution of Pure Quadratic Equations. As stated in Art. 11-5, every number has two square roots, equal in magnitude but of opposite sign. Hence, all quadratic equations have two roots. In pure quadratic equations, the absolute values of the roots are equal but of opposite sign. The roots of complete quadratics are discussed in Art. 18-3.

Example 1.   Solve the equation $x^2 - 16 = 0$.

Solution: Given $\qquad\qquad x^2 - 16 = 0$
A:16, $\qquad\qquad\qquad\qquad x^2 = 16$
$\sqrt{}$ (see note below), $\qquad\qquad x = \pm 4$

Check.   Substituting in the equation either $+4$ or -4 for the value of x, because either squared results in $+16$, we have

$$(\pm 4)^2 - 16 = 0$$
or $\qquad\qquad\qquad 16 - 16 = 0$

NOTE: Hereafter, the radical sign will mean "take the square root of both members of the previous or designated equation."

Example 2.   Solve the equation $5R^2 - 89 = 91$.

Solution: Given $\qquad\qquad 5R^2 - 89 = 91$
A:89, $\qquad\qquad\qquad\qquad 5R^2 = 180$
D:5, $\qquad\qquad\qquad\qquad\quad R^2 = 36$
$\sqrt{}$, $\qquad\qquad\qquad\qquad\qquad R = \pm 6$
Check. $\qquad\qquad 5(\pm 6)^2 - 89 = 91$
$$5 \times 36 - 89 = 91$$
$$180 - 89 = 91$$
$$91 = 91$$

Example 3.   Solve the equation $\dfrac{I+4}{I-4} + \dfrac{I-4}{I+4} = \dfrac{10}{3}$.

Solution: Given $\qquad\quad \dfrac{I+4}{I-4} + \dfrac{I-4}{I+4} = \dfrac{10}{3}$

Clearing fractions,

$$3(I+4)(I+4) + 3(I-4)(I-4) = 10(I-4)(I+4)$$

Expanding,

$$3I^2 + 24I + 48 + 3I^2 - 24I + 48 = 10I^2 - 160$$

Collecting terms, $\qquad\qquad\qquad -4I^2 = -256$
D: -4, $\qquad\qquad\qquad\qquad\quad I^2 = 64$
$\sqrt{}$, $\qquad\qquad\qquad\qquad\qquad\quad I = \pm 8$
Check by the usual method.

PROBLEMS 18-1

Solve the following equations.   If the answers are not integral, solve to three significant figures:

1. $x^2 - 25 = 0$.

2. $R^2 - 0.09 = 0$.

3. $r^2 - 89 = 200$.

4. $I^2 - 0.70 = 0.99$.

5. $7e^2 - 30 = 5$.

6. $y^2 = \frac{25}{64}$.

7. $0 = 0.80 - 0.03i^2 + 0.28.$ **8.** $3\theta^2 = \frac{27}{100}.$

9. $\frac{125}{36} = 5Z^2.$ **10.** $4R = 3(R + 5) - R(R - 1).$

11. $\dfrac{2R^2 + 4}{5} - \dfrac{3R^2 - 7}{3} = \dfrac{11}{15}.$ **12.** $I^2R = P.$

13. $3R(6R - 5) + 5(3R - 10) = 0.$ **14.** $\dfrac{E - 6}{2} = \dfrac{4E^2 - 9E - 90}{3E}.$

15. $4x^2 - 9 = 0.$

18-3. Complete Quadratic Equations—Solution by Factoring.

As an example, let it be assumed that all that is known about two expressions x and y is that $xy = 0$. We know that it is impossible to find the value of either, unless the value of the other is known. However, we do know that, if $xy = 0$, *either* $x = 0$ or $y = 0$; for the product of two numbers can be zero if, and only if, one of them is zero.

Example 1. Solve the equation $x(5x - 2) = 0$.
Solution: Here we have the product of two numbers x and $(5x - 2)$, equal to zero, and in order to satisfy the equation one of them must be equal to zero. Therefore, $x = 0$, or $5x - 2 = 0$.
Solving the latter equation,
$$x = \tfrac{2}{5}$$
Hence, $x = 0$ *or* $x = \tfrac{2}{5}$
Check.   If $x = 0$, $x(5x - 2) = 0(5 \cdot 0 - 2) = 0(-2) = 0$
         If $x = \tfrac{2}{5}$, $x(5x - 2) = \tfrac{2}{5}(5 \cdot \tfrac{2}{5} - 2) = \tfrac{2}{5}(2 - 2) = 0$

It is evident that the roots of a complete quadratic may be of unequal absolute value and may or may not have the same signs.

It is incorrect to say $x = 0$ *and* $x = \tfrac{2}{5}$, for x cannot be equal to both 0 and $\tfrac{2}{5}$ at the same time. This will be more apparent in the following examples.

Example 2. Solve the equation $(x - 5)(x + 3) = 0$.
Solution: Again, we have the product of two numbers $(x - 5)$ and $(x + 3)$, equal to zero. Hence, either $(x - 5) = 0$, *or* $(x + 3) = 0$.
$$\therefore x = 5, \quad or \quad x = -3$$
Check.   If $x = 5$, $(x - 5)(x + 3) = (5 - 5)(5 + 3) = 0(8) = 0$
         If $x = -3$, $(x - 5)(x + 3) = (-3 - 5)(-3 + 3) = (-8)0 = 0$

Example 3. Solve the equation $x^2 - x - 6 = 0$.
Solution: Given $x^2 - x - 6 = 0$
Factoring, $(x - 3)(x + 2) = 0$
Then, if $x - 3 = 0, \quad x = 3$
Also, if $x + 2 = 0, \quad x = -2$
$$\therefore x = 3, \ or \ -2$$

Check.   If $x = 3$, $x^2 - x - 6 = 3^2 - 3 - 6 = 9 - 3 - 6 = 0$
   If $x = -2$, $x^2 - x - 6 = (-2)^2 - (-2) - 6 = 4 + 2 - 6 = 0$

Example 4.   Solve the equation $(E - 3)(E + 2) = 14$.

Solution: Given $(E - 3)(E + 2) = 14$
Expanding, $E^2 - E - 6 = 14$
S : 14, $E^2 - E - 20 = 0$
Factoring, $(E - 5)(E + 4) = 0$
Then, if $E - 5 = 0$, $E = 5$
Also, if $E + 4 = 0$, $E = -4$
              $\therefore E = 5 \ or \ -4$

Check.   If $E = 5$, $(E - 3)(E + 2) = (5 - 3)(5 + 2) = (2)(7) = 14$
   If $E = -4$, $(E - 3)(E + 2) = (-4 - 3)(-4 + 2) = (-7)(-2)$
                                                    $= 14$

PROBLEMS 18-2

Solve by factoring:

1. $x^2 + 3x - 4 = 0$.

2. $x^2 - 4x + 3 = 0$.

3. $R^2 - 2R - 35 = 0$.

4. $7R = 18 - R^2$.

5. $16 = 25I^2$.

6. $3R + 9 = R^2 - 9$.

7. $0 = E^2 - 7E + 12$.

8. $8r^2 + 14r = 15$.

9. $R - \dfrac{3}{R} = 1 + \dfrac{3}{R}$.

10. $\dfrac{1}{y^2} + \dfrac{2}{y} - 24 = 0$.

11. $14 + \dfrac{2}{I} = \dfrac{1}{I^2} - \dfrac{3}{I}$.

12. $\dfrac{E - 2}{E - 4} + \dfrac{1}{2} = \dfrac{7}{E - 3}$.

13. $0 = \dfrac{2}{R - 3} + 1 - \dfrac{6}{R - 8}$.

14. $\dfrac{12}{3 - i} = \dfrac{4 - i}{1 - i}$.

15. $\dfrac{36}{(E + 3)^2} - 1 = \dfrac{E + 2}{E + 3}$.

18-4. Solution by Completing the Square.

Some quadratic equations are not readily solved by factoring.   Frequently such quadratic equations are readily solved by another method known as *completing the square.*

In Probs. 11-5, missing terms were supplied in order to form a perfect trinomial square.   This is the basis for the method of completing the square.   For example, in order to make a perfect square of the expression $x^2 + 10x$, 25 must be added as a term to obtain $x^2 + 10x + 25$, which is the square of the quantity $x + 5$.

Example 1.   Solve the equation $x^2 - 10x - 20 = 0$.
Solution: Inspection of the given equation shows that it cannot be factored with integral numbers.   Therefore the solution will be accomplished by the method of completing the square.

Given $x^2 - 10x - 20 = 0$
A : 20, $x^2 - 10x = 20$

Squaring one-half the coefficient of x and adding to both members,

$$x^2 - 10x + 25 = 20 + 25$$

Collecting terms, $x^2 - 10x + 25 = 45$

Factoring, $(x - 5)^2 = 45$

$\sqrt{}$, $x - 5 = \pm 6.71$

S:5, $x = 5 \pm 6.71$

or $x = 11.71 \; or \; -1.71$

The above answers are correct to three significant figures. The values of x are more precisely stated by maintaining the radical sign in the final roots. That is, if

$$(x - 5)^2 = 45$$

$\sqrt{}$, $x - 5 = \pm\sqrt{45}$

or $x - 5 = \pm 3\sqrt{5}$

A:5, $x = 5 \pm 3\sqrt{5}$

That is, $x = 5 + 3\sqrt{5} \; or \; 5 - 3\sqrt{5}$

Example 2. Solve the equation $3x^2 - x - 1 = 0$.

Solution: Given $3x^2 - x - 1 = 0$

D:3 (because the coefficient of x^2 must be 1), $x^2 - \frac{1}{3}x - \frac{1}{3} = 0$

Transpose the constant term. $x^2 - \frac{1}{3}x = \frac{1}{3}$

Square one-half the coefficient of x, and add to both members.

$$x^2 - \frac{1}{3}x + \frac{1}{36} = \frac{1}{3} + \frac{1}{36}$$

Collecting terms, $x^2 - \frac{1}{3}x + \frac{1}{36} = \frac{13}{36}$

Factoring, $(x - \frac{1}{6})^2 = \frac{13}{36}$

$\sqrt{}$, $x - \frac{1}{6} = \pm\dfrac{\sqrt{13}}{6}$

$$\therefore x = \frac{1 + \sqrt{13}}{6} \; or \; \frac{1 - \sqrt{13}}{6}$$

To summarize the method, we have the following:

Rule: *To solve by completing the square,*

1. *If the coefficient of the square of the unknown is not* **1**, *divide both members of the equation by the coefficient.*

2. *Transpose the constant terms (those not containing the unknown) to the right member.*

3. *Find one-half the coefficient of the unknown of the first degree; square the result; add this square to both members of the equation. This makes the left member a perfect trinomial square.*

4. *Take the square root of both members of the equation, writing the $\pm$ sign before the square root of the right member.*

5. *Solve the resulting simple equation.*

PROBLEMS 18-3

Solve by completing the square:

1. $x^2 - 3x + 2 = 0$.

2. $x^2 + x - 30 = 0$.

3. $E^2 + 10E + 24 = 0$.

4. $0 = 15 + I^2 + 10I$.

5. $R^2 - 11 - 9R = 0$.

6. $r^2 = 1 - 5r$.

7. $R^2 = 2 - \frac{3}{7}R$.

8. $I^2 - \frac{1}{8} = -\frac{3}{8}I$.

9. $3E^2 = 7E - 2$.

10. $\dfrac{5}{e - 1} = \dfrac{2e}{e + 2}$.

11. $\dfrac{5}{Z^2} = 6 - \dfrac{3}{Z}$.

12. $7 - 6R^2 = 6R(2R + 1)$.

13. $55R - 75 = 75 + 3R^2$.

14. $\dfrac{2}{I} = 3 - \dfrac{3}{3I^2 - 2I}$.

15. $E + 4 = \dfrac{1}{2E} - \dfrac{E^2 + 25}{7E}$.

18-5. Standard Form. Any quadratic equation may be written in the general form

$$ax^2 + bx + c = 0$$

This is called the *standard form* of the quadratic. Written this way, a represents the coefficient of the term containing x^2, b represents the coefficient of the term containing x, and c represents the constant term. Note that all terms of the equation, when written in standard form, are in the left member of the equation.

Example 1. Given $2x^2 + 5x - 3 = 0$. In this equation, $a = 2$, $b = 5$, and $c = -3$.

Example 2. Given $R^2 - 5R - 6 = 0$. In this equation, $a = 1$, $b = -5$, and $c = -6$.

Example 3. Given $9E^2 - 25 = 0$. In this equation, $a = 9$, $b = 0$, and $c = -25$.

18-6. Deriving a Formula for Solving Any Quadratic Equation. Because the standard form $ax^2 + bx + c = 0$ represents *any* quadratic equation, it follows that the roots of $ax^2 + bx + c = 0$ represent the roots of *any* quadratic equation. Therefore, if the standard quadratic equation can be solved for the unknown, the values, or roots, thereby obtained will serve as a formula for finding the roots of *any* quadratic equation.

This formula is derived by solving the standard form by the method of completing the square as follows:

Given $\qquad\qquad ax^2 + bx + c = 0$

Divide by a (Rule 1). $x^2 + \dfrac{bx}{a} + \dfrac{c}{a} = 0$

Transpose the constant term (Rule 2).

$$x^2 + \frac{bx}{a} = -\frac{c}{a}$$

Add the square of one-half the coefficient of x to both members (Rule 3).

$$x^2 + \frac{bx}{a} + \frac{b^2}{4a^2} = \frac{b^2}{4a^2} - \frac{c}{a}$$

Factor the left member, and add terms in right member.

$$\left(x + \frac{b}{2a}\right)^2 = \frac{b^2 - 4ac}{4a^2}$$

Take the square root of both members.

$$x + \frac{b}{2a} = \pm\,\frac{\sqrt{b^2 - 4ac}}{2a}$$

Subtract $\dfrac{b}{2a}$. $\qquad\qquad x = -\dfrac{b}{2a} \pm \dfrac{\sqrt{b^2 - 4ac}}{2a}$

Collect terms of right member. $x = \dfrac{-b \pm \sqrt{b^2 - 4ac}}{2a}$

This equation is known as the *quadratic formula.* Instead of attempting to solve a quadratic equation by factoring or by completing the square, we now make use of this general formula. Upon becoming proficient in the use of the formula, the student will find this method of solution a great convenience.

Example 1.   Solve the equation $5x^2 + 2x - 3 = 0$.
Solution: Comparing this equation with the standard form

$$ax^2 + bx + c = 0,$$

we have $a = 5$, $b = 2$, and $c = -3$.

Substituting in the quadratic formula $x = \dfrac{-b \pm \sqrt{b^2 - 4ac}}{2a}$,

$$x = \frac{-2 \pm \sqrt{2^2 - 4 \cdot 5 \cdot (-3)}}{2 \cdot 5}$$

Hence,
$$x = \frac{-2 \pm \sqrt{64}}{10}$$
$$= \frac{-2 \pm 8}{10}$$
$$= \frac{-2 + 8}{10} \text{ or } \frac{-2 - 8}{10}$$
$$\therefore x = \tfrac{3}{5} \text{ or } -1$$

Check by substituting the values of x in the given equation.

NOTE: It must be remembered that the expression $\sqrt{b^2 - 4ac}$ is the square root of the *quantity* $(b^2 - 4ac)$, *taken as a whole.*

Example 2. Solve the equation $\dfrac{3}{5 - R} = 2R$.

Solution: Clearing the fractions results in $2R^2 - 10R + 3 = 0$. Comparing this equation with the standard form $ax^2 + bx + c = 0$, we have $a = 2$, $b = -10$, and $c = 3$.

Substituting in the quadratic formula $x = \dfrac{-b \pm \sqrt{b^2 - 4ac}}{2a}$,

$$R = \frac{-(-10) \pm \sqrt{(-10)^2 - 4 \cdot 2 \cdot 3}}{2 \cdot 2}$$

Hence,
$$R = \frac{10 \pm \sqrt{76}}{4}$$

Factoring the radicand, $R = \dfrac{10 \pm 2\sqrt{19}}{4}$

Dividing both terms of the fraction by 2, $R = \dfrac{5 \pm \sqrt{19}}{2}$

$$= \frac{5 + \sqrt{19}}{2} \text{ or } \frac{5 - \sqrt{19}}{2}$$

$$\therefore R = 4.68 \text{ or } 0.320$$

These final answers are correct to three significant figures. Check the solution by the usual method.

PROBLEMS 18-4

Solve the following, using the quadratic formula:

1. $x^2 + 2x + 1 = 0$.
2. $x^2 + 2x = 8$.
3. $2x^2 + 4x - 6 = 0$.
4. $12x^2 - 6 + x = 0$.
5. $6R^2 + R - 12 = 0$.
6. $0 = 1 + 5R + 3R^2$.
7. $3I^2 = 7I - 2$.
8. $15E^2 = 22E + 5$.
9. $r^2 + 2 = 4r$.
10. $e^2 + e = 1$.
11. $\dfrac{3}{\theta} + 5 = \dfrac{2}{\theta - 1}$.
12. $\dfrac{3}{d - 2} = 1 + \dfrac{2}{d + 3}$.
13. $\dfrac{i - 2}{i} = 1 - i$.
14. $ax^2 + 2x = bx$.

15. $\dfrac{3R + 2}{2R + 4} = \dfrac{R + 2}{2R}.$ **16.** $\dfrac{3R - 5}{2R - 5} = 1 + \dfrac{2R + 5}{3R + 5}.$

17. $\dfrac{I}{5 - I} = \dfrac{3}{2} - \dfrac{5I}{12}.$ **18.** $\dfrac{E^2}{E - 5} = -\dfrac{5}{2}.$

19. $\dfrac{2}{R - 2} - \dfrac{1}{R + 2} + \dfrac{15}{8} = 0.$ **20.** $0 = 6 - \dfrac{R - 2}{R + 2} + \dfrac{R - 1}{R + 1}.$

In solving problems involving quadratic equations, two sets of results are obtained (roots). In some cases, both satisfy the conditions of the problem; in other cases, only one satisfies the conditions. Therefore, we reject obviously impossible answers and retain the ones that satisfy the conditions of the problem.

21. The square of a certain number plus four times the number is 12 Find the number.

Solution: Let x = the number.

Then x^2 = square of the number
and $4x$ = four times the number
From the problem, $x^2 + 4x = 12$
S:12, $x^2 + 4x - 12 = 0$
Factoring, $(x + 6)(x - 2) = 0$
Hence, $x = -6$ or $+2$
Substituting -6 for x in the equation, $(-6)^2 + 4(-6) = 12$
$$36 - 24 = 12$$

This root satisfies the equation.
Substituting 2 for x in the equation, $(2)^2 + 4 \cdot 2 = 12$
$$4 + 8 = 12$$

This root also satisfies the equation. Hence, both answers are correct.

22. Find two positive consecutive numbers whose product is 600.

23. The sum of a certain number and its reciprocal is $2\frac{1}{12}$. Find the number.

24. Find the dimensions of a rectangle whose area is 2394 sq ft if the sum of its length and width is 101 ft.

25. Find the dimensions of a right triangle if its hypotenuse is 40 ft and the base exceeds the altitude by 8 ft.

In any right triangle, $c^2 = a^2 + b^2$ as shown in Fig. 18-1.

$$c = 40, \qquad a = b - 8,$$
$$1600 = (b - 8)^2 + b^2.$$

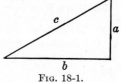

Fig. 18-1.

26. One number is 5 less than another number, and the sum of their squares is 277. Find the numbers.

27. Can the sides of a right triangle ever be consecutive even integers? If so, find these integers.

28. The formula for kinetic energy is given by K.E. $= \frac{1}{2}mv^2$. Find the value of v when $m = 10$, and K.E. $= 2 \times 10^7$.

29. Given $F = \dfrac{Wv^2}{32r}$. Solve for v. If W is doubled and F and r are held constant, what happens to v?

30. A ball bearing rolls down a sloping groove and travels a length $L = 6t + \dfrac{t^2}{2}$ in t sec. Solve for t.

31. The impedance of an a-c series circuit is given by the formula

$$Z = \sqrt{R^2 + X^2},$$

where R is the resistance and X is the reactance, both in ohms. Find the value of the reactance if $Z = 100 \ \Omega$ and $R = 40 \ \Omega$.

32. The conductance factor of an a-c circuit is given by the formula $g = \dfrac{R}{R^2 + X^2}$. Find the value of X, if $R = 50 \ \Omega$ and $g = 4 \times 10^{-3}$ mho.

33. If an object is thrown straight upward with a velocity of v ft per second, its height t sec later is given by the formula $h = vt - 16t^2$. If a shell were shot upward with a velocity of 1600 ft per second, at what time would its height be 10,000 ft (a) on the way up, (b) on the way down?

34. In an a-c series circuit, resonance exists when $2\pi fL = \dfrac{1}{2\pi fC}$. Solve for f.

35. In the formula for resonant frequency found in the preceding problem, f is in cycles, L is in henrys, and C is in farads. Find the frequency in kilocycles when $C = 250 \ \mu\mu$f and $L = 200 \ \mu$h.

36. In a series circuit containing resistance and inductance, the formula for the current is $I = \dfrac{E}{\sqrt{R^2 + \omega^2 L^2}}$, where E is the voltage across the circuit, R is the resistance in ohms, and L is the inductance in henrys. Find the value of L to three significant figures if $E = 282$ v, $R = 100 \ \Omega$, $I = 2$ a, $\omega = 2\pi f$, and $f = 60 \sim$.

37. The volume of a circular cylinder is given by the formula $v = \pi r^2 h$, where r is the radius and h is the altitude. Find the diameter when $v = 1$ qt and $h = 6$ in. (1 gal = 231 cu in.)

38. Given $W = \dfrac{I^2 R}{N}$. Solve for I.

39. The distance s in feet through which an object will fall in t sec is given by the formula $s = \frac{1}{2}gt^2$, where $g = 32.2$. The velocity attained by the object after t sec is given by $v = gt$. Solve for the velocity in terms of g and s.

40. $P = \dfrac{R(r^2 + x^2)}{r(Rr + Xx)}$. Solve for r and x.

41. The susceptance factor of an a-c circuit is given by $b = \dfrac{X}{R^2 + X^2}$ Find the value of R to three significant figures if $X = 40 \ \Omega$ and $b = 0.0111$ mho.

42. The following relations exist in the Wien bridge:

$$\omega^2 = \frac{1}{R_1 R_2 c_1 c_2}, \qquad \frac{c_1}{c_2} = \frac{R_b - R_2}{R_a R_1}$$

Solve for c_1 and c_2 in terms of resistance components and ω.

43. The e.m.f. of a storage battery is 6.3 v, and its internal resistance is 0.015 Ω. The battery is used to drive a dynamotor that requires 300 w. What current will the battery deliver to the dynamotor, and what will be the voltage reading across the battery terminals while supplying this current?

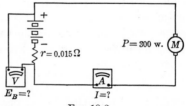

Solution: The circuit is represented in Fig. 18-2.

FIG. 18-2.

Let P = power consumed by dyna-
          motor = 300 w,

E_B = voltage across battery terminals when dynamotor is delivering
          300 w.

Since $I = \dfrac{P}{E_B}$

then $I = \dfrac{300}{E_B}$

Now $E_B = 6.3 - rI$

Substituting for r, $E_B = 6.3 - 0.015I$

Substituting for I, $E_B = 6.3 - 0.015 \left(\dfrac{300}{E_B}\right)$

Multiplying, $E_B = 6.3 - \dfrac{4.5}{E_B}$

Clearing fractions, $E_B{}^2 = 6.3 \, E_B - 4.5$

Transposing, $E_B{}^2 - 6.3 E_B + 4.5 = 0$

This equation is a quadratic in E_B; hence, $a = 1$, $b = -6.3$, and $c = 4.5$. Substituting these values in the quadratic formula,

$$E_B = \frac{-(-6.3) \pm \sqrt{(-6.3)^2 - 4 \cdot 1 \cdot 4.5}}{2 \cdot 1}$$

or $$E_B = \frac{6.3 \pm \sqrt{21.7}}{2}$$

$$\therefore E_B = 5.48 \text{ v or } 0.82 \text{ v}$$

$$I = \frac{300}{E_B} = \frac{300}{5.48} = 54.7 \text{ a}$$

Why was 5.48 v chosen instead of 0.82 v in the above solution?

44. A generator with an e.m.f. of 120 v and an internal resistance of 0.10 Ω is delivering 2.5 kw to a load through two No. 0 feeders that are 1500 ft long. What is the voltage across the load?

45. A generator with an e.m.f. of 240 v and an internal resistance of 0.25 Ω is delivering 5 kw to a load through two No. 8 feeders that are 500 ft long. What is the generator terminal voltage?

18-7. Graphical Solution of Quadratic Equations.

The graphs of quadratic equations may be plotted in a manner similar to the straight-line graphs of Chap. XV. Because the quadratic equations with which we are concerned in this article contain only one unknown, or variable, it becomes necessary to express these equations in terms of another variable in order to plot values using both X and Y axes. For example, the equation

$$x^2 - 10x + 16 = 0$$

could not be plotted in its present form because the equation contains no dependent variable. Therefore, we agree to set such quadratic equations equal to y, which will represent the dependent variable. That is, for the above equation,

$$y = x^2 - 10x + 16$$

The equation in this form may be plotted, because, for every value assigned to x, there will be corresponding values of y.

Example 1. Graph the equation $x^2 - 10x + 16 = 0$.
Solution: Setting the equation equal to y,

$$y = x^2 - 10x + 16$$

Make a table of the values of y corresponding to assigned values of x, as shown:

If x =	0	1	3	4	5	6	7	8	9	10
Then x^2 =	0	1	9	16	25	36	49	64	81	100
$10x$ =	0	10	30	40	50	60	70	80	90	100
$x^2 - 10x$ =	0	−9	−21	−24	−25	−24	−21	−16	−9	0
$\therefore y = x^2 - 10x + 16$ =	16	7	−5	−8	−9	−8	−5	0	7	16

Plotting the corresponding values of x and y as pairs of coordinates and drawing a smooth curve through the points result in the graph shown in Fig.18-3.

From the figure, it is apparent that the graph has two X intercepts at $x = 2$ and $x = 8$. That is, when $y = 0$, the graph crosses the X axis at $x = 2$ and $x = 8$. This is to be expected; for when $y = 0$, the given equation $x^2 - 10x + 16 = 0$ can be solved algebraically to obtain $x = 2$ or 8.   Hence, it is evident that the points at which the graph crosses the X axis denote the values of x when $y = 0$, which are the roots of the equation.

Another interesting fact regarding this graph is that the curve goes through a *minimum value.*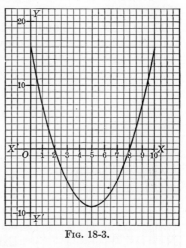
Suppose it is desired to solve for the coordinates of the point of minimum value. First, if the equation is changed to standard form, we obtain $a = 1, b = -10$, and $c = 16$. If the value of $\dfrac{-b}{2a}$ is computed, the result is the x value, or abscissa, of the minimum point on the curve. That is,

$$x = -\frac{b}{2a} = -\frac{(-10)}{2 \times 1} = \frac{10}{2} = 5$$

FIG. 18-3.

Substituting this value of x in the original equation,

$$y = x^2 - 10x + 16$$
$$y = 5^2 - 10 \cdot 5 + 16 = -9$$

Thus, the point $(5, -9)$ is where the curve passes through a minimum value.   That is, the dependent variable y is a minimum and equal to -9 when x, the independent variable, is equal to 5.

Every quadratic function of the form $ax^2 + bx + c = 0$ has a curve of this general shape.   Such a curve is called a *parabola.* The parabola opens *upward* if a is positive and *downward* if a is negative.

Example 2.   Graph the equation $27 - 3x - 4x^2 = 0$.
Solution: Equating $y = 27 - 3x - 4x^2$ and assigning values to x results in a table of values, as shown:

If x =	-4	-3	-2	-1	0	1	2	3
Then $3x$ =	-12	-9	-6	-3	0	3	6	9
$27 - 3x$ =	39	36	33	30	27	24	21	18
x^2 =	16	9	4	1	0	1	4	9
$4x^2$ =	64	36	16	4	0	4	16	36
$\therefore y = 27 - 3x - 4x^2$ =	-25	0	17	26	27	20	5	-18

Plotting the corresponding values of x and y as pairs of coordinates and drawing a smooth curve through them result in the graph shown in Fig. 18-4.

From the graph of the equation, it is observed:

(a) The roots (solution) of the equation are denoted by the X intercepts.

These are $x = -3$ and $x = 2.25$.   These may be checked algebraically to obtain

$$27 - 3x - 4x^2 = 0$$

Factoring, $(3 + x)(9 - 4x) = 0$

$$x = -3 \text{ or } 2.25$$

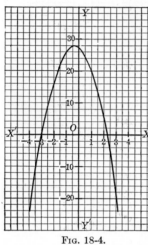

Fig. 18-4.

(b) The parabola opens *downward* because the coefficient of x^2 is negative.   ($a = -4$.)

(c) Because the parabola opens downward, the graph goes through a *maximum* value. The point of maximum value is found in the same manner as the minimum point of Example 1.   That is,

$$x = \frac{-b}{2a} = \frac{-(-3)}{2(-4)} = -\frac{3}{8}$$

Substituting $-\frac{3}{8}$ for x in the original equation,

$$y = 27 - 3(-\tfrac{3}{8}) - 4(-\tfrac{3}{8})^2 = 27.6$$

Thus, the dependent variable y is a maximum and equal to 27.6 when x, the independent variable, is equal to $-\frac{3}{8}$.

Example 3.   Graph the equations

(a) $y = x^2 - 8x + 12$
(b) $y = x^2 - 8x + 16$
(c) $y = x^2 - 8x + 20$

Solution: As before, make up a table of y values for each equation, corresponding to assigned values of x. Using these x and y values as pairs of coordinates, plot the graphs of the equations. These graphs are shown in Fig. 18-5.

The coefficients of the equations are the same except for the values of the constant term c.

From the graphs of the equations, it is observed that

(*a*) The curve of (*a*) intercepts the *X* axis at $x = 2$ and $x = 6$, and the roots of the equation are thus denoted as $x = 2$ or 6. This checks with the algebraic solution.

(*b*) The curve of (*b*) just *touches* the *X* axis at $x = 4$. Solving (*b*) algebraically shows that the roots are *equal*, both roots being 4.

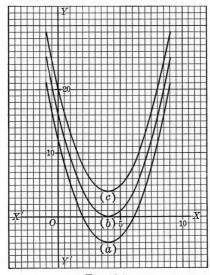

Fig. 18-5.

(*c*) The curve of (*c*) does not intersect or touch the *X* axis. Solving (*c*) algebraically results in the "imaginary" roots $x = 4 \pm j2$.

(*d*) All curves pass through minimum values at points having equal *x* values. This is as expected, for the *x* value of a maximum or a minimum is given by $x = -\dfrac{b}{2a}$, and these values are equal in each of the given equations.

(*e*) Checking the *y* values of the minima, it is seen that they must be affected by the constant terms; for, as previously mentioned, the other coefficients of the equations are the same.

PROBLEMS 18-5

Graph the following equations all on the same sheet with the same axes:

1. (*a*) $x^2 - 6x - 16 = 0.$ (*d*) $x^2 - 6x + 5 = 0.$
   (*b*) $x^2 - 6x - 7 = 0.$ (*e*) $x^2 - 6x + 9 = 0.$
   (*c*) $x^2 - 6x = 0.$ (*f*) $x^2 - 6x + 12 = 0.$
   (*g*) $x^2 - 6x + 15 = 0.$

Does changing the constant term change only the position of the graphs and the solutions of the equations? Do all the parabolas open upward? Explain your answer. Do all the graphs pass through minimum values at the same value of x? Explain your answer.

2. Solve the foregoing equations algebraically. Do these solutions check with the graph of the equations?

3. Find the value of $(b^2 - 4ac)$ for each equation. Do you see any connection between these values and the graphs?

18-8. The Discriminant of a Quadratic Equation. The quantity under the radical in the quadratic formula $(b^2 - 4ac)$ is called the *discriminant* of the quadratic equation. The two roots of the equation are

$$x = \frac{-b + \sqrt{b^2 - 4ac}}{2a} \qquad \text{and} \qquad x = \frac{-b - \sqrt{b^2 - 4ac}}{2a}$$

Now, if $b^2 - 4ac = 0$, it is apparent that the two roots are equal. Also, if $b^2 - 4ac$ is *positive*, each of the roots is a *real* number. But if $b^2 - 4ac$ is *negative*, the roots are *imaginary*. Therefore, there is a direct relationship between the value of the discriminant and the roots, and hence the graph, of a quadratic equation.

For example, the discriminants of the equations of Example 3 in the preceding article are

(a) $b^2 - 4ac = (-8)^2 - 4 \cdot 1 \cdot 12 = 16$
(b) $b^2 - 4ac = (-8)^2 - 4 \cdot 1 \cdot 16 = 0$
(c) $b^2 - 4ac = (-8)^2 - 4 \cdot 1 \cdot 20 = -16$

Upon checking these values with the curves of Fig. 18-5, and also the values of the discriminants found in the preceding exercises with their respective curves, it is evident that the roots of a quadratic equation are

1. Real and unequal if and only if $b^2 - 4ac$ is positive.
2. Real and equal if and only if $b^2 - 4ac = 0$.
3. Imaginary and unequal if and only if $b^2 - 4ac$ is negative.
4. Rational if and only if $b^2 - 4ac$ is a perfect square.

18-9. Maximum and Minimum Conditions. As previously stated, in the general quadratic equation $ax^2 + bx + c = 0$, the relation $x = \dfrac{-b}{2a}$ gives the value of the independent variable x at which the dependent variable y will be maximum or minimum.

Then by substituting this value of x, the independent variable, in the equation the corresponding value of y may be obtained. Also, it has been shown that the function will be maximum if a, the coefficient of x^2, is negative because the curve opens downward. Similarly, if the coefficient of x^2 is positive, the curve will pass through a minimum because the curve opens upward.

This knowledge facilitates the solutions of many problems that heretofore would have involved considerable labor.

Example 1.   A source of electromotive force E, with an internal resistance r, is connected to a load of variable resistance R.   What will be the value of R, with respect to r, when maximum power is being delivered to the load?

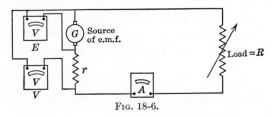

Fig. 18-6.

Solution: The circuit may be represented as shown in Fig. 18-6.   By Ohm's law, the current flowing through the circuit is

$$I = \frac{E}{r + R} \tag{1}$$

The power delivered to the external circuit is

$$P = VI = I^2 R \tag{2}$$

where V is the terminal voltage of the source and is

$$V = E - Ir \tag{3}$$

Now the terminal voltage V will decrease as the current I increases.   Therefore, the power P supplied to the load is a function of the two variables V and I.   Substituting Eq. (3) in Eq. (2),

$$P = (E - Ir)I = EI - I^2 r$$

that is, $$P = -rI^2 + EI \tag{4}$$

Equation (4) is a quadratic in I, where $a = -r$ and $b = E$.   Then, since, for maximum conditions, $I = \dfrac{-b}{2a}$,

$$I = \frac{-b}{2a} = \frac{-E}{2(-r)} = \frac{E}{2r} \tag{5}$$

which is the value of the current through the circuit when maximum power is being delivered to the load.

Substituting Eq. (5) in Eq. (1), $\dfrac{E}{2r} = \dfrac{E}{r + R}$ (6)

Solving equation (6) for R, $R = r$ (7)

Equation (7) shows that maximum power will be delivered to any load when the resistance of that load is equal to the internal resistance of the source of electromotive force.   This is one of the most important concepts in communication engineering.   For example, we are concerned with obtaining maximum power output from several types of power amplifier.   This is accomplished when the amplifier load resistance matches the plate resistance of the associated vacuum tube.   Also, maximum power is delivered to an antenna circuit when the impedance of the antenna is made to match that of the transmission line that feeds it.

In Fig. 18-7, power delivered to the load is plotted against values of the load resistance R_L when a storage battery is used,

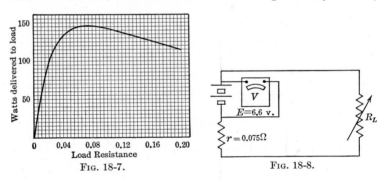

Fig. 18-7.   Fig. 18-8.

with an electromotive force E of 6.6 volts and an internal resistance $r = 0.075$ ohm.   The circuit is as shown in Fig. 18-8.

It is apparent that, when the battery or any other source of electromotive force is delivering maximum power, half the power is lost within the battery.   Under these conditions, therefore, the efficiency of the battery is 50 per cent.

At what value of R_L does maximum *current* flow in the circuit of Fig. 18-8?   When the current is maximum how much power is dissipated within the battery?   What is the terminal voltage under these conditions?

Example 2. If an object is thrown vertically upward with an initial velocity of V_0 feet per second, the height h it will reach after t seconds may be found by the formula $h = V_0 t - 16t^2$. Derive a formula for the maximum height attained for any initial velocity V_0.

Solution: Given
$$h = V_0 t - 16t^2 \tag{1}$$

Equation (1) is a quadratic in t; and, in standard form, $a = -16$, and $b = V_0$. Because h, the dependent variable, will be maximum when $t = \dfrac{-b}{2a}$,

$$t = \frac{-b}{2a} = \frac{-V_0}{2(-16)} = \frac{V_0}{32}$$

Substituting $\dfrac{V_0}{32}$ for t in Eq. (1), $\quad h = V_0 \left(\dfrac{V_0}{32}\right) - 16 \left(\dfrac{V_0}{32}\right)^2 = \dfrac{V_0^2}{64}$

Therefore, any object thrown vertically upward with an initial velocity of V_0 feet per second will attain a maximum height of $h = \dfrac{V_0^2}{64}$ ft.

Check this solution by assigning some initial velocity and plotting height in feet against time in seconds.

CHAPTER XIX

KIRCHHOFF'S LAWS

An understanding of Kirchhoff's laws, plus the ability to apply them in analyzing circuit conditions, furnishes the student with a keener insight into the behavior of electric circuits and, in addition, enables him to solve circuit problems that, with only a knowledge of Ohm's law, would be very difficult in some cases and impossible in others.

19-1. Direction of Current Flow. As stated in Art. 9-1, the most generally accepted concept of an electric current is that it consists of a motion of electrons from a negative toward a more positive point in a circuit. That is, a positively charged body is taken to be one that is deficient in electrons, whereas a negatively

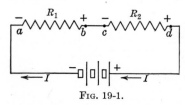

FIG. 19-1.

charged body carries an excess of electrons. When the two are joined by a conductor, electrons flow from the negative charge to the positive charge. Hence, if two such points in a circuit are maintained at a difference of potential, a *continuous* flow of electrons, or current, will take place from negative to positive. Therefore, in the consideration of Kirchhoff's laws, current will be considered as flowing from the negative terminal of a source of electromotive force, through the external circuit, and back to the positive terminal of the source. Thus, in Fig. 19-1, the current flows away from the negative terminal of the battery, through R_1 and R_2, and back to the positive terminal of the battery. Note that point b is positive with respect to point a and that point d is positive with respect to point c.

19-2. Statement of Kirchhoff's Laws. In 1847, G. R. Kirchhoff extended Ohm's law by two important statements which have become known as Kirchhoff's laws. These laws may be stated as follows:

258

1. *The algebraic sum of the currents at any junction of conductors is zero.* That is, at any point in a circuit, there is as much current flowing away from the point as there is flowing toward it.

2. *The algebraic sum of the electromotive forces and voltage drops around any closed circuit is zero.* That is, in any closed circuit, the applied electromotive force is equal to the voltage drops around the circuit.

These laws are straightforward and need no proof here; for the first is self-evident from the study of parallel circuits, and the second was stated in different words in Art. 9-8. When properly applied, they enable one to set up equations for any circuit and solve for the unknown circuit components, voltages, or currents as required.

19-3. Application of Second Law to Series Circuits. The second law is considered first because of its applications to problems with which the student is already familiar.

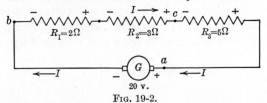

Fig. 19-2.

Figure 19-2 represents a 20-volt generator connected to three series resistances. The validity of Kirchhoff's second law was demonstrated in Art. 9-8; that is, in any closed circuit the applied electromotive force is equal to the sum of the voltage drops around the circuit. Thus, neglecting the internal resistance of the generator and the resistance of the connecting wires in Fig. 19-2,

$$E = IR_1 + IR_2 + IR_3 \qquad (1)$$

or $\qquad 20 = 2I + 3I + 5I$

Hence, $\qquad I = 2$ a

Equation (1) is satisfactory for a circuit containing one source of electromotive force. However, by considering the circuit from a different viewpoint, the voltage relations around the circuit become more understandable. For example, by starting at any point in the circuit, such as point *a*, we proceed completely around the circuit, in the direction of current flow, remembering that when current passes through a resistance there is a voltage drop that represents a loss and therefore is subtractive. Also, in going around the circuit, sources of electromotive force represent a gain in voltage if they tend to aid current flow and therefore are additive. By this method, according to the second law, the algebraic sum of all electromotive forces and voltage drops around the circuit is zero. For example, in starting at point a in Fig. 19-2 and proceeding around the circuit in the direction of current flow, the first thing encountered is the positive terminal of a source of electromotive force of 20 volts. Because this causes current to flow in the direction we are going, it is written $+20$. This is easily remembered, for the positive terminal was the first one encountered; therefore, write it plus. Next comes R_1 which is responsible for a *drop* in voltage due to the current I passing through it. Hence, this voltage drop is written $-IR_1$ or $-2I$, for R_1 is known to be 2 ohms. R_2 and R_3 are treated in a similar manner because both represent voltage *drops*. This completes the trip around the circuit; and, by equating the algebraic sum of the electromotive force and voltage drops to zero,

$$20 - 2I - 3I - 5I = 0 \qquad (2)$$

or
$$I = 2 \text{ a}$$

Note that Eq. (2) is simply a different form of Eq. (1). If the polarities of the sources of electromotive force are marked, they will serve as an aid in remembering whether to add or subtract. In going around the circuit, if the first terminal of a source of electromotive force is positive, it is added; if negative, the electromotive force is subtracted.

The point at which to start around the circuit is purely a matter of choice, for the algebraic sum of all voltages around the circuit is equal to zero. For example, starting at point b,

$$-2I - 3I - 5I + 20 = 0$$
$$I = 2 \text{ a}$$

Starting at point c,

$$-5I + 20 - 2I - 3I = 0$$
$$I = 2 \text{ a}$$

Example. Find the amount of current flowing in the circuit represented in Fig. 19-3 if the internal resistance of battery E_1 is 0.3 ohm, that of E_2 is 0.2 ohm, and that of E_3 is 0.5 ohm.

Solution: Figure 19-4 is a diagram of the circuit in which the internal resistances are represented as an aid in setting up the circuit equation.

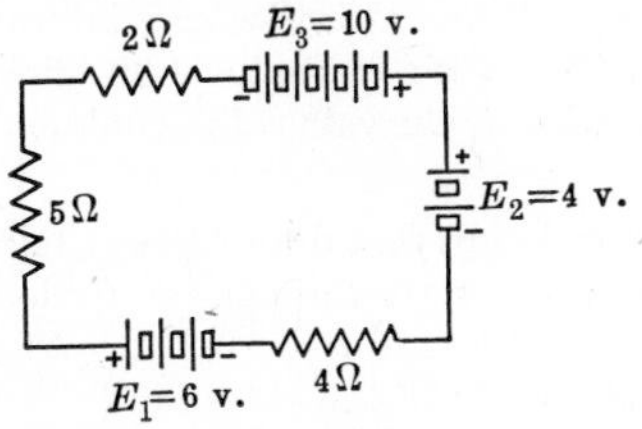

Fig. 19-3. 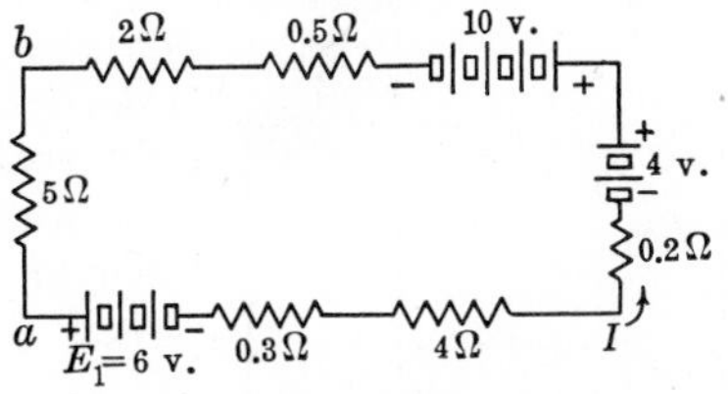   Fig. 19-4.

Beginning at point *a* and going around the circuit in the direction of current flow,

$$6 - 0.3I - 4I - 0.2I - 4 + 10 - 0.5I - 2I - 5I = 0$$

Hence, $$I = 1 \text{ a}$$

In more complicated circuits the direction of the current is often in doubt. However, this need cause no confusion, for the direction of current flow may be *assumed* and the circuit equation written in the usual manner. If the current results in a negative value when the equation is solved, the negative sign denotes that the assumed direction was wrong. As an example, let it be assumed that the current in the circuit of Fig. 19-4 flows in the direction from *a* to *b*. Then, starting at point *a* and going around the circuit in the assumed direction,

$$-5I - 2I - 0.5I - 10 + 4 - 0.2I - 4I - 0.3I - 6 = 0$$
$$I = -1 \text{ a}$$

As stated above, the minus sign shows that the assumed direction of the current was wrong; therefore, the current flows in the direction from *b* to *a*.

PROBLEMS 19-1

Solve the following problems by using Kirchhoff's second law:

1. Three resistors $R_1 = 4 \ \Omega$, $R_2 = 2 \ \Omega$, and $R_3 = 5.5 \ \Omega$ are connected in series across a 12-v battery whose internal resistance is 0.5 Ω. How much current flows in the circuit?

2. Four resistors $R_1 = 23 \ \Omega$, $R_2 = 16 \ \Omega$, $R_3 = 35 \ \Omega$, and $R_4 = 9 \ \Omega$ are connected in series across a 120-v battery whose internal resistance is 5.9Ω. How much current flows in the circuit?

3. Three resistors $R_1 = 1.5 \ \Omega$, $R_2 = 2.3 \ \Omega$, and $R_3 = 2.1 \ \Omega$ are connected in series across a battery whose internal resistance is 0.1 Ω. If 0.5 a flows through the circuit, what is the terminal voltage of the battery?

HINT: Let E equal the unknown terminal voltage.

4. Three resistors $R_1 = 1$ Ω, $R_2 = 3.6$ Ω, $R_3 = 2.55$ Ω, and an unknown resistance are connected in series across a 12-v battery whose internal resistance is 0.05 Ω. If a current of 1.39 a flows in the circuit, what is the value of the unknown resistance?

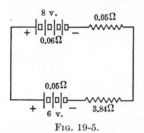

FIG. 19-5.

5. A bank of lamps that draws 25 a at 110 v is connected to a generator through two feeders, each of which has a resistance of 0.2 Ω. What is the terminal voltage of the generator?

6. A generator with a terminal voltage of 240 v is supplying 56.8 a to a motor through two feeders each of which has a resistance of 0.088 Ω. What is the voltage across the motor?

7. How much current flows in the circuit represented by Fig. 19-5?

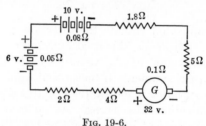

FIG. 19-6.

8. How much current flows in the circuit of Fig. 19-6?

9. What is the value of R in Fig. 19-7?

10. What is the value of the current in Fig. 19-8?

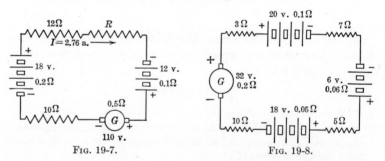

FIG. 19-7.   FIG. 19-8.

19-4. Simple Applications of Both Laws. Although the circuits of the following examples can be solved by Ohm's law, they are included here because the student is familiar with such circuits. No trouble will be encountered in solving circuits that appear to be complicated if one understands the applications of

Kirchhoff's laws to simple circuits, for all circuits are combinations of the fundamental series and parallel circuits.

Example 1.   A generator supplies 7 amperes to two resistances of 40 ohms and 30 ohms connected in parallel.   Neglecting the internal resistance of the generator and the resistance of the connecting wires, what is the generator voltage and the current through each resistance?

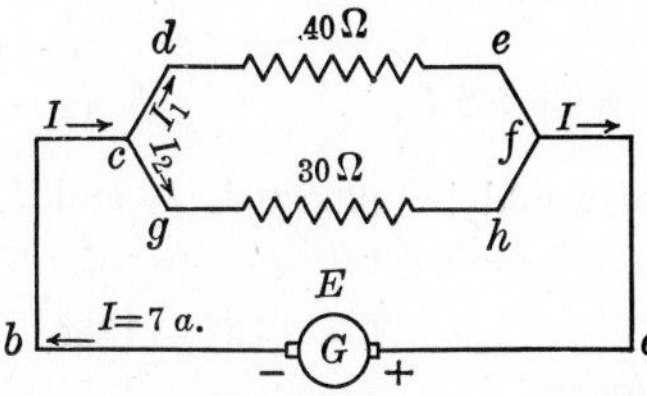

Solution: Figure 19-9 is a diagram of the circuit.   From our knowledge of parallel circuits, it is evident that the line current I divides at junction c into the branch currents I_1 and I_2. Similarly, I_1 and I_2 combine at junction f to form the line current I. Therefore,

FIG. 19-9.

$$I = I_1 + I_2$$

which is the same as $I - I_1 - I_2 = 0$ (3)

These are algebraic expressions for Kirchhoff's first law and, when used in conjunction with the second law, facilitate solution of circuits.

Upon starting at the point a and going around the circuit in the direction of current flow, the equation for the voltages around path $abcdefa$ is

$$E - 40I_1 = 0$$

$$I_1 = \frac{E}{40}$$ (4)

The equation for the voltages around path $abcghfa$ is

$$E - 30I_2 = 0$$

$$I_2 = \frac{E}{30}$$ (5)

Substituting the known values in Eq. (3),

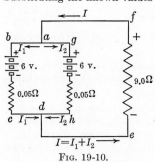

FIG. 19-10.

$$7 - \frac{E}{40} - \frac{E}{30} = 0$$

$$E = 120 \text{ v}$$

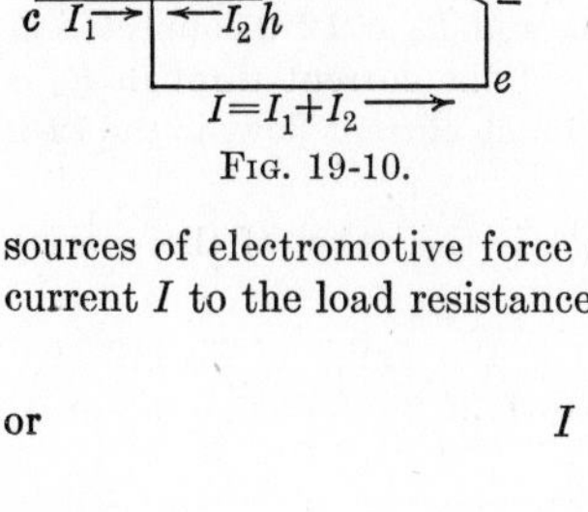

$I_1 = 3$ amperes and $I_2 = 4$ amperes are found from Eqs. (4) and (5), respectively.

Example 2.   Two 6-volt batteries, each with an internal resistance of 0.05 ohm, are connected in parallel to a load resistance of 9.0 ohms.   How much current flows through the load resistance?

Solution: Figure 19-10 is a diagram of the circuit.   In this circuit, two identical sources of electromotive force are connected in parallel to supply the line current I to the load resistance.   Again,

$$I = I_1 + I_2$$

or $I - I_1 - I_2 = 0$

Starting at junction a, the equation for the voltages around path $abcdefa$ is

$$6 - 0.05I_1 - 9I = 0$$

Solving for I_1, $I_1 = 120 - 180I$ (6)

Starting at junction a, the equation for the voltages around path $aghdefa$ is

$$6 - 0.05I_2 - 9I = 0$$

Solving for I_2, $I_2 = 120 - 180I$ (7)

As would be expected, I_1 and I_2 are equal. Substituting the values of I_1 and I_2 in Eq. (3),

$$I - (120 - 180I) - (120 - 180I) = 0$$

Hence, $I = 0.6648$ a

The foregoing solution assumes three unknowns I, I_1, and I_2. However, in writing the equations for the voltages around any path, only two unknowns may be used, for $I = I_1 + I_2$. Thus, around path $abcdefa$,

$$6 - 0.05I_1 - 9(I_1 + I_2) = 0$$

Collecting terms, $9.05I_1 + 9I_2 = 6$ (8)

Voltages around path $aghdefa$,

$$6 - 0.05I_2 - 9(I_1 + I_2) = 0$$

Collecting terms, $9I_1 + 9.05I_2 = 6$ (9)

Since Eqs. (8) and (9) are simultaneous equations, they can be solved for I_1 and I_2. Hence,

$$I_1 = 0.3324 \text{ a}$$
and $$I_2 = 0.3324 \text{ a}$$
$$I = I_1 + I_2 = 0.6648 \text{ a}$$

PROBLEMS 19-2

1. A battery supplies 8 a to two resistances of 12 Ω and 20 Ω connected in parallel. What is the voltage across the resistors?

2. A generator supplies 9 a to three resistances of 3, 6, and 4 Ω connected in parallel. What is the voltage across the resistors?

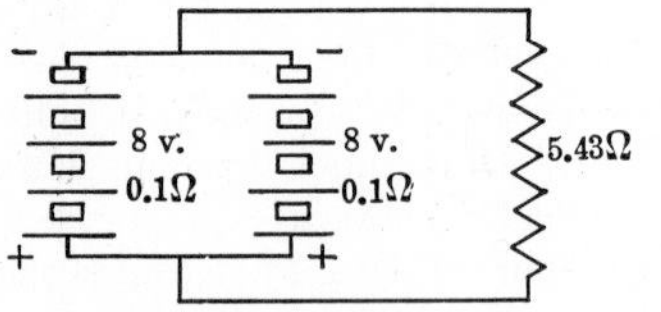

3. A circuit consists of $R_1 = 3$ Ω, $R_2 = 9$ Ω, and $R_3 = 12$ Ω connected in parallel. If the current through R_2 is 6 a, how much current flows in the 12-Ω branch?

Fig. 19-11.

4. What is the value of the current in the circuit of Fig. 19-11?

5. What would be the value of the current in the circuit of Fig. 19-11 if the load resistance was changed from 5.43 Ω to 1 Ω?

6. In a circuit connected as in Fig. 19-11, each battery has an e.m.f. of 12 v and an internal resistance of 0.2 Ω.   How much current flows through the load resistance which is 13 Ω?

7. (*a*) What is the generator current in the circuit of Fig. 19-12?

   (*b*) In what direction does the current flow?

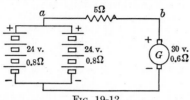

FIG. 19-12.

8. (*a*) What is the value of the generator current in the circuit of Fig. 19-12 if the generator terminal voltage is decreased to 12 v?

   (*b*) In what direction does the current flow?

19-5. Three-wire Distribution Systems.   Three-wire distribution systems are widely used for both direct- and alternating-current systems.   A three-wire system may receive its energy either from a three-wire generator or from two generators of equal voltage connected in series.   In either case, in solving such circuits, it is convenient to consider the three-wire system as receiving its energy from two generators as illustrated in Fig. 19-13. The wire that is connected at the junction between the generators is called the *neutral* wire because, when *equal* loads are connected at the same point between the outside wires and the neutral wire, the latter carries no current.

Example 1.   In the three-wire system represented in Fig. 19-13, load 1 draws 10 amperes and load 2 draws 12 amperes.   If the terminal voltage of each generator is 120 volts. determine the voltage across each load.

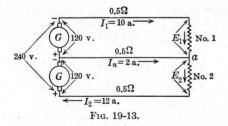

FIG. 19-13.

Solution: Label the direction and amount of each current as in Fig. 19-13. Thus a current I_1 of 10 amperes, due to load 1, flows *toward* junction *a*. Also, $I_n = 2$ amperes, in the neutral wire, flows *toward* junction *a* in order to make a total of $I_2 = 12$ amperes for load 2.   This latter current flows *away* from junction a. By assigning positive values for currents flowing toward the junction and a negative value for the current leaving the junction,

$$I_1 + I_n - I_2 = 0$$

Substituting values, $10 + 2 - 12 = 0$

which checks according to Kirchhoff's first law.

Let E_1 and E_2 be the voltages across loads 1 and 2, respectively. Then, starting at the positive terminal of each generator and going around the corresponding closed circuit in the direction of load current, the voltage equations are

For generator G_1, $120 - (10 \times 0.5) - E_1 + (2 \times 0.5) = 0$ (10)

$$E_1 = 116 \text{ v}$$

For generator G_2, $120 - (2 \times 0.5) - E_2 - (12 \times 0.5) = 0$ (11)

$$E_2 = 113 \text{ v}$$

In Eq. (10) the difference of potential due to the resistance of the neutral wire was *added* because the path around the circuit was against the direction of current in the neutral wire. In Eq. (11), this difference of potential was *subtracted* because the path around the circuit was in the direction of the current and therefore represented a voltage drop.

In dealing with three-wire distribution systems, it is well to remember that the difference between the currents in the outside wires flows in the neutral wire and that its direction is the same as that of the smaller of the currents in the outside wires. This is demonstrated in Fig. 19-13.

Example 2.   Figure 19-14 represents a three-wire distribution circuit in which loads 1, 2, 3, and 4 consist of lamps, each of which draws 1 ampere. In addition, a motor M, which draws 25 amperes, is connected across the outside wires. Determine the voltage across each group of lamps and the voltage across the motor.

Solution: First determine the amount and direction of the currents in all the wires of the system. This is conveniently accomplished by starting with the load at the end of the line and working back toward the generator until the currents in the outside wires are determined. From these, the neutral-wire currents are found. Thus, starting with the motor M of Fig. 19-14, it is apparent that the outside wires from loads 2 and 4 will carry 25 amperes. Because load 2 draws 15 amperes, the outside wire between loads 1 and 2 must carry this current plus the motor current, or $15 + 25 = 40$ a. Similarly, load 1 draws 10 amperes which must be carried by the outside wire between generator G_1 and load 1, in addition to the 40 amperes drawn by load 2 and the motor, or $10 + 40 = 50$ amperes. In like manner, the currents in the other outside wires are found, and their direction is marked. Then, because the neutral wire must supply the difference in currents between outside wires, the neutral current for each section is found, the

direction being that of the smallest current in the outside wires.   The work
can then be checked by Kirchhoff's first law: There must be as much current
flowing away from a junction as there is current flowing toward it.

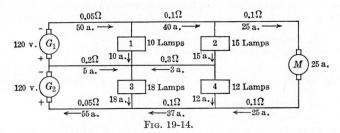

Fig. 19-14.

Let E_1, E_2, E_3, E_4, and E_M represent the voltages across loads 1, 2, 3, 4,
and M, respectively.   Equations may now be written for the closed loops
in the circuit.

Loop containing G_1 and load 1,

$$120 - (50 \times 0.05) - E_1 + (5 \times 0.2) = 0$$
$$E_1 = 118.5 \text{ v}$$

Loop containing loads 1 and 2,

$$E_1 - (40 \times 0.1) - E_2 - (3 \times 0.3) = 0$$

Substituting for E_1 $118.5 - 4 - E_2 - 0.9 = 0$
$$E_2 = 113.6 \text{ v}$$

Loop containing G_2 and load 3,

$$120 - (5 \times 0.2) - E_3 - (55 \times 0.05) = 0$$
$$E_3 = 116.25 \text{ v}$$

Loop containing loads 3 and 4,

$$E_3 + (3 \times 0.3) - E_4 - (37 \times 0.1) = 0$$

Substituting for E_3, $116.25 + 0.9 - E_4 - 3.7 = 0$
$$E_4 = 113.45 \text{ v}$$

Loop containing loads 2, 4, and M,

$$E_2 - (25 \times 0.1) - E_M - (25 \times 0.1) + E_4 = 0$$

Substituting for E_2 and E_4,
$$113.6 - 2.5 - E_M - 2.5 + 113.45 = 0$$
$$E_M = 222.05 \text{ v}$$

Check.   Voltage equation for outer loop containing motor,

$$120 + 120 - (50 \times 0.05) - (40 \times 0.1) - (25 \times 0.1) - E_M - (25 \times 0.1)$$
$$- (37 \times 0.1) - (55 \times 0.05) = 0$$
$$E_M = 222.05 \text{ v}$$

PROBLEMS 19-3

Solve the following problems by using Kirchhoff's laws:

1. In Fig. 19-15, each generator has a terminal voltage of 120 v. The resistance of each feeder is 0.1 Ω, load A draws 15 a, and load B draws 20 a.

    (*a*) Determine voltage across load A.

    (*b*) Determine voltage across load B.

2. In Fig. 19-15, each generator has a terminal voltage of 115 v. The resistance of each feeder is 0.05 Ω, load A draws 20 a, and load B draws 25 a.

    (*a*) What is the voltage across load A?

    (*b*) What is the voltage across load B?

3. In Fig. 19-15, each generator has a terminal voltage of 125 v. The resistance of each outside feeder is 0.15 Ω, and the resistance of the neutral wire is 0.2 Ω. Load A draws 30 a, and load B draws 40 a.

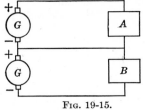

    (*a*) What is the voltage across load A?

    (*b*) How much power is dissipated in load B?

Fig. 19-15.

4. In Fig. 19-15, each generator has an e.m.f. of 125 v and an internal resistance of 0.2 Ω. The resistance of each outside feeder is 0.1 Ω, and the resistance of the neutral wire is 0.5 Ω. Load A draws 10 a, and load B draws 8 a.

    (*a*) What is the voltage across load B?

    (*b*) How much power is dissipated in load A?

5. In Fig. 19-16, the terminal voltage of each generator is 120 v, and each lamp draws 1 a. Find the voltage across each group of lamps.

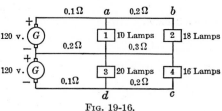

Fig. 19-16.

6. In Fig. 19-16, disconnect lamp group 1, and determine the voltage across each of the remaining groups.

7. In the original circuit of Fig. 19-16, connect five additional lamps across group 1, disconnect three lamps from group 2, disconnect five lamps from group 3, and disconnect one from group 4. Find the voltage existing across each group of lamps.

8. In the original circuit of Fig. 19-16, connect a motor load of 10 a across group 3. How much power is dissipated in group 4?

9. In the original circuit of Fig. 19-16, connect a motor load of 15 a across points a and d. Find the voltage across each group of lamps.

10. In the original circuit of Fig. 19-16, connect a motor load of 20 a across points b and c. Find the voltage across each group of lamps.

19-6. Further Applications of Kirchhoff's Laws.

In previous examples and problems if two sources of electromotive force were connected to the same circuit, the values of electromotive force and internal resistance have been equal. However, there are many types of circuits that contain more than one source of power, each with a different electromotive force and different internal resistance.

Example 1. Figure 19-17 represents two batteries connected in parallel supplying current to a resistance of 2 ohms. One battery has an electromotive force of 6 volts with an internal resistance of 0.15 ohm, and the other battery has an electromotive force of 5 volts with an internal resistance of 0.05 ohm. Determine the current through the batteries and the current in the external circuit. Neglect the resistance of the connecting wires.

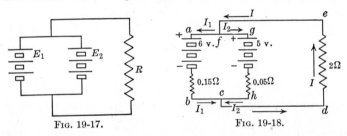

FIG. 19-17.   FIG. 19-18.

Solution: Draw a diagram of the circuit representing the internal resistance of the batteries, and label the circuit with all the known values as shown in Fig. 19-18. Label the unknown currents, and mark the direction each current is assumed to flow.

There are three currents of unknown value in the circuit, I_1, I_2, and the current I which flows through the external circuit. However, because $I = I_1 + I_2$, the unknown currents can be reduced to two unknowns by considering a current of $(I_1 + I_2)$ amperes flowing through the external circuit.

For the path *abcdefa*, $6 - 0.15I_1 - 2(I_1 + I_2) = 0$

Collecting terms, $2.15I_1 + 2I_2 = 6$ (12)

For the path *ghcdefg*, $5 - 0.05I_2 - 2(I_1 + I_2) = 0$

Collecting terms, $2I_1 + 2.05I_2 = 5$ (13)

Equations (12) and (13) are simultaneous equations that, when solved, result in

$$I_1 = 5.64 \text{ a}$$

and $$I_2 = -3.07 \text{ a}$$

The negative sign of the current I_2 denotes that this current is flowing in a direction opposite to that assumed.   The value of the line current is

$$I = I_1 + I_2$$
$$= 5.64 + (-3.07)$$
$$= 2.57 \text{ a}$$

The student should check this solution by changing the direction of I_2 in Fig. 19-18 and rewriting the voltage equations accordingly, remembering that now, at junction f, for example, $I + I_2 - I_1 = 0$.   This will demonstrate that it is immaterial which way the arrows point; for the signs preceding the current values, when found, determine whether or not the assumed directions are correct.   As previously mentioned, however, it must be remembered that going through a resistance in a direction opposite to the current arrow represents a voltage (rise) which must be added, whereas going through a resistance in the same direction of the current arrow represents a voltage (drop) which must be subtracted.

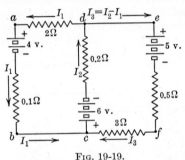

Fig. 19-19.

Example 2.   Figure 19-19 represents a network containing three unequal sources of electromotive force.   Find the current flowing in each branch.

Solution: Assume a direction for each of the unknown currents I_1, I_2, and I_3, and label them as shown in the circuit diagram.

Although three unknown currents are involved, they may be reduced to two unknowns by expressing one current in terms of the other two.   This is accomplished by applying Kirchhoff's first law to some junction such as c. By considering current flow toward a junction as positive and that flowing away from a junction as negative,

$$I_1 + I_3 - I_2 = 0$$
$$I_3 = I_2 - I_1 \qquad (14)$$

Since there are now only two unknown currents I_1 and I_2, Kirchhoff's second law may be applied to any two different closed loops in the network.

For path $abcda$, $4 - 0.1I_1 + 6 - 0.2I_2 - 2I_1 = 0$
Collecting terms, $2.1I_1 + 0.2I_2 = 10$ (15)
For path $efcde$, $5 - 0.5(I_2 - I_1) - 3(I_2 - I_1) + 6 - 0.2I_2 = 0$
Collecting terms, $3.5I_1 - 3.7I_2 = -11$ (16)

Equations (15) and (16) are simultaneous equations that, when solved, result in

$$I_1 = 4.109 \text{ a}$$
and $$I_2 = 6.860 \text{ a}$$
Substituting in Eq. (14), $$I_3 = 6.860 - 4.109$$
$$= 2.751 \text{ a}$$

The assumed directions of current flow are correct because all values are positive.

The solution may be checked by applying Kirchhoff's second law to a path not previously used. When the current values are substituted in the equation for this path, an identity should result. Thus, for path *adefcba*,

$$2I_1 + 5 - 0.5(I_2 - I_1) - 3(I_2 - I_1) + 0.1I_1 - 4 = 0$$

Collecting terms, $5.6I_1 - 3.5I_2 = -1$ (17)

The substitution of the numerical values of I_1 and I_2 in Eq. (17) verifies the solution within reasonable limits of accuracy.

19-7. Outline for Solving Networks. In common with all other problems, the solution of a circuit or a network should not be started until the conditions are analyzed and it is clearly understood what is to be found. Then a definite procedure should be adopted and followed until the solution is completed.

In order to facilitate solutions of networks by means of Kirchhoff's laws, the following procedure is suggested:

1. Draw a large, neat diagram of the network, arranging the circuits so that they appear in their simplest form.

2. Letter the diagram with all the known values such as sources of electromotive force, currents, and resistances. Carefully mark the polarities of the known electromotive forces.

3. Assign a symbol to each unknown quantity.

4. Indicate with arrows the assumed direction of current flow in each branch of the network. The number of unknown currents may be reduced by assigning a direction to all but one of the unknown currents at a junction. Then, by Kirchhoff's first law, the remaining current can be expressed in terms of the others.

5. Using Kirchhoff's second law, set up as many equations as there are unknowns to be determined. In order that each equation contain some relation that has not been expressed in another equation, each circuit path followed should cover some part of the circuit not used for other paths.

6. Solve the resulting simultaneous equations for the values of the unknown quantities.

7. Check the values obtained by substituting them in a voltage equation that has been obtained by following a circuit path not previously used.

PROBLEMS 19-4

1. How much current flows in R_3 in the circuit represented by Fig. 19-20?

2. In the circuit of Fig. 19-21, how much current flows through R?

3. Other values remaining unchanged in Fig. 19-21, how much power will be expended in R if it is changed to 0.05 Ω?

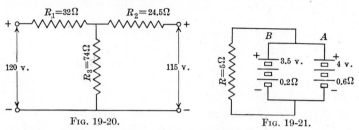

Fig. 19-20.   Fig. 19-21.

4. What are the terminal voltages of the batteries in Prob. 3?

5. In Fig. 19-22,

     (*a*) How much current flows through battery A?
     (*b*) What is the terminal voltage of battery C?
     (*c*) What is the potential difference across R?

6. In Fig. 19-22, how much current will flow through battery C if R is short-circuited?

7. In the original circuit of Fig. 19-22, how much current will flow through R if battery C is reversed?

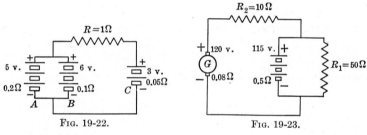

Fig. 19-22.   Fig. 19-23.

8. In the circuit of Fig. 19-23,

     (*a*) How much current flows through R_1?
     (*b*) What is the voltage across R_2?

9. In Fig. 19-24, each generator has a terminal voltage of 120 v. Battery A has an e.m.f. of 102 v and an internal resistance of 2 Ω. Battery B has an e.m.f. of 108 v and an internal resistance of 2.5 Ω. The resistance of each feeder is 0.1 Ω.

     (*a*) How much current flows through battery A?
     (*b*) How much current flows through battery B?

10. In Fig. 19-24, each generator has an e.m.f. of 122 v and an internal resistance of 0.05 Ω. Battery A has an e.m.f. of 114 v and an internal resistance of 1.5 Ω. Battery B has an e.m.f. of 108 v and an internal resistance of 1 Ω. The resistance of each feeder is 0.2 Ω.

(a) How much current flows through battery A?

(b) How much power is expended in battery B?

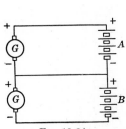

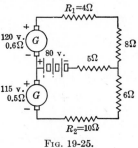

Fig. 19-24.   Fig. 19-25.

11. In the circuit of Fig. 19-25,

(a) How much current flows through R_1?

(b) How much power is expended in R_2?

12. Repeat Prob. 11, but with the battery reversed.

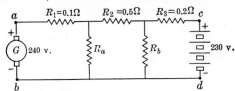

Fig. 19-26.

13. Figure 19-26 represents a generator and a bank of batteries supplying power to loads R_a and R_b, with R_1, R_2, and R_3 representing the lumped line resistances. R_b is disconnected, and R_a draws 50 a. Neglecting the internal resistances of generator and batteries,

(a) What is the voltage across R_2?

(b) How much current is flowing in the batteries, and in what direction is it flowing?

14. R_b is connected in the circuit of Fig. 19-26 and draws 75 a. If R_a draws 50 a,

(a) What is the voltage across R_b?

(b) How much power is expended in R_2?

15. In the circuit represented by Fig. 19-26, the loads are adjusted until R_a draws 150 a and R_b draws 25 a. How much power is lost in R_2?

Fig. 19-27.

16. Determine the currents through the branches of the network of Fig. 19-27, and find the equivalent resistance between points a and c.

Solution: Assume directions for all the currents, and label them in the figure.

By Kirchhoff's second law,

Path *efabce*,	$10 - 3I_2 - 4I_4 = 0$	(18)
Path *efadce*,	$10 - 2I_1 - 5I_3 = 0$	(19)
Path *abda*,	$-3I_2 + 6I_5 + 2I_1 = 0$	(20)
Path *dbcd*,	$-6I_5 - 4I_4 + 5I_3 = 0$	(21)
Path *abcda*,	$-3I_2 - 4I_4 + 5I_3 + 2I_1 = 0$	(22)

By Kirchhoff's first law,

Junction *a*,	$I - I_1 - I_2 = 0,$	$\therefore I = I_1 + I_2$	(23)
Junction *b*,	$I_2 + I_5 - I_4 = 0,$	$\therefore I_4 = I_2 + I_5$	(24)
Junction *c*,	$I_4 + I_3 - I = 0,$	$\therefore I = I_3 + I_4$	(25)
Junction *d*,	$I_1 - I_5 - I_3 = 0,$	$\therefore I_3 = I_1 - I_5$	(26)

Substituting I_4 from Eq. (24) in Eq. (18),

$$10 - 3I_2 - 4(I_2 + I_5) = 0$$

or
$$7I_2 + 4I_5 = 10 \qquad (27)$$

Substituting I_3 from Eq. (26) in Eq. (19),

$$10 - 2I_1 - 5(I_1 - I_5) = 0$$

or
$$7I_1 - 5I_5 = 10 \qquad (28)$$

Substituting I_4 from Eq. (24) and I_3 from Eq. (26) in Eq. (21),

$$-6I_5 - 4(I_2 + I_5) + 5(I_1 - I_5) = 0$$

or
$$5I_1 - 4I_2 - 15I_5 = 0 \qquad (29)$$

Solving Eqs. (27), (28), and (29) simultaneously,

$$I_1 = 1.540 \text{ a}$$
$$I_2 = 1.339 \text{ a}$$
$$I_5 = 0.1562 \text{ a}$$

Substituting these values in equations not used before,

$$I_3 = 1.383 \text{ a}$$
$$I_4 = 1.496 \text{ a}$$

By Eq. (23), $I = I_1 + I_2 = 1.540 + 1.339 = 2.879$ a

The equivalent resistance between points *a* and *c* is

$$\frac{E}{I} = \frac{10}{2.879} = 3.47 \ \Omega$$

By expressing the branch currents in terms of other currents and labeling the circuit accordingly, this problem can be solved with a smaller number of equations. This is left as a problem for the student.

19-8. Equivalent Star and Delta Circuits. The solution of Prob. 16 of the preceding article indicates that solution by Kirchhoff's laws of networks containing such arrangements can be complicated. However, there are many cases where such networks may be replaced with more convenient equivalent circuits.

The three resistances R_1, R_2, and R_3, represented in Fig. 19-28, are said to be connected in *delta* (Greek letter Δ) and R_a, R_b, and R_c of Fig. 19-29 are connected in *star*, or Y.

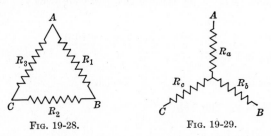

FIG. 19-28.   FIG. 19-29.

If these two circuits are to be made equivalent, then the resistance between terminals A and B, B and C, and A and C must be the same in each circuit. Hence, in Fig. 19-28, the resistance from A to B is

$$R_{AB} = \frac{R_1(R_2 + R_3)}{R_1 + R_2 + R_3} \qquad (30)$$

In Fig. 19-29 the resistance from A to B is

$$R_{AB} = R_a + R_b \qquad (31)$$

Equating Eqs. (30) and (31),

$$R_a + R_b = \frac{R_1 R_2 + R_1 R_3}{R_1 + R_2 + R_3} \qquad (32)$$

Similarly,

$$R_b + R_c = \frac{R_1 R_2 + R_2 R_3}{R_1 + R_2 + R_3} \qquad (33)$$

and

$$R_a + R_c = \frac{R_1 R_3 + R_2 R_3}{R_1 + R_2 + R_3} \qquad (34)$$

Equations (32), (33), and (34) are simultaneous and, when solved, result in

$$R_a = \frac{R_1 R_3}{R_1 + R_2 + R_3} = \frac{R_1 R_3}{\Sigma R_\Delta} \qquad (35)$$

$$R_b = \frac{R_1 R_2}{R_1 + R_2 + R_3} = \frac{R_1 R_2}{\Sigma R_\Delta} \qquad (36)$$

and

$$R_c = \frac{R_2 R_3}{R_1 + R_2 + R_3} = \frac{R_2 R_3}{\Sigma R_\Delta} \qquad (37)$$

Since Σ (Greek letter sigma) is used to denote "the summation of,"

$$\Sigma R_\Delta = R_1 + R_2 + R_3$$

Example 1.   In Fig. 19-28, $R_1 = 2$ ohms, $R_2 = 3$ ohms, and $R_3 = 5$ ohms. What are the values of the resistances in the equivalent Y circuit of Fig 19-29?

Solution: $\Sigma R_\Delta = 2 + 3 + 5 = 10 \ \Omega$

Substituting in Eq. (35), $R_a = \dfrac{2 \times 5}{10} = 1 \ \Omega$

Substituting in Eq. (36), $R_b = \dfrac{2 \times 3}{10} = 0.6 \ \Omega$

Substituting in Eq. (37), $R_c = \dfrac{3 \times 5}{10} = 1.5 \ \Omega$

Example 2.   Determine the equivalent resistance between points a and c in the circuit of Fig. 19-30.

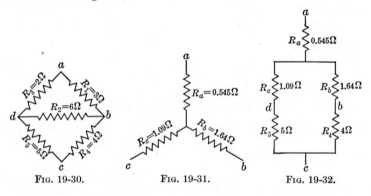

FIG. 19-30.   FIG. 19-31.   FIG. 19-32.

Solution: Convert one of the delta circuits of Fig. 19-30 to its equivalent Y circuit.   Thus, for the delta abd,

$$\Sigma R_\Delta = 3 + 6 + 2 = 11 \ \Omega$$

and the equivalent Y resistances which are shown in Fig. 19-31 are

$$R_a = \frac{3 \times 2}{11} = 0.545 \ \Omega$$

$$R_b = \frac{3 \times 6}{11} = 1.64 \ \Omega$$

and $$R_c = \frac{2 \times 6}{11} = 1.09 \ \Omega$$

The equivalent Y circuit is connected to the remainder of the network as shown in Fig. 19-32 and is solved as an ordinary series-parallel combination.

Thus,

$$R_{ac} = R_a + \frac{(R_c + R_5)(R_b + R_4)}{R_c + R_5 + R_b + R_4}$$

$$= 0.545 + \frac{(1.09 + 5)(1.64 + 4)}{1.09 + 5 + 1.64 + 4} = 3.47 \ \Omega$$

Note that the values of Fig. 19-30 are the same as those of Fig. 19-27.

The equations for converting a Y circuit to its equivalent delta circuit are obtained by solving Eqs. (35), (36), and (37) simultaneously. This results in

$$R_1 = \frac{\Sigma R_Y}{R_c} \qquad (38)$$

$$R_2 = \frac{\Sigma R_Y}{R_a} \qquad (39)$$

and $$R_3 = \frac{\Sigma R_Y}{R_b} \qquad (40)$$

where $$\Sigma R_Y = R_a R_b + R_b R_c + R_a R_c$$

A convenient method for remembering the $\Delta - Y$ and $Y - \Delta$ conversions is illustrated in Fig. 19-33.

In converting from Δ to Y, each equivalent Y resistance is equal to the product of the two *adjacent* Δ resistances divided by the summation of the Δ resistances. For example, R_1 and R_3 are adjacent to R_a; therefore,

$$R_a = \frac{R_1 R_3}{\Sigma R_\Delta}$$

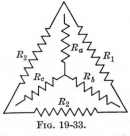

Fig. 19-33.

In converting from Y to Δ, each equivalent Δ resistance is found by dividing ΣR_Y by the *opposite* Y resistance. For example, R_1 is opposite R_c; therefore, $R_1 = \dfrac{\Sigma R_Y}{R_c}$.

PROBLEMS 19-5

1. In the circuit of Fig. 19-28, $R_1 = 10 \ \Omega$, $R_2 = 7 \ \Omega$, and $R_3 = 8 \ \Omega$. Find the resistances of the equivalent Y circuit.

2. In the circuit of Fig. 19-28, $R_1 = 2.4 \ \Omega$, $R_2 = 3 \ \Omega$, and $R_3 = 6.6 \ \Omega$. Determine the resistances of the equivalent Y circuit.

3. In the circuit of Fig. 19-29, $R_a = 6.40 \ \Omega$, $R_b = 4.48 \ \Omega$, and

$$R_c = 5.60 \ \Omega.$$

Find the resistances of the equivalent Δ circuit.

4. In the circuit of Fig. 19-29, $R_a = 3 \ \Omega$, $R_b = 4 \ \Omega$, and $R_c = 5 \ \Omega$. Find the resistances of the equivalent Δ circuit.

5. In the circuit of Fig. 19-34, $R_1 = 5$ Ω, $R_2 = 4$ Ω, $R_3 = 1$ Ω, $R_4 = 3$ Ω, $R_5 = 6$ Ω, and $E = 15$ v.   What is the value of the current I?

6. How much current flows through R_4 in Prob. 5?

7. How much current flows through R_3 in Prob. 5?

8. In the circuit of Fig. 19-34, $R_1 = 18$ Ω, $R_2 = 10$ Ω, $R_3 = 12$ Ω, $R_4 = 5.5$ Ω, $R_5 = 7$ Ω, and $E = 20$ v.   What is the value of I?

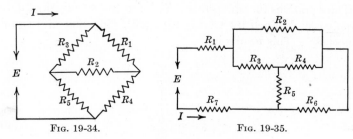

FIG. 19-34.   FIG. 19-35.

9. How much current flows through R_5 in Prob. 8?

10. How much current flows through R_1 in Prob. 8?

11. In the circuit of Fig. 19-35, $R_1 = 1.67$ Ω, $R_2 = 0.73$ Ω, $R_3 = 1$ 21 Ω, $R_4 = 2.1$ Ω, $R_5 = 9.5$ Ω, $R_6 = 3.75$ Ω, $R_7 = 0.09$ Ω, and $E = 108$ v.   What is the value of the current I?

12. How much current flows through R_6 in Prob. 11?

13. How much current flows through R_2 in Prob. 11?

14. In the circuit of Fig. 19-36, $R_1 = R_6 = 500$ Ω,

$$R_2 = R_3 = R_4 = R_5 = 400 \ \Omega,$$

$R_L = 600$ Ω, and $E = 60$ v.   What is the value of the current flowing through the load resistance R_L?

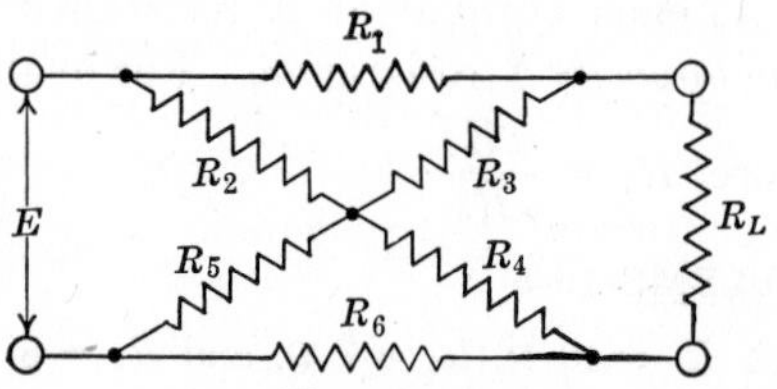

FIG. 19-36. 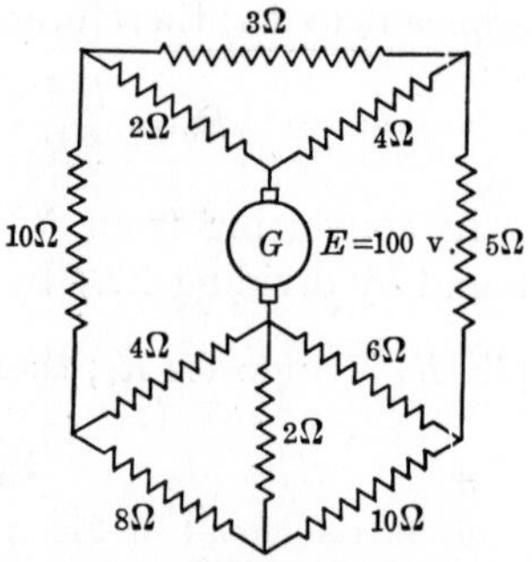   FIG. 19-37.

15. How much current does the generator supply to the circuit of Fig. 19-37?

16. In the circuit of Fig. 19-34, $E = 15.5$ v, $R_1 = 2$ Ω, $R_3 = 6$ Ω, $R_4 = 3.8$ Ω, $R_5 = 1.4$ Ω, and $I = 5$ a.   What is the resistance of R_2?

17. With the values of Prob. 16, R_2 is varied until $I = 5.03$ a.   What is the resistance of R_2?

CHAPTER XX

LOGARITHMS

In problems pertaining to engineering, there often occurs the need for numerical computations involving multiplication, division, powers, or roots. Many of these problems can be solved more readily by the use of logarithms than by ordinary arithmetical processes.

The credit for the invention of logarithms is chiefly due to John Napier, whose tables appeared in 1614. This was an extremely important event in the development of mathematics; for, by the use of logarithms,

1. Multiplication is reduced to addition.
2. Division is reduced to subtraction.
3. Raising to a power is reduced to one multiplication.
4. Extracting a root is reduced to one division.

In many phases of engineering, computation by logarithms is utilized to a great extent because of the high degree of accuracy desired and the amount of labor saved by their use. Because the slide rule is convenient and because slide-rule results meet the ordinary demands for accuracy in problems relating to electricity and radio, it is not necessary to make wide use of logarithms for computations in the general field. However, it is essential that the electrical engineer and, more particularly, the communication engineer have a thorough understanding of logarithmic processes.

20-1. Definition. The *logarithm* of a quantity is the exponent of the power to which a given number, called the *base*, must be raised in order to equal the quantity.

Example 1. Since $10^3 = 1000$,

then $\qquad\qquad$ 3 = logarithm of 1000 to the base 10

Example 2. Since $2^3 = 8$,

then $\qquad\qquad$ 3 = logarithm of 8 to the base 2

Example 3. Since $a^x = b$,

then $\qquad\qquad$ x = logarithm of b to the base a

279

20-2. Notation.   If $b^x = N$ (1)

then x is the logarithm of N to the base b.   This statement is abbreviated by writing

$$x = \log_b N   (2)$$

It is evident that Eqs. (1) and (2) mean the same thing and are simply different methods of expressing the same relation among b, x, and N.   Equation (1) is called the *exponential form*, and Eq. (2) is called the *logarithmic form*.

As an aid in remembering that a logarithm is an exponent, Eq. (1) may be written in the form

$$(\text{Base})^{\log} = \text{number}$$

The following examples illustrate relations between exponential and logarithmic forms.

Examples.

Exponential Notation	Logarithmic Notation
$2^4 = 16$	$4 = \log_2 16$
$3^5 = 243$	$5 = \log_3 243$
$25^{0.5} = 5$	$0.5 = \log_{25} 5$
$10^2 = 100$	$2 = \log_{10} 100$
$10^4 = 10,000$	$4 = \log_{10} 10,000$
$a^b = c.$	$b = \log_a c$
$\epsilon^x = y$	$x = \log_\epsilon y$

From the foregoing examples, it is apparent that any positive number, other than 1, may be selected as a base for a system of logarithms.   Because 1 raised to any power is 1, it cannot be used as a base.

PROBLEMS 20-1

Express the following equations in logarithmic form:

1. $10^3 = 1000.$ **2.** $10^5 = 100,000.$

3. $5^2 = 25.$ **4.** $4^3 = 64.$

5. $6^0 = 1.$ **6.** $a^0 = 1.$

7. $5^4 = 625.$ **8.** $9^{0.5} = 3.$

9. $r^s = t.$ **10.** $3^{2x} = M.$

Express the following equations in exponential form:

11. $2 = \log_{10} 100.$ **12.** $\log_{10} 1000 = 3.$

13. $\log_7 49 = 2.$ **14.** $\log_4 64 = 3.$

15. $\log_4 2 = 0.5$.

16. $\log_\epsilon \epsilon = 1$.

17. $\log_a a = 1$.

18. $\log_{10} 10 = 1$.

19. $\log_a 1 = 0$.

20. $\log_{10} 1 = 0$.

Find the value of x:

21. $2^x = 4$.

22. $3^x = 81$.

23. $10^x = 100,000$.

24. $x = \log_3 27$.

25. $3^x = \sqrt{3}$.

26. $\log_5 x = 3$.

27. Show that $\log_{10} 100 = \log_{10} 100,000 - \log_{10} 1000$.

28. Show that $\log_b b = 1$.

29. What are the logarithms of 2, 4, 8, 16, 32, 64, 128, 256, and 512 to the base 2?

30. What are the logarithms of 3, 9, 27, 81, 243, and 729 to the base 3?

20-3. The Logarithm of a Product. *The logarithm of a product is equal to the sum of the logarithms of the factors.*

Consider the two factors M and N, and let x and y be their respective logarithms to the base a; then,

$$x = \log_a M \tag{3}$$

and

$$y = \log_a N \tag{4}$$

Writing Eq. (3) in exponential form,

$$a^x = M \tag{5}$$

Writing Eq. (4) in exponential form,

$$a^y = N \tag{6}$$

Then

$$M \cdot N = a^x \cdot a^y = a^{x+y}$$

Therefore,

$$\log_a (M \cdot N) = x + y = \log_a M + \log_a N$$

Example. $2 = \log_{10} 100$,   or $10^2 = 100$
              $4 = \log_{10} 10,000$,   or $10^4 = 10,000$

Then $100 \times 10,000 = 10^2 \cdot 10^4 = 10^{2+4} = 10^6$

Therefore, $\log_{10}(100 \times 10,000) = 2 + 4 = \log_{10} 100 + \log_{10} 10,000$

The above proposition is also true for the product of more than two factors. Thus, by successive applications of the proof, it can be shown that

$$\log_a (A \cdot B \cdot C \cdot D) = \log_a A + \log_a B + \log_a C + \log_a D$$

20-4. The Logarithm of a Quotient. *The logarithm of the quotient of two numbers is equal to the logarithm of the dividend minus the logarithm of the divisor.*

As in the preceding proof,

let	$x = \log_a M$	(3)
and	$y = \log_a N$	(4)
Writing Eq. (3) in exponential form,	$a^x = M$	(5)
Writing Eq. (4) in exponential form,	$a^y = N$	(6)
Dividing Eq. (5) by Eq. (6),	$\dfrac{a^x}{a^y} = \dfrac{M}{N}$	
That is,	$a^{x-y} = \dfrac{M}{N}$	(7)

Writing Eq. (7) in logarithmic form, $x - y = \log_a \dfrac{M}{N}$ (8)

Substituting in Eq. (8) for the values of x and y,

$$\log_a M - \log_a N = \log_a \frac{M}{N}$$

Example. $2 = \log_{10} 100,$ or $10^2 = 100$
         $4 = \log_{10} 10,000,$ or $10^4 = 10,000$

Then $\dfrac{10,000}{100} = \dfrac{10^4}{10^2} = 10^{4-2} = 10^2$

Therefore, $\log_{10} \dfrac{10,000}{100} = 4 - 2 = \log_{10} 10,000 - \log_{10} 100$

20-5. The Logarithm of a Power. *The logarithm of a power of a number equals the logarithm of the number multiplied by the exponent of the power.*

Again, let	$x = \log_a M$	(3)
Then	$M = a^x$	(9)

Raising both sides of Eq. (9) to the nth power,

$$M^n = a^{nx} \tag{10}$$

Writing Eq. (10) in logarithmic form,

$$\log_a M^n = nx \tag{11}$$

Substituting in Eq. (11) for the value of x,

$$\log_a M^n = n \log_a M$$

Example $2 = \log_{10} 100,$ or $100 = 10^2$
Since $(10^2)^2 = 10^{2 \cdot 2} = 10^4 = 10,000$
then $\log_{10} 10,000 = 4$
Therefore, $\log_{10} 100^2 = 2 \log_{10} 100 = 2 \cdot 2 = 4$

20-6. The Logarithm of a Root. *The logarithm of a root of a number is equal to the logarithm of the number divided by the index of the root.*

Again, let $x = \log_a M$ (3)
Then $M = a^x$ (9)

Extracting the nth root of both sides of Eq. (9),

$$M^{\frac{1}{n}} = a^{\frac{x}{n}} \tag{12}$$

Writing Eq. (12) in logarithmic form,

$$\log_a M^{\frac{1}{n}} = \frac{x}{n} \tag{13}$$

Substituting in Eq. (13) for the value of x,

$$\log_a M^{\frac{1}{n}} = \frac{\log_a M}{n}$$

Example. $4 = \log_{10} 10,000,$ or $10,000 = 10^4$
Since $\sqrt{10,000} = \sqrt{10^4} = 10^{\frac{4}{2}} = 10^2 = 100$
then $\log_{10} \sqrt{10,000} = \dfrac{\log_{10} 10,000}{2} = \dfrac{4}{2} = 2$

20-7. Summary. It is evident that if the logarithms of numbers are used for computations, instead of the numbers themselves, then *multiplication, division, raising to powers,* and *extracting roots* are replaced by *addition, subtraction, multiplication,* and *division,* respectively. Because the student is familiar with the laws of exponents, especially as applied to the powers of ten, the foregoing operations with logarithms involve no new ideas. The sole idea behind logarithms is that every positive number may be expressed as a power of some base. That is,

$$\text{Any positive number} = (\text{base})^{\log}$$

20-8. The Common System. Since 10 is the base of our number systems, both integral and decimal, the base 10 has been chosen for a system of logarithms. This system is called the *common system* or *Briggs's system*. The natural system, of which the base to five decimal places is 2.71828, will be discussed later.

Hereafter, when no other base is stated, the base will be 10. For example, $\log_{10} 625$ will be written log 625, the base 10 being understood.

20-9. Characteristics. The following table illustrates the connection between the power of ten and the logarithms of certain numbers:

Exponential Form	Logarithmic Form
$10^4 = 10,000$	$\log 10,000 = 4$
$10^3 = 1000$	$\log 1000 = 3$
$10^2 = 100$	$\log 100 = 2$
$10^1 = 10$	$\log 10 = 1$
$10^0 = 1$	$\log 1 = 0$
$10^{-1} = 0.1$	$\log 0.1 = -1$
$10^{-2} = 0.01$	$\log 0.01 = -2$
$10^{-3} = 0.001$	$\log 0.001 = -3$
$10^{-4} = 0.0001$	$\log 0.0001 = -4$

Inspection of the table shows that only powers of ten have integers for logarithms. Also, it is evident that the logarithm of any number between 10 and 100, for example, is between 1 and 2; that is, it is 1 plus a decimal. Similarly the logarithm of any number between 100 and 1000 is between 2 and 3, and so on. Therefore, to represent all numbers, it is necessary to utilize fractional powers. For example,

$$\log 37 = 1.5682$$
That is, $$37 = 10^{1.5682}$$
Also, $$\log 461 = 2.6637$$
That is, $$461 = 10^{2.6637}$$

In the same manner, it follows that the logarithm of a number between 0.01 and 0.001 is -3 plus a decimal or -2 minus a decimal. In order that the decimal part of a logarithm may always be positive, it has been agreed that the logarithm of a number less than 1 is to be taken so that the integral part only is negative.

From the foregoing, it follows that every logarithm has two parts, an integer and a decimal fraction.

The *integral* part is called the *characteristic* and may be positive or negative.

The *fractional part* is called the *mantissa* and is *always positive*.

20-10. Rules for Determining the Characteristic. The use of the base 10 makes it possible to simplify computation by logarithms and to express them in a compact tabulated form. For example, determining the characteristic becomes a matter of inspection, as is evident from the following:

Rule : 1. *The characteristic of a number greater than 1 is positive and is one less than the number of digits to the left of the decimal point.*

2. *The characteristic of a positive number less than 1 is negative and is one more than the number of zeros immediately to the right of the decimal point.*

If the characteristic is negative, it is customary to write the negative sign *above* the characteristic to emphasize that the characteristic alone is negative. For example, in

$$\log 0.000647 = \bar{4}.8109$$

the $\bar{4}.8109$ means $-4 + 0.8109$. To write it -4.8109 would indicate that both characteristic and mantissa were negative. This would be incorrect, for it has been agreed that the mantissa shall always be considered positive.

To avoid the use of a negative characteristic, it is convenient to add 10 to the characteristic and subtract 10 at the right of the mantissa. Thus $\log 0.000647 = \bar{4}.8109$ would be written $6.8109 - 10$. In writing logarithms in this form, *the characteristic, when 10 is added, is 9 minus the number of zeros immediately at the right of the decimal point.* For example,

$$\log 0.0001 = 6 - 10$$

or -4.

The application of the rules for determining the characteristic becomes a simple matter if the notation is remembered for expressing all numbers as a number between 1 and 10, times the proper power of ten. By so doing, the power of ten is always the characteristic of the logarithm of the number so expressed. This is illustrated in the following table:

Number	Standard notation	Characteristic	Refer to rule
682	6.82×10^2	2	1
3765	3.765×10^3	3	1
14	1.4×10^1	1	1
1	1×10^0	0	
0.00425	4.25×10^{-3}	-3 or $7-10$	2
0.1	1×10^{-1}	-1 or $9-10$	2
0.000072	7.2×10^{-5}	-5 or $5-10$	2

20-11. The Mantissa. Note that all numbers whose logarithms are given below have the same significant figures. These logarithms were obtained by first finding log 2.207 from a table, as will be discussed later. The remaining logarithms were then obtained by applying the properties of logarithms as stated in Arts. 20-3 and 20-4.

$$\log 2207 \quad = \log 1000\,(2.207) = \log 1000 + \log 2.207$$
$$= 3 + 0.3438$$

$$\log 220.7 \quad = \log 100(2.207) \quad = \log 100 \;\; + \log 2.207$$
$$= 2 + 0.3438$$

$$\log 22.07 \quad = \log 10(2.207) \quad = \log 10 \;\;\; + \log 2.207$$
$$= 1 + 0.3438$$

$$\log 2.207 \quad = \log 1(2.207) \quad = \log 1 \;\;\; + \log 2.207$$
$$= 0 + 0.3438$$

$$\log 0.2207 \quad = \log \frac{2.207}{10} \quad = \log 2.207 - \log 10$$
$$= -1 + 0.3438$$

$$\log 0.02207 = \log \frac{2.207}{100} \quad = \log 2.207 - \log 100$$
$$= -2 + 0.3438$$

From the above examples, it is apparent that the mantissa is not affected by a shift of the decimal point. That is, *the mantissa of the logarithm of a number depends only on the sequence of the significant figures in the number*. Because of this, 10 is ideally suited as a base for a system of logarithms to be used for computation.

PROBLEMS 20-2

Write the characteristics of the logarithms of the following numbers:

1. 63.   **2.** 106.   **3.** 784.   **4.** 43.2.

5. 432.   **6.** 4320.   **7.** 0.432.   **8.** 4.32.

9. 8425.   **10.** 0.08425.   **11.** 8.425.   **12.** 84.25.

13. 5060.   **14.** 0.5060.   **15.** 5.060.   **16.** 506,000.

17. 0.0004.   **18.** 0.00723.   **19.** 8.642.   **20.** 0.9463.

Find the value of each of the following expressions:

21. $\log 100 + \log 0.001$.   **22.** $\log \sqrt{100}$.

23. $\log \sqrt{\dfrac{1000}{10}}$.   **24.** $\log \sqrt{1000} - \log 100$.

25. $\log \sqrt{0.001}$.

Write the following expressions in expanded form:

26. $\log \dfrac{642 \times 8.63}{37.2}$.

Solution: $\log \dfrac{642 \times 8.63}{37.2} = \log 642 + \log 8.63 - \log 37.2$

27. $\log \dfrac{3793 \times 70.2}{264}$.   **28.** $\log \dfrac{9.30 \times 479}{3.42 \times 4869}$.

29. $\log \sqrt{\dfrac{893 \times 0.642}{2.376 \times 20.4}}$.   **30.** $\log \sqrt[4]{7182 \times 17.53 \times 69.3}$.

31. $\log \dfrac{abc}{de}$.   **32.** $\log \dfrac{x^3 y^4}{a \sqrt[3]{b}}$.

Given $\log 48.54 = 1.6861$, find the logarithms of the following numbers:

33. 4.854.   **34.** 4854.   **35.** 0.04854.

36. 0.0004854.   **37.** 48,540.   **38.** 4854×10^{-4}.

39. 48.54×10^6.   **40.** 0.004854×10^{-3}.

Given $\log 8.162 = 0.9118$, find the numbers that correspond to the following logarithms:

41. 1.9118.   **42.** 3.9118.   **43.** $6.9118 - 10$.

44. 6.9118.   **45.** $9.9118 - 10$.   **46.** $1.9118 - 10$.

47. 2.9118.   **48.** $7.9118 - 10$.   **49.** 10.9118.

50. $2.9118 - 10$.

20-12. Tables of Logarithms. Because the characteristic of the logarithm of any number is obtainable by inspection, it is necessary to tabulate only the mantissas of the logarithms of numbers. Though mantissas can be computed by use of advanced mathematics, for convenience the mantissas of the logarithms up to a certain number of significant figures have been computed and arranged in logarithmic tables. Table VI is a four-place table of logarithms. That is, the mantissas found there have been computed and rounded off to four decimal places.

20-13. To Find the Logarithm of a Given Number. The following is a portion of Table VI (page 509):

N	0	1	2	3	4	5	6	7	8	9
40	6021	6031	6042	6053	6064	6075	6085	6096	6107	6117
41	6128	6138	6149	6160	6170	6180	6191	6201	6212	6222
42	6232	6243	6253	6263	6274	6284	6294	6304	6314	6325
43	6335	6345	6355	6365	6375	6385	6395	6405	6415	6425

Examination of the table shows that the first column has **N** at top and bottom. **N** is an abbreviation for "number." The other columns are labeled **0, 1, 2, 3, 4,** · · · **9.** Therefore, any number consisting of three significant figures has its first two figures in the **N** column and its third figure in another column. This will be illustrated in the following examples.

When finding the logarithm of a number, *always write the characteristic at once, before looking for the mantissa.*

Example 1.   Find log 40.
Solution: The characteristic is 1, because 40 is a number between 10 and 100.

Since 40 has no third significant figure, other than zero, the mantissa of 40 is found at the right of 40 in the *N* column, in the column headed zero. It is 0.6021.

$$\therefore \log 40 = 1.6021$$

Example 2.   Find log 416.
Solution: The characteristic is 2.

The first two digits of 416 are found in the *N* column and the third digit in the column headed 6. Then the mantissa is read in the row containing 41 and in the column headed 6. It is 0.6191.

$$\therefore \log 416 = 2.6191$$

Similarly,
$$\log 4.16 = 0.6191$$
$$\log 41.6 = 1.6191$$
$$\log 4160 = 3.6191$$
$$\log 0.00416 = 7.6191 - 10, \text{ etc.}$$

That is, the mantissa of any number having 416 as significant figures is 0.6191.

Example 3. Find log 4347.
Solution: The characteristic is 3.
Since 4347 is between 4340 and 4350, its mantissa must be between the mantissas of 4340 and 4350.

$$\text{Mantissa of } 4350 = 0.6385$$
$$\text{Mantissa of } 4340 = 0.6375$$
$$\text{Difference} = \overline{0.0010}$$

The *tabular difference* between these mantissas is 0.0010, and it is apparent that an *increase* of 10 in the number causes the mantissa to *increase* by 0.0010. Therefore an increase of 7 in the number will increase the mantissa 0.7 as much.   Hence the increase in the mantissa will be $0.0010 \times 0.7 = 0.0007$, **and** the mantissa of 4347 will be

$$0.6375 + 0.0007 = 0.6382$$
$$\therefore \log 4347 = 3.6382$$

Similarly,
$$\log 43.47 = 1.6382$$
$$\log 4.347 = 0.6382$$
$$\log 434{,}700 = 5.6382$$
$$\log 0.0004347 = 6.6382 - 10, \text{ etc.}$$

That is, the mantissa of any number having 4347 as significant figures is 0.6382.

The foregoing process of finding the mantissa is called *interpolation* and is based on the assumption that the increase in the logarithm is proportional to the increase in the number.

Example 4.   Find log 0.000042735.
Solution: The characteristic is -5, or $5 - 10$.
Since 42,735 is between 42,700 and 42 800, its mantissa must be between the mantissas of 42,700 and 42,800.

$$\text{Mantissa of } 42{,}800 = 0.6314$$
$$\text{Mantissa of } 42{,}700 = 0.6304$$
$$\text{Tabular difference} = \overline{0.0010}$$

Since an increase of 100 in the number causes the mantissa to increase 0.0010, an increase of 35 in the number would cause an increase in the mantissa of $0.0010 \times 0.35 = 0.000350$.   Then the mantissa of 42,735 will be

$$0.6304 + 0.000350 = 0.630750$$

This mantissa, as written above, is another example of how the retention of decimals might easily give a false impression of accuracy. The table from which the mantissa is taken is correct to four significant figures. Therefore, any mantissa found by interpolation from such a table cannot be correct beyond four significant figures. Hence, it is correct to write

$$\log 0.000042735 = 5.6308 - 10$$

Summarizing, we have the following:

Rule : *To find the logarithm of a number containing three significant figures,*

1. *Determine the characteristic.*

2. *Locate the first two significant figures in the column headed N.*

3. *In the same row and in the column headed by the third significant figure, find the required mantissa.*

Rule : *To find the logarithm of a number containing more than three significant figures,*

1. *Determine the characteristic.*

2. *Find the mantissa for the first three significant figures of the number.*

3. *Find the next higher mantissa, and take the tabular difference of the two mantissas.*

4. *Add to the lesser mantissa the product of the tabular difference and the remaining figures of the number considered as a decimal.*

PROBLEMS 20-3

Find the logarithms of the following:

1. 3.	**2.** 300.	**3.** 30.
4. 356.	**5.** 642.	**6.** 747.
7. 101.	**8.** 500.	**9.** 242,000.
10. 0.0000499.	**11.** 8425.	**12.** 4,672,000.
13. 0.9792.	**14.** 141,700.	**15.** 342.56.
16. 246,300.	**17.** 1.493×10^{-5}.	**18.** 703.3×10^{7}.
19. 6.28.	**20.** 3.1416.	**21.** 2.7183.
22. 376.92.	**23.** 0.000982.	**24.** 746,000.
25. 79,990.	**26.** 5,645,000.	**27.** 5.645×10^{5}.
28. 0.00006.	**29.** 8×10^{-12}.	**30.** 34.63×10^{-5}.

20-14. To Find the Number Corresponding to a Given Logarithm. The number corresponding to a given logarithm is called the *antilogarithm* and is written "antilog." For example, if log 692 = 2.8401, then the number corresponding to the logarithm 2.8401 is 692. That is,

$$\text{antilog } 2.8401 = 692$$

To find the antilog of a given logarithm, we reverse the process of finding the logarithm when the number is given.

Example 1.   Find the number whose logarithm is 3.9101.

Solution: The characteristic tells only the position of the decimal point. Therefore, to find the significant figures of the number (antilog), the mantissa must be found in Table VI (page 509).   To the left of the mantissa 0.9101 in column N, find the first two significant figures of the number, which are 81; and, at the head of the column of the mantissa, find the third significant figure, which is 3.   Hence the number has the significant figures 813.   The position of the decimal point is fixed by the characteristic; and because the characteristic is 3, there must be four figures to the left of the decimal point.

Thus,

antilog 3.9101 = 8130

Similarly,   antilog 0.9101 = 8.13

antilog 7.9101 − 10 = 0.00813

antilog 6.9101 = 8,130,000, etc.

A change in the characteristic changes only the position of the decimal point.

Example 2.   Find the number whose logarithm is 2.3680.

Solution: Examination of Table VI shows that there the mantissa of the logarithm is not given exactly.

Find the two consecutive mantissas between which the given mantissa lies.   These are 0.3674 and 0.3692.   Then, considering only significant figures,

0.3692   = mantissa of log 234
0.3674   = mantissa of log 233

Tabular difference = 0.0018, number difference = 1

Hence a difference of 0.0018 in the mantissa makes a difference of 1 in the number.   Now the given mantissa is 0.0006 larger than the smaller one (0.3680 − 0.3674 = 0.0006).   Then the required number is

$$\frac{0.0006}{0.0018} \times 1 = 0.33$$

larger than 233.   The sequence of significant figures is 233.33 or 233.3, for results were computed from a four-place table.

$$\therefore \text{ antilog } 2.3680 = 233.3$$

or   2.3680 = log 233.3

Example 3. Find the number whose logarithm is 6.9793 − 10.

Solution:

$$0.9795 = \text{mantissa of log } 954$$
$$0.9791 = \text{mantissa of log } 953$$

Tabular difference = $\overline{0.0004}$, number difference = $\overline{1}$

$$\text{Given mantissa} = 0.9793$$
$$\text{Next lower mantissa} = 0.9791$$
$$\text{Difference} = \overline{0.0002}$$

Since the difference between numbers is proportional to the difference of the corresponding mantissas, the fourth significant figure to be added to 953 is

$$\frac{0.0002}{0.0004} \times 1 = 0.5$$

The required significant figures are 953.5.

$$\therefore \text{antilog } 6.9793 - 10 = 0.0009535$$
$$= 9.535 \times 10^{-4}$$

or

$$6.9793 - 10 = \log 9.535 \times 10^{-4}$$

PROBLEMS 20-4

Find the antilogarithm of each of the following logarithms:

1. 0.8785.	**2.** 3.8785.	**3.** 8.8785 − 10.
4. 2.9948.	**5.** 1.5911.	**6.** 4.1335.
7. 6.1335 − 10.	**8.** 5.8686.	**9.** 8.9440.
10. 3.9440 − 10.	**11.** 0.00000.	**12.** 0.3010.
13. 0.4969.	**14.** 0.7980.	**15.** 3.7067 − 10.
16. 0.8952.	**17.** 1.8515.	**18.** 4.8295.
19. 7.4138 − 10.	**20.** 2.5061.	**21.** 9.5904 − 10.
22. 3.7707.	**23.** 9.9918 − 10.	**24.** 0.4627.
25. 5.9636.	**26.** 2.5412.	**27.** 8.4300 − 10.
28. 8.9600 − 20.	**29.** 3.1245.	**30.** 9.8560 − 20.

20-15. Addition and Subtraction of Logarithms. Since the mantissa of a logarithm is always positive, care must be exercised in adding or subtracting logarithms.

Adding logarithms with positive characteristics is the same as adding arithmetical numbers.

Example 1. Add the logarithms 2.7642 and 4.3046.

Solution:

$$2.7642$$
$$4.3046$$
$$\overline{7.0688}$$

In adding logarithms whose characteristics are negative, it is best to express them as logarithms with a positive characteristic, writing the proper multiple of negative 10 after the mantissa.

Example 2.   Add the logarithms $\overline{4}.3265$ and 6.2843.

Solution: $\overline{4}.3265 = 6.3265 - 10$

$$6.3265 - 10$$
$$6.2843$$
$$\overline{12.6108 - 10} = 2.6108$$

If, in the sum, -10, -20, -30, -40, etc., appears after the mantissa and the characteristic is greater than 9, subtract from both characteristic and mantissa a multiple of 10 that will make the characteristic less than 10.

Example 3.   Add the logarithms $6.3283 - 10$, $7.7642 - 10$, and $9.1048 - 10$.

Solution: $6.3283 - 10$
$$7.7642 - 10$$
$$9.1048 - 10$$
$$\overline{23.1973 - 30}$$
S:20,   Sum $=$ $3.1973 - 10$

In subtracting a larger logarithm from a smaller, the characteristic of the smaller should be increased by 10, and -10 written after the mantissa to preserve equality.

Example 4.   Subtract the logarithm 6.9860 from the logarithm 4.1073.

Solution: $4.1073 = 14.1073 - 10$
$$6.9860$$
$$\overline{7.1213 - 10}$$

Also, in subtracting a negative logarithm from a positive logarithm, the characteristic of the minuend should be made positive by adding to it the proper multiple of 10 and writing that multiple negative after the mantissa to preserve equality.

Example 5.   Subtract the logarithm $5.7856 - 10$ from the logarithm 1.6725.

Solution: Adding 10 to the characteristic, $1.6725 = 11.6725 - 10$.

$$11.6725 - 10$$
$$5.7856 - 10$$
$$\overline{5.8869}$$

Example 6.   Subtract the logarithm $8.6754 - 20$ from the logarithm 2.4625.

Solution: Adding 20 to the characteristic, 2.4625 = 22.4625 − 20.

$$\begin{array}{r} 22.4625 - 20 \\ 8.6754 - 20 \\ \hline 13.7871 \end{array}$$

PROBLEMS 20-5

Add the following logarithms:

1. 3.6874 + 2.3265.   **2.** 8.7263 + 1.1289.

3. $\overline{6}$.2642 + 3.7655.   **4.** $\overline{3}$.7827 + $\overline{4}$.4683.

5. 8.7112 + $\overline{6}$.8683.   **6.** $\overline{7}$.2863 + 3.4433.

Perform the indicated subtractions:

7. 0.3680 − $\overline{2}$.2562.   **8.** 0.1400 − $\overline{4}$.5611.

9. $\overline{3}$.1875 − 0.2178.   **10.** $\overline{1}$.6532 − $\overline{2}$.1227.

11. 8.9316 − $\overline{4}$.4208.   **12.** $\overline{6}$.3217 − 4.6483.

20-16. Multiplication by Logarithms.

It was shown in Art 20-3 that the logarithm of a product is equal to the sum of the logarithms of the factors. This property, with the aid of the tables, is of value in multiplication.

Example 1.   Find the product of 2.79 × 684.
Solution: Let p = the desired product.

Then $p = 2.79 \times 684$ (14)

Taking the logarithms of both members of Eq. (14),

$$\log p = \log 2.79 + \log 684$$

Looking up the logarithms and tabulating them,

$$\log 2.79 = 0.4456$$
$$\log 684 = 2.8351$$

Adding logarithms, $\log p = \overline{3.2807}$

Interpolating to find the value of p,

$$\begin{array}{ll} \log 1910 = 3.2810 & \log p \quad= 3.2807 \\ \log 1900 = 3.2788 & \log 1900 = 3.2788 \\ \text{Tabular difference} = \overline{0.0022}, & \text{difference} = \overline{0.0019} \end{array}$$

Then the value of p is $\dfrac{0.0019}{0.0022} \times 10 = 8 +$ larger than 1900. There is no need to express the result of the above division beyond one significant figure, for interpolation in a four-place table is not correct beyond four significant figures. Thus,

$$p = 1900 + 8 = 1908$$

The above quotient to three significant figures is 8.64. Adding this to 1900 would have resulted in a product of 1908.64, whereas the product obtained by actual multiplication is 1908.36.

Example 2. Given $X_L = 2\pi fL$. Find the value of X_L when $f = 10,600,000$ and $L = 0.0000251$. Use $2\pi = 6.28$.

Solution: $X_L = 6.28 \times 10,600,000 \times 0.0000251$
Taking logarithms,

$$\log X_L = \log 6.28 + \log 10,600,000 + \log 0.0000251$$

Tabulating,
$$\log 6.28 = 0.7980$$
$$\log 10,600,000 = 7.0253$$
$$\log 0.0000251 = \underline{5.3997 - 10}$$
$$\log X_L = \overline{13.2230 - 10}$$
$$= 3.2230$$

By interpolation, $X_L = 1671$

In using logarithms, a form should be written out for all the work before beginning any computations. The form should provide places for all logarithms as taken from Table VI and for other work necessary to complete the problem.

20-17. Computation with Negative Numbers. Because a negative number has an imaginary logarithm the logarithms of negative numbers cannot be used in computation. However, the numerical results of multiplications and divisions are the same regardless of the algebraic signs of the factors. Therefore, to make computations involving negative numbers, first determine whether the final result will be positive or negative. Then find the numerical value of the expression by logarithms, considering all numbers as positive, and affix the proper sign to the result.

PROBLEMS 20-6

Compute by logarithms:

1. 16×6.
2. 84×3.
3. 2×50.
4. 4×250.
5. $2 \times 25 \times 0.02$.
6. $38 \times (-42)$.
7. $(-76) \times 3.4$.
8. $0.0025 \times (-45)$.
9. 682×4.03.
10. $0.906 \times (-0.0024)$.
11. 81.2×542.
12. $2046 \times (-1.052)$.
13. $6.282 \times (-0.1592)$.
14. $5 \times 8 \times 42$.
15. $7.24 \times 38.6 \times 462$.
16. $5.96 \times 888 \times 0.00604$.
17. $(-0.00253) \times 700 \times 985$.
18. $17.62 \times (-8.772) \times 0.2275$.
19. $846.4 \times 405 \times 1922$.
20. $(-2846) \times 9438 \times (-6848)$.

20-18. Division by Logarithms. It was shown in Art. 20-4 that the logarithm of the quotient of two numbers is equal to the logarithm of the dividend minus the logarithm of the divisor. This property allows division by the use of logarithms.

Example 1.   Find the value of $\frac{948}{237}$, using logarithms.

Solution: Let q = quotient.

Then $q = \frac{948}{237}$

Taking logarithms, $\log q = \log 948 - \log 237$

Tabulating, $\log 948 = 2.9768$

                                         $\log 237 = 2.3747$

Subtracting, $\log q = \overline{0.6021}$

Taking antilogs, $q = 4$

Example 2.   Find the value of $\dfrac{-24.68}{682,700}$, using logarithms.

Solution: By inspection the quotient will be negative.   Let

                                       q = quotient

Then $q = \dfrac{-24.68}{682,700}$

Taking logarithms, $\log q = \log 24.68 - \log 682,700$

Interpolating and tabulating, $\log 24.68 = \quad 11.3923 - 10$

                                        $\log 682,700 = \quad 5.8342$

Subtracting, $\log q = \overline{\quad 5.5581 - 10}$

Taking antilogs, $q = -3.615 \times 10^{-5}$

NOTE: $\log 24.68 = 1.3923$, but 10 was added to the characteristic and subtracted after the mantissa, in order to facilitate the subtraction of a larger logarithm, as explained in Art. 20-15.

PROBLEMS 20-7

Compute by logarithms:

1. $\frac{10}{5}$.

2. $\frac{60}{12}$.

3. $\frac{288}{36}$.

4. $\dfrac{2450}{-3.5}$.

5. $\dfrac{0.423}{0.0047}$.

6. $\dfrac{786}{-943}$.

7. $\dfrac{-1397}{8.742}$.

8. $\dfrac{0.0006043}{-5.763}$.

9. $\dfrac{2804}{0.0009006}$.

10. $\dfrac{-74.23}{-0.008040}$.

20-19. Cologarithms. The logarithm of the reciprocal of a number is called the *cologarithm* of that number.   It is abbreviated *colog*.   Hence, to express the cologarithm of the number N, we write colog N.   Because, by definition,

$$\text{colog } N = \log \frac{1}{N}$$

then $\qquad\qquad \text{colog } N = \log 1 - \log N$

Since $\log 1 = 0$, by substituting in the above equation,

$$\log \frac{1}{N} = 0 - \log N$$

$$\therefore \ \log \frac{1}{N} = -\log N$$

The foregoing illustrates that the cologarithm of a number equals *minus* the logarithm of the number. The minus sign affects the entire logarithm; that is, both characteristic and mantissa of a cologarithm are negative. However, to avoid a negative mantissa in the cologarithm, we agree to subtract the logarithm of the number from $10.0000 - 10$. Note that this is the same as subtracting from zero, except for the resulting sign of the mantissa.

Example 1.   Find colog 40.

Solution:	$\text{colog } 40 = \log \frac{1}{40} = \log 1 - \log 40$
Now	$\log 1 = 0$
or	$\log 1 = 10.0000 - 10$
Also,	$\log 40 = \ \underline{1.6021}$
Subtracting,	$\text{colog } 40 = \ 8.3979 - 10$

Example 2.   Find colog 0.00075.

Solution:	$\log 1 = 10.0000 - 10$
	$\log 0.00075 = \ \underline{6.8751 - 10}$
Subtracting,	$\text{colog } 0.00075 = \ 3.1249$

To divide by any number is the same as multiplying by the reciprocal of that number. That is,

$$\frac{873}{432} \text{ is the same as } 873 \times \frac{1}{432}$$

or, in general, $\qquad\qquad \frac{A}{N} = A\left(\frac{1}{N}\right)$

Therefore, *in computing a quotient, add the cologarithm of each factor of the denominator to the logarithm of the numerator.*

Example 3.   Evaluate $\alpha = \dfrac{14.63}{0.00362 \times 8767}$.

Solution: The above could be expressed as

$$\alpha = 14.63 \cdot \frac{1}{0.00362} \cdot \frac{1}{8767}$$

That is,   log α = log 14.63 + colog 0.00362 + colog 8767
Tabulating,   log 14.63 = 1.1652
log 0.00362 = 7.5587 − 10; hence,   colog 0.00362 = 2.4413
log 8767 = 3.9428; hence,   colog 8767 = 6.0572 − 10
Adding,   log α = 9.6637 − 10
Taking antilogs. α = 0.461

Example 4.   Evaluate $\phi = \dfrac{64.28 \times 0.00973}{4006 \times 0.05134 \times 0.002085}$.

Solution: Always make up a skeleton form before looking up the logarithms in the tables, thus: log 64.28 =
                                                log 0.00973 =
log 4006   =   colog 4006 =
log 0.05134   =   colog 0.05134 =
log 0.002085 =   colog 0.002085 = _____
                                                    log ϕ =
                                                      ϕ =
Tabulating,   log 64.28 = 1.8080
                                               log 0.00973 = 7.9881 − 10
      log 4006 = 3.6027   colog 4006 = 6.3973 − 10
  log 0.05134 = 8.7105 − 10   colog 0.05134 = 1.2895
log 0.002085 = 7.3191 − 10   colog 0.002085 = 2.6809
                                                 log ϕ = 0.1638
                                                 ∴ ϕ = 1.458

PROBLEMS 20-8

Using logarithms, compute the results of the following:

1. $\dfrac{3.8 \times 2.6}{4.3}$.

2. $\dfrac{7.3 \times 9.8}{6.3 \times 8.5}$.

3. $\dfrac{44.1 \times 1.82}{10.27 \times 0.32}$.

4. $\dfrac{57.4 \times 0.0347}{0.6258}$.

5. $\dfrac{0.335}{326.1 \times 0.00276}$.

6. $\dfrac{1.001}{3.141 \times 0.703}$.

7. $\dfrac{0.000008604}{5.28 \times 0.000000117}$.

8. $\dfrac{1}{27.98 \times 0.395 \times 0.00148}$.

9. $\dfrac{1}{8.96 \times 7333 \times 0.000801}$.

10. $\dfrac{6.28 \times 0.159 \times 10^{-3}}{0.00425 \times 235 \times 10^{2}}$.

20-20. Raising to a Power by Logarithms.

It was shown in Art. 20-5 that the logarithm of a power of a number is equal to the logarithm of the number multiplied by the exponent of the power.

Example 1.   Find by logarithms the value of 12^3.

Solution: $\log 12^3 = 3 \log 12$

$\log 12 = 1.0792$

Multiplying by 3, 3

$\overline{3.2376} = \log 1728$

$\therefore 12^3 = 1728$

Example 2.   Find by logarithms the value of $(0.0563)^5$.

Solution: $\log (0.0563)^5 = 5 \log 0.0563$

$\log 0.0563 = 8.7505 - 10$

Multiplying by 5, 5

$5 \log 0.0563 = \overline{43.7525 - 50}$

$= 3.7525 - 10$

antilog $3.7525 - 10 = 5.656 \times 10^{-7}$

$\therefore (0.0563)^5 = 5.656 \times 10^{-7}$

Example 3.   Find by logarithms the value of 5^{-3}.

Solution: By the laws of exponents,

$$5^{-3} = \frac{1}{5^3}$$

Then $\log 5^{-3} = \log 1 - \log 5^3$

$= \log 1 - 3 \log 5$

$\log 5 = 0.6990$ $\log 1 = 10.0000 - 10$

Multiplying, 3 $3 \log 5 = 2.0970$

$3 \log 5 = \overline{2.0970}$ $\log 5^{-3} = \overline{7.9030 - 10}$

antilog $7.9030 - 10 = 0.008$

$\therefore 5^{-3} = 0.008$

20-21. Extracting Roots by Logarithms.

It was shown in Art. 20-6 that the logarithm of a root of a number is equal to the logarithm of the number divided by the index of the root.

Example 1.   Find by logarithms the value of $\sqrt[3]{815}$.

Solution: By the laws of exponents,

$\sqrt[3]{815} = (815)^{\frac{1}{3}}$

Then $\log (815)^{\frac{1}{3}} = \frac{1}{3} \log 815$

$\log 815 = 2.9112$

$\frac{1}{3} \log 815 = \dfrac{2.9112}{3} = 0.9704$

antilog $0.9704 = 9.34$

$\therefore \sqrt[3]{815} = 9.34$ to three significant figures.

Example 2.   Find by logarithms the value of $\sqrt[4]{0.00955}$.

Solution: $\sqrt[4]{0.00955} = (0.00955)^{\frac{1}{4}}$

Then $\log (0.00955)^{\frac{1}{4}} = \frac{1}{4} \log 0.00955$

$\log 0.00955 = 7.9800 - 10$

$\frac{1}{4} \log 0.00955 = 1.9950 - 2.5$

This result, though correct, is not in the standard form for a negative characteristic. This inconvenience can be obviated by writing the logarithm in such a manner that the negative part when divided results in a quotient of −10. Thus,

$$\log 0.00955 = 7.9800 - 10$$

would be written $\log 0.00955 = 37.9800 - 40.$

Since it is necessary to divide the logarithm by 4 in order to obtain the fourth root, 30 was subtracted from the negative part to make it exactly divisible by 4. Therefore, to preserve equality, it was necessary to add 30 to the positive part.

Then $$\log \sqrt[4]{0.00955} = \frac{37.9800 - 40}{4} = 9.4950 - 10$$

$$\text{antilog } 9.4950 - 10 = 0.3126$$
$$\therefore \sqrt[4]{0.00955} = 0.3126$$

20-22. Fractional Exponents.   Computations involving fractional exponents are made by combining the operations of raising to powers and extracting roots.

Example.   Find by logarithms the value of $\sqrt[4]{(0.0542)^3}$.

Solution: $\sqrt[4]{(0.0542)^3} = (0.0542)^{\frac{3}{4}}$
Then $\log (0.0542)^{\frac{3}{4}} = \frac{3}{4} \log 0.0542$
$\log 0.0542 = 8.7340 - 10$
$3 \log 0.0542 = 26.2020 - 30$

Adding 10 to the characteristic and subtracting 10 from the negative part in order to make it evenly divisible by 4,

$$3 \log 0.0542 = 36.2020 - 40$$
$$\frac{3}{4} \log 0.0542 = \frac{36.2020 - 40}{4} = 9.0505 - 10$$
$$\text{antilog } 9.0505 - 10 = 0.112$$
$$\therefore \sqrt[4]{(0.0542)^3} = 0.112$$

Instead of adding 10 to the characteristic, as above, it would also have been correct to subtract 10 from the characteristic and add 10 to the mantissa, thus obtaining $16.2020 - 20$. It is immaterial what numbers are added and subtracted as long as the resulting negative part of the logarithm will result in an integral quotient.

PROBLEMS 20-9

Using logarithms, compute the results of the following:

1. $(18.7)^3$.   **2.** $(63.9)^6$.   **3.** $(0.0293)^4$.

4. $(0.761)^4$.   **5.** $\sqrt[3]{987}$.   **6.** $\sqrt[4]{815}$.

7. $(0.00563)^{\frac{1}{3}}$.   **8.** $(0.715)^{\frac{1}{6}}$.   **9.** $(0.850)^{\frac{1}{4}}$.

10. $\sqrt[4]{928}$.   **11.** $(143)^{\frac{2}{3}}$.   **12.** $\sqrt[3]{(8.91)^4}$.

13. $(25.7)^{\frac{3}{4}}$.   **14.** $(0.00314)^3$.

15. $\sqrt{\dfrac{163 \times 0.977}{14.4}}$.   **16.** $\sqrt[3]{\dfrac{0.541 \times 47.3}{0.0157}}$.

17. $(\frac{198}{276})^{\frac{2}{3}}$.   **18.** $(\frac{534}{175})^{\frac{2}{3}}$.

19. $\sqrt[5]{0.000230} \times \sqrt[4]{387}$.   **20.** $\left(\dfrac{10^7 \times 0.000000683}{10^8 \times (0.00000343)^3}\right)^{\frac{2}{3}}$.

20-23. Change of Base. The natural system of logarithms has for its base the number $\epsilon = 2.71828 \cdots$. There are many formulas in the various branches of science where this base is used. A table of natural logarithms has not been included in this book because, for purposes of computation, all that is necessary is to remember that the natural logarithm of a number is approximately 2.3026 times the common logarithm of the same number. The common logarithm of a number is 0.4343 times the natural logarithm of the same number. These relations may be written

$$\log_\epsilon N = 2.3026 \log_{10} N. \tag{15}$$
$$\log_{10} N = 0.4343 \log_\epsilon N \tag{16}$$

Example 1. $\begin{aligned} \log_\epsilon 1000 &= 2.3026 \log_{10} 1000 \\ &= 2.3026 \times 3 \\ &= 6.9078 \end{aligned}$

Example 2. $\begin{aligned} \log_{10} 100 &= 0.4343 \log_\epsilon 100 \\ &= 0.4343 \times 4.6052 \\ &= 2.0000 \end{aligned}$

Example 3. Given $x = \log_\epsilon 48$. Solve for x.
Solution: $\begin{aligned} \log_\epsilon 48 &= 2.3026 \log_{10} 48 \\ &= 2.3026 \times 1.6812 \\ x &= 3.871 \end{aligned}$

20-24. Graph of $y = \log_{10} x$. The graph of $y = \log_{10} x$ is shown in Fig. 20-1. A study of this graph shows the following:

1. A negative number has no real logarithm.
2. The logarithm of a positive number less than 1 (a decimal between 0 and 1) is negative.
3. The logarithm of 1 is zero.
4. The logarithm of a positive number greater than 1 is positive.

5. As the number approaches zero, its logarithm decreases without limit.

6. As the number increases indefinitely, its logarithm increases without limit.

Is the method of interpolation that treats a short distance on the logarithmic curve as a straight line sufficiently accurate for computation?

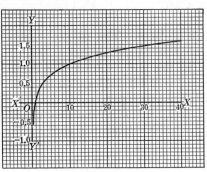

Fig. 20-1.

20-25. Logarithmic Equations. An equation in which there appears the logarithm of some expression involving the unknown quantity is called a *logarithmic equation*.

Logarithmic equations have wide application in electric-circuit analysis. In addition, the communication engineer uses them in computations involving decibels and transmission-line characteristics.

Example 1.   Solve the equation $4 \log x + 3.7960 = 4.6990 + \log x$.

Solution: Given $4 \log x + 3.7960 = 4.6990 + \log x$.

Transposing, $4 \log x - \log x = 4.6990 - 3.7960$

Collecting terms, $3 \log x = 0.9030$

D : 3, $\log x = 0.3010$

From tables or slide rule, $x = 2$

In solving logarithmic equations, the logarithm of the unknown, as log x in Example 1, is considered as any other literal coefficient. That is, in general, the rules for solving ordinary algebraic equations apply to logarithmic equations.

A common error made by students in solving logarithmic equations is confusing coefficients of logarithms with coefficients of the unknown. For example,

$$3 \log x \neq \log 3x$$

because the left member denotes the product of 3 times the logarithm of x, whereas the right member denotes the logarithm of the quantity 3 times x, that is, log $(3x)$.

Example 2.   Given $500 = 276 \log \dfrac{d}{0.05}$.   Solve for d.

Solution: Given $\qquad\qquad 500 = 276 \log \dfrac{d}{0.05}$

Then, $\qquad\qquad\qquad 500 = 276\,(\log d - \log 0.05)$

D : 276, $\qquad\qquad\quad 1.81 = \log d - \log 0.05$

Transposing, $\qquad\qquad\qquad\qquad \log d = 1.81 + \log 0.05$

Substituting $8.6990 - 10$ for log 0.05, $\quad \log d = 1.81 + 8.6990 - 10$

Collecting terms, $\qquad\qquad\qquad\qquad \log d = 0.5090$

From tables or slide rule, $\qquad\qquad\quad d = 3.23$

  Alternate Solution: Given $\qquad\qquad 500 = 276 \log \dfrac{d}{0.05}$

D : 276, $\qquad\qquad\qquad\qquad 1.81 = \log \dfrac{d}{0.05}$

Taking antilog of both members, $\qquad 64.6 = \dfrac{d}{0.05}$

Solving for d, $\qquad\qquad\qquad\qquad\quad d = 3.23$

20-26. Exponential Equations. An equation in which the unknown appears in an exponent is called an *exponential equation*. In the equation

$$x^3 = 125$$

it is necessary to find some value of x that, when cubed, will equal 125.   In this equation *the exponent is a constant.*

In the *exponential equation*

$$5^x = 125$$

the situation is different.   *The unknown appears as an exponent,* and it is now necessary to find what power 5 must be raised to obtain 125.

Some exponential equations can be solved by inspection.   For example, the value of x in the foregoing equation is 3.   In general, taking the logarithms of both sides of an exponential equation will result in a logarithmic equation that can be solved by the usual methods.

Example 1.   Given $4^x = 256$.   Solve for x.

Solution: Given $\qquad\qquad\qquad\qquad\qquad 4^x = 256$

Taking the logarithms of both members, $\quad \log 4^x = \log 256$

or $x \log 4 = \log 256$

D: $\log 4$, $x = \dfrac{\log 256}{\log 4}$

From tables or slide rule, $x = \dfrac{2.408}{0.602} = 4$

Check. $4^4 = 256$

Example 2.   Given $5^{x-3} = 52$. Solve for x.

Solution: Given $5^{x-3} = 52$

Taking the logarithms of both members, $\log 5^{x-3} = \log 52$

or $(x - 3) \log 5 = \log 52$

D: $\log 5$, $x - 3 = \dfrac{\log 52}{\log 5}$

From tables or slide rule, $x - 3 = \dfrac{1.716}{0.699}$

A: 3, $x = \dfrac{1.716}{0.699} + 3$

or $x = 5.46$

How is this solution checked?

PROBLEMS 20-10

Solve the following equations:

1. $x = \log_\epsilon 508$.

2. $x = \log_\epsilon 1.25$.

3. $\log x + 2 \log x = 3$.

4. $\log x + \log 10x = 101$.
(HINT: $\log 10x = \log 10 + \log x$.

5. $\log 3x + 3 \log x = 20$.

6. $\log \dfrac{P}{4} = 16$.

7. $\log \dfrac{P_1}{6} = 1.3$.

8. $\log \dfrac{6}{E} = 0.1$.

9. $\log x^2 - \log x = 0.3$.

10. $x^3 = 216$.

11. $2^x = 16$.

12. $3^x = 81$.

13. $2^x = 10$.

14. $3^{x-2} = 10$.

15. $4^{2x} = 100$.

16. $x^{2.3} = 14$.

17. In an inductive circuit, the equation for the growth of current is given by

$$i = \frac{E}{R}(1 - \epsilon^{-\frac{Rt}{L}}) \tag{17}$$

where i = current in amperes at any elapsed time t sec after the switch is closed,

E = constant impressed voltage in volts,
L = inductance of the circuit in henrys,
R = circuit resistance in ohms,
ϵ = base of the natural system of logarithms.

A circuit of 0.75 h inductance and 15 Ω resistance is connected across a 12-v battery. What is the value of the current at the end of 0.06 sec after the circuit is closed?

Solution: The circuit is shown in Fig. 20-2.

Given
$$i = \frac{E}{R} (1 - \epsilon^{-\frac{Rt}{L}})$$

Substituting the known values,
$$i = \tfrac{12}{15}(1 - \epsilon^{-\frac{15 \times 0.06}{0.75}})$$
$$= 0.8(1 - \epsilon^{-1.2})$$

Multiplying,
$$i = 0.8 - 0.8\epsilon^{-1.2}$$

or
$$i = 0.8 - \frac{0.8}{\epsilon^{1.2}} \tag{18}$$

Now
$$\log_{10} \epsilon^{1.2} = 1.2 \log_{10} \epsilon$$
$$= 1.2 \times 0.4343$$
$$= 0.5212$$

Then, since
$$\log_{10} \epsilon^{1.2} = 0.5212$$
taking antilogs,
$$\epsilon^{1.2} = 3.32$$

Substituting the value of $\epsilon^{1.2}$ in Eq. (18),

$$i = 0.8 - \frac{0.8}{3.32}$$
$$\therefore i = 0.559 \text{ a}$$

The growth of the current in the circuit of Fig. 20-2 is shown graphically in Fig. 20-3.

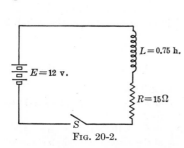

FIG. 20-2.

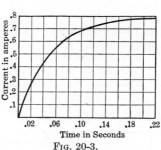

FIG. 20-3.

18. The inductance of the circuit of Fig. 20-2 is doubled, and the resistance is thus increased 1.4 times its original value. Other circuit values remaining the same, what will be the value of the current 0.06 sec after the switch is closed?

19. Using the circuit values of Fig. 20-2, what will be the value of the current

    (*a*) 1 sec after the switch is closed?
    (*b*) 2 sec after the switch is closed?

20. In the circuit of Fig. 20-2, after the switch is closed, how long will it take the current to reach 50% of its maximum value?

21. If $\dfrac{L}{R}$ is substituted for t in the equation $i = \dfrac{E}{R}(1 - \epsilon^{-\frac{Rt}{L}})$, show that

the value of the current i will be 63.2% of its steady-state value. The

numerical value of $\dfrac{L}{R}$, in seconds, is known as the circuit *time constant*. It is

useful in determining the rapidity with which current rises or falls in one inductive circuit in comparison with others.

22. A certain 220-v generator shunt field has an inductance of 15 h and a resistance of 100 Ω. How long, after the line voltage is applied, does it take for the current to reach 75% of its maximum value?

23. A relay of 1.2 h inductance and 500 Ω resistance is to be used for keying a radio transmitter. The relay is to be operated from a 110-v line, and 0.175 a is required to close the contacts. How many words per minute will the relay carry if each word is considered as five letters of five impulses per letter? The time of opening of the contacts is the same as the time required to close them.

HINT: $0.175 = \tfrac{110}{500}(1 - \epsilon^{-\frac{500t}{1.2}})$. t is the time required to close the relay.

24. Using the relay of Prob. 23, how many words per minute would it carry if 50 Ω resistance were connected in series with the relay? The line voltage remains at 110 v.

25. In a capacitive circuit the equation for the current is given by

$$i = \frac{E}{R}\epsilon^{-\frac{t}{RC}} \tag{19}$$

where i = current in amperes at any elapsed time t sec after the switch is

  closed,

  E = impressed voltage in volts,

  C = capacitance of the circuit in farads,

  R = circuit resistance in ohms,

  ϵ = base of the natural system of logarithms.

A capacitance of 20 μf in series with 500 Ω is connected across a 110-v generator.

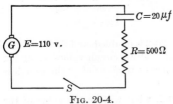

FIG. 20-4.

(*a*) What is the value of the current at the instant the switch is closed? HINT: $t = 0$.

(*b*) What is the value of the current 0.007 sec after the switch is closed? The circuit is shown in Fig. 20-4.

26. In the circuit of Fig. 20-4, how long after the switch is closed will the current have decayed to 30% of its initial value?

Solution: $E = 110$ v, $R = 500$ Ω, $C = 20$ μf, and $i = \dfrac{0.3E}{R}$. $t = ?$

$$i = \frac{0.3E}{R} = \frac{0.3 \times 110}{500} = 0.066 \text{ a}$$

Substituting in Eq. (19), $0.066 = \frac{110}{500}(\epsilon^{-\frac{t}{500\times20\times10^{-6}}})$

Simplifying, $0.066 = 0.22\,\epsilon^{-\frac{t}{10^{-2}}}$

or $0.066 = 0.22\,\epsilon^{-100t}$

D : 0.22, $0.3 = \epsilon^{-100t}$

By the law of exponents, $0.3 = \dfrac{1}{\epsilon^{100t}}$

M : ϵ^{100t} $0.3\,\epsilon^{100t} = 1$

D : 0.3, $\epsilon^{100t} = 3.33$

Taking logarithms, $\log_{10}\epsilon^{100t} = \log_{10} 3.33$

That is, $100t\,\log_{10}\epsilon = \log_{10} 3.33$

Then $100t \times 0.4343 = 0.5224$

or $43.43t = 0.5224$

    $\therefore t = 0.012$ sec

The decay of the current in the circuit of Fig. 20-4 is shown graphically in Fig. 20-5.

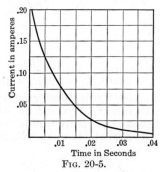

FIG. 20-5.

27. A 30-μf condenser in series with a resistance of 1000 Ω is connected across a 220-v source.

  (a) What is the initial value of the current?

  (b) How long after the switch is closed will the current have decayed to 36.8% of its initial value?

  (c) Is the time obtained in (b) equal to CR sec? The product of CR, in seconds, is the time constant of a capacitive circuit.

28. The quantity of charge on a condenser is given by

$$q = CE(1 - \epsilon^{-\frac{t}{CR}}) \qquad (20)$$

where q is the quantity of electricity in coulombs.

  (a) Calculate the charge q in coulombs on a condenser of 50 μf in series with a resistance of 2000 Ω, 0.03 sec after being connected across a 100-v source.

  (b) What is the voltage across the condenser at the end of 0.03 sec?

29. A key-click filter consisting of a 2-μf condenser in series with a resistance is connected across the keying contacts of a transmitter. If the average time of impulse is 0.004 sec, calculate the value of the series resistance required in order that the condenser may discharge 90% in this time.

HINT: Under steady-state conditions, $q = CE$. Then

$$0.9CE = CE(1 - \epsilon^{-\frac{t}{RC}})$$

30. The emission current in amperes of a heated filament is given by

$$I = AT^2 \epsilon^{-\frac{B}{T}} \tag{21}$$

For a tungsten filament, $A = 60$ and $B = 52,400$. Find the current of such a filament at a temperature $T = 2500°K$.

31. An important triode formula is

$$I_p + I_g = K\left(E_g + \frac{E_p}{\mu}\right)^{\frac{3}{2}}$$

where I_p = plate current,
       I_g = grid current,
      E_g = grid voltage,
      E_p = plate voltage,
      μ = amplification factor.
Calculate $I_p + I_g$ if $K = 0.0005$, $E_g = 5$ v, $E_p = 250$ v, and $\mu = 8$.

32. The diameter of No. 0000 wire is 460 mils, and that of No. 36 is 5 mils. There are 38 wire sizes between No. 0000 and No. 36; therefore the ratio between cross-sectional areas of successive sizes is the thirty-ninth root of the ratio of the area of No. 0000 wire to that of No. 36 wire; or

$$\sqrt[39]{\frac{(460)^2}{5^2}}$$

Compute the value of this ratio. Because this ratio is nearly equal to $\sqrt[3]{2}$, we can use the approximation that the cross-sectional area of a wire doubles for every decrease of three sizes, as explained in Art. 10-5.

CHAPTER XXI

APPLICATION OF LOGARITHMS TO DECIBELS AND TRANSMISSION LINES

Proficiency in the use of logarithmic equations will be an asset to the student as he studies their application to decibels and transmission lines in this chapter.

Derived from the original international transmission unit, which is called the "bel" in honor of the inventor of the telephone, Alexander Graham Bell, the decibel is probably the most widely used unit in communication engineering. A thorough understanding of the applications and uses of this unit is essential to the student of communication engineering.

21-1. The Transmission Unit—Power Ratios. The ear responds logarithmically to variations in sound intensity. That is, it is much more sensitive to changes of volume at low sound levels than it is at high sound levels. Therefore, any unit used for expressing power gains or losses in communication circuits must, in order to be practical, vary logarithmically. This unit is the *decibel* which is one-tenth (deci) of the bel mentioned above. The abbreviation for decibel is db. A difference of 1 decibel between two sound intensities is just discernible to the ear. By definition,

$$\text{Decibels} = \text{db} = 10 \log_{10} \frac{P_2}{P_1} \tag{1}$$

where $\frac{P_2}{P_1}$ is the ratio of the two powers being compared.

Example 1. A power of 10 milliwatts is required to drive an audio-frequency amplifier. The output of the amplifier is 120 milliwatts. What is the gain, expressed in decibels?

Solution: $P_1 = 10$ milliwatts, and $P_2 = 120$ milliwatts. db = ?

Substituting in Eq. (1), db $= 10 \log \frac{120}{10}$
$= 10 \log 12 = 10.8$ db gain

Example 2. A network has a loss of 16 decibels. What power ratio corresponds to this loss?

Solution: Given $\qquad$ db $= 10 \log \frac{P_2}{P_1}$ $\tag{1}$

309

Substituting 16 for db, $16 = 10 \log \dfrac{P_2}{P_1}$

D : 10, $1.6 = \log \dfrac{P_2}{P_1}$

Taking antilogs of both members.

$$39.8 = \dfrac{P_2}{P_1}$$

Thus, a loss of 16 decibels corresponds to a power ratio of 39.8 to 1.

Because db is 10 times the log of the power ratio, it is evident that power ratios of $10 = 10$ db, $100 = 20$ db, $1000 = 30$ db, etc. Therefore, it could have been determined by inspection that the 16-decibel loss in the previous example represented a power ratio somewhere between 10 and 100. This is evident by the figure 1 of 16 decibels. The second digit 6 of 16 decibels is ten times the logarithm of 3.98; hence, 16 decibels represents a power ratio of 39.8.

A loss in decibels is customarily denoted by the minus sign. Thus, a loss of 16 decibels is written -16 decibels.

Example 3.   A certain radio receiver utilizes a type 6F6 vacuum tube as a final audio stage that delivers 4500 milliwatts to the loud-speaker. The owner is considering modifying the circuit in order to substitute a type 6L6 tube for the 6F6. The 6L6 tube will deliver 6500 milliwatts to the speaker. Is the gain in power sufficient to warrant the expense of making this change?

Solution: By changing to the 6L6 tube the power output is increased by a ratio of 1.44, nearly 1.5 times. Those not familiar with the use of the decibel would probably think that an increase in power of almost 45 per cent would justify making the change. However, by expressing the power ratio in terms of decibels, it is evident that, as far as the ear is concerned, very little is gained.

Substituting in Eq. (1), $db = 10 \log \frac{6500}{4500}$
        $= 10 \times 0.1596 = 1.6$ db

Such an increase in power would hardly be noticeable.

Expressing the gain or loss of various circuits or apparatus in terms of decibels obviates the necessity of computing gains or losses by multiplication and division. Because the decibel is a logarithmic unit, the total gain of a circuit is found by adding the individual decibel gains and losses of the various circuit components.

Example 4.   A dynamic microphone with an output of -85 decibels is connected to a preamplifier with a gain of 60 decibels. The output of the preamplifier is connected through an attenuation pad with a loss of 10 deci-- bels to a final amplifier with a gain of 90 decibels.   What is the total gain?

Solution: In this example, all decibel values have been taken from a common reference level.   Because the microphone is 85 decibels below refer- ence level, the preamplifier brings the level up to $-85 + 60 = -25$ db. The attenuation pad then reduces the level to $-25 - 10 = -35$ db. Finally, the final amplifier causes a net gain of $-35 + 90 = 55$ db gain.   Hence, it is apparent that the over-all gain in any system is simply the algebraic sum of the decibel gains or losses of the associated circuit com- ponents.   Thus, $-85 + 60 - 10 + 90 = 55$ db gain.

21-2. Reference Levels.   Because the decibel is an expression for a power ratio, it would be meaningless to say, for example, that an amplifier has an output of so many decibels unless that output is referred to some power level.

Several zero-decibel levels are in use.   For example, telephone engineers commonly use 0.006 watt (6 milliwatts) as the refer- ence, or zero, level.   This level is also used by several receiver and amplifier manufacturers.   For example, if an amplifier is rated at 40 decibels, this means that the power-output capability of the amplifier is 40 decibels *above* reference level.   If reference level is 6 milliwatts, the amplifier has a power-output capability of 60 watts.   As a general rule, the power output of an amplifier is specified in addition to the over-all decibel gain of the amplifier.

In broadcasting, 12.5 milliwatts is generally taken as standard because this is based upon "peak" values of speech, whereas the 6-milliwatt level is based upon average values.

At least one prominent microphone manufacturer uses a zero- decibel level as 1 volt per bar.   That is, a microphone will have zero-decibel output if, when subjected to a sound intensity of 1 dyne per square centimeter, there is developed 1 volt across its output terminals.   This is a very high zero level for micro- phones, as is the 12.5-milliwatt level.

From the foregoing the student will realize the necessity of knowing what zero level is being used in expressing gain or loss in decibels.   Unless otherwise specified, zero decibel will here be taken as 6 milliwatts.

Example 1.   How much power is represented by a gain of 23 decibels?
Solution: Substituting 23 for db and 6 for P_1 in Eq. (1),

$$23 = 10 \log \frac{P_2}{6}$$

D : 10,
$$2.3 = \log \frac{P_2}{6}$$

Taking antilogs of both members, $199.5 = \dfrac{P_2}{6}$

$$\therefore P_2 = 1197 \text{ mw}$$

Check. $23 = 10 \log \tfrac{1197}{6}$

$$23 = 10 \log 199.5$$

$$23 = 10 \times 2.3$$

Alternate Solution: $2.3 = \log \dfrac{P_2}{6}$

or $2.3 = \log P_2 - \log 6$

Transposing, $\log P_2 = 2.3 + \log 6$

Substituting the value of log 6, $\log P_2 = 2.3 + 0.778$

$$\log P_2 = 3.078$$

Taking antilogs, $P_2 = 1197 \text{ mw}$

Example 2. How much power is represented by -64 decibels?

Solution: Substituting -64 for db and 6 for P_1 in Eq. (1),

$$-64 = 10 \log \frac{P_2}{6}$$

$D:10,$ $-6.4 = \log \dfrac{P_2}{6}$

The left member of the above equation is a logarithm with a negative mantissa because the entire number 6.4 is negative. Hence, to express this logarithm with a positive mantissa the equation is written

$$(3.6 - 10) = \log \frac{P_2}{6}$$

Taking antilogs of both members, $3.98 \times 10^{-7} = \dfrac{P_2}{6}$

$$\therefore P_2 = 2.39 \times 10^{-6} \text{ mw}$$

Check. $-64 = 10 \log \dfrac{2.39 \times 10^{-6}}{6} = 10 \log 3.98 \times 10^{-7}$

$$-64 = 10(3.6 - 10)$$

$$-64 = -64$$

Alternate Solution: $-6.4 = \log \dfrac{P_2}{6}$

Then $-6.4 = \log P_2 - \log 6$

Transposing, $\log P_2 = \log 6 - 6.4$

Substituting the value of log 6, $\log P_2 = 0.778 - 6.4$

$$= (10.778 - 10) - 6.4$$

$$\therefore P_2 = 2.39 \times 10^{-6} \text{ mw}$$

By always placing the larger power in the numerator of the power ratio, the quotient will always be greater than 1; hence, the characteristic of the logarithm of the ratio will always be zero or a positive value. In this manner the use of a negative characteristic is avoided. As an illustration, from Example 2,

$$-6.4 = \log \frac{P_2}{6}$$

which is the same as $6.4 = \log 6 - \log P_2$

Hence, $6.4 = \log \dfrac{6}{P_2}$

It is always apparent whether there is a gain or a loss in decibels; therefore, the proper sign may be affixed after working the problem.

21-3. Current and Voltage Ratios. Fundamentally, the decibel is a measure of the ratio of two powers. However, voltage ratios and current ratios may be utilized for computing the decibel gain or loss provided that the input and output impedances are taken into account.

In the following derivations, P_1 and P_2 will represent the power input and power output, respectively, and R_1 and R_2 will represent the input and output impedances, respectively.

Then $P_1 = \dfrac{E_1{}^2}{R_1}$ and $P_2 = \dfrac{E_2{}^2}{R_2}$

Since $\mathrm{db} = 10 \log \dfrac{P_2}{P_1}$

substituting for P_1 and P_2, $\mathrm{db} = 10 \log \dfrac{E_2{}^2/R_2}{E_1{}^2/R_1}$

Therefore, $\mathrm{db} = 10 \log \dfrac{E_2{}^2 R_1}{E_1{}^2 R_2} = 10 \log \left(\dfrac{E_2}{E_1}\right)^2 \dfrac{R_1}{R_2}$

That is, $\mathrm{db} = 10 \log \left(\dfrac{E_2}{E_1}\right)^2 + 10 \log \dfrac{R_1}{R_2}$

or $\mathrm{db} = 20 \log \dfrac{E_2}{E_1} + 10 \log \dfrac{R_1}{R_2}$ (2)

This may be written $\mathrm{db} = 20 \log \dfrac{E_2 \sqrt{R_1}}{E_1 \sqrt{R_2}}$ (3)

Similarly, $P_1 = I_1{}^2 R_1$ and $P_2 = I_2{}^2 R_2$

Then, since $\mathrm{db} = 10 \log \dfrac{P_2}{P_1}$

by substituting for P_1 and P_2, $\mathrm{db} = 10 \log \dfrac{I_2{}^2 R_2}{I_1{}^2 R_1}$

That is, $\mathrm{db} = 20 \log \dfrac{I_2}{I_1} + 10 \log \dfrac{R_2}{R_1}$ (4)

This may be written $\mathrm{db} = 20 \log \dfrac{I_2 \sqrt{R_2}}{I_1 \sqrt{R_1}}$ (5)

If, in both the above cases, the impedances R_1 and R_2 are equal, they will cancel, and the following formulas will result:

$$db = 20 \log \frac{E_2}{E_1} \qquad (6)$$

and

$$db = 20 \log \frac{I_2}{I_1} \qquad (7)$$

It is evident that voltage or current ratios may be translated into decibels *only* when the impedances across which the voltages exist, or into which the currents flow, are taken into account.

Example. An amplifier has an input resistance of 200 and an output resistance of 6400. When 0.5 v. is applied across the input, a voltage of 400 v. appears across the output.

(a) What is the power output of the amplifier?

(b) What is the gain in decibels?

Solution: (a) Power output $= P_o = \dfrac{E_o{}^2}{R_o} = \dfrac{400^2}{6400} = 25$ w

       (b) Power input $= P_i = \dfrac{E_i{}^2}{R_i} = \dfrac{0.5^2}{200} = 1.25 \times 10^{-3}$ w

Power gain, $db = 10 \log \dfrac{P_o}{P_i} = 10 \log \dfrac{25}{1.25 \times 10^{-3}} = 43$ db

Check the solution by substituting the values of the voltages and resistances in Eq. (3).

$$db = 20 \log \frac{E_o}{E_i} \sqrt{\frac{R_i}{R_o}}$$

$$= 20 \log \frac{400}{0.5} \sqrt{\frac{200}{6400}} = 43 \text{ db}$$

21-4. The Merit, or Gain, of an Antenna.

The merit of an antenna, especially one designed for directive transmission or reception, is usually expressed in terms of antenna *gain*. The gain is generally taken as the ratio of the power that must be supplied to some standard-comparison antenna to the power that must be supplied the antenna under test, in order to produce the same field strengths in the desired direction at the receiving antenna. Similarly, the gain of one antenna over another could be taken as the ratio of their respective radiated fields.

Example. One kilowatt is supplied to a rhombic antenna which results in a field strength of 20 microvolts per meter at the receiving station. In order to produce the same field strength at the receiving station, a half-wave antenna, properly oriented and located near the rhombic, must be supplied with 16.6 kw.   What is the gain of the rhombic?

Solution: Because the same antenna is used for reception, both transmitting antennas deliver the same power to the receiver.

Hence, $$db = 10 \log \frac{P_2}{P_1} = 10 \log \frac{16.6}{1} = 12.2 \text{ db}$$

PROBLEMS 21-1

1. How many decibels correspond to a power ratio of

(a) 25?   (b) 47.5?

(c) $\frac{1}{195}$?   (d) $\frac{1}{38}$?

2. Referred to impedances of the same value, how many decibels correspond to a voltage ratio of

(a) 57?   (b) 13.9?

(c) $\frac{1}{115}$?   (d) $\frac{1}{76}$?

3. If zero decibel is taken as 6 mw, how much voltage across a 600-Ω load does this represent?   How much current flows through the load?

4. If zero decibel is taken as 6 mw, how much voltage across a 500-Ω load does this represent?   How much current flows through the load?

5. If reference level is taken as 12.5 mw, how much voltage across a 600-Ω load does this represent?   How much current flows through the load?

6. If reference level is taken as 12.5 mw, how much voltage across a 500-Ω load does this represent?   How much current flows through the load?

7. If zero power level corresponds to 12.5 mw, in a 600-Ω load, compute the output in milliwatts and voltage across the load for the following output meter readings:

(a)   2 db.   (b)   10 db.

(c) −12 db.   (d) −4 db.

8. If zero power level corresponds to 6 mw in a 600-Ω load, compute the output in milliwatts and voltage across the load for the following output meter readings:

(a)   5 db.   (b)   12 db.

(c) −6 db.   (d) −10 db.

9. An amplifier is rated as having a 90-db gain.   What power ratio does this represent?

10. If the amplifier of Prob. 9 has equal output and input impedances, what is the ratio of the output current to input current?

11. A network has a loss of 20 db.   What power ratio corresponds to this loss?

12. If the network of Prob. 11 has the same input and output impedances, what is the ratio of the output voltage to input voltage?

13. A certain crystal microphone is rated at −80 db. There is on hand a final audio amplifier with a rating of 40 db. How much gain must a preamplifier have to drive the final amplifier to full output if an attenuator pad between the microphone and preamplifier has a loss of 15 db? (All decibel ratings taken from same reference.)

14. An amplifier has a normal output of 25 w. A selector switch is arranged to reduce the output in 5-db intervals. What power outputs correspond to reductions in output of 5, 10, 15, 20, and 25 db?

15. A broadcasting station is rated at 1 kw. If the received signals vary as the square root of the radiated power, how much gain in decibels would be apparent to a near-by listener if the broadcasting station doubled its power?

16. A broadcasting station increases its power from 500 w to 10 kw. How many decibels gain does this represent to the listener?

17. The noise level of a certain telephone line used for carrying broadcast programs is 55 db down from the program level. If the program level is 12.5 mw, how much power is there in the noise level?

18. The output of a 200-Ω dynamic microphone is rated at −85 db from a reference level of 12.5 mw. This microphone is to be used with an amplifier which is to have a power output of 15 w. What must be the decibel gain between microphone and amplifier output?

19. If the amplifier of Prob. 18 has an output impedance of 3500 Ω, what is the over-all voltage amplification from microphone to amplifier output?

20. What is the equivalent power amplification in the above amplifier?

21. It is desired to use the above amplifier with a phonograph pickup which is rated at −30 db from a reference level of 6 mw. To keep from overloading the amplifier, how many decibels loss must be introduced between pickup and input?

22. An amplifier has an input impedance of 500 Ω and an output impedance of 4500 Ω. When 0.10 v is applied across the input, a voltage of 350 v appears across the output.

  (a) What is the power output of the amplifier?
  (b) What is the power gain in decibels?
  (c) What is the voltage gain of the amplifier?

23. An amplifier has an input impedance of 600 Ω and an output impedance of 6000 Ω. The power output is 30 w when 1.9 v is applied across the input.
  (a) What is the voltage gain of the amplifier?
  (b) What is the power gain in decibels?
  (c) What is the power input?

24. A dynamic microphone with an output level of −72 db is connected to a speech amplifier consisting of three voltage-amplifier stages. The first voltage-amplifier stage has a voltage gain of 100, and the second has a voltage gain of 9. The interstage transformer between the second and third voltage-amplifier stages has a step-up ratio of 3 to 1, and the third stage has a

voltage gain of 8.   The driver stage and modulator have a gain of 23 db.
If zero power level is 6 mw, what is the output power of the modulator?

Microphone −72 db		Amplifier 100		Amplifier 9		Transformer 3		Amplifier 8		Modulator 23 db

25. The voltage amplification of an amplifier was measured at various
frequencies as tabulated below:

Frequency, cycles per second	Output voltage	Frequency, cycles per second	Output voltage
60	16	1,000	29
100	21	2,000	30
200	24	3,000	31
400	25	5,000	30
700	27	10,000	12

   (*a*) Plot a curve of voltage amplification against frequency.
   (*b*) Choosing the amplification at 400 $\sim$ as reference level, plot the
        relative amplification in decibels against frequency.   Which
        curve best illustrates the performance of the amplifier?

26. How many decibels gain is necessary to produce a 60-μw signal in
600-Ω telephones if the received signal supplies 9 μv to the 80-Ω line that
feeds the receiver?

27. In the receiver of Prob. 26, if the over-all gain is increased to 96 db,
what received signal will produce the 60-μw signal in the telephones?

28. The voltage across the 600-Ω telephones of the above receiver is
adjusted to 1.73 v.   When the audio filter is cut in, the voltage is reduced
to 1.44 v.   What is the "insertion loss" of the filter?

29. The input power to a line is 10 mw.   Forty microwatts is delivered at
the end of the line which is 50 miles long.   What is the attenuation in
decibels per mile?

30. It is desired to raise the power level at the end of the line of Prob. 29
to that of the original input.   What would be the voltage gain of the
required amplifier?

31. In Prob. 29, what is the ratio of input power to output power?

32. One of the original attenuation units was the *neper* which is given by

$$\text{Nepers} = \log_\epsilon \frac{I_1}{I_2}$$

Since
$$\text{db} = 20 \log_{10} \frac{I_1}{I_2}$$

what is the relation between nepers and decibels for equal impedances?

HINT:
$$\log_\epsilon \frac{I_1}{I_2} = 2.30 \log_{10} \frac{I_1}{I_2}$$

33. Five hundred watts are supplied to a directive antenna which results in a field strength of 5 μv per meter at a receiving station. In order to produce the same field strength at the receiving station, the standard-comparison antenna must be supplied with 8 kw. What is the gain of the directive system in decibels?

34. A rhombic antenna used for transmitting results in a field strength of 60 μv per meter at a receiving station. The standard-comparison antenna lays down a field strength of 3 μv per meter. What is the decibel gain of the rhombic antenna?

35. A directive antenna system used for receiving a fixed station supplies 75 μv across the input of the receiver. The comparison antenna when receiving the same station supplies 15 μv across the receiver input.
What is the gain of the directive system?

21-5. Transmission Lines. A transmission line is a device consisting of one or more electrical conductors and designed for

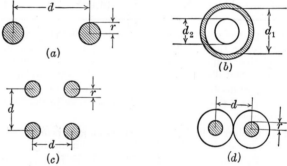

Fig. 21-1.

the purpose of transferring electrical energy from one point to another. The transmission line has a wide variety of uses. In one form, it may carry electrical power to a city several miles distant from the power plant; in another form, it may be used for carrying chain broadcast programs from one studio to several broadcast stations; and, in still another form, it may carry radio-frequency energy from a radio transmitter to an antenna or from an antenna to a radio receiver, etc.

The most common types of transmission lines are

1. The two-wire open-air line as shown in Fig. 21-1(*a*). This line consists of two parallel conductors whose spacing is carefully held constant.

2. The concentric-conductor line, as illustrated in Fig. 21-1(*b*), which consists of tubular conductors, one inside of the other.

3. The four-wire open-air line as shown in Fig. 21-1(*c*). In this type of line the diagonally opposite wires are connected to each other for effecting an electrical balance.

4. The twisted-pair line, as shown in Fig. 21-1(*d*), which may consist of lamp cord, a telephone line, or other insulated conductors.

Any conductor has a definite amount of self-inductance, capacitance, and resistance per unit length. These properties account for the behavior of transmission lines in their various forms and uses.

The derivations of the transmission-line equations that follow may be found in advanced engineering texts.

21-6. The Inductance of a Line. The inductance of a two-wire open-air line is given by the equation

$$L = l\left(0.161 + 1.48 \log_{10} \frac{d}{r}\right) \times 10^{-3} \qquad (8)$$

where L = inductance of line and return in henrys,

l = length of line in miles,

d = distance between conductor centers,

r = radius of each wire (in same units as d).

Example. What is the inductance of a line 90 miles long consisting of No. 0000 copper wires spaced 5 feet apart?

Solution: Diameter of No. 0000 = 460 mils,   ∴ radius = 0.230 in.

$$\frac{d}{r} = \frac{60}{0.23} = 261$$

$$\log_{10} 261 = 2.42$$

Then $L = 90(0.161 + 1.48 \times 2 42) \times 10^{-3} = 0.337$ h

For radio frequencies, more accurate results are obtained by the approximate relation

$$L \cong 9.21 \times 10^{-9} \log_{10} \frac{d}{r} \qquad (9)$$

where L is the inductance in henrys per centimeter, with d and r having the same values as in Eq. (8).

21-7. The Capacitance of a Line. The capacitance of a two-wire open-air line is

$$C = \frac{0.0194l}{\log_{10} \dfrac{d}{r}} \qquad (10)$$

where C = capacitance of line in microfarads,

l = length of line in miles,

d = distance between wire centers,

r = radius of each wire (in same units as d).

Example 1.   What is the capacitance per mile of a line consisting of No. 00 copper wires spaced 4 feet apart?

Solution: Diameter of No. 00 = 365 mils,   ∴ radius = 0.1825 in.

$$\frac{d}{r} = \frac{48}{0.182} = 263$$

$$\log_{10} 263 = 2.42$$

Then $$C = \frac{0.0194}{2.42} = \frac{19.4 \times 10^{-3}}{2.42}$$

$$= 8.02 \times 10^{-3} \ \mu f \text{ per mile}$$

For radio frequencies, more accurate results are obtained by the equation

$$C \cong \frac{1}{9.21 \times 10^{-9} \ c^2 \log_{10} \dfrac{d}{r}} \tag{11}$$

where C is the capacitance in farads per centimeter and c is the velocity of light (3×10^{10} centimeters per second), with d and r having the same values as in Eq. (10).

The capacitance of submarine cables and of cables laid in metal sheaths is given by

$$C = \frac{0.0388Kl}{\log_{10} \dfrac{d_1}{d_2}} \tag{12}$$

where C = capacity of line in microfarads,

K = relative dielectric constant of insulation,

l = length of line in miles,

d_1 = inside diameter of outer conductor,

d_2 = outside diameter of inner conductor.

Example 2.   A No. 14 copper wire is lead-sheathed.   The wire is insulated with ⅛-inch gutta percha.   (K = 4.1.)   What is the capacitance for 1000 feet of this cable?

Solution: d_2 = diameter of No. 14 = 0.0640 in.

d_1 = 0.0640 + 2(⅛) = 0.314 in.

$$\log \frac{d_1}{d_2} = \log \frac{0.314}{0.0640} = \log 4.91 = 0.691$$

$$l = \tfrac{1000}{5280}$$

Then
$$C = \frac{0.0388Kl}{\log \dfrac{d_1}{d_2}} = \frac{0.0388 \times 4.1 \times 1000}{0.691 \times 5280}$$

$$= 0.0436 \ \mu f$$

PROBLEMS 21-2

1. What is the inductance of a 50-mile line consisting of two No. 0 copper wires spaced 3 ft between centers?

2. What is the inductance of a 14-mile line consisting of No. 10 copper wire spaced 2 ft between centers?

3. A transmission line 15,000 ft long consists of two No. 00 solid copper wires having a spacing of 20 in. between centers. Determine

(a) The inductance of the line.
(b) The capacity of the line.

4. If the spacing of the above line was 4 ft between wire centers, what would be

(a) The inductance of the line?
(b) The capacity of the line?

5. A two-wire line, 20 miles long, consisting of No. 0 solid copper is to be erected. In order that the capacitance of the line will not exceed 0.166 μf, what must be the minimum spacing between wire centers?

6. In order that a two-wire line, 13.5 miles long, consisting of No. 00 solid copper wire will not exceed a capacitance of 0.00750 μf per mile, what must be the minimum spacing between wire centers?

7. A lead-sheathed underground cable consists of No. 000 copper wire covered with 0.5 in. rubber insulation. ($K = 4.3$.) What is the capacitance per mile?

8. A lead-sheathed cable consisting of No. 1 copper wire with 0.5 in. rubber insulation ($K = 4.3$) is open-circuited. A capacity bridge measures 0.19 μf between the conductor and sheath. How far out is the break?

9. What is the capacitance per mile of the cable of Prob. 8?

10. The cable of Prob. 7 becomes open-circuited. A capacity bridge measures 0.622 μf. How far out is the break?

11. The value of the current in a line at a point l miles from the source of power is given by

$$i = I_o \epsilon^{-Kl}$$

where I_o is the current at the source and K is the attenuation constant. In a certain line, the attenuation $K = 0.02$ db per mile. Find the length of line where i is 10% of the original current I_o.

HINT: $0.1I_o = I_o \epsilon^{-0.02l}$. $l = ?$

12. If the attenuation of a line is 0.015 db per mile, how far from the power source will the current have decreased to 75% of its original value?

13. A two-wire open-air transmission line is used to couple a receiving antenna to the receiver. The line is 500 ft long and consists of No. 12 wire spaced $6\frac{1}{8}$ in. between centers. Using Eqs. (9) and (11),

(a) What is the inductance per centimeter of the line?
(b) What is the capacitance per centimeter of the line?
(c) What is the inductance of the entire line?
(d) What is the capacitance of the entire line?

14. A two-wire open-air transmission line is used to couple a radio transmitter to the antenna. The line is 1000 ft long and consists of No. 10 wire spaced 7.6 in. Using Eqs. (9) and (11),

(a) What is the inductance of the line?
(b) What is the capacitance of the line?

21-8. Characteristic Impedances of Radio-frequency Transmission Lines. The most important characteristic of a transmission line is the *characteristic impedance,* denoted by Z_0 and expressed in ohms. This impedance is often called "surge impedance," "surge resistance," or "iterative impedance."

The value of the characteristic impedance is determined by the construction of the line, that is, by the size of the conductors and their spacing. At radio frequencies, the characteristic impedance may be considered to be a resistance, the value of which is given by

$$Z_0 = \sqrt{\frac{L}{C}} \qquad (13)$$

where L and C are the inductance and capacitance, respectively, per unit length of line as given in Eqs. (9) and (11). The unit of length selected for L and C is immaterial so long as the *same* unit is used for both.

Substituting the values of L and C for a two-wire open-air transmission line in Eq. (13) results in

$$Z_0 = 276 \log_{10} \frac{d}{r} \qquad (14)$$

where d is the spacing between wire centers and r is the radius of the conductors *in the same units as d.* Note that the characteristic impedance is *not* a function of the length of the line.

Example 1. A transmission line is made of No. 10 wire spaced 12 in. between centers. What is the characteristic impedance of the line?

Solution: $d = 12$ in.
Diameter of No. 10 wire $= 0.102$ in., $\therefore r = 0.051$ in.

$$Z_0 = 276 \log \frac{d}{r} = 276 \log \frac{12}{0.051}$$

$$Z_0 = 276 \log 235 = 276 \times 2.37$$

$$Z_0 = 654 \ \Omega$$

The characteristic impedance of a concentric line is given by

$$Z_0 = 138 \log_{10} \frac{d_1}{d_2} \tag{15}$$

where d_1 is the inside diameter of the outer conductor and d_2 is the outside diameter of the inner conductor.

Example 2. The outer conductor of a concentric transmission line consists of copper tubing $\frac{1}{16}$ in. thick with an outside diameter of 1 in. The copper tubing comprising the inner conductor is $\frac{1}{32}$ in. thick with an outside diameter of $\frac{1}{4}$ in. What is the characteristic impedance of the line?

Solution: $d_1 = 1 - (2 \cdot \frac{1}{16}) = \frac{7}{8}$ in., $d_2 = \frac{1}{4}$ in.

$$Z_0 = 138 \log \frac{d_1}{d_2} = 138 \log \frac{\frac{7}{8}}{\frac{1}{4}}$$

$$Z_0 = 138 \log 3.5 = 138 \times 0.544$$

$$Z_0 = 75.1 \ \Omega$$

PROBLEMS 21-3

1. What is the characteristic impedance of a two-wire open-air transmission line consisting of No. 12 wire spaced 6 in. between wire centers?

2. What is the characteristic impedance of a two-wire open-air transmission line consisting of No. 10 wire spaced 8 in. between wire centers?

3. What is the characteristic impedance of a transmission line consisting of No. 14 wire spaced 2 in. between wire centers?

4. It is desired to construct a 500-Ω transmission line. Number 10 wire is the only size available. What should be the spacing between wire centers?

5. It is necessary to construct a 700-Ω transmission line to couple a radio transmitter to a rhombic antenna. Number 14 wire is the only size available. What should be the spacing between wire centers?

6. The impedance at the center of a half-wave antenna is approximately 74 Ω. For maximum power transfer between transmission line and antenna, the impedance of the transmission line must match that of the antenna. Is it physically possible to construct an open-wire line with a characteristic impedance as low as 74 Ω?

7. Plot a graph of the characteristic impedance in ohms against the ratio $\frac{d}{r}$, from $\frac{d}{r} = 1$ to $\frac{d}{r} = 150$, for two-wire open-air transmission lines.

8. It is desired to construct a 600-Ω two-wire line at a certain radio station. In the stockroom, there are on hand a large number of 10-in. spreader insulators. That is, these spreaders will space the *wires* 10 in. What sized wire should be used to obtain as near as possible the desired impedance if the 10-in. spreaders are used? HINT: $d = 10 + 2r$.

9. What sized wire should be used to obtain as near as possible an impedance of 700 Ω, by use of the spreaders described in Prob. 8?

10. What sized copper tubing should be used to construct a quarter-wave matching stub having a characteristic impedance of 250 Ω if 1.5-in. spreaders are available?

11. What sized tubing should be used to construct a quarter-wave matching stub having an impedance of 316 Ω, if the spreaders of Prob. 10 are used?

12. The outer conductor of a concentric transmission line is a copper pipe $\frac{1}{8}$ in. thick with an outside diameter of 3 in. The inner conductor is copper tubing with an outside diameter of $\frac{3}{4}$ in. What is the surge impedance of the line?

13. The inside diameter of the outer conductor of a concentric line is $\frac{1}{2}$ in. The surge impedance of the line is 80 Ω. What is the diameter of the inner conductor?

14. Plot a graph of the characteristic impedance in ohms against the ratio $\frac{d_1}{d_2}$, from $\frac{d_1}{d_2} = 2$ to $\frac{d_1}{d_2} = 10$ for concentric transmission lines.

15. A certain grade of twisted-pair transmission line, which has a surge impedance of 72 Ω, has a loss of 0.064 db per foot. For a 100-ft length of line,

(*a*) What is the total loss in decibels?

(*b*) What is the efficiency of transmission?

HINT: $\dfrac{\text{Power output}}{\text{power input}} \times 100 = \%$ efficiency

16. The twisted-pair line of Prob. 15 is replaced by a concentric cable that has a loss of 0.002 db per foot. What is the new efficiency of transmission?

17. For a two-wire transmission line, the attenuation in decibels per foot of *wire* is given by the equation

$$\alpha = \frac{0.0157 R_f}{\log_{10} \dfrac{d}{r}} \tag{16}$$

where R_f is r-f resistance per foot of *wire*.

One kilowatt of power, at a frequency of 16 Mc, is delivered to a 500-ft two-wire line consisting of No. 12 copper wire spaced 6 in. between wire centers. If the r-f resistance of No. 12 wire, at 16 Mc, is 30 times the d-c resistance,

(*a*) What is the line loss in decibels?

(*b*) What is the efficiency of transmission?

18. The transmission line of Prob. 17 is replaced by a two-wire line consisting of No. 8 wire spaced 12 in. between centers.   If the r-f resistance of No. 8 wire, at 16 Mc, is 49 times the d-c resistance,

   (*a*) What is the line loss in decibels?
   (*b*) What is the efficiency of transmission?

19. The spacing of the transmission line of Prob. 18 is reduced to 6 in. between wire centers.

   (*a*) What is the line loss in decibels?
   (*b*) What is the efficiency of transmission?

20. For a concentric transmission line, the attenuation in decibels per foot of *line* is expressed by the relation

$$\alpha = \frac{4.6 \sqrt{f}(d_1 + d_2)10^{-6}}{d_1 d_2 \log_{10} \dfrac{d_1}{d_2}} \tag{17}$$

where d_1 and d_2 are in inches and have the same meaning as in Eq. (15) and f is the frequency in megacycles.

A concentric line 500 ft in length consists of an outer conductor with an inside diameter of $\frac{7}{8}$ in. and an inner conductor that is $\frac{1}{4}$ in. in diameter. At a frequency of 16 Mc,

   (*a*) What is the line loss in decibels?
   (*b*) What is the efficiency of transmission?

21. The capacity of a vertical antenna, which is shorter than one-quarter wave length at its operating frequency, may be computed by the equation

$$C_a = \frac{17l}{\left[\left(\log_e \dfrac{24l}{d}\right) - 1\right]\left[1 - \left(\dfrac{fl}{246}\right)^2\right]} \tag{18}$$

where C_a = capacity of antenna in micromicrofarads,
   l = height of antenna in feet,
   d = diameter of antenna conductor in inches,
   f = operating frequency in megacycles.
Determine the capacity of a vertical antenna that is 125 ft high and consists of $\frac{3}{8}$-in. wire.   The antenna is being operated on 500 kc.

22. Find the capacity of a vertical antenna that is 80 ft high and operating on 375 kc.   The antenna is made of $\frac{7}{16}$-in. wire.

23. The r-f resistance of a copper concentric transmission line can be computed by the following equation:

$$r = \sqrt{f}\left(\frac{1}{d_1} + \frac{1}{d_2}\right) \times 10^{-3} \ \Omega \text{ per foot} \tag{19}$$

where f = frequency in megacycles,
   d_1 = inside diameter of outer conductor in inches,
   d_2 = outside diameter of inner conductor in inches.

What is the resistance of a concentric line 100 ft long, operating at 200 Mc, if $d_1 = 1\frac{7}{8}$ in. and $d_2 = \frac{1}{4}$ in.?

24. What is the resistance of a concentric line 100 ft long, operating at 200 Mc, if $d_1 = \frac{3}{8}$ in. and $d_2 = \frac{1}{12}$ in.?

25. If an antenna is matched to a concentric transmission line, the per cent efficiency is given by

$$\text{Efficiency} = \frac{100R_T}{Z_0 + R_T} \qquad (20)$$

where Z_0 = characteristic impedance of concentric line,
R_T = effective resistance of line due to attenuation.
R_T is obtainable from the line constants as follows:

$$R_T = Z_0(\epsilon^{\frac{rl}{Z_0}} - 1) \qquad (21)$$

where r = r-f resistance per foot of line as found in Eq. (19),
l = length of line in feet.

Find the efficiency of transmission of a matched concentric transmission line with a characteristic impedance of 70 Ω. The line is 100 ft long and has an r-f resistance of 0.15 Ω per foot.

26. What is the efficiency of transmission of a matched concentric transmission line with a characteristic impedance of 80 Ω, if the line is 500 ft long and has an r-f resistance of 0.08 Ω per foot?

CHAPTER XXII

ANGLES

This chapter deals with the study of angles as an introduction to the branch of mathematics called *trigonometry*. The word "trigonometry" is derived from two Greek words meaning "measurement" or "solution" of triangles.

Trigonometry is both algebraic and geometric in nature. It is not confined to the solution of triangles but forms a basis for more advanced subjects in mathematics. A knowledge of the subject paves the way for a clear understanding of alternating-current theory and circuits. These, in turn, are the bases of communication and electrical engineering.

22-1. Angles. In trigonometry, we are concerned primarily with the many relations that exist among the sides and angles of

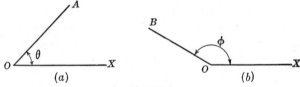

(a)   (b)

Fig. 22-1.

triangles. In order to understand the meaning and measurement of angles, it is essential we thoroughly understand these corelations.

An angle is formed when two straight lines meet at a point. In Fig. 22-1(a), lines OA and OX meet at the point O to form the angle AOX. Similarly, in Fig. 22-1(b), the angle BOX is formed by lines OB and OX meeting at the point O. This point is called the *vertex* of the angle, and the two lines are called the *sides* of the angle. The size, or magnitude, of an angle is a measure of the difference in directions of the sides. Thus, in Fig. 22-1, angle BOX is a larger angle than AOX. The lengths of the sides of an angle have no bearing on the size of the angle.

In geometry it is customary to denote an angle by the symbol $\angle$. If this notation is used, angle AOX would be written $\angle AOX$.

An angle is also denoted by the letter at the vertex or by a supplementary letter placed inside the angle. Thus, angle AOX is correctly denoted by $\angle AOX$, $\angle O$, or $\angle \theta$. Also, BOX could be written $\angle BOX$, $\angle O$, or $\angle \phi$.

If equal angles are formed when one straight line intersects another, the angles are called *right angles*. In Fig. 22-2, angles XOY, ϕ, $X'OY'$, and α are each right angles.

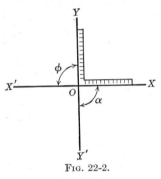

Fig. 22-2.

An *acute angle* is an angle that is less than a right angle. In Fig. 22-3(a), $\angle \alpha$ is an acute angle.

An *obtuse angle* is an angle that is greater than a right angle. In Fig. 22-3(b), $\angle \beta$ is an obtuse angle.

Two angles whose sum is one right angle are called *complementary angles*. Either one is said to be the "complement" of the other. Thus, in Fig. 22-3(c), angles ϕ and θ are complementary angles; ϕ is the complement of θ, and θ is the complement of ϕ.

Two angles whose sum is two right angles (a straight line) are called *supplementary angles*. Either one is said to be the "supplement" of the other. Thus, in Fig. 22-3(d), angles b and a

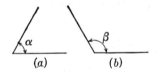

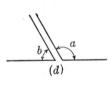

Fig. 22-3.

are supplementary angles; b is the supplement of a, and a is the supplement of b.

22-2. Generation of Angles. In the study of trigonometry, it becomes necessary to extend our concept of angles beyond the geometric definitions stated in Art. 22-1. An angle should be thought of as being generated by a line (line segment or half ray) that starts in a certain initial position and rotates about a point called the *vertex* of the angle until it stops at its final position. The original position of the rotating line is called the *initial side* of the angle, and the final position is called the *terminal side* of the angle.

An angle is said to be in *standard position* when its vertex is at the origin of a system of rectangular coordinates and its initial side extends in the positive direction along the X axis. Thus, in Fig. 22-4, the angle θ is in standard position. The vertex is at the origin, and the initial side is on the positive X axis. The angle has been generated by the line OP revolving, or sweeping, from OX to its final position.

An angle is called a *positive angle* if it is generated by a line revolving counterclockwise. If the generating line revolves clockwise, the angle is called a *negative angle*. In Fig. 22-5, all angles are in standard position. θ is a positive angle that was

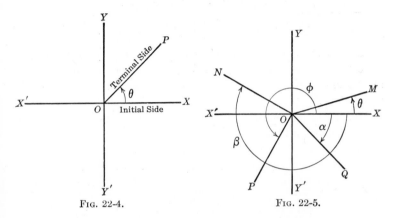

Fig. 22-4.   Fig. 22-5.

generated by the line OM revolving counterclockwise from OX. ϕ is also a positive angle whose terminal side is OP. α is a negative angle that was generated by the line OQ revolving in a clockwise direction from the initial side OX. β is also a negative angle whose terminal side is ON.

If the terminal side of an angle that is in standard position lies in the first quadrant, then that angle is said to be *an angle in the first quadrant*, etc. Thus, θ in Fig. 22-4 and θ in Fig. 22-5 are in the first quadrant. Similarly, in Fig. 22-5, β is in the second quadrant, ϕ is in the third quadrant, and α is in the fourth quadrant.

22-3. The Sexagesimal System. There are several systems of angular measurement. The three most commonly used are the right angle, the circular (or natural) system, and the sexagesimal system. The right angle is almost always used as a unit of angular measure in plane geometry and is constantly used by builders, surveyors, etc. However, for the purposes of trigonometry, it is an inconvenient unit because of its large size.

The unit most commonly used in trigonometry is the *degree*, which is one-ninetieth of a right angle. The degree is defined

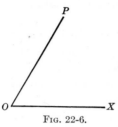

FIG. 22-6.

as that angle formed by $\frac{1}{360}$ part of a revolution of the angle-generating line. The degree is divided into 60 equal parts called *minutes*, and the minute into 60 equal parts called *seconds*. The word "sexagesimal" is derived from a Latin word pertaining to the number 60.

Instead of dividing the degrees into minutes and seconds, we shall divide them decimally for convenience. The decimal scale is coming into wide use in electric-circuit applications. For example, instead of expressing an angle of 43 degrees 36 minutes as 43°36′, we write 43.6°.

The actual measurement of an angle consists in finding how many degrees and a decimal part of a degree there are in the

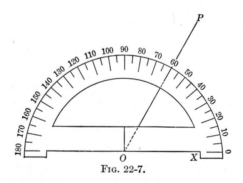

FIG. 22-7.

angle. This can be accomplished with a fair degree of accuracy by means of a *protractor*, which is an instrument for measuring or constructing angles.

To measure an angle *XOP*, as in Fig. 22-6, place the center of the protractor indicated by *O* at the vertex of the angle with, say, the line *OX* coinciding with one edge of the protractor as shown in Fig. 22-7. The magnitude of the angle, which is 60°, is indicated where the line *OP* crosses the graduated scale.

To construct an angle, say 30° from a given line OX, place the center of the protractor on the vertex O. Pivot the pro-

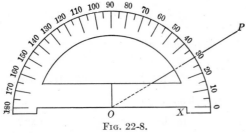

FIG. 22-8.

tractor about this point until OX is on a line with the 0° mark on the scale. In this position, 30° on the scale now marks the terminal side OP as shown in Figs. 22-8 and 22-9.

22-4. Angles of Any Magnitude. In the study of trigonometry, it

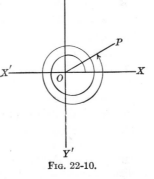

FIG. 22-10.

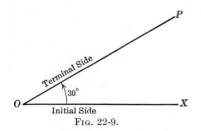

Initial Side
FIG. 22-9.

will be necessary to extend our concept of angles in order to include angles greater than 360°, either positive or negative. Thinking of an angle being generated, as explained in Art. 22-2, permits consideration of angles of any size; for the generating line may rotate from its initial position in a positive or negative direction so as to produce an angle of any size, even greater than 360°. Figure 22-10 illustrates how an angle of +750° is generated. However, for the purpose of ordinary computation, we consider such an angle to be in the same quadrant as its terminal side with a magnitude equal to the remainder after the largest multiple of 360° it will contain has been subtracted from it. Thus, in Fig. 22-10, the angle is in the first quadrant and, geometrically, is equal to 750° − 720° = 30°.

PROBLEMS 22-1

1. Construct two complementary angles each in standard position on the same pair of axes.

2. Construct two supplementary angles each in standard position on the same pair of axes.

3. What is the complement of

(a) 45°?   (b) 32°?   (c) 85°?
(d) 98°?   (e) 135°?   (f) −60°?

4. What is the supplement of

(a) 45°?   (b) 94°?   (c) 120°?
(d) 210°?   (e) 300°?   (f) −85°?

5. Using a protractor, construct the following angles, placing them in standard position on rectangular coordinates. Indicate by arrows the direction and amount of rotation necessary to generate these angles:

30°.   −80°.   145°.   −135°.   720°.   −800°.
260°.   300°.   −210°.   −315°.   −180°.   270°.

6. Through how many right angles does the minute hand of a clock turn from 11:45 A.M. to 2:30 P.M. of the same day?

7. Through how many degrees does the minute hand of a clock turn in 5 min?

8. How many degrees per minute does the minute hand of a clock rotate?

9. How many degrees per minute does the hour hand of a clock rotate?

10. A motor has a speed of 1800 r.p.m. What is the angular velocity (speed) in degrees per second?

11. The shaft of the above motor is directly connected to a pulley 18 in. in diameter. What is the pulley-rim speed in feet per second?

12. What is the approximate angular velocity of the earth in degrees per minute?

13. (a) Draw two angles in the first quadrant, differing by 360°.

(b) Draw two negative angles in the third quadrant, differing by 360°.

14. Can there be two obtuse angles in one triangle?

22-5. The Circular, or Natural System.

The circular, or natural, system of angular measurement is sometimes called *radian measure* or *π-measure*. The unit of measure is the *radian*.

A radian is an angle that, when placed with its vertex at the center of a circle, intercepts an arc equal in length to the radius of the circle. Thus, in Fig. 22-11, if the length of the arc *AP* equals the radius of the circle, then angle *AOP* is equal to 1 radian. Figure 22-12 shows a circle divided into radians.

The circular system of measure is used extensively in electrical and radio formulas and is universally used in the higher branches of mathematics.

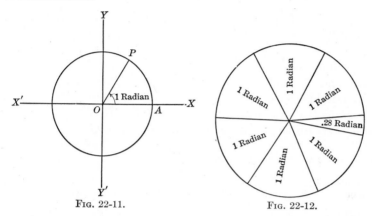

FIG. 22-11.   FIG. 22-12.

From geometry, it is known that the circumference of a circle is given by the relation

$$C = 2\pi r \tag{1}$$

where r is the radius of the circle. Dividing both sides of Eq. (1) by r,

$$\frac{C}{r} = 2\pi \tag{2}$$

Now Eq. (2) simply says that the ratio of the circumference to the radius is 2π. That is, the length of the circumference is 2π times longer than the radius. Therefore, a circle must contain 2π radians. Also, since the circumference subtends 360°, it follows that

$$2\pi \text{ radians} = 360°$$
$$\pi \text{ radians} = 180°$$

or
$$1 \text{ radian} = \frac{180°}{\pi} = 57.2959° \cong 57.3° \tag{3}$$

From Eq. (3), the following is evident:

To reduce radians to degrees, multiply the number of radians by 57.3. $\left(\text{This is very nearly equal to } \dfrac{180°}{\pi}.\right)$

To reduce degrees to radians, multiply the number of degrees by 0.01745. $\left(\text{This is very nearly equal to } \dfrac{\pi}{180°}.\right)$

Several of the modern types of slide rule have gauge marks at 57.3 on scales C and D denoted by R (for radians). These marks are a convenience in converting from radians to degrees. Since 0.01745 is the reciprocal of 57.3, the former number will be found on the reciprocal scales opposite the R gauge marks. Similarly, if 180 on scale CF is set to π on DF, 0.01745 will appear on scale D opposite the index of scale C. In this manner the rule is set up for multiplication by 0.01745.

Example 1. Reduce 1.7 radians to degrees.

Solution: 1 radian = 57.3°
Hence,   1.7 radians = 1.7 × 57.3 = 97.4°

Example 2. Convert 15.6° to radians.

Solution: 1° = 0.01745 radian
Hence,   15.6° = 15.6 × 0.01745 = 0.272 radian

PROBLEMS 22-2

1. Express in terms of π the number of radians in the following angles:

    (a) 360°.   (b) 180°.   (c) 60°.
    (d) 90°.   (e) 30°.   (f) 45°.

2. Express in terms of π the number of radians in the following angles:

    (a) 135°.   (b) 270°.   (c) 240°.
    (d) 720°.   (e) 315°.   (f) 300°.

3. Express the following angles in degrees:

    (a) 2 radians.   (b) $\dfrac{2\pi}{5}$ radians.   (c) $\dfrac{1}{\pi}$ radians.

    (d) 0.6 radian.   (e) 2.2 radians.   (f) 0.056 radian.

4. Through how many radians does the minute hand of a clock turn from 10:00 A.M. to 1:45 P.M. of the same day?

5. Through how many radians does the hour hand of a clock turn in 45 min?

6. A motor has a speed of 1500 r.p.m. What is its angular velocity in radians per second?

7. A generator has a speed of 4200 r.p.m. What is its angular velocity in radians per second?

8. A motor has an angular velocity of 60π radians per second.   What is its speed in r.p.m.?

9. A motor has an angular velocity of 25π radians per second.   What is its speed in r.p.m.?

10. What is the approximate angular velocity of the earth in radians per hour?

22-6. Similar Triangles.   Two triangles are said to be *similar* when their corresponding angles are equal.   That is, similar triangles are identical in shape but may not be the same size. The important characteristic of similar triangles is that a direct proportionality exists between corresponding sides.   The three triangles of Fig. 22-13 have been constructed so that their corresponding angles are equal.   Therefore, the three triangles are

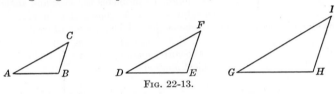

Fig. 22-13.

similar, and their corresponding sides are proportional.   This leads to the proportions

$$\frac{AB}{AC} = \frac{DE}{DF} = \frac{GH}{GI}, \qquad \frac{BC}{AB} = \frac{EF}{DE} = \frac{HI}{GH}, \cdots$$

As an example, if $AB = 0.5$ inch, $DE = 1$ inch, and $GH = 1.5$ in., then DF is twice as long as AC and GI is three times as long as AC.   Similarly, HI is three times as long as BC, and EF is twice as long as BC.

The properties of similar triangles are used extensively in measuring distance, such as the distances across bodies of water or other obstructions or the heights of various objects.   In addition, the relation between similar triangles forms the very basis of trigonometry.

Since the sum of the three angles of any triangle is $180°$, it follows that if two angles of a triangle are equal to two angles of another triangle the third angle of one must also be equal to the third angle of the other.   Therefore, two triangles are similar if two angles of one are equal to two angles of the other.

If the numerical values of the necessary parts of a triangle are known, the triangle may be drawn to scale with the use of compasses, protractor, and ruler. The completed figure may then be measured with protractor and ruler to obtain the numerical values of the unknown parts. This is conveniently accom‑ plished on squared paper.

PROBLEMS 22-3

1. Two triangles are similar. The sides of the first are 15, 12, and 8 ft The longest side of the second triangle is 25 ft. How long are the other two sides of the second triangle?

2. Two triangles are similar. The sides of the first are 20, 6, and 17 in. The shortest side of the second triangle is 31 ft. How long are the other two sides of the second triangle?

In the following problems the sides and angles of all triangles will be as represented in Fig. 22-14 That is, the angles will be represented by the capital letters A, B, C, and the sides opposite these angles will be the corresponding letters a, b, and c.

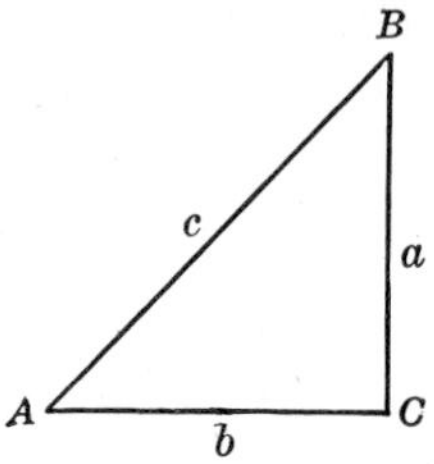

Fig. 22-14.

Solve the following by graphical methods:

3. $b = 3$, $c = 5$, $A = 53.1°$.   **4.** $a = 9$, $b = 12$, $c = 15$.

5. $a = 8$, $b = 5$, $C = 34°$.   **6.** $a = 10$, $c = 15$, $B = 100°$.

7. $c = 7$, $A = 45°$, $B = 45°$.   **8.** $C = 80°$, $b = 4$, $a = 11$.

22-7. The Right Triangle. If one of the angles of a triangle is a right angle, the triangle is called a *right triangle*. Then, since the sum of the angles of any triangle is 180°, a right triangle contains one right angle and two acute angles. Also, the sum of the acute angles must be 90°. This relation enables us to find one acute angle when the other is given. For example, in the right triangle shown in Fig. 22-15, if $\theta = 30°$, then $\phi = 60°$.

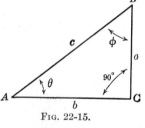

Fig. 22-15.

Since all right angles are equal, if an acute angle of one right triangle is equal to an acute angle of another right triangle, the two triangles are similar.

The side of a right triangle opposite the right angle is called the *hypotenuse*. Thus, in Fig. 22-15, the side c is the hypotenuse. When a right triangle is in standard position as in Fig. 22-15, the side a is called the *altitude* and the side b is called the *base*

Another very important property of a right triangle is that the square of the hypotenuse is equal to the sum of the squares of the other two sides. That is,

$$c^2 = a^2 + b^2$$

This relation provides a means of computing any one of the three sides if two sides are given.

Example 1. A chimney is 130 feet high. What is the length of its shadow at a time when a vertical post 5 feet high casts a shadow that is 7 feet long?

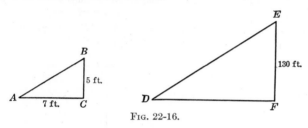

FIG. 22-16.

Solution: *BC* in Fig. 22-16 represents the post, and *EF* represents the stack. Because the rays of the sun strike both chimney and post at the same angle, right triangles *ABC* and *DEF* are similar. Then, since

$$\frac{DF}{AC} = \frac{EF}{BC}$$

by substituting, $\dfrac{DF}{7} = \dfrac{130}{5}$

or $DF = 182$ ft

Example 2. What is the length of *a* in the triangle of Fig. 22-17?

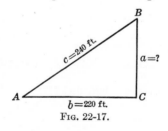

FIG. 22-17.

Solution: Given $c^2 = a^2 + b^2$.

Transposing, $a^2 = c^2 - b^2$

$\sqrt{}$, $a = \sqrt{c^2 - b^2}$

Substituting, $a = \sqrt{240^2 - 220^2} = \sqrt{9200}$

                     $\therefore a = 95.9$ ft

PROBLEMS 22-4

In the following right triangles, solve for the indicated elements:

1. $a = 15$, $b = 20$, $A = 36.9°$.   Find c and B.

2. $a = 13$, $c = 31$, $A = 24.8°$.   Find b and B.

3. $b = 105$, $c = 165$, $A = 50.4°$.   Find a and B.

4. A vessel steams east at the rate of 20 knots and another south at 14 knots. If both start from the same place at the same time, how far apart will they be in 5 hr?

5. An antenna supporting pole is 80 ft above level ground. This pole is to be guyed 6 ft from the top of the pole to a point on the ground 50 ft from the base of the pole. What is the length of the guy?

6. In Fig. 22-18, if $AC = 6$ ft, $BC = 8$ ft, and $AE = 3$ ft, find the length DE.

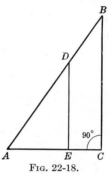

Fig. 22-18.

7. In Fig. 22-18, let $AE = 16$ ft, $EC = 12$ ft, and $AB = 40$ ft. What is the length of DE?

8. In Fig. 22-18, let $AD = 25$ ft, $DB = 10$ ft, and $BC = 24$ ft. What is the length of AE?

9. A radio tower casts a shadow 225 ft long at a time when a yardstick, held upright with one end touching the ground, casts a shadow 2 ft 3 in. long. What is the height of the tower?

10. The mast of a ship casts a shadow 66 ft 6 in. long on deck at a time when a sailor 5 ft 9 in. tall, standing on deck, casts a shadow 4 ft 5 in. long. What is the height of the mast above deck?

CHAPTER XXIII

TRIGONOMETRIC FUNCTIONS

In the preceding chapter, it was shown that plane geometry furnishes two important properties of right triangles. These are

$$A + B = 90°$$
and $$a^2 + b^2 = c^2$$

The first relation makes it possible to find one acute angle when the other is given. By means of the second, any one side may be computed if the other two sides are given. These relations, however, furnish no methods for computing the magnitude of an acute angle when two sides are given. Also, using these relations, we cannot compute two sides of a right triangle if the other side and one acute angle are given. With only this amount of knowledge, we should be forced to resort to actual measurement by graphical methods.

The results obtained by such methods are unsuitable for use in many problems, for even with the greatest care and large-scale drawings the degree of accuracy is definitely limited. It is evident, therefore, that certain other relations are needed in which the sides of a right triangle and the angles are united. Such relations form the foundation of trigonometry.

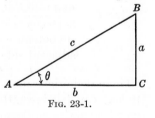

FIG. 23-1.

23-1. Trigonometric Ratios of Acute Angles. In Fig. 23-1, let θ be one of the acute angles of the right triangle ABC. If the three sides of the triangle are used, two at a time, six ratios may be expressed. These ratios are

$$\frac{a}{c}, \frac{b}{c}, \frac{a}{b}, \frac{b}{a}, \frac{c}{b}, \text{ and } \frac{c}{a}$$

and have been assigned the following names:

339

$\dfrac{a}{c}$ is called the *sine* of the angle θ, written sin θ.

$\dfrac{b}{c}$ is called the *cosine* of the angle θ, written cos θ.

$\dfrac{a}{b}$ is called the *tangent* of the angle θ, written tan θ.

$\dfrac{b}{a}$ is called the *cotangent* of the angle θ, written cot θ.

$\dfrac{c}{b}$ is called the *secant* of the angle θ, written sec θ.

$\dfrac{c}{a}$ is called the *cosecant* of the angle θ, written csc θ.

These definitions for any acute angle are readily remembered, regardless of the position of the right triangle, if we take into account the positions of two sides of the triangle with respect to the acute angle under considera-tion. Thus, in Fig. 23-2, b is called the *adjacent side* of θ, and a is called the *opposite side*. The trigonometric functions (ratios) may be defined in terms of these sides as follows:

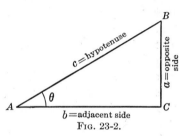

Fig. 23-2.

$$\sin \theta = \frac{\text{opposite side}}{\text{hypotenuse}} = \frac{a}{c} \qquad \cos \theta = \frac{\text{adjacent side}}{\text{hypotenuse}} = \frac{b}{c}$$

$$\tan \theta = \frac{\text{opposite side}}{\text{adjacent side}} = \frac{a}{b} \qquad \cot \theta = \frac{\text{adjacent side}}{\text{opposite side}} = \frac{b}{a}$$

$$\sec \theta = \frac{\text{hypotenuse}}{\text{adjacent side}} = \frac{c}{b} \qquad \csc \theta = \frac{\text{hypotenuse}}{\text{opposite side}} = \frac{c}{a}$$

These definitions must be memorized so thoroughly that the student can tell instantly any ratio of either acute angle of a right triangle, regardless of its position.

The sine, cosine, and tangent are the ratios most frequently used in practical work. If these are carefully learned, the others are easily remembered because they are reciprocals, as is shown in the article following.

The fact that the numerical value of any one of the trigono-**metric** functions (ratios) depends only upon the magnitude of the angle θ is of fundamental importance. This is established from a consideration of Fig. 23-3. The angle θ is generated by the line AD revolving about the point A. From the points B, B', and B'', perpendiculars are let fall to the initial line, or adjacent side, AX. These form similar triangles ABC, $AB'C'$, and $AB''C''$ because all are right triangles having a common acute angle θ (Art. 22-7). Hence,

$$\frac{BC}{AB} = \frac{B'C'}{AB'} = \frac{B''C''}{AB''}$$

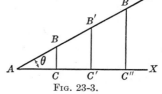

FIG. 23-3.

Each of these ratios defines the sine of θ. Similarly, it may be shown that this property is true for each of the other functions. Therefore, the size of the right triangle is immaterial, for only the *relative* lengths of the sides are of importance.

Each one of the six ratios will change in value whenever the angle changes in magnitude. Thus, it is evident that the ratios are really functions of the angle under consideration. If the angle is considered to be the independent variable, then the six functions (ratios) and the relative lengths of the sides of the triangles are dependent variables.

Example. Calculate the functions of the angle θ in the right triangle of Fig. 23-1 if $a = 6$ inches and $c = 10$ inches.

Solution: Since $c^2 = a^2 + b^2$,

then
$$b = \sqrt{c^2 - a^2} = \sqrt{100 - 36} = \sqrt{64} = 8 \text{ in.}$$

Applying the definitions of the six functions,

$$\sin \theta = \tfrac{6}{10} = \tfrac{3}{5} \qquad \cos \theta = \tfrac{8}{10} = \tfrac{4}{5}$$
$$\tan \theta = \tfrac{6}{8} = \tfrac{3}{4} \qquad \cot \theta = \tfrac{8}{6} = \tfrac{4}{3}$$
$$\sec \theta = \tfrac{10}{8} = \tfrac{5}{4} \qquad \csc \theta = \tfrac{10}{6} = \tfrac{5}{3}$$

What would be the values of the above functions if $a = 6$ meters, $b = 8$ meters, and $c = 10$ meters?

23-2. Reciprocal Relations of the Functions. As a result of the definitions of the trigonometric functions, the following reciprocal relations exist:

$$\sin \theta = \frac{a}{c} = \frac{1}{\dfrac{c}{a}} = \frac{1}{\csc \theta} \qquad \csc \theta = \frac{c}{a} = \frac{1}{\dfrac{a}{c}} = \frac{1}{\sin \theta}$$

$$\cos \theta = \frac{b}{c} = \frac{1}{\dfrac{c}{b}} = \frac{1}{\sec \theta} \qquad \sec \theta = \frac{c}{b} = \frac{1}{\dfrac{b}{c}} = \frac{1}{\cos \theta}$$

$$\tan \theta = \frac{a}{b} = \frac{1}{\dfrac{b}{a}} = \frac{1}{\cot \theta} \qquad \cot \theta = \frac{b}{a} = \frac{1}{\dfrac{a}{b}} = \frac{1}{\tan \theta}$$

The cosecant, secant, and cotangent should always be thought of as the reciprocals of the sine, cosine, and tangent, respectively.

By noting the sequence of the phrases "opposite side" and "adjacent side," it is seen that they replace each other in the definitions for sine and cosine, tangent and cotangent, and secant and cosecant. Furthermore, it will be noted that if the reciprocals of the six functions are taken in the order given the same six appear in the opposite order. The following diagram will serve as an aid in remembering these relations.

Interchangeable Sides

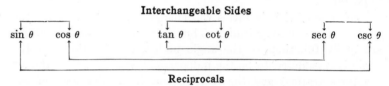

sin θ   cos θ   tan θ   cot θ   sec θ   csc θ

Reciprocals

23-3. Functions of Complementary Angles. By applying the definitions of the six functions to the angle ϕ in Fig. 23-4

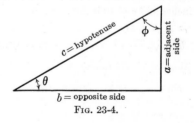

c = hypotenuse ϕ a = adjacent side θ b = opposite side

Fig. 23-4.

and noting the positions of the adjacent and opposite sides for this angle, we obtain

$$\sin \phi = \frac{\text{opposite side}}{\text{hypotenuse}} = \frac{b}{c} \qquad \cos \phi = \frac{\text{adjacent side}}{\text{hypotenuse}} = \frac{a}{c}$$

$$\tan \phi = \frac{\text{opposite side}}{\text{adjacent side}} = \frac{b}{a} \qquad \cot \phi = \frac{\text{adjacent side}}{\text{opposite side}} = \frac{a}{b}$$

$$\sec \phi = \frac{\text{hypotenuse}}{\text{adjacent side}} = \frac{c}{a} \qquad \csc \phi = \frac{\text{hypotenuse}}{\text{opposite side}} = \frac{c}{b}$$

Upon comparing these with the original definitions given for the triangle of Fig. 23-2, the following relations appear:

$$\sin \phi = \cos \theta \qquad \cos \phi = \sin \theta$$
$$\tan \phi = \cot \theta \qquad \cot \phi = \tan \theta$$
$$\sec \phi = \csc \theta \qquad \csc \phi = \sec \theta$$

Since $\phi = 90° - \theta$, the above relations may be written

$$\sin (90° - \theta) = \cos \theta \qquad \cos (90° - \theta) = \sin \theta$$
$$\tan (90° - \theta) = \cot \theta \qquad \cot (90° - \theta) = \tan \theta$$
$$\sec (90° - \theta) = \csc \theta \qquad \csc (90° - \theta) = \sec \theta$$

The above may be stated in words as follows: *A function of an acute angle is equal to the cofunction of its complementary angle.* This enables us to find the function of every acute angle greater than 45° if we know the functions of all angles less than 45°. For example, sin 56° = cos 34°, tan 63° = cot 27°, cos 70° = sin 20°, etc.

23-4. Construction of an Angle When One Function Is Given. When the trigonometric function of an acute angle is given, the angle may be constructed geometrically by using the definition for the given function. Also, the magnitude of the resulting angle can be measured by the use of a protractor.

Example 1.   Construct the acute angle whose tangent is $\frac{9}{10}$.

Solution: Erect perpendicular lines AC and BC, preferably on cross-sectional paper. Measure off 10 units along AC and 9 units along BC. Join A and B, thus forming the right triangle ABC. Tan $A = \frac{9}{10}$; therefore, A is the required angle. Measuring A with a protractor shows it to be an angle of approximately 42°. The construction is shown in Fig. 23-5.

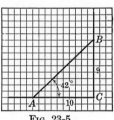

Fig. 23-5.

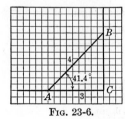

Fig. 23-6.

Example 2.   Find by construction the acute angle whose cosine is $\frac{3}{4}$.

Solution: Erect perpendicular lines AC and BC. Measure off 3 units along AC (letting three divisions of the cross-sectional paper be equal to one unit for greater accuracy). With A as a center and with a radius of 4 units, draw an arc to intersect the perpendicular at B. Connect A and B. Cos $A = \frac{3}{4}$; therefore A is the required angle. Measuring A with a protractor shows it to be an angle of approximately 41.4°. The construction is shown in Fig. 23-6.

PROBLEMS 23-1

1. In Fig. 23-7, give the values of all six trigonometric functions for the angles θ and ϕ in terms of ratios of the sides a, b, and c.

2. In Fig. 23-8, (a) $\sin \alpha = ?$ (b) $\sin \beta = ?$ (c) $\cot \beta = ?$ (d) $\sec \alpha = ?$ (e) $\tan \alpha = ?$

3. In Fig. 23-8, (a) $\dfrac{OP}{OR} = \tan?$ (b) $\dfrac{PR}{PO} = \sec?$ (c) $\dfrac{OR}{PR} = \cos?$ (d) $\dfrac{OP}{RP} = \sin?$ (e) $\dfrac{PR}{RO} = \csc?$

4. The three sides of a right triangle are 5, 12, and 13. Let θ be the acute angle opposite the side 12, and let ϕ be the other acute angle. Write the six functions of θ and ϕ.

5. In Fig. 23-9, the sides are R, X, and Z. If $X = \frac{1}{3}Z$, find the six functions of θ.

6. In Fig. 23-9, if $X = R$, find the sine, cosine, and tangent of θ.

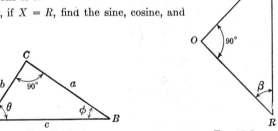

Fig. 23-7.

Fig. 23-8.

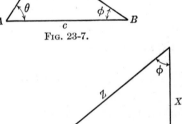

Fig. 23-9.

7. In Fig. 23-9, if $Z = 2R$, find the sine, cosine, and tangent of θ.

8. In Fig. 23-9, if $R = \frac{1}{2}X$, find the sine, cosine, and tangent of ϕ.

9. In Fig. 23-9, if $X = \frac{1}{4}R$, find the sine, cosine, and tangent of ϕ.

10. By inspection, give the value of the following:

(a) $\cos \beta = \frac{2}{3}$, $\sec \beta = ?$ (b) $\sin \alpha = \frac{1}{3}$, $\csc \alpha = ?$
(c) $\tan \phi = 1$, $\cot \phi = ?$ (d) $\sec \theta = \frac{4}{3}$, $\cos \theta = ?$
(e) $\cot \beta = \frac{3}{11}$, $\tan \beta = ?$ (f) $\csc \phi = 10$, $\sin \phi = ?$

11. Construct a triangle having sides of 9, 40, and 41. Is it a right triangle? Write the six functions of the largest acute angle.

12. Given cos $A = \frac{4}{5}$. Construct the angle A, and find the other functions.

13. Write the other functions of an acute angle whose sine is $\frac{4}{5}$.

14. In a right triangle, $c = 5$ in., and sin $A = \frac{3}{5}$. Construct the triangle, and write the functions of the angle B.

15. Construct the acute angle whose cosecant is 6, and write the remaining functions.

16. State which of the following is greater if $\theta \neq 0°$ and less than 90°:

(a) sin θ or tan θ.　　　　　(b) sec θ or tan θ.

(c) cos θ or cot θ.　　　　　(d) csc θ or cot θ.

23-5. Functions of Any Angle.　In the preceding chapter the concepts of angles were extended to include angles in any quad-

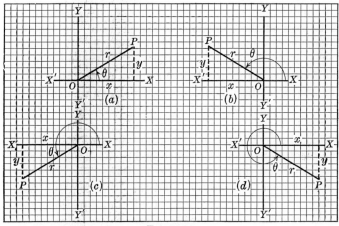

Fig. 23-10.

rant and either positive or negative. So far, the trigonometric functions have applied to acute angles only, but we are now ready to consider the functions of any angle. In Fig. 23-10, the line r is revolving about the origin of the rectangular coordinate system in a counterclockwise (positive) direction. This line, which generates the angle θ, is known as the *radius vector*. The initial side of θ is the positive X axis, and the terminal side is the radius vector. If a perpendicular is let fall from any point P along the radius vector, in any of the quadrants, a right triangle xyr will be formed with r as a hypotenuse of constant unit length and with x and y having lengths equal to the respective coordinates of P.

We then define the trigonometric functions of θ as follows:

$$\sin \theta = \frac{y}{r} = \frac{\text{ordinate}}{\text{radius}} \qquad \cos \theta = \frac{x}{r} = \frac{\text{abscissa}}{\text{radius}}$$

$$\tan \theta = \frac{y}{x} = \frac{\text{ordinate}}{\text{abscissa}} \qquad \cot \theta = \frac{x}{y} = \frac{\text{abscissa}}{\text{ordinate}}$$

$$\sec \theta = \frac{r}{x} = \frac{\text{radius}}{\text{abscissa}} \qquad \csc \theta = \frac{r}{y} = \frac{\text{radius}}{\text{ordinate}}$$

Since the values of the six trigonometric functions are entirely independent of the position of the point P along the radius vector, it follows that they depend only upon the position of the radius vector, or the size of the angle. Therefore, for every angle, there is one, and only one, value of each function.

23-6. Sign of the Functions. The signs of the functions of angles in various quadrants are very important. If we remember the signs of the abscissas (x values) and the ordinates (y values) in the four quadrants, we shall encounter no trouble.

For angles in the first quadrant, as shown in Fig. 23-10 (a), the x and y values are positive. Since the length of the radius vector r is always considered positive, it is evident that all functions of angles in the first quadrant are positive. For angles in the second quadrant, as shown in Fig. 23-10(b), the x values are negative and the y values are positive. Therefore the sine and its reciprocal are positive, and the other four functions are negative. Similarly, the signs of all the functions may be checked from their definitions as given in the preceding article. The following table should be verified:

Quadrant	$\sin \theta$	$\cos \theta$	$\tan \theta$	$\cot \theta$	$\sec \theta$	$\csc \theta$
I	+	+	+	+	+	+
II	+	−	−	−	−	+
III	−	−	+	+	−	−
IV	−	+	−	−	+	−

If the proper signs for the sine and cosine are fixed in mind, the other signs will be remembered because of an important relation.

$$\frac{\sin \theta}{\cos \theta} = \frac{\dfrac{y}{r}}{\dfrac{x}{r}} = \frac{y}{x}$$

Since $\qquad\qquad \tan \theta = \dfrac{y}{x}$

then $\qquad\qquad \dfrac{\sin \theta}{\cos \theta} = \tan \theta$

If the sine and cosine have like signs, the tangent is positive; and if they have unlike signs, the tangent is negative.   Because the signs of the sine, cosine, and tangent always agree with their respective reciprocals, the cosecant, secant, and cotangent, the signs for the latter are obtainable from the signs of the sine and

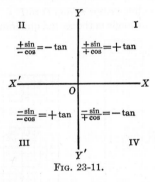

Fig. 23-11.

cosine as outlined above.   Figure 23-11 will serve as an aid in remembering the signs.

PROBLEMS 23-2

In what quadrant or quadrants is θ for each of the following conditions?

1. When $\sin \theta$ is negative. | **2.** When $\sin \theta$ is positive.

3. When $\tan \theta$ is negative. | **4.** When $\cos \theta$ is positive.

5. When $\cos \theta$ is negative. | **6.** When $\tan \theta$ is positive.

7. $\sin \theta$ positive, $\cos \theta$ negative. | **8.** $\tan \theta$ and $\sin \theta$ both positive.

9. $\sec \theta$ negative, $\tan \theta$ positive. | **10.** $\cos \theta$ negative, $\cot \theta$ negative.

11. $\cos \theta$ positive, $\sin \theta$ negative. | **12.** When all functions of θ are positive.

13. $\sin \theta$ positive, $\tan \theta$ negative. | **14.** $\cos \theta$ positive, $\tan \theta$ negative.

15. $\cot \theta$ negative, $\sec \theta$ positive. | **16.** $\sin \theta = \frac{1}{4}$.

17. $\cos \theta = -\frac{3}{5}$. | **18.** $\tan \theta = 4$.

19. $\sin \theta = 0.144$.

20. Is there an angle whose sine is positive and whose cosecant is negative?

21. Find the value of $\dfrac{\sin\theta - \cos\theta}{\sec\theta + \cot\theta}$ when $\tan\theta = \frac{2}{3}$.

Give the signs of the sine, cosine, and tangent of each of the following angles:

22. $46°$.   **23.** $82°$.   **24.** $276°$.   **25.** $210°$.

26. $95°$.   **27.** $310°$.   **28.** $-60°$.   **29.** $-130°$.

30. $-200°$.   **31.** $\dfrac{\pi}{4}$.   **32.** $\dfrac{3\pi}{2}$.   **33.** $\dfrac{-4\pi}{3}$.

Find the value of the radius vector r for each of the following positions of P, and then find the trigonometric functions of the angle θ.   ($\angle XOP$). Keep answers in fractional form.

34. $(-9, 12)$.

Solution: Draw the radius vector r from O to $P = (-9, 12)$ as shown in Fig. 23-12.   Hence, θ is an angle in the second quadrant, with a side adjacent

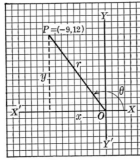

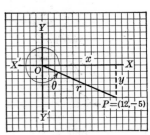

FIG. 23-12.   FIG. 23-13.

having an x value of -9 and a side opposite with a y value of 12.

Then $r = \sqrt{x^2 + y^2} = \sqrt{(-9)^2 + (12)^2} = 15$

Hence, by definition,

$$\sin\theta = \frac{y}{r} = \frac{12}{15} = \frac{4}{5} \qquad \cos\theta = \frac{x}{r} = \frac{-9}{15} = -\frac{3}{5}$$

$$\tan\theta = \frac{y}{x} = \frac{12}{-9} = -\frac{4}{3} \qquad \cot\theta = \frac{x}{y} = \frac{-9}{12} = -\frac{3}{4}$$

$$\sec\theta = \frac{r}{x} = \frac{15}{-9} = -\frac{5}{3} \qquad \csc\theta = \frac{r}{y} = \frac{15}{12} = \frac{5}{4}$$

35. $(12, -5)$.

Solution: Draw the radius vector r from O to P as shown in Fig. 23-13. θ is an angle in the fourth quadrant, with a side adjacent having an x value of 12 and a side opposite with a y value of -5.

Then $\qquad r = \sqrt{x^2 + y^2} = \sqrt{12^2 + (-5)^2} = 13$

Hence, by definition,

$$\sin \theta = \frac{y}{r} = -\frac{5}{13} \qquad \cos \theta = \frac{x}{r} = \frac{12}{13}$$

$$\tan \theta = \frac{y}{x} = -\frac{5}{12} \qquad \cot \theta = \frac{x}{y} = -\frac{12}{5}$$

$$\sec \theta = \frac{r}{x} = \frac{13}{12} \qquad \csc \theta = \frac{r}{y} = -\frac{13}{5}$$

36. (2, 3).   **37.** (−12, −5).   **38.** (6, 8).

39. (3, −4).   **40.** (−6, −8).   **41.** (−9, −3).

42. (−6, 8).   **43.** (20, −15).   **44.** (5, 5).

23-7. Computation of the Functions. Tables have been computed, giving the values of the functions of angles. However, there are a few important angles whose functions are obtainable from definite geometric relations. Because these angles occur so frequently in practical work, their functions are derived here.

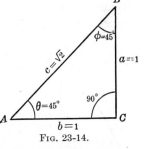

Fig. 23-14.

23-8. Functions of 45°. Construct a right triangle with the angle θ equal to 45° and the length of the opposite side a equal to one unit as shown in Fig. 23-14. Then, by construction, $\phi = 45°$ and $b = 1$ unit. Since

$$a^2 + b^2 = c^2$$
$$c = \sqrt{a^2 + b^2} = \sqrt{1 + 1} = \sqrt{2}$$

From the definitions of Art. 23-1,

$$\sin 45° = \frac{a}{c} = \frac{1}{\sqrt{2}} = \frac{1}{2}\sqrt{2} \qquad \cos 45° = \frac{b}{c} = \frac{1}{\sqrt{2}} = \frac{1}{2}\sqrt{2}$$

$$\tan 45° = \frac{a}{b} = \frac{1}{1} = 1 \qquad \cot 45° = \frac{b}{a} = \frac{1}{1} = 1$$

$$\sec 45° = \frac{c}{b} = \frac{\sqrt{2}}{1} = \sqrt{2} \qquad \csc 45° = \frac{c}{a} = \frac{\sqrt{2}}{1} = \sqrt{2}$$

23-9. Functions of 60° and 30°. Construct an equilateral triangle, making the length of each side equal to two units as ABD in Fig. 23-15. From B, draw BC perpendicular to AD

Therefore, BC bisects AD at C, making b equal to one unit. Then, in the *right* triangle ABC, $\theta = 60°$, $b = 1$, $c = 2$. Since

$$a^2 + b^2 = c^2$$
$$a = \sqrt{c^2 - b^2} = \sqrt{4 - 1} = \sqrt{3}$$

From the definitions of Art. 23-1,

$$\sin 60° = \frac{a}{c} = \frac{\sqrt{3}}{2} = \frac{1}{2}\sqrt{3} \qquad \cos 60° = \frac{b}{c} = \frac{1}{2}$$

$$\tan 60° = \frac{a}{b} = \frac{\sqrt{3}}{1} = \sqrt{3} \qquad \cot 60° = \frac{b}{a} = \frac{1}{\sqrt{3}} = \frac{1}{3}\sqrt{3}$$

$$\sec 60° = \frac{c}{b} = \frac{2}{1} = 2 \qquad \csc 60° = \frac{c}{a} = \frac{2}{\sqrt{3}} = \frac{2}{3}\sqrt{3}$$

Since an angle of 30° is the complement of an angle of 60°, the functions of 30° are equal to the corresponding cofunctions of 60°. Therefore,

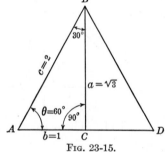

FIG. 23-15.

$$\sin 30° = \tfrac{1}{2}$$
$$\cos 30° = \tfrac{1}{2}\sqrt{3}$$
$$\tan 30° = \tfrac{1}{3}\sqrt{3}$$
$$\cot 30° = \sqrt{3}$$
$$\sec 30° = \tfrac{2}{3}\sqrt{3}$$
$$\csc 30° = 2$$

The sine and cosine of 30°, 45°, and 60° are easily remembered from the following table:

θ	30°	45°	60°
$\sin \theta$	$\tfrac{1}{2}\sqrt{1}$	$\tfrac{1}{2}\sqrt{2}$	$\tfrac{1}{2}\sqrt{3}$
$\cos \theta$	$\tfrac{1}{2}\sqrt{3}$	$\tfrac{1}{2}\sqrt{2}$	$\tfrac{1}{2}\sqrt{1}$

23-10. Functions of 0°. For an angle of 0°, the initial and terminal sides are both on OX. At any distance a from O, choose the point P as shown in Fig. 23-16. Then the coordinates of P are $(a, 0)$. That is, the x value is equal to a units, and the y value is zero. Since the radius vector r is equal to a, by definition,

$$\sin 0° = \frac{y}{r} = \frac{0}{r} = 0 \qquad \cos 0° = \frac{x}{r} = \frac{a}{a} = 1$$

$$\tan 0° = \frac{y}{x} = \frac{0}{a} = 0 \qquad \cot 0° = \frac{x}{y} = \frac{a}{0} = \infty$$

$$\sec 0° = \frac{r}{x} = \frac{a}{a} = 1 \qquad \csc 0° = \frac{r}{y} = \frac{a}{0} = \infty$$

By $\frac{a}{0} = \infty$ is meant the value of $\frac{a}{y}$ as y approaches zero without

limit. Thus, as y gets nearer and nearer to zero, $\frac{a}{y}$ gets larger

and larger. Therefore, $\frac{a}{y}$ is said to *approach* infinity as y

approaches zero. However, $\frac{a}{0}$ does not actually result in a

quotient of infinity, for division by zero is meaningless. Therefore, we say that cot 0° and csc 0° have no meaning; and whenever the symbol ∞ is used to denote
a trigonometric function, it should be
read "has no meaning."

Determining the functions of 90°,
180°, and 270° is accomplished by the
same method as that used for 0°.
These are left as problems for the
student.

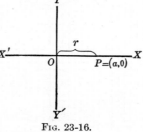

Fig. 23-16.

**23-11. Line Representation of the
Functions.** By representing the func-
tions as lengths of lines, we are able to obtain a mental picture
of the manner in which the functions vary as the radius vector
revolves and generates angles. Since we are primarily concerned with the sine, cosine, and tangent, only these functions
will be represented graphically.

In Fig. 23-17 the radius vector r, with a length of one unit, is
revolving about the origin generating the angle θ. Then, in
each of the four quadrants,

$$\sin \theta = \frac{BC}{r} = \frac{BC}{1} = BC \qquad \text{and} \qquad \cos \theta = \frac{OC}{r} = \frac{OC}{1} = OC$$

It is evident *that the sine of an angle may be represented by the
ordinate (y value) of any point where the end of the radius vector
coincides with the circumference of the circle.* Hence, the length
BC represents $\sin \theta$ in all quadrants, as shown in Fig. 23-17.

Note that the ordinate gives both the sign and the magnitude of the sine in any quadrant. Thus, in quadrants I and II, $\sin \theta = +0.6$; in quadrants III and IV, $\sin \theta = -0.6$. That is, when the radius vector is above the X axis, the ordinate, and therefore the sine, are positive. When the radius vector is below the X axis, the ordinate and, therefore, the sine are negative.

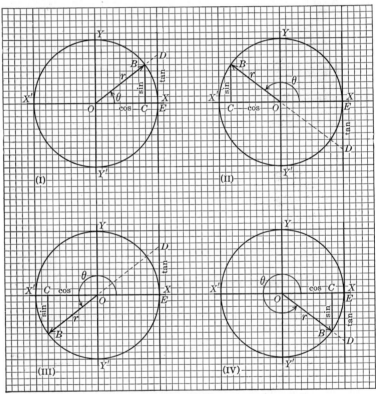

Fig. 23-17.

Similarly, *the cosine of an angle may be represented by the abscissa (x value) of any point where the end of the radius vector coincides with the circumference of the circle.* Hence, the length OC represents $\cos \theta$ in all quadrants, as shown in Fig. 23-17. The abscissa gives both the sign and the magnitude of the cosine in any quadrant. Thus, in quadrants I and IV, $\cos \theta = +0.8$; in quadrants II and III, $\cos \theta = -0.8$. That is, when the radius vector is to the right of the Y axis, the abscissa, and therefore the cosine, are positive. When the radius vector is to the left of the Y axis, the abscissa, and therefore the cosine, are negative.

In Fig. 23-17, the radius vector has been extended to intersect the tangent line DE which has been drawn tangent to the circle at the positive X axis. Since by construction, DE is perpendicular to OX, OBC and ODE are similar right triangles, for they have a common acute angle BOC. From the similar triangles,

$$\frac{BC}{OC} = \frac{DE}{OE}$$

Then, in each of the four quadrants,

$$\tan \theta = \frac{BC}{OC} = \frac{DE}{OE} = \frac{DE}{1} = DE$$

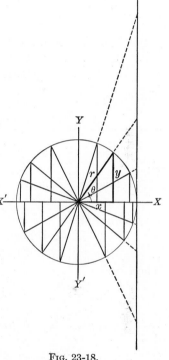

From the above, it is evident that *the tangent of an angle may be represented by the ordinate (y value) of any point where the extended radius vector intersects the tangent line*. The ordinate gives both the sign and the magnitude of the tangent in any quadrant. Thus, in quadrants I and III, tan $\theta = +0.75$; in quadrants II and IV, tan $\theta = -0.75$.

Fig. 23-18.

23-12. Variation of the Functions. As the radius vector starts from OX and revolves about the origin in a positive (counterclockwise) direction, the angle θ is generated and varies in magnitude continuously from 0° to 360° through the four quadrants. Figure 23-18 illustrates the manner in which the sine, cosine, and tangent vary as the angle θ changes in value.

Quadrant I. As θ increases from 0° to 90°,
    x is positive and decreases from r to 0.
    y is positive and increases from 0 to r.

Therefore,

$$\sin \theta = \frac{y}{r} \text{ is } \textit{positive} \text{ and increases from 0 to 1.}$$

$$\cos \theta = \frac{x}{r} \text{ is } \textit{positive} \text{ and decreases from 1 to 0.}$$

$$\tan \theta = \frac{y}{x} \text{ is } \textit{positive} \text{ and increases from 0 to } \infty.$$

Quadrant II. As θ increases from 90° to 180°,
x is negative and decreases from 0 to $-r$.
y is positive and decreases from r to 0.

Therefore,

$$\sin \theta = \frac{y}{r} \text{ is } \textit{positive} \text{ and decreases from 1 to 0.}$$

$$\cos \theta = \frac{x}{r} \text{ is } \textit{negative} \text{ and decreases from 0 to } -1.$$

$$\tan \theta = \frac{y}{x} \text{ is } \textit{negative} \text{ and increases from } -\infty \text{ to 0.}$$

Quadrant III. As θ increases from 180° to 270°,
x is negative and increases from $-r$ to 0.
y is negative and decreases from 0 to $-r$.

Therefore,

$$\sin \theta = \frac{y}{r} \text{ is } \textit{negative} \text{ and decreases from 0 to } -1.$$

$$\cos \theta = \frac{x}{r} \text{ is } \textit{negative} \text{ and increases from } -1 \text{ to 0.}$$

$$\tan \theta = \frac{y}{x} \text{ is } \textit{positive} \text{ and increases from 0 to } \infty.$$

Quadrant IV. As θ increases from 270° to 360°,
x is positive and increases from 0 to r.
y is negative and increases from $-r$ to 0.

Therefore,

$$\sin \theta = \frac{y}{r} \text{ is } \textit{negative} \text{ and increases from } -1 \text{ to 0.}$$

$$\cos \theta = \frac{x}{r} \text{ is } \textit{positive} \text{ and increases from 0 to 1.}$$

$$\tan \theta = \frac{y}{x} \text{ is } \textit{negative} \text{ and increases from } -\infty \text{ to 0.}$$

Students often become confused in comparing the variations of the functions, when represented as lines, with their actual numerical value. For example, in quadrant II as the angle θ increases from 90° to 180°, we say that cos θ *decreases* from 0 to $-r$. Actually, the abscissa representing the cosine is getting *longer;* confusion results from not remembering that a negative number is always less than zero. The *lengths* of the lines representing the functions, when compared with the radius vector, indicate only the *magnitude* of the function. The position of the lines, with respect to the X or Y axis, specifies the signs of the functions.

PROBLEMS 23-3

1. What is the least value sin θ may have?

2. What is the least value cos θ may have?

3. What is the greatest value csc θ may have in the first quadrant?

4. What is the greatest value sec θ may have in the fourth quadrant?

5. Can the secant and cosecant have values between -1 and $+1$?

CHAPTER XXIV

TABLES OF FUNCTIONS

For the purpose of making computations, it is evident that a table of trigonometric functions would be helpful, arranged somewhat like a table of logarithms.

Such a table could be made by computing the functions of all angles by graphical methods. However, this would be laborious, and the resulting functions would not be accurate. Fortunately, mathematicians have calculated the values of the trigonometric functions by the use of advanced mathematics and have tabulated the results. These tables are known as *tables of natural functions* to distinguish them from *tables of the logarithms of the functions.*

In Table VIII (page 512) are arranged the natural functions of angles for every one-tenth of a degree from 0° to 90°. It will be noted that this table is similar in form to that of the table of logarithms (Table VI). In fact, these two tables are used very much in the same manner.

24-1. Given an Angle—To Find the Desired Function. How to use the table of natural functions is best illustrated by examples.

When the Angle Is Given in the Table

Example 1. Find the sine of 36.7°.
Solution: The angle 36° is in the left column of the table. The sine of 36.7° is read in the sin row and in the column headed 0.7°. It is 0.5976.

$$\therefore \sin 36.7° = 0.5976$$

Example 2. Find the cosine of 7.9°.
Solution: The angle 7° is in the left column of the table. The cosine of 7.9° is read in the cos row and in the column headed 0.9°. It is 0.9905.

$$\therefore \cos 7.9° = 0.9905$$

Example 3. Find the tangent of 79.1°.
Solution: Opposite 79° in the tan row and in the column headed 0.1°, read 5.1929.

$$\therefore \tan 79.1° = 5.1929$$

When the Angle Is Not Given in the Table

Example 4.   Find the sine of 26.42°.

Solution: Since 26.42° is between 26.4° and 26.5°, its sine value must be between sin 26.4° and sin 26.5°.   Hence,

$$
\begin{aligned}
\text{sin } 26.5° &= 0.4462 \\
\text{sin } 26.4° &= 0.4446 \\
\hline
\text{Difference} &= 0.0016
\end{aligned}
$$

The *tabular difference* between these sines is 0.0016, and it is apparent that an increase of 0.1° from 26.4° causes the sine value to increase 0.0016. Therefore an increase from 26.4° to 26.42°, which is an increase of 0.02°, must increase the sine value 0.2 as much.   Hence, the increase in the sine value is 0.0016 × 0.2 = 0.00032.

$$\therefore \text{ sin } 26.42° = 0.4446 + 0.00032 = 0.44492$$

The sine of 26.42°, as written above, is another good example of how the retention of decimals might easily convey a false impression of accuracy.   The tables from which the sine values were taken are correct to four significant figures.   Therefore, any sine value found by interpolation cannot be correct beyond four significant figures.   Thus, it is correct to write

$$\text{sin } 26.42° = 0.4449$$

A similar case, applicable to interpolation in the logarithm tables, was discussed in Art. 20-13, Example 4.

Example 5.   Find the cosine of 53.77°.

Solution:
$$
\begin{aligned}
\text{cos } 53.7° &= 0.5920 \\
\text{cos } 53.8° &= 0.5906 \\
\hline
\text{Difference} &= 0.0014
\end{aligned}
$$

Since the value of the cosine *decreases* 0.0014 as the angle increases 0.1° from 53.7°, a subtraction must be made when interpolating.   Then the decrease in the cosine value is 0.0014 × 0.7 = 0.00098.

$$\text{cos } 53.77° = 0.5920 - 0.00098 = 0.59102$$
or $$\text{cos } 53.77° = 0.5910$$

Example 6.   Find the tangent of 48.13°.

Solution:
$$
\begin{aligned}
\text{tan } 48.2° &= 1.1184 \\
\text{tan } 48.1° &= 1.1145 \\
\hline
\text{Difference} &= 0.0039
\end{aligned}
$$

Since the value of the tangent increases 0.0039 as the angle increases 0.1° from 48.1°, then the increase of 0.03° will cause the tangent to increase 0.0039 × 0.3 = 0.00117.

$$\therefore \tan 48.13° = 1.1145 + 0.00117 = 1.11567$$

or $\tan 48.13° = 1.1157$

PROBLEMS 24-1

1. Find the sine, cosine, and tangent of

    (*a*) 13°.   (*b*) 89°.   (*c*) 4.3°.
         (*d*) 57.9°.   (*e*) 25.4°.

2. Find the sine, cosine, and tangent of

    (*a*) 17°.   (*b*) 78°.   (*c*) 8.7°.
         (*d*) 63.1°.   (*e*) 33.6°.

3. Find the sine, cosine, and tangent of

    (*a*) 25.75°.   (*b*) 73.36°.   (*c*) 2.14°.
         (*d*) 47.72°.   (*e*) 10.27°.

4. Find the sine, cosine, and tangent of

    (*a*) 37.55°.   (*b*) 69.93°.   (*c*) 53.18°.
         (*d*) 7.49°.   (*e*) 49.11°.

24-2. Inverse Trigonometric Functions. Frequently some form of notation is needed in order to express an angle in terms of one of its functions. For example, in Art. 23-4, Example 1 dealt with an angle whose tangent was $\frac{9}{10}$. Similarly, in Example 2 of the same article, we considered an angle whose cosine was $\frac{3}{4}$.

If $\sin \theta = x$, then θ is an angle whose sine is x. It has been agreed to express such a relation by the notation

$$\theta = \sin^{-1} x \qquad \text{or} \qquad \theta = \text{arc sin } x$$

Both are read "θ is equal to the angle whose sine is x," or, "the inverse sine of x." For example, the tangent of 37.2° is 0.7590. Stated as an inverse function, this would be written

$$37.2° = \text{arc tan } 0.7590$$

Similarly, in the case of a right triangle labeled as in Fig. 23-1, we should write $\theta = \text{arc tan } \frac{a}{b}$, $\theta = \text{arc cos } \frac{b}{c}$, etc. In this book, we shall not use the notation "$\theta = \sin^{-1} x$," for we prefer not to use an exponent when no exponent is intended. Although this form of notation is used in a number of texts, the student will find that nearly all recent mathematics and engineering texts are using the "θ = arc sin x" form of notation. Because more advanced mathematics employs trigonometric functions affected by exponents, it is evident that confusion would eventually result from utilizing the other notation for specifying the inverse functions.

24-3. Given a Function—To Find the Corresponding Angle. As in Art. 24-1, the use of the tables is best illustrated by examples.

When the Function Is Given in the Tables

Example 1.   Find the angle whose sine is 0.2351.

Solution: Find 0.2351 in the sin row. In the degrees column opposite the sin row in which 0.2351 is located, read 13°. The column in which 0.2351 is located is the 0.6° column. Thus, 0.2351 is the sine of 13.6°. This could be written

$$13.6° = \text{arc sin } 0.2351$$

Example 2.   Find θ, if cos θ = 0.0332.

Solution: Since the given cosine value is a very small number, we deduce that the corresponding angle must be large. Here is another example where a knowledge of how the functions vary is an asset because it saves time in looking up angles whose functions are given.

In the degrees column opposite the cos row in which 0.0332 is located, read 88°. 0.0332 is in the 0.1° column. Thus, 0.0332 is the cosine of 88.1°. This may be written

$$\cos 88.1° = 0.0332$$
or
$$88.1° = \text{arc cos } 0.0332$$

Example 3.   Find θ if θ = arc tan 1.1423.

Solution: Since tan 45° = 1 and the tangent value increases as the angle increases, it is evident that θ is somewhat larger than 45°. This knowledge enables one to begin searching for the given tangent value somewhere near its location.

In the degrees column opposite the tan row in which 1.1423 is located, read 48°. 1.1423 is in the 0.8° column. Thus, 1.1423 is the tangent of 48.8°. That is,

$$48.8° = \text{arc tan } 1.1423$$

When the Function Is Not Given in the Table

Example 4.   Find θ, if θ = arc sin 0.4452.

Solution: Examination of the table shows that 0.4452 is not given exactly in the sine values. Therefore we find the two consecutive sine values

between which the given sine value lies.   These are 0.4446 and 0.4462 which
are the sines of 26.4° and 26.5°, respectively.   Tabulating,

$$\text{sin } 26.5° = 0.4462$$
$$\text{sin } 26.4° = \underline{0.4446}$$
$$\text{Difference} = \overline{0.0016}$$

The *tabular difference* between these sine values is 0.0016, and it is apparent
that an increase of 0.1° from 26.4° causes the sine value to increase 0.0016.
Now the given sine value is 0.0006 larger than the sine of the smaller angle
taken from the table (0.4452 − 0.4446 = 0.0006).

Then, since $\dfrac{\text{increase}}{\text{difference}} = \dfrac{0.0006}{0.0016} = \dfrac{3}{8}$, the given sine value is $\dfrac{3}{8}$, or 0.375, of
the way from 0.4446 to 0.4462.   Therefore, we assume that θ is three-
eighths, or 0.375, of the way from 26.4° to 26.5°.   Hence,

$$\theta = 26.4° + 0.0375 = 26.4375°.$$

Again it becomes necessary to round off the answer in order to prevent a
false impression of accuracy.   Hence, we write

$$26.44° = \text{arc sin } 0.4452$$

Example 5.   Find θ, if cos $\theta = 0.3732$.

Solution: $0.3746 = \text{cos } 68.0°$
$$0.3730 = \text{cos } 68.1°$$
$$\text{Difference} = \overline{0.0016} \text{ for } \overline{\quad 0.1°}$$

Since the value of the cosine decreases 0.0016 as the angle increases 0.1°
from 68.0°, a subtraction must be made in interpolating.   The given cosine
value is 0.0002 larger than the smallest value taken from the table

$$(0.3732 − 0.3730 = 0.0002).$$

Then the given cosine value is $\dfrac{0.0002}{0.0016} = \dfrac{1}{8}$ of the way from 0.3730 to 0.3746.
Therefore, we assume that θ is $\frac{1}{8}$, or 0.125, of the way from 68.1° to 68.0°.
Hence, $\theta = 68.1° − 0.0125° = 68.0875°$, which, when rounded off, gives

$$68.09° = \text{arc cos } 0.3732$$

Example 6.   Find θ, if $\theta = \text{arc tan } 0.5920$.

Solution: $0.5938 = \text{tan } 30.7°$
$$0.5914 = \text{tan } 30.6°$$
$$\text{Difference} = \overline{0.0024} \text{ for } \overline{\quad 0.1°}$$

For an increase of 0.1° the tangent increases 0.0024.   The given tangent
value is 0.0006 larger than the tangent of the smaller angle taken from the
table (0.5920 − 0.5914 = 0.0006).   Then the given tangent value is
$\dfrac{0.0006}{0.0024} = \dfrac{1}{4}$, or 0.25, of the way from 0.5914 to 0.5938.   Therefore, we assume

that θ is $\frac{1}{4}$, or 0.25, of the way from 30.6° to 30.7°.   Hence,

$$\theta = 30.6° + 0.025 = 30.625°$$

which, when rounded off, gives

$$30.62° = \text{arc tan } 0.5920$$

The student will note the similarity of interpolating in the table of functions to interpolating in the table of logarithms. The methods and reasoning are identical; for, in using either of the tables, we assume that the difference between tabulated values is proportional to the difference of their respective mantissas or angles, as the case may be.

24-4. Accuracy. The methods of interpolation illustrated here are for the use of those students who require a greater degree of accuracy than that given by working with angles to the nearest tenth of a degree.   In our considerations of alternating-current circuits, we shall confine our accuracy to three significant figures and angles to the nearest tenth of a degree. This, except for isolated cases, will more than meet all practical requirements.   Also, it reduces interpolation to an inspection of the values of the tabulated functions in order to determine which tenth of a degree to choose.

The use of a slide rule obviates the necessity of using a table of trigonometric functions except for cases where an extremely high degree of accuracy is desired.   Finding an angle corresponding to a given function or finding a function corresponding to a given angle is accomplished by one setting of the indicator. It is in working with trigonometric functions that the use of the modern slide rule really begins to be rewarding in saving time and labor.

PROBLEMS 24-2

1. Find the angles having the following as sines:

(a) 0.0628.   (b) 0.9949.   (c) 0.2639.
          (d) 0.9250.   (e) 0.6037.

2. Find the angles having the following as cosines:

(a) 0.0401.   (b) 0.9789.   (c) 0.5664.
          (d) 0.4215.   (e) 0.7915.

3. Find the angles having the following tangents:

(a) 0.1388.   (b) 9.6768.   (c) 0.7292.
          (d) 1.6025.   (e) 0.0831.

4. (*a*) $\theta = $ arc sin 0.7848. $\theta = ?$
(*b*) $\theta = $ arc tan 3.5105. $\theta = ?$
(*c*) $\theta = $ arc cos 0.9974. $\theta = ?$
(*d*) $\theta = $ arc tan 1.2475. $\theta = ?$
(*e*) $\theta = $ arc sin 0.0950. $\theta = ?$

24-5. Functions of Angles Greater than 90°.   The student has noted that the trigonometric functions have been tabulated only for angles of 0° to 90°.   The signs and magnitudes for angles in all quadrants were considered in the preceding chapter, and it is evident that a table of functions for all angles will be needed.   Because the existing tables are for angles in the first quadrant, there must be methods of expressing any angle in terms of an angle of the first quadrant in order to make use of the table of functions.

24-6. To Find the Functions of an Angle in the Second Quadrant.   In Fig. 24-1, let θ represent any angle in the second quad-

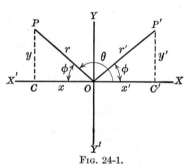

FIG. 24-1.

rant.   From any point P on the radius vector r, draw the perpendicular y, to the horizontal axis.   The acute angle that r makes with the horizontal axis is designated by ϕ.   Then, since $\theta + \phi = 180°$, θ and ϕ are supplementary angles.   Hence,

$$\phi = 180° - \theta$$

Now construct the angle XOP' in the first quadrant equal to ϕ, make r' equal to r, and draw y' perpendicular to OX.   Since the right triangles OPC and $OP'C'$ are equal, $x = -x'$ and $y = y'$.   Then

$$\sin (180° - \theta) = \frac{y}{r} = \frac{y'}{r'} = \sin \phi$$

$$\cos (180° - \theta) = \frac{x}{r} = \frac{-x'}{r'} = - \cos \phi$$

$$\tan (180° - \theta) = \frac{y}{x} = \frac{y'}{-x'} = - \tan \phi$$

These relations show that the function of an angle has the same absolute value as the same function of its supplement.   That is, if two angles are supplementary their sines are equal, and their cosines and tangents are of equal magnitude but opposite in sign.

Examples: sin 140° = sin (180° − 140°) = sin 40° = 0.6428
  cos 100° = − cos (180° − 100°) = − cos 80° = −0.1736
  tan 175° = − tan (180° − 175°) = − tan 5° = −0.0875

24-7. To Find the Function of an Angle in the Third Quadrant.

In Fig. 24-2, let θ represent any angle in the third quadrant, and let ϕ be the acute angle that the radius vector r makes with the horizontal axis.   Then

$$\phi = \theta - 180°$$

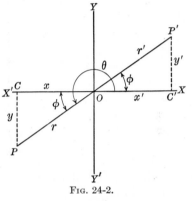

Now construct the angle XOP' in the first quadrant equal to ϕ, make r' equal to r, and draw y and y' perpendicular to the horizontal axis. Since the right triangles OPC and $OP'C'$ are equal, $x = -x'$ and $y = -y'$.   Then

Fig. 24-2.

$$\sin (\theta - 180°) = \frac{y}{r} = \frac{-y'}{r'} = - \sin \phi$$

$$\cos (\theta - 180°) = \frac{x}{r} = \frac{-x'}{r'} = - \cos \phi$$

$$\tan (\theta - 180°) = \frac{y}{x} = \frac{-y'}{-x'} = \tan \phi$$

These relations show that the function of an angle in the third quadrant has the same absolute value as the same function of the acute angle between the radius vector and the horizontal axis.   The signs of the functions are the same as for any angle in the third quadrant, as discussed in Art. 23-6.

Examples: sin 200° = − sin (200° − 180°) = − sin 20° = −0.3420
  cos 260° = − cos (260° − 180°) = − cos 80° = −0.1736
  tan 234° = tan (234° − 180°) = tan 54° = 1.3764

24-8. To Find the Functions of an Angle in the Fourth Quadrant. In Fig. 24-3, let θ represent any angle in the fourth quadrant, and let ϕ be the acute angle that the radius vector r

makes with the horizontal axis.   Then

$$\phi = 360° - \theta$$

Now construct the angle XOP' in the first quadrant equal to ϕ, make r' equal to r, and draw y and y' perpendicular to the

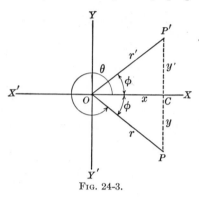

Fig. 24-3.

horizontal axis.   Since the right triangles OPC and $OP'C$ are equal, $y = -y'$.   Then

$$\sin (360° - \theta) = \frac{y}{r} = \frac{-y'}{r'} = -\sin \phi$$

$$\cos (360° - \theta) = \frac{x}{r} = \frac{x}{r'} = \cos \phi$$

$$\tan (360° - \theta) = \frac{y}{x} = \frac{-y'}{x} = -\tan \phi$$

These relations show that the functions of an angle in the fourth quadrant have the same absolute value as the same functions of an acute angle in the first quadrant equal to $(360° - \theta)$. The signs of the functions, however, are those for an angle in the fourth quadrant, as discussed in Art. 23-6.

Examples: $\sin 300° = -\sin (360° - 300°) = -\sin 60° = -0.8660$
    $\cos 285° = \cos (360° - 285°) = \cos 75° = 0.2588$
    $\tan 316° = -\tan (360° - 316°) = -\tan 44° = -0.9657$

24-9. To Find the Function of an Angle Greater than 360°. Any angle θ greater than 360° has the same trigonometric functions as θ minus an integral multiple of 360°.   That is, a function of an angle larger than 360° is found by dividing the angle by

360° and finding the required function of the remainder.   Thus θ, in Fig. 24-4, is a positive angle of 955°.   To find any function of 955°, divide 955° by 360° which gives 2 with a remainder of 235°.   Hence,

$$\sin 955° = \sin 235° = -\sin(235° - 180°)$$
$$= -\sin 55° = -0.8192$$
$$\cos 955° = \cos 235° = -\cos(235° - 180)°$$
$$= -\cos 55° = -0.5736$$
$$\tan 955° = \tan 235° = \tan(235° - 180°)$$
$$= \tan 55° = 1.4281$$

24-10. To Find the Function of a Negative Angle.   In Fig. 24-5, let $-\theta$ represent a negative angle in the fourth quadrant

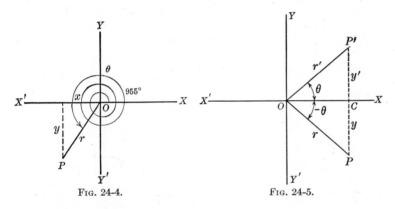

Fig. 24-4.   Fig. 24-5.

made by the radius vector r and the horizontal axis.   Construct the angle θ in the first quadrant equal to $-\theta$, make r' equal to r, and draw y and y' perpendicular to the horizontal axis.   Since the right triangles OPC and $OP'C$ are equal, $y = -y'$.   Then

$$\sin(-\theta) = \frac{y}{r} = \frac{-y'}{r'} = -\sin\theta$$

$$\cos(-\theta) = \frac{x}{r} = \frac{x}{r'} = \cos\theta$$

$$\tan(-\theta) = \frac{y}{x} = \frac{-y'}{x'} = -\tan\theta$$

These relations are true for any values of $-\theta$, regardless of the quadrant or the magnitude of the angle.

Examples: sin $(-65°)$ = $-$ sin 65° = -0.9063
cos $(-150°)$ = cos 150° = $-$ cos $(180° - 150°)$ = $-$ cos 30° = -0.8660
tan $(-287°)$ = $-$ tan 287° = $-$ tan $(360° - 287°)$ = $-(-$ tan 73°)
$$= 3.2709$$

24-11. To Reduce the Functions of Any Angle to the Functions of an Acute Angle.

It has been shown in the preceding articles that all angles can be reduced to terms of $(180° - \theta)$, $(\theta - 180°)$, $(360° - \theta)$, or θ. These results may be summarized as follows:

Rule: *To find any function of any angle θ, take the same function of the acute angle formed by the terminal side (radius vector) and the horizontal axis, and prefix the proper algebraic sign for that quadrant.*

When finding the functions of angles, the student should make a sketch showing the approximate location of the angle. This procedure will clarify the trigonometric relationships, and, in addition, many errors will be avoided.

Example 1. Find the functions of 143°.

Solution: Construct the angle 143°, and mark the signs of the radius vector, abscissa, and ordinate, as shown in Fig. 24-6. (The radius vector is always

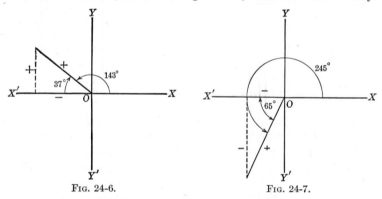

FIG. 24-6.   FIG. 24-7.

positive.) Since $180° - 143° = 37°$, the acute angle for the functions is 37°. Hence,

$$\text{sin } 143° = \text{sin } 37° = 0.6018$$
$$\text{cos } 143° = -\text{cos } 37° = -0.7986$$
$$\text{tan } 143° = -\text{tan } 37° = -0.7536$$

Example 2. Find the functions of 245°.

Solution: Construct the angle 245° as shown in Fig. 24-7. Since

$$245° - 180° = 65°,$$

the acute angle for the functions is 65°.   Hence,

$$\sin 245° = - \sin 65° = -0.9063$$
$$\cos 245° = - \cos 65° = -0.4226$$
$$\tan 245° = \tan 65° = 2.1445$$

Example 3.   Find the functions of 312°.

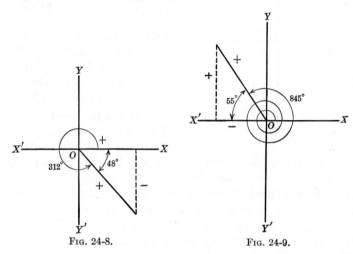

FIG. 24-8.   FIG. 24-9.

Solution: Construct the angle 312° as shown in Fig. 24-8.   Since

$$360° - 312° = 48°$$

the acute angle for the functions is 48°.   Hence,

$$\sin 312° = - \sin 48° = -0.7431$$
$$\cos 312° = \cos 48° = 0.6691$$
$$\tan 312° = - \tan 48° = -1.1106$$

Example 4.   Find the functions of 845°.

Solution: $\frac{845°}{360°} = 2 + 125°$.   Therefore, the functions of 125° will be identical with those of 845°.   The construction is shown in Fig. 24-9. Since $180° - 125° = 55°$, the acute angle for the functions is 55°.   Hence,

$$\sin 845° = \sin 55° = 0.8192$$
$$\cos 845° = - \cos 55° = -0.5736$$
$$\tan 845° = - \tan 55° = -1.4281$$

Example 5.   Find the functions of −511°.

Solution: $\dfrac{-511°}{360°} = -(1 + 151°)$.   Therefore, the functions of $-151°$ will be identical with those of $-511°$.   The construction is shown in Fig. 24-10.

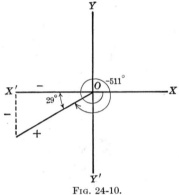

Since $180° - 151° = 29°$, the acute angle for the functions is $29°$.   Hence,

$\sin(-151°) = -\sin 29° = -0.4848$
$\cos(-151°) = -\cos 29° = -0.8746$
$\tan(-151°) = \tan 29° = 0.5543$

FIG. 24-10.

24-12. Angles Corresponding to Inverse Functions. Now that we are able to express all angles as acute angles in order to use the table of functions from $0°$ to $90°$, it has probably occurred to the student that an important distinction exists between the direct trigonometric functions and the inverse trigonometric functions. The trigonometric functions of any given angle have only one value, whereas a given function corresponds to an infinite number of angles. For example, an angle of $30°$ has but one sine value which is 0.5000; but an angle whose sine is 0.5000 (arc sin 0.5000) may be taken as $30°$, $150°$, $390°$, $480°$, $510°$, etc.

To avoid confusion, it has been agreed that the values of arc sin θ and arc tan θ which lie between $+90°$ and $-90°$, in the first and fourth quadrants, are to be known as the *principal values* of arc sin θ and arc tan θ. The principal value is often denoted by using a capital letter, as Arc sin θ. Thus, Arc sin $0.5750 = 35.1°$, and Arc sin $(-0.9980) = -86.4°$. Also, Arc tan $1.4826 = 56°$, and Arc tan $(-0.0699) = -4°$.

The principal values of arc cos θ are taken as the values between $0°$ and $180°$ and are denoted by Arc cos θ. Thus, Arc cos $0.1736 = 80°$, and Arc cos $(-0.9816) = 169°$.

PROBLEMS 24-3

1. Find the sine, cosine, and tangent of

    (*a*) $99°$.   (*b*) $164°$.   (*c*) $136.5°$.

           (*d*) $159.1°$.   (*e*) $178.1°$.

2. Find the sine, cosine, and tangent of

    (*a*) $103°$.   (*b*) $169°$.   (*c*) $114.3°$.

           (*d*) $152.3°$.   (*e*) $146.8°$.

3. Find the sine, cosine, and tangent of

    (a) 186°.   (b) 261°.   (c) 220.7°.
        (d) 197.4°.   (e) 250.6°.

4. Find the sine, cosine, and tangent of

    (a) 189°.   (b) 247°.   (c) 193.3°.
        (d) 200.4°.   (e) 233.9°.

5. Find the sine, cosine, and tangent of

    (a) 352°.   (b) 277°.   (c) 348.1°.
        (d) 285.7°.   (e) 331.2°.

6. Find the sine, cosine, and tangent of

    (a) 274°.   (b) 349°.   (c) 320.3°.
        (d) 292.4°.   (e) 338.8°.

7. Find the sine, cosine, and tangent of

    (a) 385°.   (b) 847°.   (c) 1376°.
        (d) −480°.   (e) −667°.

8. Find the sine, cosine, and tangent of

    (a) 590°.   (b) −1080°.   (c) 1038°.
        (d) −406°.   (e) −923°.

9. Find θ if

    (a) $\theta = $ Arc tan 0.3899.   (b) $\theta = $ Arc sin (−0.1253).
    (c) $\theta = $ Arc tan (−0.7508).   (d) $\theta = $ Arc cos (−0.1288).
    (e) $\theta = $ Arc sin 0.0279.

10. Find θ if

    (a) $\theta = $ Arc sin (−0.8181).   (b) $\theta = $ Arc cos 0.2706.
    (c) $\theta = $ Arc tan (−0.4557).   (d) $\theta = $ Arc sin 0.8771.
    (e) $\theta = $ Arc tan (−7.3962).

11. The illumination on a surface that is not perpendicular to the rays of light from a source of light is given by the formula

$$E = \frac{I \cos \theta}{d^2}$$

where $E = $ illumination at the point on the surface in foot-candles,
      $I = $ luminous intensity of the source in candles,
      $d = $ distance in feet from the source of light,
      $\theta = $ angle between incident ray and a line perpendicular to the surface.
Solve for d, I, and θ.

12. In the formula of Prob. 11, find the value of d if $I = $ 265 cp, $\theta = 65°$, and $E = $ 12 ft-candles.

13. A certain 100-w lamp has a luminous intensity of 108 cp. Disregarding reflection, compute the illumination at a point on a surface 10 ft from the lamp if the plane of the surface is at an angle of 20° from the incident rays.

14. In the formula of Prob. 11, at what angle to the incident ray will the plane of the surface be, for the greatest amount of light?

15. The illumination on a horizontal surface from a source of light at a given vertical distance from the surface is given by the formula

$$E_h = \frac{I}{h^2} \cos^3 \theta$$

where E_h = illumination in foot-candles at a point on the horizontal surface,
   I = luminous intensity of the source in foot-candles,
   h = vertical distance in feet from the horizontal surface to the source of light,
   θ = angle between incident ray and a vertical line, as shown in Fig. 24-11.

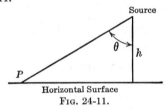

Source
θ
h
P
Horizontal Surface
Fig. 24-11.

NOTE: $\cos^3 \theta$ means $\cos \theta$ raised to the third power. Thus,

$$\cos^3 \theta = (\cos \theta)^3.$$

Solve for h, I, and θ.

16. Using the formula of Prob. 15, solve for E_h if $I = 225$ ft-candles, $h = 15$ ft, and $\theta = 35°$.

17. Using the formula of Prob. 15, find the value of I if $h = 10$ ft, $E_h = 25$ ft-candles, and $\theta = 70°$.

18. According to present standards, 8 to 12 ft-candles of illumination on the printed page should be used for ordinary reading purposes. A 50-w 45-cp lamp is suspended 6 ft above a reading table. The reflector used with the lamp projects 70% of the light downward. Does this produce enough illumination for reading a book directly under the lamp?

19. To produce 10 ft-candles on the book in the above problem, what candle-power lamp would be required?

20. According to formula of Prob. 15, at what angle is the greatest light obtained for a given distance?

CHAPTER XXV

SOLUTION OF RIGHT TRIANGLES

One of the most important applications of trigonometry is the solution of triangles, both right and oblique. This chapter is concerned with the former. The right triangle is probably the most universally used geometric figure; with the aid of trigonometry, it is applied to numerous problems in measurement that otherwise might be impossible to solve.

A large percentage of the problems relating to the analysis of alternating-current circuits and communication networks involves the solution of the right triangle in one form or another. It is essential that we, who would understand the functioning of such circuits, have a thorough knowledge of the solution of right triangles.

25-1. Facts Concerning Right Triangles. Before proceeding with the actual solutions of right triangles, the following useful facts regarding the properties of the right triangle should be reviewed:

1. *The square of the hypotenuse is equal to the sum of the squares of the other two sides.* ($c^2 = a^2 + b^2$. Fig. 23-1.)

2. *The acute angles are complements of each other; that is, the sum of the two acute angles is 90°.* ($A + B = 90°$. Fig. 23-1.)

3. *The hypotenuse is greater than either of the other sides and is less than their sum.*

4. *The greater angle is opposite the greater side, and the greater side is opposite the greater angle.*

These facts will often serve as a material aid in checking computations made by trigonometric methods.

25-2. Procedure for Solution of Right Triangles. Every triangle has three sides and three angles, and these are called the six *elements* of the triangle. To *solve* a triangle is to find the values of the unknown elements.

A triangle may be solved by two methods:

1. By constructing the triangle accurately from known elements with scale, protractor, and compasses. The unknown elements may then be measured with the scale and the protractor.

2. By computing the unknown elements from those that are known.

The first method has been used to some extent in preceding chapters. However, as previously discussed, the graphical method is cumbersome and has a limited degree of accuracy.

Trigonometry, combined with simple algebraic processes, furnishes us with a powerful tool for solving triangles by the second method listed above. Moreover, the degree of accuracy is limited only by the number of significant figures to which the elements have been measured and the number of significant figures in the table of functions used for the solution.

As pointed out in earlier chapters, every type of problem should be approached and solved in a planned and systematic manner. Only in this way are the habits of clear and ordered thinking aeveloped, the principles of the problem understood, and the possibility of errors reduced to a minimum. With the foregoing in mind, the following suggestions for solving right triangles are listed as a guide:

1. Make an accurate drawing to scale of the triangle, and mark the known (given) elements. This shows the relation of the elements, helps in choosing the functions needed, and will serve as a check for the solution. List what is to be found.

2. To find an unknown element, select a formula that contains two known elements and the required unknown element. Substitute the known elements in the formula, and solve for the unknown.

3. As a rough check on the solution, compare the results with the drawing. To check the values accurately, note whether they satisfy relations different from those already employed for the solution of the values being checked. A convenient check for the sides of a right triangle is the relation

$$a^2 = c^2 - b^2 = (c + b)(c - b)$$

4. In the computations, round off the numbers representing the lengths of sides to three significant figures and all angles to the nearest tenth of a degree. This means that the values of the functions employed in computations are to be used to only three significant figures. As previously stated, such accuracy is sufficient for ordinary practical circuit computations.

Heretofore, the right triangles used in figures for illustrative examples have been lettered in the conventional manner, as shown in Figs. 23-1, 23-2, etc.   At this point the notation for the various elements will be changed to that of Fig. 25-1.   This change of lettering in no way has any effect on the fundamental relations existing among the elements of a right triangle; nor are any new ideas involved in connection with the trigonometric functions.   Because certain alternating-current problems will employ this form of notation, this is a convenient place to introduce it in order that we may become accustomed to solving right triangles lettered in this manner.

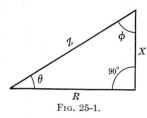
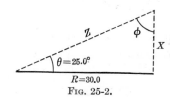

Fig. 25-1.   Fig. 25-2.

The following articles illustrate all the possible conditions encountered in the solution of right triangles.

25-3. Given an Acute Angle and a Side Not the Hypotenuse.

Example 1.   Given $R = 30.0$ and $\theta = 25.0°$.   Solve for Z, X, and ϕ.
Solution: The construction is shown in Fig. 25-2.

$$\phi = 90° - \theta$$
$$= 90° - 25° = 65°$$

An equation containing the two known elements and one unknown is

$$\tan \theta = \frac{X}{R}$$

Solving for X, $X = R \tan \theta$

Substituting the values of R and $\tan \theta$, $X = 30 \times 0.466 = 14.0$

Also, since $\sin \theta = \frac{X}{Z}$

solving for Z, $Z = \frac{X}{\sin \theta}$

Substituting the values of X and $\sin \theta$, $Z = \frac{14.0}{0.423} = 33.1$

This solution may be checked by using some relation other than the ones used in solving.   Thus, substituting values in

$$X^2 = (Z + R)(Z - R)$$

results in $14.0^2 = (33.1 + 30.0)(33.1 - 30.0)$

$$196 = 63.1 \times 3.10 = 196$$

Since all results were rounded off to three significant figures, the check shows the solution to be correct for this degree of accuracy.

The value of Z may be checked by employing a function not used in the solution. Thus, since

$$R = Z \cos \theta$$

by substituting the values, $30 = 33.1 \times 0.906$

Still another check could be made by use of an inverse function employing two of the elements found in the solution. For example,

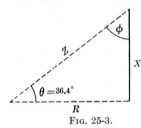

FIG. 25-3.

$$\phi = \text{arc cos} \frac{X}{Z} = \frac{14.0}{33.1} = 0.423 = \cos 65°$$

Example 2. Given $X = 106$ and $\theta = 36.4°$. Solve for Z, R, and ϕ.

Solution: The construction is shown in Fig. 25-3.

$$\phi = 90° - \theta$$
$$= 90° - 36.4° = 53.6°$$

An equation containing two known elements and one unknown is

$$\sin \theta = \frac{X}{Z}$$

Solving for Z, $Z = \dfrac{X}{\sin \theta}$

Substituting the values of X and $\sin \theta$, $Z = \dfrac{106}{0.593} = 179$

Also, since $\cos \theta = \dfrac{R}{Z}$

solving for R, $R = Z \cos \theta$

Substituting the values of Z and $\cos \theta$, $R = 179 \times 0.805 = 144$

Check the solution by one of the methods previously explained.

Example 3. Given $R = 8.35$ and $\phi = 62.7°$. Find Z, X, and θ.

Solution: The construction is shown in Fig. 25-4.

$$\theta = 90° - \phi$$
$$= 90° - 62.7° = 27.3°$$

When θ is found, the methods to be used in the solution of this example become identical with those of Example 1. Hence,

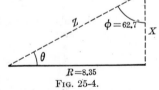

FIG. 25-4.

$$X = R \tan \theta = 8.35 \tan 27.3° = 8.35 \times 0.516 = 4.31$$

$$Z = \frac{X}{\sin \theta} = \frac{4.31}{\sin 27.3°} = \frac{4.31}{0.459} = 9.39$$

Check the solution by a method considered most convenient.

Example 4. Given $X = 1290$ and $\phi = 41.9°$. Find Z, R, and θ.
Solution: The construction is shown in Fig. 25-5.

$$\theta = 90° - \phi$$
$$= 90° - 41.9° = 48.1°$$

When θ is found, the methods to be used in the solution of this example become identical with those of Example 2. Hence,

$$Z = \frac{X}{\sin \theta} = \frac{1290}{\sin 48.1°} = \frac{1290}{0.744} = 1730$$
$$R = Z \cos \theta = 1730 \cos 48.1° =$$
$$1730 \times 0.688 = 1160$$

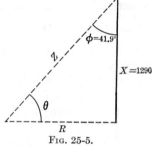

Check the solution by a method considered most convenient.

Fɪɢ. 25-5.

With the exception of finding the unknown acute angle, which involves subtraction, any of the foregoing examples and the following problems may be solved with two movements on many types of slide rules.

PROBLEMS 25-1

Solve the following right triangles for the unknown elements. Check each by making a construction and by substituting into a formula not used in the solution.

1. $R = 63.5$, $\theta = 25.0°$.   **2.** $R = 10.3$, $\theta = 78.5°$.
3. $R = 175$, $\theta = 12.3°$.   **4.** $R = 0.423$, $\theta = 64.9°$.
5. $R = 525$, $\theta = 37.4°$.   **6.** $X = 48.4$, $\theta = 84.1°$.
7. $X = 9.21$, $\theta = 5.2°$.   **8.** $X = 867$, $\theta = 57.6°$.
9. $X = 1250$, $\theta = 25.7°$.   **10.** $X = 0.290$, $\theta = 46.0°$
11. $R = 100$, $\phi = 38.9°$.   **12.** $R = 1750$, $\phi = 69.3°$,
13. $R = 1.23$, $\phi = 2.5°$.   **14.** $R = 76.3$, $\phi = 15.4°$.
15. $R = 0.932$, $\phi = 79.6°$.   **16.** $X = 2.91$, $\phi = 80.9°$
17. $X = 6800$, $\phi = 41.2°$.   **18.** $X = 250$, $\phi = 27.7°$,
19. $X = 17.5$, $\phi = 53.8°$.   **20.** $X = 57.3$, $\phi = 3.2°$.

25-4. Given an Acute Angle and the Hypotenuse.

Example 1. Given $Z = 45.3$ and $\theta = 20.3°$. Find R, X, and ϕ.
Solution: The construction is shown in Fig. 25-6.

$$\phi = 90° - \theta$$
$$= 90° - 20.3° = 69.7°$$

An equation containing two known elements and one unknown is

$$\cos \theta = \frac{R}{Z}$$

Solving for R, $R = Z \cos \theta$

Substituting the values of Z and $\cos \theta$, $R = 45.3 \times 0.938 = 42.5$

Another convenient equation is $\sin \theta = \frac{X}{Z}$

Solving for X, $X = Z \sin \theta$

Substituting the values of Z and $\sin \theta$, $X = 45.3 \times 0.347 = 15.7$

The solution may be checked by any of the usual methods.

Example 2.   Given $Z = 265$ and $\phi = 22.4°$.   Find R, X, and θ.

Solution: The construction is shown in Fig. 25-7.

$$\theta = 90° - \phi$$
$$= 90° - 22.4° = 67.6°$$

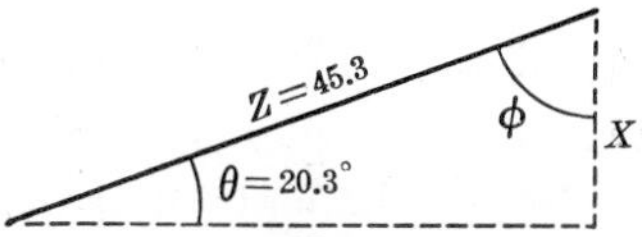

Fig. 25-6. 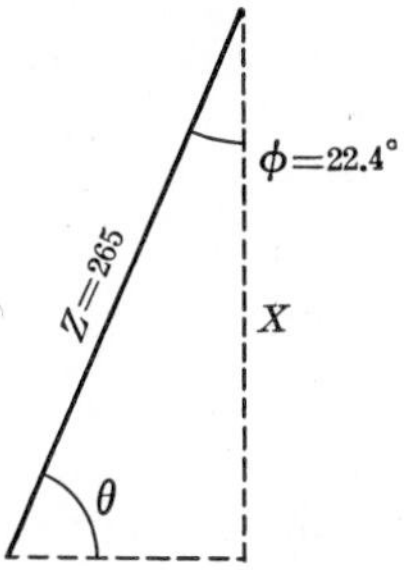   Fig. 25-7.

When θ is found, this triangle is solved by the methods used in Example 1. Hence,

$$R = Z \cos \theta = 265 \cos 67.6° = 265 \times 0.381 = 101$$
$$X = Z \sin \theta = 265 \sin 67.6° = 265 \times 0.924 = 245$$

Check the solution by one of the several methods.

PROBLEMS 25-2

Solve the following right triangles for the unknown elements. Check each by construction and by substituting in a formula not used in the solution.

1. $Z = 42.0$, $\theta = 81.2°$.   2. $Z = 108$, $\theta = 10.9°$.

3. $Z = 1.92$, $\theta = 40.0°$.   4. $Z = 1600$, $\theta = 73.5°$.

5. $Z = 600$, $\theta = 2.3°$.   6. $Z = 350$, $\phi = 66.7°$.

7. $Z = 500$, $\phi = 39.4°$.   8. $Z = 10^4$, $\phi = 51.6°$.

9. $Z = 0.238$, $\phi = 26.1°$.   10. $Z = 73$, $\phi = 3.8°$.

25-5. Given the Hypotenuse and One Other Side.

Example 1.   Given $Z = 38.3$ and $R = 23.1$.   Find X, θ, and ϕ.

Solution: The construction is shown in Fig. 25-8.

An equation containing two known elements and one unknown is

$$\cos \theta = \frac{R}{Z}$$

Substituting the values of R and Z, $\cos \theta = \dfrac{23.1}{38.3} = 0.603$

$$\therefore \theta = 52.9°$$
$$\phi = 90° - \theta$$
$$= 90° - 52.9° = \mathbf{37.1°}$$

Then, since $\sin \theta = \dfrac{X}{Z}$

solving for X, $X = Z \sin \theta$

Substituting the values of Z and $\sin \theta$, $X = 38.3 \times 0.798 = \mathbf{30.5}$

Example 2.   Given $Z = 10.7$ and $X = 8.10$.   Find R. θ, and ϕ.
Solution: The construction is shown in Fig. 25-9.

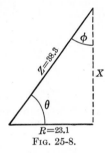

$R=23.1$
Fig. 25-8.

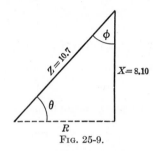

R
Fig. 25-9.

An equation containing two known elements and one unknown **is**

$$\sin \theta = \frac{X}{Z}$$

Substituting the values of X and Z, $\sin \theta = \dfrac{8.10}{10.7} = 0.757$

$$\therefore \theta = 49.2°$$
$$\phi = 90° - \theta$$
$$= 90° - 49.2° = \mathbf{40.8°}$$

Then, since $\cos \theta = \dfrac{R}{Z}$

solving for R, $R = Z \cos \theta$

Substituting the values of Z and $\cos \theta$, $R = 10.7 \times 0.653 = \mathbf{6.99}$

PROBLEMS 25-3

Solve the following right triangles, and check each as in the preceding problems:

1. $Z = 60.0,\ R = 40.0.$ **2.** $Z = 752,\ R = 70.2.$

3. $Z = 15.3,\ R = 2.84.$ **4.** $Z = 22.6,\ R = 8.10.$

5. $Z = 407,\ R = 403.$ **6.** $Z = 96.2,\ X = 24.1.$

7. $Z = 13.9,\ X = 8.50.$ **8.** $Z = 73,\ X = 7.02.$

9. $Z = 500,\ X = 43.3.$ **10.** $Z = 1.02,\ X = 0.994.$

25-6. Given Two Sides Not the Hypotenuse.

Example. Given $R = 76.0$ and $X = 37.4$. Find Z, θ, and ϕ.

Solution: The construction is shown in Fig. 25-10.

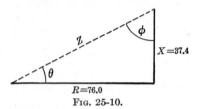

$R = 76.0$
Fig. 25-10.

An equation containing two known elements and one unknown is

$$\tan \theta = \frac{X}{R}$$

Substituting the values of X and R, $\tan \theta = \dfrac{37.4}{76.0} = 0.492$

$$\therefore \theta = 26.2°$$
$$\phi = 90° - \theta$$
$$= 90° - 26.2° = 63.8°$$

$Z = 84.7$ may be found by one of the methods explained in the preceding articles.

PROBLEMS 25-4

Solve the following right triangles, and check each as in the preceding problems:

1. $R = 65.2$, $X = 14.1$.
2. $X = 512$, $R = 106$.
3. $R = 10.9$, $X = 4.65$.
4. $R = 32.3$, $X = 32.3$.
5. $X = 408$, $R = 249$.
6. $X = 10^3$, $R = 162$.
7. $R = 21.7$, $X = 52.0$.
8. $X = 195$, $R = 95.9$.
9. $R = 31.4$, $X = 430$.
10. $X = 600$, $R = 527$.

25-7. Terms Relating to Miscellaneous Trigonometric Problems.

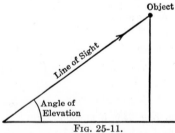

Fig. 25-11.

If an object is higher than an observer's eye, the *angle of elevation* of the object is the angle between the horizontal and the line of sight to the object. This is illustrated in Fig. 25-11.

If an object is lower than an observer's eye, the *angle of depression* of the object is the angle between the horizontal and the line of sight to the object. This is illustrated in Fig. 25-12.

The *horizontal distance* between two points is the distance from one of the two points to a vertical line drawn through the other. Thus, in Fig. 25-13, the line AC is a vertical line through the point A, and CB is a horizontal line through the point B. Then the horizontal distance from A to B is the distance between C and B.

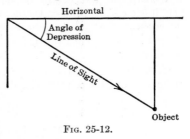

FIG. 25-12.

The *vertical distance* between two points is the distance from one of the two points to the horizontal line drawn through the other. Thus, the vertical distance from A to B, in Fig. 25-13, is the distance between A and C.

Calculations of distance in the vertical plane are made by means of right triangles having horizontal and vertical sides.

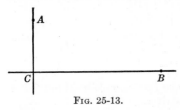

FIG. 25-13.

The horizontal side is usually called the *run;* and the vertical side is called the *rise* or *fall*, as the case may be.

The *slope* or *grade* of a line is the rise or fall divided by the run. Thus if a road rises 5 feet in a run of 100 feet, the grade of the road is $\frac{5}{100} = 0.05 = 5$ per cent.

PROBLEMS 25-5

1. What is the angle of inclination of a stairway with the floor if the steps have a tread of 11 in. and a rise of 6 in.?

2. What angle does a rafter make with the horizontal if it has a rise of 4 ft in a run of 6 ft?

3. A road rises 350 ft in a run of 2500 ft. What is the percentage of grade? What is the angle of inclination of the roadbed with the horizontal?

4. A radio tower cast a shadow 473 ft long. At the same time the angle of elevation of the sun was observed to be 32.4°. What is the height of the tower?

5. A radio tower 600 ft high cast a shadow 262 ft long. What was the angle of elevation of the sun at this time?

6. At a horizontal distance of 125 ft from the foot of a radio tower, the angle of elevation to the top is found to be 62°. How high is the tower?

7. A telephone pole 40 ft high is to be guyed from its middle, and the guy is to make an angle of 45° with the ground. Allowing 2 ft extra for splicing, how long must the guy wire be?

8. A ladder 35 ft in length rests against a vertical wall. The foot of the ladder is 10 ft from the wall. How far up the wall does the ladder reach? What angle does the ladder make with the ground?

9. A ladder 50 ft long can be placed so that it will reach a point on a wall 42 ft above the ground. By tipping the ladder back without moving its foot, it will reach a point on another wall 32 ft above the ground. What is the horizontal distance between the walls?

10. From the top of a cliff 426 ft high the angle of depression of a ship is observed to be 18.2°. How far out is the ship?

11. In order to find the width *BC* of a river, a distance *AB* was laid off along the bank, the point *B* being directly opposite a tree *C* on the opposite

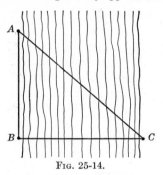

Fig. 25-14.

side, as shown in Fig. 25-14. If the angle *BAC* was observed to be 51.6° and *AB* was 325 ft, find the width of the river.

12. In order to measure the distance *AC* across a pond, a surveyor lays off a line *AB* such that the angle *BAC* = 90°, as shown in Fig. 25-15. At

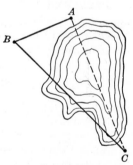

Fig. 25-15.

point *B*, 500 ft from *A*, he observes that angle *ABC* = 68.2°. Find the distance *AC*.

CHAPTER XXVI

PERIODIC FUNCTIONS

In Art. 23-11, it was shown that the trigonometric functions could be represented by the ratios of lengths of certain lines to the unit radius vector. Also, in Art. 23-12, the variation of the functions was represented by lines.

The complete variation of the functions is more clearly illustrated and better understood by plotting their continuous values on rectangular coordinates.

26-1. The Graph of the Sine Curve, $y = \sin x$. The equation $y = \sin x$ may be plotted just as the graphs of algebraic equations are plotted, that is, by assigning values to the angle x (the independent variable), computing the corresponding value of y (the dependent variable), plotting the points whose coordinates are thus obtained, and drawing a smooth curve through the points. This is the same procedure as that used for plotting linear equations in Chap. XV and for plotting quadratic equations in Chap. XVIII.

The first questions that come to mind in preparing to graph this equation are, "What values shall be assigned to x? Shall they be in radians or degrees?" Either might be used, but it is more reasonable to use radians. In Art. 22-5, it was shown that an angle measured in radians may be represented by the arc intercepted by this angle on the circumference of a circle of unit radius. Since, as previously mentioned, the functions of an angle may be represented by suitable lengths of lines, it follows that if an angle is expressed in radian measure both the angle and its functions can be expressed in terms of a common unit of length. Therefore, we shall select a suitable unit of length and plot both x and y values in terms of this unit. Then to graph the equation $y = \sin x$, the procedure is as follows:

1. Assign values to x.

2. From the slide rule or the tables, determine the corresponding values of y.

3. Take each pair of values of x and y as coordinates of a point, and plot the point.

4. Draw a smooth curve through the points.

x, degrees	x, radians (π-measure)	x, radians (unit measure)	y (sin x)	Point
0	0	0	0	$P_0 = (0, 0)$
30	$\dfrac{\pi}{6}$	0.52	0.50	$P_1 = (0.52, 0.50)$
60	$\dfrac{\pi}{3}$	1.05	0.87	$P_2 = (1.05, 0.87)$
90	$\dfrac{\pi}{2}$	1.57	1.00	$P_3 = (1.57, 1.00)$
120	$\dfrac{2\pi}{3}$	2.09	0.87	$P_4 = (2.09, 0.87)$
150	$\dfrac{5\pi}{6}$	2.62	0.50	$P_5 = (2.62, 0.50)$
180	π	3.14	0	$P_6 = (3.14, 0)$

It is not necessary to tabulate values of sin x between π radians and 2π radians (180° to 360°), for these values are negative but

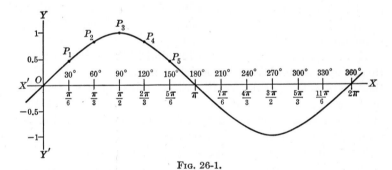

Fig. 26-1.

equal in magnitude to the sines of the angles between 0 radians and π radians (0° to 180°). The curve should be plotted with the angle and the function having the same unit or scale; that is, one unit on the Y axis should be the same length as that representing 1 radian on the X axis. When the curve is so plotted, it is called a *proper sine curve*, as shown in Fig. 26-1. This wave-shaped curve is called the *sine curve* or *sinusoid*.

If additional values of x are chosen, both positive and negative, the curve continues indefinitely in both directions, repeating in value. Notice that, as x increases from 0 to $\frac{\pi}{2}$, sin x increases from 0 to 1; as x increases from $\frac{\pi}{2}$ to π, sin x decreases from 1 to 0; as x increases from π to $\frac{3\pi}{2}$, sin x decreases from 0 to -1; and as x increases from $\frac{3\pi}{2}$ to 2π, sin x increases from -1 to 0.   Thus the curve repeats itself for every multiple of 2π radians.

26-2. The Graph of the Cosine Curve $y = \cos x$. By following the procedure for plotting the sine curve, it is easily shown that the graph of $y = \cos x$ appears as shown in Fig. 26-2.

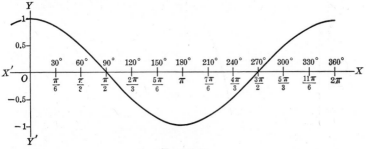

FIG. 26-2.

Note that, as x increases from 0 to $\frac{\pi}{2}$, cos x decreases from 1 to 0; as x increases from $\frac{\pi}{2}$ to π, cos x decreases from 0 to -1; as x increases from π to $\frac{3\pi}{2}$, cos x increases from -1 to 0; and as x increases from $\frac{3\pi}{2}$ to 2π, cos x increases from 0 to 1.   If additional values of x are chosen, both positive and negative, the curve will repeat itself indefinitely in both directions. The cosine curve is identical in shape with the sine curve except that there is a difference of 90° between corresponding points on the two curves. Another similarity between these curves is that both curves repeat their values for every multiple of 2π radians.

26-3. The Graph of the Tangent Curve $y = \tan x$. The graph of the equation $y = \tan x$, shown in Fig. 26-3, has different characteristics from the sine or cosine curves. The curve slopes upward and to the right. At points where x is an odd multiple of $\frac{\pi}{2}$, the curve is discontinuous. This is to be expected from the discussion of the tangent function in Art. 23-12.

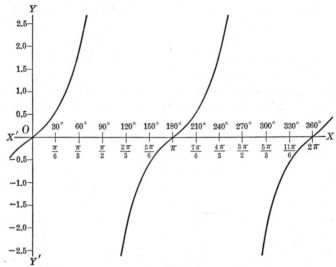

Fig. 26-3.

The tangent curve repeats itself at intervals of π radians and is thus seen to be a series of separate curves, or branches, rather than a continuous curve.

PROBLEMS 26-1

1. Plot the equation $y = \sin x$ from -2π radians to 2π radians.

2. Plot the equation $y = \cos x$ from -2π radians to 2π radians.

3. Plot the equation $y = \cot x$ from 0 radians to 2π radians.

4. Plot the equation $y = \sec x$ from 0 radians to 2π radians.

5. Plot the equation $y = \csc x$ from 0 radians to 2π radians.

6. Plot the equation $y = \sin^2 x$ and $y = \cos^2 x$ on the same coordinates and to the same scale. In computing points, remember that when a negative number is squared the result is positive. Add the respective ordinates of the curves for several different values of angle, and plot the results. What conclusion do you draw from these results?

26-4. Periodicity. From the graphs plotted in the preceding figures and from earlier considerations of the trigonometric functions, it is evident that each trigonometric function repeats itself exactly in the same order and at regular intervals.   A function that repeats itself periodically is called a *periodic function*. From this definition, it is apparent that the trigonometric functions are periodic functions.

Owing to the fact that many natural phenomena are periodic in character, the sine and cosine curves lend themselves ideally to graphical representation and mathematical analysis of these recurrent motions.   For example, the rise and fall of tides, motions of certain machines, the vibrations of a pendulum, the rhythm of our bodily life, sound waves, and water waves are all familiar happenings that may be represented and analyzed by the use of these curves.   An alternating current follows these variations, as will be shown in Chap. XXVIII, and it is because of this fact that we must have a good grounding in trigonometry. It is essential that the student understand the mathematical expressions for various periodic functions and especially their applications to alternating-current circuits.

The tangent, cotangent, secant, and cosecant curves are not used to represent recurrent happenings; for although these curves are periodic, they are discontinuous for certain values of angles.

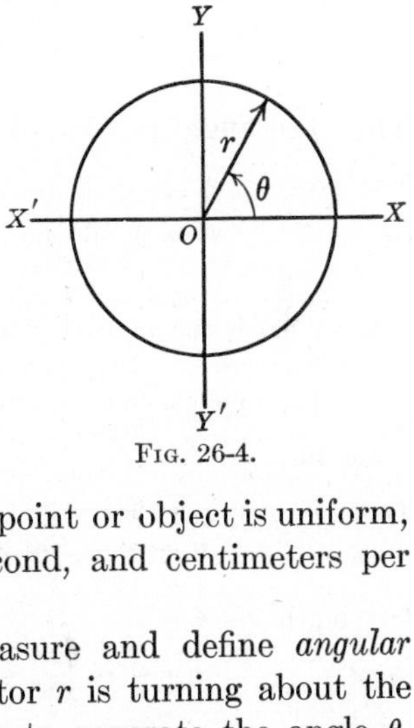

26-5. Angular Motion.   The *linear velocity* of a point or object moving in a particular direction is the rate at which distance is traveled by the point or object.   The unit of velocity is the distance traveled

Fig. 26-4.

in unit time when the motion of the point or object is uniform, such as miles per hour, feet per second, and centimeters per second.

The same concept is used to measure and define *angular velocity*.   In Fig. 26-4 the radius vector r is turning about the origin in a counterclockwise direction to generate the angle θ. The *angular velocity* of such a rotating line is the rate at which an angle is generated by rotation.   When the rotation is uniform, the unit of angular velocity is the angle generated per unit of time.   Thus, angular velocity is measured in degrees per second or radians per second, the latter being the more widely used.

Angular velocity may be expressed in terms of revolutions per minute (r.p.m.) or revolutions per second (r.p.s.). For example, if f is the number of revolutions per second of the vector of Fig. 26-4, then $2\pi f$ is the number of radians generated per second. The angular velocity in radians per second is denoted by ω (Greek letter omega). Thus, if the radius vector is rotating f revolutions per second,

$$\omega = 2\pi f \text{ radians per second}$$

If the armature of a generator is rotating at 1800 revolutions per minute, which is 30 revolutions per second, it has an angular velocity of

$$\omega = 2\pi f = 2\pi \times 30 = 188.4 \text{ radians per second}$$

The total angle θ generated by a rotating line in t seconds at an angular velocity of ω radians per second is

$$\theta = \omega t$$

Thus the angle generated by the armature in 0.01 second is

$$\theta = \omega t = 188.4 \times 0.01 = 1.884 \text{ radians}$$
or $\qquad \theta = 1.884 \times 57.3° = 108°$

Example. A flywheel has a velocity of 300 revolutions per minute.
(a) What is the angular velocity?
(b) What angle will be generated in 0.2 second?
(c) How much time is required for the wheel to generate 628 radians?

Solution: (a) $f = \dfrac{300 \text{ r.p.m.}}{60} = 5$ r.p.s.

Then, $\qquad \omega = 2\pi f = 2\pi \times 5 = 10\pi$, or 31.4 radians per second
(b) $\qquad \theta = \omega t = 10\pi \times 0.2 = 2\pi$ radians
$\qquad\qquad \theta = 360°$
(c) Since $\quad \theta = \omega t$
then $\qquad t = \dfrac{\theta}{\omega} = \dfrac{628}{10\pi} = 20$ sec

PROBLEMS 26-2

1. What is the angular velocity in terms of π radians per second of

    (a) The hour hand of a clock?
    (b) The minute hand of a clock?
    (c) The second hand of a clock?

2. Express the angular velocity of 6 r.p.s. in

(*a*) Radians per second.
(*b*) Degrees per second.

3. A revolution counter on an armature shaft recorded 750 revolutions in 30 sec. What is the angular velocity of the armature in radians per second?

4. The radius vector r of Fig. 26-4 is rotating at the rate of 3600 r.p.m. What is the value of θ in radians at the end of

(*a*) 0.001 sec?
(*b*) 0.005 sec?
(*c*) 0.3 sec?

5. If the radius vector r of Fig. 26-4 is rotating at the rate of 1 r.p.s., what is the value of sin ωt at the end of

(*a*) 0.10 sec?
(*b*) 0.30 sec?
(*c*) 0.65 sec?
(*d*) 0.80 sec?

26-6. Projection of a Point Having Uniform Circular Motion.

In Fig. 26-5 the radius vector r rotates about a point in a counter-

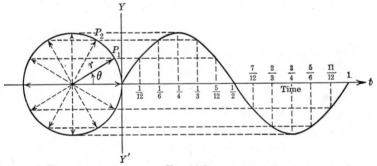

FIG. 26-5.

clockwise direction with a uniform angular velocity of 1 revolution per second. Then every point on the radius vector, such as the end point P, rotates with uniform angular velocity. If the radius vector starts from 0°, at the end of $\frac{1}{12}$ second it will have rotated 30°, or 0.5236 radian, to P_1; at the end of $\frac{1}{6}$ second, it will have rotated to P_2 and generated an angle of 60°, or 1.047 radians, etc.

The projection of the end point of the radius vector, that is, its ordinate value at any time, may be plotted as a curve. This is accomplished by extending the horizontal diameter of the circle to the right for use as an X axis along which time is to be plotted. Choosing a convenient length along the X axis, divide it into as many intervals as there are angle values to be plotted. In Fig. 26-5, projections have been made every 30°, starting from 0°. Therefore the X axis is divided into 12 divisions; and since one complete revolution takes place in 1 second, each division on the time axis will represent $\frac{1}{12}$ second, or 30° rotation.

Through the points of division on the time axis (X axis), construct vertical lines; and through the corresponding points, made by the end point of the radius vector at that particular time, draw lines parallel to the time axis. Draw a smooth curve through the points of intersection. Thus the resulting sine curve traces the ordinate of the end point of the radius vector for any time t, and from it we could obtain the sine value for any angle generated by the radius vector.

As the vector continues to rotate, successive revolutions will generate repeating, or periodic, curves.

Since the y value of the curve is proportional to the sine of the generated angle and the length of the radius vector, we have

$$y = r \sin \theta$$

Then, since the radius vector rotates through 2π radians in 1 second, the y value at any time t is

$$y = r \sin 2\pi t$$
or $$y = r \sin 6.28t$$

which is the equation of the sine curve of Fig. 26-5.

From the foregoing considerations, it is apparent that if a straight line of length r rotates about a point with a uniform angular velocity of ω radians per unit time, starting from a horizontal position when the time $t = 0$, the projection y of the end point upon a vertical straight line will have a motion that may be represented by the relation

$$y = r \sin \omega t \tag{1}$$

This equation is of fundamental importance in describing the motion of any object or quantity that varies periodically, or with simple harmonic motion. Thus the value of an alternating electromotive force at any instant may be completely described in terms of such an equation as will be shown in Chap. XXVIII. Any motion that can be described by this equation, that is, if the motion or variation may be represented by a sine curve, is said to be *sinusoidal* or to vary *sinusoidally*.

Example. A crank 6 inches long, starting from 0°, turns in a counter-clockwise direction at the rate of 1 revolution in 10 seconds.

(a) What is the equation for the projection of the crank handle upon a vertical line at any instant? That is, what is the vertical distance from the crankshaft at any time?

(b) What is the vertical distance from the handle to the shaft at the end of 3 seconds?

(c) At the end of 8 seconds?

Solution: (a) The general equation for the projection of the end point on a vertical line is

$$y = r \sin \omega t \qquad (1)$$

where r = length of the rotating object,

ω = angular velocity in radians per second,

t = time in seconds at any instant.

Then, since the crank makes 1 revolution, or 2π radians, in 10 seconds, the angular velocity is

$$\omega = \frac{2\pi}{10} = \frac{\pi}{5} \text{ or } 0.628 \text{ radians per second}$$

Substituting the values of r and ω in Eq. (1),

$$y = 6 \sin 0.628t \text{ in.}$$

(b) At the end of 3 seconds the crank will have turned through

$$0.628 \times 3 = 1.88 \text{ radians}$$

which is $1.88 \times 57.3° = 108°$. Substituting this value for $0.628t$ in Eq. (1) results in

$$y = 6 \sin 108°$$
$$= 6 \times 0.951 = 5.71 \text{ in.}$$

which is the vertical distance of the handle from the shaft at the end of 3 seconds.

(c) At the end of 8 seconds the crank will have turned through

$$0.628 \times 8 = 5.02 \text{ radians}$$

which is $5.02 \times 57.3° = 288°$. Substituting this value for $0.628t$ in the above equation results in

$$y = 6 \sin 288°$$
$$= 6 \times (-0.951) = -5.71 \text{ in.}$$

which is the vertical distance of the handle from the shaft at the end of 8 seconds. The negative sign denotes that the handle is *below* the shaft; that is, the distance is measured downward, whereas the distance in (b) above was taken as positive, or *above* the shaft.

If it is desired to express the projection of the end point of the radius vector upon the horizontal, the relation is

$$y = r \cos \omega t \tag{2}$$

which, when plotted, results in a cosine curve. Thus, in the foregoing example, the horizontal distance (Art. 25-7) between the handle and shaft at the end of 8 seconds will be

$$y = 6 \cos 288°$$
$$= 6 \times 0.309 = 1.85 \text{ in.}$$

26-7. Amplitude. The graphs of Fig. 26-1, Fig. 26-2, and Fig. 26-5 have an equal amplitude of 1, that is, an equal vertical displacement from the horizontal axis. The value of the radius vector r determines the amplitude of a general curve, and for this reason the factor r in the general equation

$$y = r \sin \omega t$$

is called the *amplitude factor*. Thus the amplitude of a periodic curve is taken as the maximum displacement, or value, of the

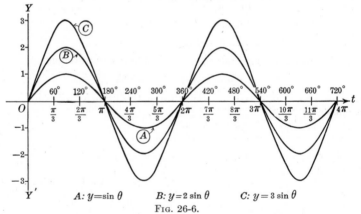

A: $y = \sin \theta$ B: $y = 2 \sin \theta$ C: $y = 3 \sin \theta$
Fig. 26-6.

curve. It is apparent that, if the length of the radius vector which generates a sine wave is varied, the amplitude of the sine wave will be varied accordingly. This is illustrated in Fig. 26-6.

26-8. Frequency. When the radius vector makes one complete revolution, regardless of its starting point, it has generated one complete sine wave; hence, we say the sine wave has gone through one complete *cycle*. Thus the number of cycles occurring in a periodic curve in a unit of time is called the *frequency* of the curve. For example, if the radius vector rotated 5 revolutions per second, the curve describing its motion would go through 5 cycles in 1 second of time. The frequency f in cycles per second is obtained by dividing the angular velocity ω by 360° when the latter is measured in degrees or by 2π when measured in radians. That is,

$$f = \frac{\omega}{2\pi} \sim$$

Curves for different frequencies are shown in Fig. 26-7.

In the equation $y = r \sin \frac{1}{2}t$, since $\omega t = \frac{1}{2}t$, the angular velocity ω is $\frac{1}{2}$ radian per second. That is, at the end of 2π, or 6.28, seconds the curve has gone through one-half cycle, or 3.14 radians of angle, as shown in Fig. 26-7.

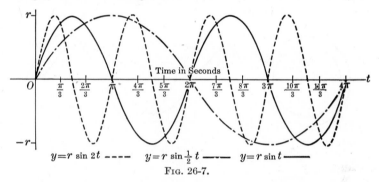

$$y = r \sin 2t \text{ ----} \qquad y = r \sin \frac{1}{2} t \text{ ---} \qquad y = r \sin t \text{ ---}$$

FIG. 26-7.

In the equation $y = r \sin t$, since $\omega t = t$, the angular velocity ω is 1 radian per second. Thus at the end of 2π seconds the curve has gone through one complete cycle, or 2π radians of angle.

Similarly, in the equation $y = r \sin 2t$, the angular velocity ω is 2 radians per second. Then at the end of 2π seconds the curve has completed two cycles, or 4π radians of angle.

26-9. Period. The time T required for a periodic function, or curve, to complete one cycle is called the *period*. Hence if the frequency f is given by

$$f = \frac{\omega}{2\pi} \sim$$

it follows that

$$T = \frac{2\pi}{\omega} = \frac{1}{f} \text{ sec.}$$

For example, if a curve repeats itself 60 times in 1 second, it has a frequency of 60 cycles per second and a period of

$$T = \tfrac{1}{60} = 0.0167 \text{ sec.}$$

Similarly, in Fig. 26-7, the curve represented by $y = r \sin \tfrac{1}{2}t$ has a frequency of $\dfrac{\omega}{2\pi} = \dfrac{0.5}{2\pi} = 0.0796$ cycle per second and a period of 12.6 seconds. The curve of $y = r \sin t$ has a frequency of $\dfrac{\omega}{2\pi} = \dfrac{1}{2\pi} = 0.159$ cycle per second and a period of 6.28 seconds. The curve of $y = r \sin 2t$ has a frequency of 0.318 cycle per second and a period of 3.14 seconds.

26-10. Phase. In Fig. 26-8, two radius vectors are rotating about a point with equal angular velocities of ω and separated

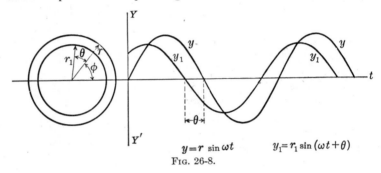

$$y = r \sin \omega t \qquad y_1 = r_1 \sin (\omega t + \theta)$$
Fig. 26-8.

by the constant angle θ. That is, if r starts from the horizontal axis, then r_1 starts ahead of r by the angle θ and maintains this angular difference.

When $t = 0$, r starts from the horizontal axis to generate the curve $y = r \sin \omega t$. At the same time, r_1 is ahead of r by an angle θ; hence, r_1 generates the curve $y_1 = r_1 \sin (\omega t + \theta)$. It will be noted that this *displaces* the y_1 curve along the horizontal by an angle θ as shown in the figure.

The angular difference θ between the two curves is called the *phase angle;* and since y_1 is *ahead* of y, we say that y_1 leads y. Thus, in the equation $y_1 = r_1 \sin (\omega t + \theta)$, θ is called the *angle of lead.* In Fig. 26-8, y_1 leads y by 30°; therefore the equation for y_1 becomes

$$y_1 = r_1 \sin (\omega t + 30°)$$

In Fig. 26-9, the radius vectors r and r_1 are rotating about a point with equal angular velocities of ω, except that now r_1 is *behind* r by a constant angle θ. The phase angle between the two curves is θ; but, in this case, y_1 lags y. Hence the equation for the curve generated by r_1 is

$$y_1 = r_1 \sin (\omega t - \theta)$$

In Fig. 26-9, the *angle of lag* is $\theta = 60°$; therefore, the equation for y_1 becomes

$$y_1 = r_1 \sin (\omega t - 60°)$$

26-11. Summary. The general equation

$$y = r \sin (\omega t \pm \theta) \tag{3}$$

describes a periodic event, and its graph results in a periodic curve. By choosing the proper values for the three arbitrary constants r,

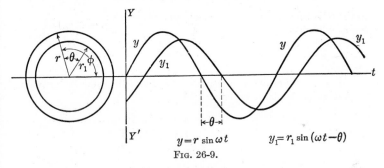

$$y = r \sin \omega t \qquad y_1 = r_1 \sin (\omega t - \theta)$$
Fig. 26-9.

ω, and θ, we can describe or plot any periodic sequence of events because a change in any one of these will change the curve accordingly. Hence,

1. If r is changed, the *amplitude* of the curve will be changed proportionally. For this reason, r is called the *amplitude factor*.

2. If ω is changed, the *frequency*, or period, of the curve will be changed. Thus, ω is called the *frequency factor*.

3. If θ is changed, the curve is moved along the time axis with no other change. Thus, if θ is made larger, the curve is displaced to the left and results in a leading phase angle. If θ is made smaller, the curve is moved to the right and results in a lagging phase angle. Hence the angle θ in the general equation is called the *phase angle* or the *angle of lead or lag*.

Example. Discuss the equation $y = 147 \sin (377t + 30°)$.

Solution: Given $y = 147 \sin (377t + 30°)$.

Comparing the given equation with the general equation, it is seen that $r = 147$, $\omega = 377$ radians per second, and $\theta = 30°$. Therefore the curve represented by this equation is a sine curve with an amplitude of 147. The angular velocity is 377 radians per second; hence the frequency is

$$f = \frac{\omega}{2\pi} = \frac{377}{2\pi} = 60 \sim$$

The period is $\qquad T = \dfrac{1}{f} = \dfrac{1}{60} = 0.0167 \text{ sec}$

The curve has been displaced to the left 30°; that is, it leads the curve $y = r \sin 377t$ by a phase angle of 30°. Therefore, when $t = 0$, the curve begins at an angle of 30° with a value of

$$\begin{aligned} y &= 147 \sin (\omega t + 30°) \\ &= 147 \sin (0° + 30°) \\ &= 147 \times 0.5 = 73.5 \end{aligned}$$

PROBLEMS 26-3

In the following equations of periodic curves, specify:

(*a*) Amplitude.
(*b*) Angular velocity.
(*c*) Frequency.
(*d*) Period.
(*e*) Angle of lead or lag with respect to a curve of the same frequency but having no displacement angle.

1. $y = 25 \sin (2\pi t + 30°)$.   **2.** $y = 32 \sin (37.7t - 10°)$.

3. $e = 325 \sin (314t - 18°)$.   **4.** $e = E_m \sin (157t + 17°)$.

$\qquad$ **5.** $i = I_m \sin (6.28 \times 10^3 - 90°)$.

Plot the curves that represent the following motions:

6. $y = \sin 2\pi t$.   **7.** $y = 5 \sin 15t$.

8. $y = 16 \sin 120t$.   **9.** $y = 8 \sin^° (120t + 30°)$.

$\qquad$ **10.** $y = 32 \sin (120t - 30°)$.

11. A crank 10 in. long starts from a horizontal position (0°) and turns in a counterclockwise (positive) direction in a vertical plane at the rate of 6 r.p.s.

(*a*) Plot the curve that shows the projection of the handle upon a vertical line at any time.
(*b*) Write the equation of the curve.
(*c*) What is the distance of the handle from the horizontal at the end of 0.1 sec?
(*d*) What is the horizontal distance from the handle to the shaft at the end of 0.06 sec?
(*e*) Through how many radians will the crank turn in 0.45 sec?

12. A crank 12 in. long starts from a position of 23° with the horizontal and turns in a positive direction at the rate of 14 r.p.s.

(a) Plot the curve that shows the projection of the handle upon a vertical line at any time.

(b) Write the equation of the curve.

(c) What is the height of the handle above the horizontal at the end of 0.714 sec?

(d) What is the horizontal distance from the handle to the shaft at the end of 0.5 sec?

(e) Through how many radians will the crank turn in 3 sec?

CHAPTER XXVII

ELEMENTARY PLANE VECTORS

Many physical quantities can be expressed by specifying a certain number of units. For example, the volume of a tank may be expressed as so many cubic feet, the temperature of a room is expressed as a certain number of degrees, the speed of a moving object may be expressed by a number of linear units per unit of time such as miles per hour and feet per second. Such quantities are *scalar quantities*, and the numbers that represent them are called *scalars*. A scalar quantity is one having only magnitude; that is, it is a quantity fully described by a number, but it does not involve any concept of direction.

27-1. Definitions. Many other types of physical quantities need to be expressed more definitely than is possible by specifying magnitude alone. For example, the velocity of a moving object has a direction as well as a magnitude. Also, a force due to a push or a pull is not completely described unless the direction as well as the magnitude of the force is given. In addition, the entire system of electric-circuit analysis is built up around the idea of expressing the directions and magnitudes of voltages and currents. Those quantities which have both magnitude and direction are called *vector quantities*. A vector quantity is conveniently represented by a directed straight-line segment called a *vector*, whose length is proportional to the magnitude and whose head points in the direction of the vector quantity.

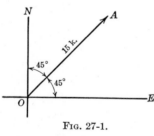

FIG. 27-1.

Example 1. If a vessel steams northeast at a speed of 15 knots, its speed can be represented by a line whose length represents 15 knots, to some convenient scale, as shown in Fig. 27-1. The direction of the line represents the direction in which the vessel is traveling. Thus the line OA is a vector that completely describes the velocity of the vessel.

396

Example 2.   In Fig. 27-2, the vector OA represents a force of 80 pounds pulling on a body at O in a direction of 60°.   The vector OB represents a force of 40 pounds acting on the same body in a direction of 310° or −50°.

Two vectors are equal if they have the same magnitude and direction.   Thus, in Fig. 27-3, vectors, A, B, and C are equal.

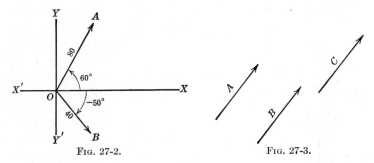

FIG. 27-2.   FIG. 27-3.

27-2. Notation.   As the student progresses in the study of vectors, it will be found that vectors and scalars satisfy different algebraic laws.   For example, a scalar when reduced to its simplest terms is simply a number and as such obeys all the laws of ordinary algebraic operations.   Since a vector involves direction, in addition to magnitude, it does not obey the usual algebraic laws and therefore has an analysis peculiar to itself.

From the foregoing, it is apparent that it is desirable to have a notation that indicates clearly which quantities are scalars and which are vectors.   Several methods of notation are used, but the student will find little cause for confusion, for most authors specify and explain their particular system of notation.

A vector may be denoted by two letters, the first indicating the origin, or initial point, and the second indicating the head, or terminal point.   This form of notation was used in Examples 1 and 2 of the preceding article.   Sometimes a small arrow is placed over these letters to emphasize that the quantity considered is a vector.   Thus, $\overrightarrow{OA}$ could be used to represent the vector from O to A as in Fig. 27-2.   In several texts, vectors are indicated by boldface type; thus, **A** denotes the vector A.   Other common forms of specifying a vector quantity, as, for example, the vector A, are $\bar{A}$, $\dot{A}$, and $\underline{A}$.

27-3. Addition of Vectors.   Scalar quantities are added algebraically.

Thus   20 cents + 8 cents = 28 cents
and   16 insulators − 7 insulators =   9 insulators

Since vector quantities involve direction as well as magnitude, they cannot be added algebraically unless their directions are parallel. Figure 27-4 illustrates vectors OA and AB. Vector OA may be considered as a motion from O to A, and vector AB as a motion from A to B. Then the sum of the vectors represents the sum of the motions from O to A and from A to B which is the motion from O to B. This sum is the vector OB; that is, the *vector sum* of OA and AB is OB. Thus, the sum of two vectors is the vector joining the initial point of the first to the terminal

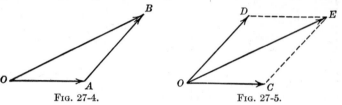

FIG. 27-4.   FIG. 27-5.

point of the second, if the initial point of the second vector is joined to the terminal point of the first vector as shown in Fig. 27-4.

In Fig. 27-5, vectors OC and OD are equal to vectors OA and AB, respectively, of Fig. 27-4. In Fig. 27-5, however, the vectors start from the same origin. That their sum may be represented by the diagonal of a parallelogram of which the vectors are adjacent sides is evident by comparing Figs. 27-4 and 27-5. This is known as the *parallelogram law* for the composition of forces and holds for the composition or addition of all vector quantities.

The addition of vectors that are not at right angles to each other will be considered from a mathematical viewpoint in a later chapter. At this time, it is sufficient to know that two forces acting simultaneously on a point, or an object, may be replaced by a single force called the *resultant*. That is, the resultant force will produce the same effect on the object as the joint action of the two forces. Thus, in Fig. 27-4, the vector OB is the resultant of vectors OA and AB. Similarly, in Fig. 27-5, the vector OE is the resultant of the vectors OC and OD. Note that $OB = OE$.

Example. Three forces, A, B, and C are acting on point O as shown in Fig. 27-6. Force A exerts 150 pounds at an angle of 60°, B exerts 100 pounds at an angle of 135°, and C exerts 150 pounds at an angle of 260°. What is the resultant force on point O?

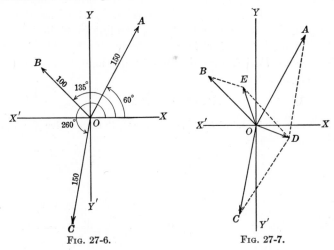

FIG. 27-6.   FIG. 27-7.

Solution: The resultant of vectors A, B, and C can be found graphically by two methods.

(*a*) First draw the vectors to scale. Find the resultant of any two vectors, such as OA and OC, by constructing a parallelogram with OA and OC as adjacent sides. Then the resultant of OA and OC will be the diagonal OD of the parallelogram $OADC$ as shown in Fig. 27-7. In effect, there are now but two forces, OB and OD, acting on point O. The resultant of these two forces is found as before by constructing a parallelogram with OB and OD as adjacent sides. The resultant force on point O is then the diagonal OE of the parallelogram $OBED$. Upon measuring with scale and protractor, OE is found to be 57 pounds acting at an angle of 112°.

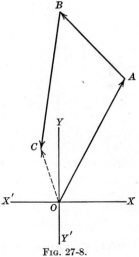

FIG. 27-8.

(*b*) Draw the vectors to scale as shown in Fig. 27-8, joining the initial point of B to the terminal point of A and then joining the initial point of C to the terminal point of B. The vector drawn from the point O to the terminal point of C is the resultant force, and measurements show it to be the same as that found by the method illustrated in Fig. 27-7.

A figure such as $OABCO$, in Fig. 27-8, is called a *polygon of forces*. The vectors may be joined in any order as long as the initial point of one vector joins the terminal point of another vector and the vectors are drawn with the proper magnitude and direction. The length and direction of the line that is necessary to close the polygon, that is, the line from the original initial point to the terminal point of the last vector drawn, constitute a vector that represents the magnitude and the direction of the resultant.

PROBLEMS 27-1

Find the magnitude and direction, with respect to the positive X axis, of the following vectors:

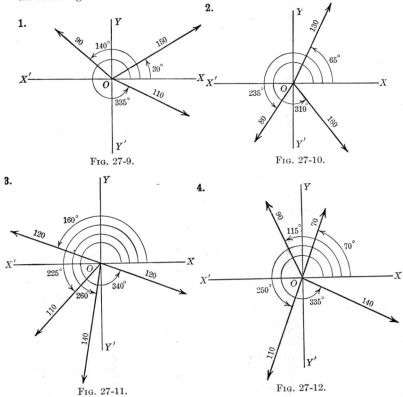

Fig. 27-9.   Fig. 27-10.

Fig. 27-11.   Fig. 27-12.

27-4. Components of a Vector. From what has been considered regarding combining or adding vectors, it follows that a vector may be resolved into components along any two specified directions. For example, in Fig. 27-4, the vectors OA and AB

are components of the vector *OB*.   If the directions of the components are chosen so that they are at right angles to each other, the components are called *rectangular components*.

By placing the initial point of a vector at the origin of the *X* and *Y* axes, the rectangular components are readily obtained either graphically or mathematically.

Example 1.   A vector with a magnitude of 10 makes an angle of 53.1° with the horizontal.   What are the vertical and horizontal components?

Solution: The vector is illustrated in Fig. 27-13 as the directed line segment *OA*, whose length drawn to scale represents the magnitude of 10, and making an angle of 53.1° with the *X* axis.

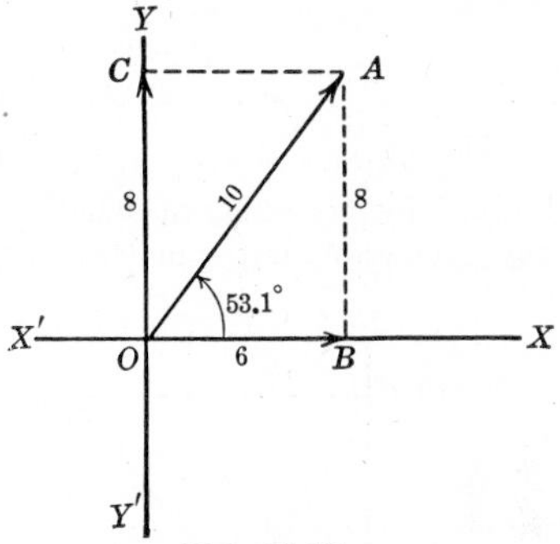

The *horizontal component* of *OA* is the horizontal distance (Art. 25-7) from *O* to *A* and is found graphically by projecting the vector *OA* upon the *X* axis. Thus the vector *OB* is the horizontal component of *OA*.

Fig. 27-13.

The *vertical component* of *OA* is the vertical distance from *O* to *A* and is found graphically by projecting the vector *OA* upon the *Y* axis.   Similarly, the vector *OC* is the vertical component of *OA*.

Finding the horizontal and vertical components of *OA* by mathematical methods is simply a problem in solving a right triangle as outlined in Art. 25-4.   Hence,

$$OB = 10 \cos 53.1° = 6$$

and $\qquad OC = BA = 10 \sin 53.1° = 8$

Check. $\qquad \theta = \text{arc tan } \tfrac{8}{6} = \text{arc tan } 1.33 = \tan 53.1°$

or $\qquad 10^2 = 6^2 + 8^2 = 36 + 64 = 100$

The foregoing may be summarized as follows:

Rule: 1. *The horizontal component of a vector is the projection of the vector upon a horizontal line and equals the magnitude of the vector multiplied by the cosine of the angle made by the vector with the horizontal.*

2. *The vertical component of a vector is the projection of the vector upon a vertical line and equals the magnitude of the vector multiplied by the sine of the angle made by the vector with the horizontal.*

Example 2.   An airplane is flying on a course of 40° at a speed of 250 m.p.h.   How many miles per hour is the plane advancing in a due eastward direction?   In a direction due north?

Solution: Draw the vector diagram as shown in Fig. 27-14. (Courses are measured from the north.) The vector *OB*, which is the horizontal component of *OA*, represents the velocity of the airplane in an eastward direction. The vector *OC*, which is the vertical component of *OA*, represents the velocity of the airplane in a northward direction.

Again, the process of finding the magnitude of *OB* and *OC* resolves into a problem in solving the right triangle *OBA*. Hence,

$$OB = 250 \cos 50° = 161 \text{ m.p.h. eastward}$$
and $$OC = BA = 250 \sin 50° = 192 \text{ m.p.h. northward}$$

If the vector diagram has been drawn to scale, an approximate check can be made by measuring the lengths of *OA* and *OC*. Such a check will disclose any large errors in the mathematical solution.

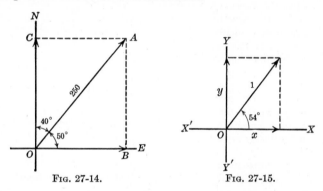

FIG. 27-14.   FIG. 27-15.

Example 3. A radius vector of unit length is rotating about a point with a velocity of 2π radians per second. What are its horizontal and vertical components?

(a) At the end of 0.15 second?

(b) At the end of 0.35 second?

(c) At the end of 0.75 second?

Solution: (a) At the end of 0.15 second the rotating vector will have generated $2\pi \times 0.15 = 0.942$ radians, or $0.942 \times 57.3° = 54°$ as shown in Fig. 27-15. The horizontal component, measured along the *X* axis, is

$$x = 1 \cos 54° = 0.588$$

The vertical component, measured along the *Y* axis, is

$$y = 1 \sin 54° = 0.809$$

Check the solution by measurement or any other method considered convenient.

(b) At the end of 0.35 second the rotating vector will have generated an angle of $2\pi \times 0.35 = 2.20$ radians, or $2.20 \times 57.3° = 126°$ as shown in Fig. 27-16.

The horizontal component, measured along the X axis, is

$$x = 1 \cos 126° = 1(-\cos 54°) = -0.588 \qquad \text{(Art. 24-11)}$$

The vertical component, measured along the Y axis, is

$$y = 1 \sin 126° = 1 \sin 54° = 0.809 \qquad \text{(Art. 24-11)}$$

Check by some convenient method.

(c) At the end of 0.75 second the rotating vector will have generated $2\pi \times 0.75 = 4.71$ radians, or $4.71 \times 57.3° = 270°$ as shown in Fig. 27-17.

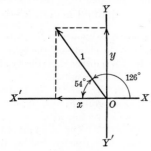

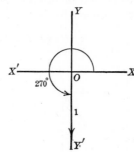

Fɪɢ. 27-16.   Fɪɢ. 27-17.

The horizontal component is

$$x = 1 \cos 270° = 0$$

The vertical component is

$$y = 1 \sin 270° = -1$$

PROBLEMS 27-2

Find the horizontal and vertical components, denoted by h and v, respectively, of the following vectors.   Check the mathematical solution of each by drawing a vector diagram to scale.

1. 15 at 36.9°.
3. 7.15 at 69.1°.
5. 234 at 166.2°.
7. 80.7 at 270°.
9. 364 at 285.1°.

2. 105 at 25.8°.
4. 40.9 at 116.5°.
6. 61.2 at 221.4°.
8. 9.78 at 340.6°.
10. 508 at 180°.

11. A shell is fired at an angle of 45° with a velocity of 2000 ft per second. Find its initial horizontal velocity.

12. The resultant of two forces acting at right angles is a force of 810 lb that makes an angle of 22.5° with one of the forces.   Find the two component forces.

13. A vessel sails 53 miles northwest.   How far west has it moved?

14. Resolve a force of 48 lb into two rectangular components, one of which is 23.2 lb.

15. The resultant of two forces acting at right angles is 139 lb. One of the forces is 64.6 lb. What is the other?

27-5. Vector Addition of Rectangular Components.

If two forces that are at right angles to each other are acting on a body, their resultant may be found by the usual methods of vector addition as outlined in Art. 27-3. However, the resultant may be obtained by geometric or trigonometric methods, for the problem is that of solving for the hypotenuse of a right triangle when the other two sides are given, as outlined in Art. 25-6.

Example. Two vectors are acting on a point. One with a magnitude of 6 is directed along the horizontal to the right of the point, and the other with a magnitude of 8 is directed vertically above the point. Find the resultant.

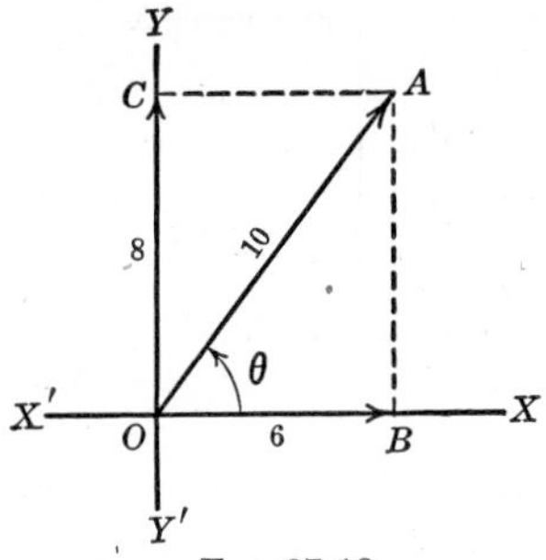

FIG. 27-18.

Solution 1: In Fig. 27-18 the horizontal vector, with a magnitude of 6, is shown as *OB*. The vertical vector, with a magnitude of 8, is shown as *OC*. The resultant of these two vectors may be obtained graphically by completing the parallelogram of forces *OCAB*, as outlined in Art. 27-3. Thus, the magnitude of the resultant will be represented by the length of *OA* in Fig. 27-18. The angle, or direction of the resultant, may be measured with the protractor.

Graphical methods have a limited degree of accuracy, as pointed out in earlier articles. They should be used as an approximate check for more precise mathematical methods.

Solution 2: Since $BA = OC$ in Fig. 27-18, then OBA is a right triangle the hypotenuse of which is the resultant OA. Therefore the magnitude of the resultant is

$$OA = \sqrt{\overline{OB}^2 + \overline{BA}^2} = \sqrt{6^2 + 8^2} = 10$$

The angle, or direction of the resultant, is

$$\theta = \text{arc tan} \frac{BA}{OB} = \frac{8}{6} = 1.33 = \text{arc tan } 53.1°$$

Although the method of Solution 2 is accurate and mathematically correct, there are several operations involved. For example, in finding the magnitude, 6 and 8 must be squared, these squares must be added, and then the square root of this sum must be extracted. This involves four operations.

Solution 3: Since OBA is a right triangle for which OB and BA are given, the hypotenuse (resultant) can be computed as explained in Art. 25-6. Hence,

$$\tan \theta = \frac{BA}{OB} = 1.33$$

$$\therefore \theta = 53.1°$$

Then

$$OA = \frac{OB}{\cos 53.1°} = \frac{6}{0.6} = 10$$

or

$$OA = \frac{BA}{\sin 53.1°} = \frac{8}{0.8} = 10$$

The method of Solution 3 is to be preferred, owing to the minimum number of operations involved; in addition, this is the method used when the slide rule is used for solving the resultant. It is worthy of note that this solution may be completed with a total of three movements on many types of slide rules, and without referring to a table of trigonometric functions.

It should be noted that Example 1 of Art. 27-4 involves the same quantities as those used in the example of this article and that Figs. 27-13 and 27-18 are alike. In the earlier example a vector is given that is resolved into its rectangular components In the example of this article, the same components are given as vectors which are added vectorially to obtain the vector of the first example. From this it is apparent that resolving a vector into its rectangular components and adding vectors that are separated by 90° are inverse operations. Basically, either problem resolves itself into the solution of a right triangle.

PROBLEMS 27-3

Find the resultant forces of the following vectors:

1. 9 at 0° and 5.8 at 90°. **2.** 108 at 0° and 145 at 90°.

3. 44.5 at 90° and 12 at 0°. **4.** 730 at 0° and 234 at 90°.

5. 16.3 at 0° and 8.2 at 0°. **6.** 80.2 at 180° and 21.5 at 90°.

7. 30.6 at 90° and 13.4 at 90°. **8.** 50 at 0° and 42.1 at 270°.

9. 110 at 270° and 32 at 180°. **10.** 201 at 90° and 117 at 180°.

11. 92.6 at 90° and 108 at 270°. **12.** 46.2 at 0°, 71.4 at 90°, and 38 at 0°.

13. 78 at 180°, 49 at 90°, 19.7 at 270°, and 46 at 0°.

14. 89 at 90°, 56 at 180°, 239 at 0°, and 201 at 270°.

15. 13 at 0°, 21 at 90°, 4.8 at 270°, 25 at 90°, 15 at 0°, and 69.2 at 270°.

16. Two forces of 42.1 and 22.5 lb act at right angles to each other. Find the resultant force and the angle between the resultant and the 22.5-lb force

17. An airplane is heading north flying at 220 m.p.h. The wind is blowing from the west with a speed of 35 m.p.h. At the end of 30 min, how much distance has the airplane covered and in what direction is it flying?

18. A river flows at the rate of 4 m.p.h. A man is rowing a boat across the river at the rate of 3.5 m.p.h. What is the speed of the boat? If the river is 2 miles wide, where will the boat land on the opposite bank?

19. A vessel that steams 10 knots in still water steers directly across a river that has a current of 3 knots. Find the actual velocity and direction of the vessel with respect to the current.

20. In preceding Prob. 19, if it is desired to dock the vessel directly across the river from the starting point, in what direction with respect to the current must the ship be steered?

CHAPTER XXVIII

ALTERNATING CURRENTS—FUNDAMENTAL IDEAS

Thus far, we have considered direct voltages and direct currents, that is, voltages that do not change in polarity and currents that do not change in their directions of flow.

In this chapter, we begin the study of mathematics as applied to alternating currents. An *alternating current* is one that alternates, or changes its direction, periodically.

The fact that over 90 per cent of the electrical energy produced is generated in the form of alternating current makes this subject very important to the electrician. The radioman is even more concerned, for the operation of all radio and communication circuits is based on alternating-current phenomena. The first requisite in the study of radio engineering is a solid foundation in the principles of alternating currents.

28-1. Generation of an Alternating Electromotive Force. A coil of wire, with its ends connected to slip rings, rotating in a counterclockwise direction in a uniform magnetic field is illustrated in Fig. 28-1. That an alternating electromotive force will be generated in the coil is apparent from a consideration of generated currents. For example, when the side of the coil *ab* moves from its present position away from the *S* pole, the electromotive force generated in it will be directed from *b* to *a*; that is, *a* will be positive with respect to *b*. At the same time, the side of the coil *cd* is moving away from the *N* pole, thus cutting magnetic lines of force with a motion opposite to that of *ab*. Then the electromotive force generated in *cd* will be directed from *c* to *d* and will add to the electromotive force from *b* to *a* to send a current I_1 through the resistance *R*.

When the coil has rotated 90° from the position shown in Fig. 28-1, the plane of the coil is perpendicular to the magnetic field, and at this instant the sides of the coil are moving parallel to the magnetic field, thus cutting no lines of force. There is no electromotive force generated at this instant.

As the side of the coil *ab* begins to move up toward the *N* pole, the electromotive force generated in it will now be directed from *a* to *b*. Similarly, because the side of the coil *cd* is now moving down toward the *S* pole, the electromotive force in *cd* will be directed from *d* to *c*. This reversal of the direction of generated electromotive force is due to a change of direction of motion with respect to the direction of the lines of force. Therefore, the flow of current I_2 through *R* will be in the direction indicated by the arrow.

When the coil rotates so that the plane of the coil is again

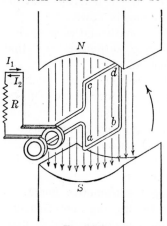

perpendicular to the lines of force (270° from the position shown in Fig. 28-1), no electromotive force will be generated at that instant. Rotation beyond this position, however, causes an electromotive force to be generated such that current flows in the original direction I_1. Such an electromotive force, which periodically reverses its direction, is known as an *alternating electromotive force*, and the resulting current is known as an *alternating current*.

Fig. 28-1.

In some engineering textbooks the generation of an electromotive force is explained as due to the change of magnetic flux through the rotating coil. In the final analysis, the results are the same. Here we are interested mainly in the behavior of the circuits connected to sources of alternating currents.

28-2. Variation of an Alternating Electromotive Force. The first questions that come to mind are, "In what manner does an alternating electromotive force vary? How may we represent that variation graphically?"

Figure 28-2 shows a cross section of the elementary generator of Fig. 28-1. The circles represent either side of the rotating coil at successive instants during the rotation.

When a conductor passes through a magnetic field, there must be a component of its velocity at right angles to the lines of force in order to generate an electromotive force. For example, a

conductor must actually *cut* lines in order to develop an electromotive force the amount of which will be proportional to the
number of lines cut and the rate of cutting.

From studies of rotation and a consideration of Fig. 28-2, it is
evident that the component of horizontal velocity of the rotating
conductor is proportional to the sine of the angle of rotation.
Because the horizontal velocity is perpendicular to the magnetic
field, it is this component that develops an electromotive force.

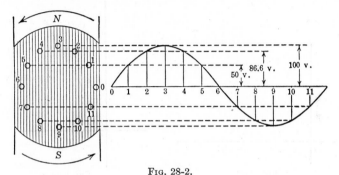

FIG. 28-2.

For example, at position 0, where the angle of rotation is zero,
the conductor is moving parallel to the field; hence, no voltage is
generated. As the conductor rotates toward 90°, the component
of horizontal velocity becomes greater, thus generating a higher
voltage. Therefore, the sine curve of Fig. 28-2 is a graphical
representation of the induced electromotive force in a conductor
rotating in a uniform magnetic field. The voltage starts from
zero, increases in a positive direction to a maximum value
(100 volts in the figure) at 90°, decreases to zero at 180°, increases
in the opposite or negative direction until it attains maximum
negative value at 270°, and finally decreases to zero value again
at 360°. It follows, then, that the induced electromotive force
may be completely described by the relation

$$e = E_m \sin \theta \qquad (1)$$

where e = instantaneous value of electromotive force at any
angle θ,

E_m = maximum value of electromotive force,

θ = angular position of coil.

28-3. Vector Representation. Since the sine wave of electromotive force is a periodic function, a simpler method of representing the relation of the electromotive force induced in a coil to the angle of rotation is available. The rotating conductor may be replaced by a rotating radius vector whose length represents the magnitude of the maximum generated voltage E_m. Then the instantaneous value for any position of the conductor

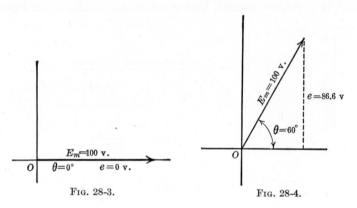

Fig. 28-3.   Fig. 28-4.

may be represented by the vertical component of the vector (Art. 27-4).

In Fig. 28-3, which is the vector diagram for the conductor at position 0 in Fig. 28-2, the vector E_m is at 0° position and therefore has no vertical component. Thus the value of the electromotive force in this position is zero. Or, since

$$e = E_m \sin \theta,$$

by substituting the values of E_m and θ, $e = 100 \sin 0°$.

$$e = 0.$$

In Fig. 28-4, which is the vector diagram for the conductor at position 2 in Fig. 28-2, the coil has moved 60° from the zero position. The vector E_m is therefore at an angle of 60° from the reference axis, and the instantaneous value of the induced electromotive force is represented by the vertical component of E_m. Then, since

$$e = E_m \sin \theta,$$

by substituting the values of E_m and θ, $e = 100 \sin 60°$.

$$e = 86.6 \text{ v}.$$

Example 1.   What is the instantaneous value of an alternating electro-motive force when it has reached 58° of its cycle?   The maximum value is 500 volts.

Solution: Draw the vector diagram to scale as shown in Fig. 28-5.   The instantaneous value is the vertical component of the vector E_m.   Then, since

$$e = E_m \sin \theta,$$

by substituting the values of E_m and θ, $e = 500 \sin 58°.$

$$e = 424 \text{ v.}$$

Example 2.   What is the instantaneous value of an alternating electro-motive force when it has reached 216° of its cycle?   The maximum value is 163 volts.

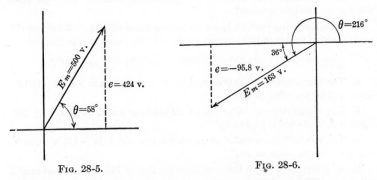

FIG. 28-5.   FIG. 28-6.

Solution: Draw the vector diagram to scale as shown in Fig. 28-6.   The instantaneous value is the vertical component of the vector E_m.   Then, since

$$e = E_m \sin \theta,$$

by substituting the values of E_m and θ, $e = 163 \sin 216°.$

$$e = 163[- \sin (216° - 180°)]$$
$$= 163(- \sin 36°).$$
$$e = -95.8 \text{ v.}$$

A vector diagram drawn to scale should be made for every alternating-current problem.   This gives the student a better insight into the functioning of alternating currents and at the same time serves as a good check on the mathematical solution.

Since the current in a circuit is proportional to the applied voltage, it follows that an alternating electromotive force which varies periodically will produce a current of similar variation. Hence the instantaneous current of a sine wave of alternating current is given by

$$i = I_m \sin \theta \tag{2}$$

where i = instantaneous value of current,
I_m = maximum value of current,
θ = angular position of coil.

PROBLEMS 28-1

1. An alternating e.m.f. has a maximum value of 325 v. What are the instantaneous values of this e.m.f. at the following positions in its cycle:

(a) 11°?   (b) 62°?   (c) 140°?   (d) 243°?   (e) 340°?

2. The instantaneous value of an alternating e.m.f. is 122 v when 24° of its cycle has been completed. What is its maximum value? (Art. 25-3.)

3. The instantaneous value of an alternating e.m.f. is 70 v at 119°. What is its maximum value?

4. An alternating current has a maximum value of 90 a. What are the instantaneous values of this current at the following positions in its cycle:

(a) 69°?   (b) 322.5°?   (c) 196°?   (d) 172.4°?   (e) 124°?

5. The instantaneous value of an alternating current is 3.4 a at 166.6°. What will be its value at 215°?

6. The instantaneous value of an alternating e.m.f. is 206 v at 29°. What will be its value at 344.3°?

7. The instantaneous value of an alternating e.m.f. is −117 v at 229°. What will be its value at 103°?

8. An alternating e.m.f. has a maximum value of 750 v. At what angles will it be at 70.7% of its positive maximum value?

9. At what angles are the instantaneous values of an alternating current equal to 22.5% of the maximum negative value?

10. Find the instantaneous value of an alternating current 114° after its maximum positive value of 12 a.

28-4. Cycles, Frequency, and Poles. Each revolution of the coil in Fig. 28-1 results in one complete *cycle* which consists of one positive and one negative loop of the sine wave (Art. 26-8). The number of cycles generated in 1 second is called the *frequency* of the alternating electromotive force, and the *period* is the time required to complete one cycle. One-half cycle is called an *alternation*. Thus, by a 60-cycle alternating current is meant that the current passes through 60 cycles per second, which results in a period of 0.0167 second. Also, a 60-cycle current completes 120 alternations per second.

Figure 28-7 represents a coil rotating in a four-pole machine. When one side of the coil has rotated from position 0 to position 4, it has passed under the influence of an N and an S pole, thus generating one complete sine wave, or electrical cycle. This corresponds to 2π electrical radians, or 360 electrical degrees, although the coil has rotated only 180 space-degrees. Therefore, in one complete revolution the coil will generate two complete cycles, or 720 electrical degrees, so that for every *space-degree* there result two *electrical time-degrees*.

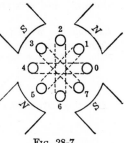

Fig. 28-7.

In any alternator the armature, or field, must move an angular distance equal to the angle formed by two consecutive like poles in order to complete one cycle. It is evident, then, that a two-pole machine must rotate at twice the speed of a four-pole machine to produce the same frequency. Therefore, to find the frequency of an alternator in cycles per second, *the number of pairs of poles is multiplied by the speed of the armature in revolutions per second.* That is,

$$f = \frac{PS}{60} \tag{3}$$

where f = frequency in cycles per second,
$\quad P$ = number of pairs of poles,
$\quad S$ = revolutions per minute of armature, or field.

Example. What is the frequency of an alternator having four poles with a speed of 1800 revolutions per minute?

Solution: $\qquad f = \frac{2 \times 1800}{60} = 60 \sim$

28-5. Equations of Voltages and Currents. Since each cycle consists of 360 electrical degrees, or 2π electrical radians, the variation of an alternating electromotive force can be expressed in terms of time. Thus, a frequency of f cycles per second results in $2\pi f$ radians per second which is denoted by ω (Art. 26-5). Hence, the instantaneous electromotive force at any time t is given by the relation

$$e = E_m \sin \omega t \tag{4}$$

The instantaneous current is

$$i = I_m \sin \omega t \tag{5}$$

The student should review Arts. 26-6 to 26-10 to ensure a complete understanding of the relations between the general equation for a periodic function and Eqs. (4) and (5) above. Thus, E_m and I_m are the amplitude factors of their respective equations, and ω is the frequency factor.

Example 1.   Write the equation of a 60-cycle alternating voltage that has a maximum value of 156 volts.

Solution: The angular velocity ω is 2π times the frequency or

$$2\pi \times 60 = 377 \text{ radians per second.}$$

Substituting 156 volts for E_m and 377 for ω in Eq. (4),

$$e = 156 \sin 377t$$

Example 2.   Write the equation of a radio-frequency current of 700 kilocycles that has a maximum value of 21.2 amperes.

Solution: $I_m = 21.2$ amperes and $f = 700$ kilocycles $= 7 \times 10^5$ cycles Then $\omega = 2\pi f = 2\pi \times 7 \times 10^5 = 4.4 \times 10^6$.   Substituting these values in Eq. (5),

$$i = 21.2 \sin (4.4 \times 10^6)t$$

Example 3.   If the time $t = 0$ when the voltage of Example 1 is zero and increasing in a positive direction, what is the instantaneous value of the voltage at the end of 0.002 second?

Solution: Substituting 0.002 for t in the equation for the voltage,

$$e = 156 \sin (377 \times 0.002)$$
$$= 156 \sin 0.754$$

where 0.754 is the time-angle in *radians*.   Then, since 1 radian $= 57.3°$,

$$e = 156 \sin (0.754 \times 57.3°)$$
$$= 156 \sin 43.2°$$

Hence, $e = 107 \text{ v}$

PROBLEMS 28-2

1. An alternator with 24 poles has a speed of 300 r.p.m. and develops a maximum voltage of 622 v.

(*a*) What is the frequency of the alternating current?

(*b*) How many times does the current change its direction in 1 min?

(*c*) Write the equation for the instantaneous voltage at any time t.

2. An alternator with 12 poles has a speed of 250 r.p.m. and supplies a maximum current of 63.6 a.

(*a*) What is the frequency?

(*b*) Write the equation for the instantaneous current at any time t.

3. A 25-cycle generator that develops a maximum voltage of 933 v has a speed of 250 r.p.m.

(*a*) How many poles has it?
(*b*) Write the equation for the voltage.
(*c*) What is the instantaneous voltage when the time *t* is equal to 0.005 sec?

4. An 800-cycle alternator generates a maximum voltage of 170 v at 4000 r.p.m.

(*a*) How many poles has it?
(*b*) Write the equation for the voltage.
(*c*) What is the value of the voltage when the time *t* is equal to 0.000796 sec?

5. At what speed must a 24-pole 50-cycle generator be driven in order to develop its rated frequency?

6. The equation for a certain alternating voltage is $e = 707 \sin 314t$. What is its frequency?

7. The equation for an alternating current is $i = 14.1 \sin (2.23 \times 10^6)t$. What is its frequency?

8. The equation for an alternating voltage is

$$e = (1.5 \times 10^{-4}) \sin (2.02 \times 10^8)t$$

(*a*) What is the maximum voltage in microvolts?
(*b*) What is the frequency in megacycles?

9. A 60-Mc r-f current has a maximum value of 55 μa. Write the equation of the current.

10. A broadcasting station operating on 710 kc develops a maximum potential of 0.155 mv across a listener's antenna. Write the equation for this voltage.

28-6. Average Value of Current or Voltage. Since an alternating current or voltage is of sine-wave form, it follows that the average current or voltage of 1 cycle is zero owing to the reversal of direction each half cycle. The term *average value* is usually understood to mean the average value of one alternation without regard to positive or negative values. The average value of a sine wave, such as that shown in Fig. 28-2, may be computed to a fair degree of accuracy by taking the average of many instantaneous values between two consecutive zero points of the curve, the values chosen being separated by equal values of angle. Thus, the average value is equal to the average height of any voltage or current loop. The exact average value is $\dfrac{2}{\pi} \cong 0.637$

times the maximum value. Thus, if I_{av} and E_{av} denote the average values of alternating current and voltage, respectively, we obtain

$$I_{av} = \frac{2}{\pi} I_m \cong 0.637 I_m \tag{6}$$

and

$$E_{av} = \frac{2}{\pi} E_m \cong 0.637 E_m \tag{7}$$

Example. The maximum value of an alternating voltage is 622 volts. What is its average value?

Solution: $E_{av} = 0.637 E_m = 0.637 \times 622 = 396$ v

28-7. Effective Value of Current or Voltage. If a direct current of I amperes is caused to flow through a resistance of R ohms, the resulting energy converted into heat equals I^2R watts. We should not expect an alternating current with a maximum value of 1 ampere to produce as much heat as a direct current of 1 ampere, for the former does not maintain a constant value. Thus, the above alternating-current ampere is not so effective as the direct-current ampere. The *effective value* of an alternating current is rated in terms of direct current; that is, an alternating current has an effective value of 1 ampere if, flowing through a given resistance, it will produce heat at the same rate as a direct-current ampere.

The effective value of a sine wave of current may be computed to a fair degree of accuracy by taking equally spaced instantaneous values and extracting the square root of their average, or mean, squared values. For this reason, the effective value is often called the *root-mean-square* (r.m.s.) value. The exact effective value of an alternating current or voltage is $\frac{1}{\sqrt{2}} \cong 0.707$ times the maximum value. Thus, if I and E denote the effective values of current and voltage, respectively, we obtain

$$I = \frac{I_m}{\sqrt{2}} \cong 0.707 I_m \tag{8}$$

and

$$E = \frac{E_m}{\sqrt{2}} \cong 0.707 E_m \tag{9}$$

It should be noted that *all meters, unless marked to the contrary, read effective values of current and voltage.*

Example 1.   The maximum value of an alternating voltage is 311 volts. What is the effective value?

Solution: $E = 0.707E_m = 0.707 \times 311 = 220$ v

Example 2.   An alternating-current ammeter reads 15 amperes.   What is the maximum value of the current?

Solution: Since $I = 0.707I_m$

then $I_m = \dfrac{I}{0.707}$

Substituting 15 amperes for I, $I_m = \dfrac{15}{0.707} = 21.2$ a

Alternate Solution: Since $I = \dfrac{I_m}{\sqrt{2}}$

then $I_m = I \sqrt{2} = 1.41I$

Substituting for I, $I_m = 1.41 \times 15 = 21.2$ a

Hence the maximum value of an alternating current or voltage is equal to 1.41 times the effective value.

PROBLEMS 28-3

1. What is the average value of an alternating voltage whose maximum value is 600 v?

2. An alternating voltage has an average value of 191 v.   What is the maximum value?

3. The average value of an alternating current is 4.2 a.   What is the maximum value?

4. The maximum value of an alternating voltage is 44 v.   What is the average value?

5. What is the effective value of an alternating voltage whose maximum value is 311 v?

6. A switchboard meter reads 440 v of alternating voltage.   What is the maximum value of the voltage?

7. What is the maximum value of an alternating current that has an effective value of 28 a?

8. What is the average value of an alternating voltage that has an effective value of 38.5 v?

9. What is the effective value of an alternating voltage that has an average value of 145 v?

10. An alternating-current switchboard ammeter reads 7.5 a.   What is the average value of the current?

28-8. Phase Relations—Phase Angles.   Nearly all alternating-current circuits contain circuit elements, or components, that cause the voltage and current to pass through their corresponding

zero values at different times. The effects of such conditions are given detailed consideration in the next chapter.

An alternating voltage and the resulting alternating current of the same frequency passing through corresponding zero values at the same instant are said to be *in phase*.

If the current passes through a zero value before the corresponding zero value of the voltage, the current and voltage are *out of phase* and the current is said to *lead* the voltage.

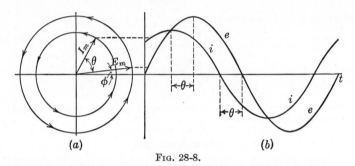

(a) (b)

Fig. 28-8.

Figure 28-8 illustrates a vector diagram and the corresponding sine waves for a current of i amperes leading a voltage of e volts by a *phase angle* of θ (Art. 26-10). Hence, if the voltage is taken as reference, the general equation of the voltage is

$$e = E_m \sin \omega t \tag{10}$$

and the current is given by

$$i = I_m \sin (\omega t + \theta) \tag{11}$$

The instantaneous values of the voltage and current for any angle ϕ of the voltage are

$$e = E_m \sin \phi \tag{12}$$

and $\qquad\qquad\qquad i = I_m \sin (\phi + \theta) \tag{13}$

Example 1.   In Fig. 28-8, the maximum values of the voltage and the current are 156 volts and 113 amperes, respectively. The frequency is 60 cycles per second, and the current leads the voltage by 40°.

(*a*) Write the equation for the voltage at any time *t*.

(*b*) Write the equation for the current at any time *t*.

(*c*) What is the instantaneous value of the current when the voltage has reached 10° of its cycle?

Solution: Given   Maximum voltage $= E_m = 156$ v
Maximum current $= I_m = 113$ a
Frequency $= f = 60 \sim$
Phase angle $= \theta = 40°$ lead
Voltage angle $= \phi = 10°$

Draw a vector diagram as shown in Fig. 28-8(a).   (The circles are not necessary, they simply denote rotation of the vectors.)

(a) Substituting given values in Eq. (10),

$$e = 156 \sin 2\pi \times 60t$$

or $$e = 156 \sin 377t \text{ v}$$

(b) Substituting given values in Eq. (11),

$$i = 113 \sin (377t + 40°)$$

Note: The quantity $377t$ is in *radians*.

(c) Substituting given values in Eq. (13),

$$i = 113 \sin (10° + 40°)$$

or $$i = 113 \sin 50° = 86.6 \text{ a}$$

Figure 28-9 illustrates a vector diagram and the corresponding sine waves for a current of i amperes lagging a voltage of e volts

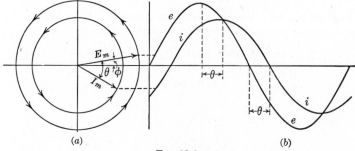

(a)   (b)

Fig. 28-9.

by a *phase angle* of θ.   Therefore, if the voltage is taken as reference, the general equation of the voltage will be as given by Eq. (10) and the current will be

$$i = I_m \sin (\omega t - \theta) \tag{14}$$

The instantaneous value of the current for any angle ϕ of the voltage is

$$i = I_m \sin (\phi - \theta) \tag{15}$$

Example 2.   In Fig. 28-9, the maximum values of the voltage and the current are 170 volts and 14.1 amperes, respectively.   The frequency is 800 cycles per second, and the current lags the voltage by 40°.

(a) Write the equation for the voltage at any time t.

(b) Write the equation for the current at any time t.

(c) What is the instantaneous value of the current when the voltage has reached 10° of its cycle?

Solution: Given   Maximum voltage $= E_m = 170$ v

                 Maximum current $= I_m = 14.1$ a

                     Frequency $= f = 800 \sim$

                   Phase angle $= \theta = 40°$ lag

                  Voltage angle $= \phi = 10°$

Draw a vector diagram as shown in Fig. 28-9(a).

(a) Substituting given values in Eq. (10),

$$e = 170 \sin 2\pi \times 800t$$

or
$$e = 170 \sin 5030t \text{ v}$$

(b) Substituting given values in Eq. (14),

$$i = 14.1 \sin (5030t - 40°) \text{ a}$$

(c) Substituting given values in Eq. (15),

$$i = 14.1 \sin (10° - 40°)$$

or
$$i = 14.1 \sin (-30°) = -7.05 \text{ a}$$

Example 3. In a certain alternating-current circuit a current of 14 amperes lags a voltage of 220 volts by an angle of 60°. What is the instan-

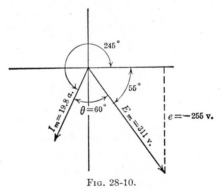

Fig. 28-10.

taneous value of the voltage when the current has completed 245° of its cycle?

NOTE: Unless otherwise specified, all voltages and currents are to be considered *effective* values.

Solution: Draw the vector diagram as shown in Fig. 28-10.

$$E_m = \sqrt{2}E = \sqrt{2} \times 220 = 311 \text{ v}$$
$$\phi = 245° + \theta = 245° + 60° = 305° = -55°$$

Then, by substituting the values of E_m and θ in Eq. (12),

$$e = 311 \sin (-55°) = -255 \text{ v}$$

PROBLEMS 28-4

1. A 60-cycle alternator generates a maximum voltage of 9330 v and a maximum current of 1410 a. The current leads the voltage by an angle of 30°.

(a) Write the equation for the current at any time t.

(b) What is the instantaneous value of the current when the voltage has completed 20° of the cycle?

2. A 25-cycle alternator is generating 6600 v at 700 a. The current lags the voltage by an angle of 22°.

(a) Write the equation for the current at any time t.

(b) What is the instantaneous value of the current when the voltage has completed 50° of its cycle?

3. In the alternator of Prob. 1, what will be the instantaneous value of the current when the voltage has completed 190° of its cycle?

4. In the alternator of Prob. 2, what will be the instantaneous value of the current when the voltage has completed 184° of its cycle?

5. A 50-cycle alternator generates 2300 v with a current of 200 a. The phase angle is 25° lagging.

(a) Write the equation for the current at any time t.

(b) What is the instantaneous value of the current when the voltage has completed 70° of its cycle?

6. In the alternator of Prob. 5, what is the instantaneous value of the voltage when the current has completed 230° of its cycle?

7. An alternating voltage has a maximum value of 170 v and a maximum current of 42.4 a. If the instantaneous value of the voltage is 66.4 v when the instantaneous value of the current is 30 a, what is the phase angle between current and voltage?

8. In Prob. 7, what will be the instantaneous value of the current when the voltage has reached its maximum negative value?

9. A 60-cycle current has a value of 30 a at 230 v. If the instantaneous value of the voltage is -67.6 v when the instantaneous value of the current is 26.1 a, what is the phase angle between current and voltage?

10. (a) Write the equation for the current in Prob. 9.

(b) In Prob. 9, what will be the instantaneous value of the voltage when the current has reached its maximum positive value?

CHAPTER XXIX

ALTERNATING CURRENTS—SERIES CIRCUITS

The phenomena occurring in alternating-current circuits make them a very interesting subject for study. For example, unlike circuits carrying direct currents, in alternating-current circuits the product of the voltage and current is seldom equal to the reading of a wattmeter connected in the circuit; the current may lag or lead the voltage, or the potential difference across an inductance or capacitance may be several times the supply voltage. This chapter deals with the computation of such effects in series circuits.

In the application of Ohm's law to alternating-current circuits, there is always the possibility of confusion until the student clearly understands that Ohm's law applies with respect to the relations existing among *voltage, current,* and *resistance* only. These relations as stated in Art. 9-2 always hold true, either with direct currents or with alternating currents, as long as the relative values of these three are concerned. However,

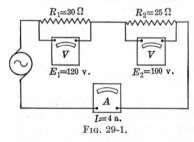

$R_1 = 30\,\Omega$ $R_2 = 25\,\Omega$
V V
$E_1 = 120$ v. $E_2 = 100$ v.
A
$I = 4$ a.
Fig. 29-1.

counter electromotive forces resulting from the presence of inductances or capacitors, or a combination of both, introduce voltage reactions that must be taken into account in the analysis of alternating-current circuits. Ohm's law does not concern itself with these effects.

29-1. The Resistance Circuit. Figure 29-1 represents a 60-cycle alternator supplying 220 volts to two resistances connected in series.

This circuit contains resistance only; therefore, Ohm's law applies in every respect. The internal resistance of the alternator and the resistance of the connecting wires being neglected, the current through the circuit is given by the familiar relation

422

$$I = \frac{E}{R_t} = \frac{E}{R_1 + R_2} = \frac{220}{30 + 25} = \frac{220}{55} = 4 \text{ a}$$

Again, as with direct currents, the voltage drops, or potential differences, across the resistances are

$$E_1 = IR_1 = 4 \times 30 = 120 \text{ v}$$

and $\quad\quad\quad\quad\; E_2 = IR_2 = 4 \times 25 = \underline{100 \text{ v}}$

$$\text{Applied voltage} = \overline{220 \text{ v}}$$

In an alternating-current circuit containing only resistance the voltage and current are in phase. That is, the voltage and current pass through corresponding parts of their cycles at the same instant. Hence, if

$$e = E_m \sin \omega t = 311 \sin 377t$$

is the equation for the alternator voltage of Fig. 29-1, then the current through the circuit is

$$i = I_m \sin (\omega t + \theta) = I_m \sin (\omega t + 0°) = 5.66 \sin 377t \text{ a}$$

Figure 29-2 is the vector diagram for the circuit of Fig. 29-1. It will be noted that the voltage vector and the current vector coincide. This is as anticipated from the equations for the voltage and current, for they differ only in amplitude factors; the frequency factors are equal, and the phase angle is 0° (Arts. 26-7 to 26-9).

It is evident that Ohm's law says nothing about maximum, average, or effective values of current and

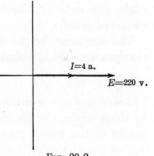

Fig. 29-2.

voltage. Any of these values may be used; that is, maximum voltage may be used to find maximum current or average voltage to find average current, etc. Naturally, maximum voltage is not used to find effective current unless the proper conversion constant is introduced into the equation. As previously stated, all voltage and current values here are to be considered as effective values unless otherwise specified (Art. 28-7).

29-2. Power in the Resistive Circuit. In direct-current circuits the power is equal to the product of the voltage and the current (Art. 9-5).   This is true for alternating-current circuits for *instantaneous values* of voltage and current.   That is, the *instantaneous power* is

$$p = ei \tag{1}$$

When a sine wave of voltage is impressed across a resistance, the relations among voltage, current, and power are as shown in Fig. 29-3.   The voltage existing across the resistance is in phase with the current flowing through it.   The power delivered to the resistance at any instant is represented by the height of the

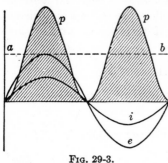

power curve which is the product of the instantaneous values of voltage and current at that instant.   The shaded area under the power curve represents the total power delivered to the circuit during one complete cycle of voltage.   It will be noted that the power curve is of sine-wave form, having a frequency twice that of the voltage.   Also, the power

FIG. 29-3.

curve lies entirely above the *X* axis, there being no negative values of power.

The maximum height of the power curve is the product of the maximum values of voltage and current.   Stated as an equation,

$$P_m = E_m I_m \tag{2}$$

The average power delivered to a resistance load is represented by the height of the line *ab* in Fig. 29-3 which is half the maximum height of the power curve, or its average height.   Then, since

$$\text{Average power} = P = \frac{P_m}{2}$$

by dividing both members of Eq. (2) by 2 we obtain

$$\frac{P_m}{2} = \frac{E_m I_m}{2}$$

Substituting for the value of $\frac{P_m}{2}$ and factoring the denominator of the right member,

$$P = \frac{E_m I_m}{\sqrt{2}\,\sqrt{2}}$$

Substituting for the values in the right member (Art. 28-7),

$$P = EI. \tag{3}$$

Hence, the alternating power consumed by a resistance load is equal to the product of the effective values of voltage and current. As in direct-current circuits, alternating power is measured in watts and kilowatts.

Example. What is the power expended in the resistances of Fig. 29-1?

> *Solution:*
> Voltage across $R_1 = E_1 = 120$ v
> Voltage across $R_2 = E_2 = 100$ v
> Current through circuit $= I = 4$ a
> Power expended in $R_1 = P_1 = E_1 I = 120 \times 4 = 480$ w
> Power expended in $R_2 = P_2 = E_2 I = 100 \times 4 = \underline{400\ \text{w}}$
> Total $= 880$ w

Also, the total power is $P_t = EI = 220 \times 4 = 880$ watts.

Because $P = EI$, the usual Ohm's law relations hold for resistances in alternating-current circuits. Hence,

$$P = I^2 R \tag{4}$$

and

$$P = \frac{E^2}{R} \tag{5}$$

Thus, the power consumed by R_1 of Fig. 29-1 can be computed by using Eq. (4) or (5). Hence,

$$P_1 = I^2 R_1 = 4^2 \times 30 = 480 \text{ w}$$

or

$$P_1 = \frac{E_1^2}{R_1} = \frac{120^2}{30} = 480 \text{ w}$$

PROBLEMS 29-1

1. A 25-cycle alternator supplies 660 v across a combination of three series resistors of 100, 50, and 90 Ω.

    (*a*) How much current flows in the circuit?
    (*b*) Write the equations of the voltage across the series combination and the circuit current.
    (*c*) How much power is dissipated in the 50-Ω resistance?
    (*d*) What is the difference of potential across the 90-Ω resistance?
    (*e*) What is the instantaneous value of the current when the instantaneous voltage is 319 v?

2. Given the circuit of Fig. 29-4,

(*a*) Write the equation for the e.m.f. of the alternator.

(*b*) Write the equation for the total current of the circuit.

(*c*) What is the potential difference across R_4?

(*d*) How much power is dissipated in R_3?

(*e*) How much current flows through R_2?

(*f*) What is the instantaneous value of the current through R_1 when the instantaneous voltage across R_1 is 68.4 v?

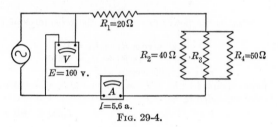

$R_1 = 20\,\Omega$

$R_2 = 40\,\Omega$ R_3 $R_4 = 50\,\Omega$

V

$E = 160$ v.

A

$I = 5.6$ a.

Fig. 29-4.

3. In the circuit of Fig. 29-4, what is the instantaneous value of the voltage across R_2 when the instantaneous value of the current through R_4 is 1.33 a?

4. A 25-cycle alternator is connected to a resistance of 100 Ω. A wattmeter connected in the circuit shows the resistance to be dissipating 300 w. What is the maximum difference of potential developed across the resistance?

5. What is the maximum value of the current in the circuit of Prob. 4?

29-3. The Inductive Circuit. A circuit, or an inductance coil, has the property of inductance when there is an electromotive force set up in it due to a *change* of current through it. Thus, a circuit has an inductance of 1 henry when a change of current of 1 ampere per second induces an electromotive force of 1 volt (Art. 8-6). Expressed as an equation,

$$E_{\text{av}} = L\frac{I}{t} \tag{6}$$

where E_{av} is the average voltage induced in a circuit of L henrys by a *change* of current of I amperes in t seconds.

An alternating current of I_m amperes makes *four changes* during each cycle. These are

1. From zero to maximum positive value.

2. From maximum positive value to zero.

3. From zero to maximum negative value.

4. From maximum negative value to zero.

The time required for one complete cycle of alternating current is $T = \dfrac{1}{f}$ seconds (Art. 26-9), and each of the above changes occur in $\frac{1}{4}$ of the time required for the completion of each cycle. Then the time for each change is $\dfrac{1}{4f}$ seconds. Substituting this value of t, and I_m for I, in Eq. (6),

$$E_{av} = L \frac{I_m}{\dfrac{1}{4f}} = 4fLI_m \qquad (7)$$

Equation (7) is cumbersome if used in its present form, for it contains an average voltage term and a maximum current term. The equation may be expressed in terms of the relation between average and maximum values as given in Art. 28-6.

$$E_{av} = \frac{2}{\pi} E_m$$

Substituting in Eq. (7) for this value of E_{av},

$$\frac{2}{\pi} E_m = 4fLI_m$$

which becomes $\qquad E_m = 2\pi fLI_m \qquad (8)$

Because both voltage and current in Eq. (8) are now in terms of maximum values, effective values may be used. **Thus,**

$$E = 2\pi fLI \qquad \textbf{(9)}$$

The factors $2\pi fL$ in Eqs. (8) and (9) represent **a reaction due to** the frequency of the alternating current and **the amount of** inductance contained in the circuit. Hence the **alternating** voltage E required to cause a current of I amperes with a frequency of f cycles per second to flow through an inductance of L henrys is given by Eq. (9). That is, the voltage must overcome the reaction $2\pi fL$ which is called the *inductive reactance*. From Eq. (9) the inductive reactance, which is denoted by X_L and expressed in ohms, is given by

$$\frac{E}{I} = 2\pi fL$$

or $\qquad X_L = 2\pi fL = \omega L \qquad \textbf{(10)}$

where f = frequency in cycles per second,

   L = inductance in henrys.

Note the similarity of the relations between voltage and current for inductive reactance and resistance. Both inductive reactance and resistance offer an opposition to a flow of alternating current, both are expressed in ohms, and both are equal to the voltage divided by the current. Here the similarity ends; there is no inductive reactance to steady-state direct currents

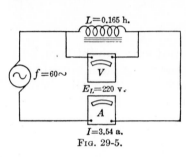

L=0.165 h.

$f=60\sim$

$E_L=220$ v.

$I=3.54$ a.

FIG. 29-5.

because there is no *change* in current, and, as explained later, inductive reactances consume no alternating power.

Figure 29-5 represents a 60-cycle alternator delivering 220 volts to a coil having an inductance of 0.165 henry. The opposition, or inductive reactance, to the flow of current is

$$X_L = 2\pi f L = 2\pi \times 60 \times 0.165 = 62.2\ \Omega$$

Although it is impossible to construct an inductance containing no resistance, to simplify basic considerations we shall consider the coil of Fig. 29-5 as being an inductance with negligible resistance. (The effects of inductance and resistance acting together are discussed in Art. 29-7.) The current in the circuit due to the action of voltage and inductive reactance is

$$I = \frac{E_L}{X_L} = \frac{220}{62.2} = 3.54\ \text{a}$$

Example 1.   What is the inductive reactance of an inductance of 17 microhenrys at a frequency of 2500 kilocycles?

Solution: $f = 2500\ \text{kc} = 2.5 \times 10^6 \sim$
   $L = 17\ \mu\text{h} = 1.7 \times 10^{-5}\ \text{h}$
   $X_L = 2\pi f L$
      $= 2\pi \times 2.5 \times 10^6 \times 1.7 \times 10^{-5}$
      $= 2\pi \times 1.7 \times 2.5 \times 10 = 267\ \Omega$

Example 2.   An inductance coil is connected to 115 volts, 60 cycles. An ammeter connected in series with the coil reads 0.714 ampere. On the assumption that the coil contains negligible resistance, what is its inductance?

Solution: $E_L = 115$ v

                  $f = 60 \sim$

                  $I = 0.714$ a

                  $X_L = \dfrac{E_L}{I} = \dfrac{115}{0.714} = 161 \ \Omega$

Since $X_L = 2\pi fL$

then $L = \dfrac{X_L}{2\pi f} = \dfrac{161}{2\pi \times 60} = 0.427$ h

In a circuit containing inductance, a change of current induces an electromotive force of such polarity that it always opposes the change of current. Because an alternating current is constantly changing, in an inductive circuit there is always present a reaction that opposes this change. The net effect of this, in a *purely inductive circuit*, is to cause the *current to lag the voltage by* 90°. This is illustrated by the vector diagram of Fig. 29-6 which shows the voltage of

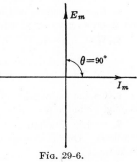

Fig. 29-6.

the circuit of Fig. 29-5 to be at maximum positive value when the current is passing through zero.

The instantaneous voltage across the inductance is given by

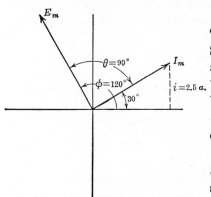

Fig. 29-7.

$$e = E_m \sin \omega t$$
or $$e = 311 \sin 377t$$

Since the current lags the voltage by a phase angle θ of 90°, the equation for the current through the inductance is

$$i = I_m \sin (\omega t - \theta) \quad (11)$$
or $$i = 5\sin (377t - 90°) \quad (12)$$

If the voltage has completed ϕ degrees of its cycle, the instantaneous current is

$$i = 5 \sin (\phi - 90°) \quad (13)$$

Example 3. What is the instantaneous value of the current in Fig. 29-5 when the voltage has completed 120° of its cycle?

Solution: Draw a vector diagram of the current and voltage relations as shown in Fig. 29-7. The instantaneous value of the current is found from

Eq. (13) and is

$$i = I_m \sin (\phi - 90°) = 5 \sin (120° - 90°) = 5 \sin 30° = 2.5 \text{ a}$$

PROBLEMS 29-2

1. What would be the reactance of a coil having an inductance of 0.19 h when connected to a 60-cycle e.m.f.?

2. What is the reactance of a 5-h choke at a frequency of 120 cycles?

3. A coil in a radio transmitter has an inductance of 150 μh. What is its reactance at a frequency of 950 kc?

4. A certain choke coil in a radio receiver has an inductance of 4.57 μh. What is its reactance at a frequency of 200 Mc?

5. What happens to the inductive reactance of a circuit when

    (a) The inductance is held constant and the frequency is varied?
    (b) The frequency is held constant and the inductance is varied?

6. On the assumption of negligible resistance, what current would flow through an inductance of 0.0326 h at a potential of 120 v, 800 $\sim$?

7. If there are 110 volts, 25 $\sim$ across an inductance, a current of 215 ma flows. On the assumption of negligible resistance in the coil, what is its inductance?

8. A current of 425 ma, 50 $\sim$ flows through an inductance of 1.65 h. On the assumption that the inductance has negligible resistance, what is the potential difference across it?

9. What is the instantaneous value of the current of Prob. 8 when the voltage has completed 26° of its cycle?

10. What is the instantaneous value of the voltage of Prob. 8 when the current has completed 230° of its cycle?

29-4. The Capacitive Circuit.

A capacity is formed between two conductors when there is an insulating material between them. A circuit, or a condenser, is said to have a capacitance of 1 farad when a *change* of 1 volt per second produces a current of 1 ampere (Art. 8-7). Expressed as an equation,

$$I_{av} = C \frac{E}{t} \tag{14}$$

where I_{av} is the average current in amperes that is caused to flow through a capacitance of C farads by a *change* of E volts in t seconds.

In all probability the above definition does not clearly indicate to the student *how much* electricity, or charge, a given condenser will contain. Perhaps a more understandable definition is that a circuit, or a condenser, has a capacitance of 1 farad when a difference of potential of 1 volt will produce on it 1 coulomb of charge. Expressed as an equation,

$$Q = CE \qquad (15)$$

where Q is the charge in coulombs placed on a condenser of C farads by a difference of potential of E volts across the condenser.

It was shown in Art. 29-3 that the time t required for one change of an alternating electromotive force was $\dfrac{1}{4f}$ seconds. Therefore, if an alternating electromotive force of E_m volts at a frequency of f cycles per second is impressed across a condenser of C farads, by substituting the above value of t, and E_m for E, in Eq. (14),

$$I_{av} = C\,\frac{E_m}{\dfrac{1}{4f}} = 4fCE_m \qquad (16)$$

Again, as in Eq. (7), the above equation contains an average term and a maximum term. As given in Art. 28-6,

$$I_{av} = \frac{2}{\pi} I_m$$

Substituting in Eq. (16) for this value of I_{av},

$$\frac{2}{\pi} I_m = 4fCE_m$$

which becomes

$$I_m = 2\pi fCE_m \qquad (17)$$

Because both voltage and current in Eq. (17) are now in terms of maximum values, effective values may be used. Thus,

$$I = 2\pi fCE \qquad (18)$$

The factors $2\pi fC$ represent a reaction due to the frequency of the alternating electromotive force and the amount of capacitance; hence, it is evident that the amount of current in a purely capacitive circuit depends upon these factors. As in the case of resistive circuits and inductive circuits, the opposition to the flow of current is obtained by dividing the voltage by the current. Then, from Eq. (18),

$$\frac{E}{I} = \frac{1}{2\pi fC} \qquad (19)$$

The right member of Eq. (19), which represents the opposition to a flow of alternating current in a purely capacitive circuit, is called the *capacitive reactance*. It is denoted by X_c and expressed in ohms. Thus,

$$X_c = \frac{1}{2\pi f C} = \frac{1}{\omega C} \tag{20}$$

where f = frequency in cycles per second,
C = capacitance in farads.

Figure 29-8 represents a 60-cycle alternator delivering 220 volts to a condenser having a capacitance of 14.5 microfarads. The opposition, or capacitive reactance, to the flow of current is

$$X_c = \frac{1}{2\pi f C} = \frac{1}{2\pi \times 60 \times 14.5 \times 10^{-6}} = \frac{10^4}{2\pi \times 6 \times 1.45} = 183\ \Omega$$

Neglecting the resistance of the connecting leads and the extremely small losses at low frequencies in a well-constructed condenser, the current in the circuit due to the action of the voltage and capacitive reactance is

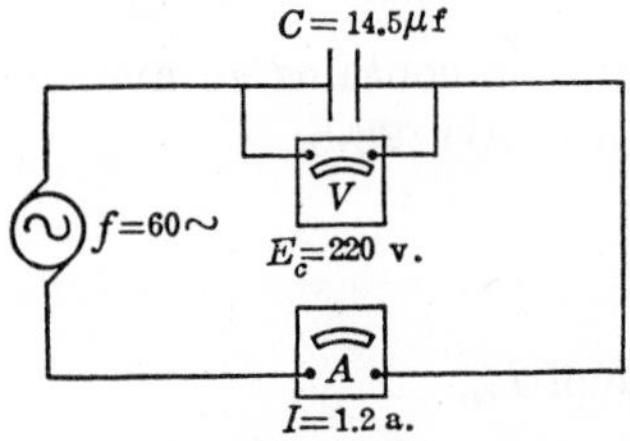

$C = 14.5\mu f$

$f = 60 \sim$

$E_c = 220$ v.

$I = 1.2$ a.

Fig. 29-8.

$$I = \frac{E_c}{X_c} = \frac{220}{183} = 1.20\ a$$

Example 1.   What is the capacitive reactance of a 350-micromicrofarad condenser at a frequency of 1200 kilocycles?

Solution: $f = 1200$ kc $= 1.2 \times 10^6 \sim$
$C = 350\ \mu\mu f = 3.5 \times 10^{-10}$ f

$$X_c = \frac{1}{2\pi f C} = \frac{1}{2\pi \times 1.2 \times 10^6 \times 3.5 \times 10^{-10}}$$

$$= \frac{10^4}{2\pi \times 1.2 \times 3.5} = 379\ \Omega$$

Example 2.   A condenser is connected across 110 volts, 60 cycles. A milliammeter connected in series with the condenser reads 350 milliamperes. What is the capacitance of the condenser?

Solution: $E_c = 110$ v
$f = 60 \sim$
$I = 350$ ma $= 0.350$ a

$$X_c = \frac{E_c}{I} = \frac{110}{0.35} = 314\ \Omega$$

Since $X_c = \dfrac{1}{2\pi f C}$

then $\qquad C = \dfrac{1}{2\pi f X_c} = \dfrac{1}{2\pi \times 60 \times 314}$

$\qquad\qquad = \dfrac{10^{-3}}{2\pi \times 6 \times 3.14} = 8.44 \times 10^{-6}\,\text{f} = 8.44\ \mu\text{f}$

Because current flows in a condenser only when the voltage across it is changing, it is evident that, when an alternating voltage is impressed, current is flowing at all times because the potential difference across the condenser is constantly changing. Furthermore, the greatest amount of current will flow when the voltage is changing most rapidly, this occurring when the voltage passes through zero value. This property, in conjunction with the effects of the counter electromotive force, *causes the current to lead the voltage by 90° in a purely capacitive circuit.* This is illustrated by the vector diagram of Fig. 29-9 which shows the current through the circuit of Fig. 29-8 to be at maximum positive value when the voltage is passing through zero.

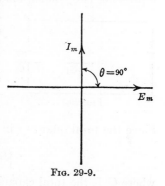

Fig. 29-9.

The instantaneous voltage across the condenser is given by

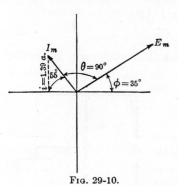

Fig. 29-10.

$$e = E_m \sin \omega t \qquad (21)$$
$$\text{or} \qquad e = 311 \sin 377t \qquad (22)$$

Therefore, the equation for the current is

$$i = I_m \sin (377t + \theta) \qquad (23)$$
or
$$i = 1.70 \sin (377t + 90°) \qquad (24)$$

If the voltage has completed ϕ degrees of its cycle, the instantaneous current is

$$i = I_m \sin (\phi + 90°) \qquad (25)$$

Example 3. What is the instantaneous value of the current in **Fig. 29-8** when the voltage has completed 35° of its cycle?

Solution: Draw a vector diagram of the current and voltage relations as shown in Fig. 29-10. The instantaneous value of the current is found from Eq. (25) and is

$$i = I_m \sin (\phi + 90°) = 1.70 \sin (35° + 90°) = 1.70 \sin 125° = 1.39 \text{ a}$$

29-5. Condensers in Parallel and in Series.

Figure 29-11 represents two condensers C_1 and C_2 connected across a voltage E. The quantity of charge in condenser C_1 will be

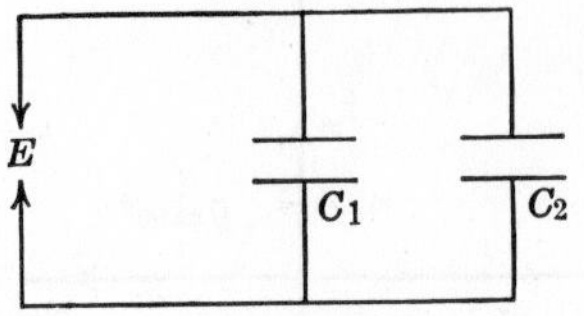

$$Q_1 = C_1 E \qquad (26)$$

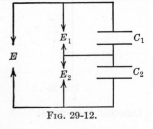

and that in condenser C_2 will be

$$Q_2 = C_2 E \qquad (27)$$

Fig. 29-11.

Since the total quantity in both condensers is $Q_1 + Q_2$, then

$$Q_1 + Q_2 = C_t E \qquad (28)$$

where C_t is the total capacity of the combination.
Adding Eq. (26) and Eq. (27),

$$Q_1 + Q_2 = C_1 E + C_2 E$$

or
$$Q_1 + Q_2 = (C_1 + C_2)E$$

Substituting the value of $(Q_1 + Q_2)$ from Eq. (28),

$$C_t E = (C_1 + C_2)E$$

which results in
$$C_t = C_1 + C_2 \qquad (29)$$

From the foregoing, it is apparent that condensers in parallel combine like resistances in series; that is, the capacitance of paralleled condensers is equal to the sum of the individual capacitances.

Figure 29-12 represents two condensers C_1 and C_2 connected in series with a voltage E across the combination. Because the condensers are in series, the same quantity of electricity must be sent into each of them. Then, if E_1 and E_2 represent the potential

Fig. 29-12.

differences across C_1 and C_2, respectively, Q represents the quantity of electricity in each condenser, and C_t is the capacity of the combination. Hence,

$$E = \frac{Q}{C_t}$$

$$E_1 = \frac{Q}{C_1}$$

and $\qquad\qquad E_2 = \frac{Q}{C_2}$

Since $\qquad\qquad E = E_1 + E_2 \qquad\qquad\qquad\qquad (30)$

by substituting the values for all voltages into Eq. (30),

$$\frac{Q}{C_t} = \frac{Q}{C_1} + \frac{Q}{C_2}$$

or $\qquad\qquad \frac{1}{C_t} = \frac{1}{C_1} + \frac{1}{C_2} \qquad\qquad\qquad (31)$

Equation (31) resolves into

$$C_t = \frac{C_1 C_2}{C_1 + C_2} \qquad\qquad\qquad (32)$$

The above illustrates the fact that condensers in series combine like resistances in parallel; that is, the reciprocal of the combined capacitance of condensers in series is equal to the sum of the reciprocals of the capacitances of the individual condensers.

Example.   (a) What is the capacitance of a 6-μf condenser in parallel with a condenser of 4 μf?

(b) What is the capacitance of these condensers when connected in series?

Solution: $\qquad\qquad$ (a) $C_t = 6 + 4 = 10$ μf

$\qquad\qquad\qquad$ (b) $C_t = \dfrac{6 \times 4}{6 + 4} = 2.4$ μf

PROBLEMS 29-3

1. What is the capacitive reactance of a condenser of 12 μf at a frequency of 60 ∼?

2. What is the capacitive reactance of a condenser of 6 μf at a frequency of 60 ∼?

3. A blocking condenser in a radio transmitter has a capacity of 0.004 μf. What is its reactance at a frequency of 1250 kc?

4. What will be the reactance of the condenser of Prob. 3 if the frequency is increased to 2500 kc?

5. What is the reactance of a condenser of 50 μμf at a frequency of 400 Mc?

6. What happens to the capacitive reactance of a circuit when

(*a*) The capacitance is held constant and the frequency is varied?

(*b*) The frequency is held·constant and the capacitance is varied?

7. How much current will flow in a condenser of 4 μf when 120 v, 800 $\sim$ is impressed across it?

8. If there are 240 volts, 60 $\sim$ across a condenser, a current of 452 ma is the result. What is the capacitance of the condenser?

9. A current of 603 ma, 800 $\sim$ flows through a 1-μf condenser. What is the potential difference across the condenser?

10. What is the instantaneous value of the current of Prob. 9 when the voltage has completed 257° of its cycle?

11. What is the instantaneous value of the voltage of Prob. 9 when the current has completed 156° of its cycle?

12. (*a*) What is the capacitance of a combination consisting of a 350-$\mu\mu f$ condenser in parallel with a condenser of 500 $\mu\mu f$?

(*b*) What is the resulting capacitance when these condensers are connected in series?

13. Two condensers, 8 μf and 4 μf, are connected in series across 180 v, 120 $\sim$.

(*a*) How much current flows through the condensers?

(*b*) Which condenser has the greater potential difference across it?

14. Two condensers, 50 $\mu\mu f$ and 200 $\mu\mu f$, are connected in parallel. A current of 500 ma, 3500 kc flows through the condenser of 200 $\mu\mu f$. How much current flows through the other condenser?

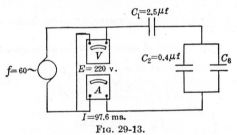

Fig. 29-13.

15. Given the circuit of Fig. 29-13, and neglecting resistance of leads,

(*a*) Write the equation for the e.m.f. of the alternator.

(*b*) Write the equation for the circuit current.

(*c*) What is the potential difference across C_1?

(*d*) What is the capacitance of C_3?

(*e*) How much current flows through $\dot{C}_2$?

29-6. Power in Circuits Containing Only Inductance or Capacity.
Figure 29-14 illustrates the voltage, current, and power

relations when a sine wave of electromotive force is impressed across an inductance whose resistance is negligible.

When the current is increasing from zero to maximum positive value, during the time interval from 1 to 2, power is being taken from the source of electromotive force and is being stored in the magnetic field about the coil. As the current through the inductance decreases from maximum positive value to zero, during the time from 2 to 3, the magnetic field is collapsing, thus returning its power to the circuit. Thus, during the intervals from 1 to 2 and from 3 to 4, the inductance is taking power from the source

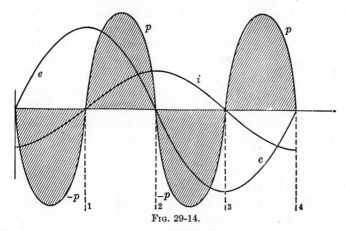

Fig. 29-14.

that is represented by the *positive* power in the figure. During the intervals from 0 to 1 and 2 to 3, the inductance is returning power to the source that is represented by the *negative* power in the figure. As previously stated, the instantaneous power is equal to the product of the voltage and current, being positive when the voltage and current are of like sign and negative when of unlike sign. Note that between points 3 and 4, although the voltage and current are both negative, the power is positive.

When an alternating electromotive force is impressed across a condenser, power is taken from the source and stored in the condenser as the voltage increases from zero to maximum positive value. As the voltage decreases from maximum positive value to zero, the condenser discharges and returns power to the source. As in the case of the inductance, half of the power loops are positive and half are negative; therefore, no power is expended in either circuit, for the power alternately flows to and from the source. This power is called *reactive* or *apparent power* and is given by the relation

$$P = EI$$

and is measured in *volt-amperes* or *kilovolt-amperes*, abbreviated va and kva, respectively.

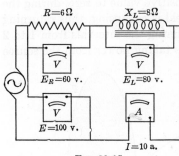

$R = 6\,\Omega$ $X_L = 8\,\Omega$

V

$E_R = 60$ v.

V

$E_L = 80$ v.

V

A

$E = 100$ v.

$I = 10$ a.

Fig. 29-15.

29-7. Resistance and Inductance in Series.

It has been explained that in a circuit containing only resistance the voltage applied across the resistance and the current through the resistance are in phase and that in a circuit containing only reactance the voltage and current are 90° out of phase. However, circuits encountered in practice contain both resistance and reactance. Such a condition is shown in Fig. 29-15 where an alternating electromotive force of 100 volts is impressed across a combination of 6 ohms resistance in series with 8 ohms inductive reactance.

As with direct-current circuits, the sum of the voltage drops around the circuit comprising the load must equal the applied electromotive force. In the consideration of resistance and reactance, however, we are dealing with voltages that can no longer be added or subtracted arithmetically. This is because the voltage drop across the resistance is in phase with the current and the voltage drop across the inductive reactance is 90° ahead of the current.

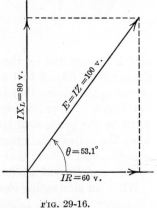

$IX_L = 80$ v.

$E = IZ = 100$ v.

$\theta = 53.1°$

$IR = 60$ v.

Fig. 29-16.

Because the current is the same in all parts of a series circuit, we may use it as a reference and plot the voltage across the resistance and that across the inductive reactance as shown in Fig. 29-16. The resultant of these two voltages, which can be treated as rectangular components (Art. 27-4), must be equal to the applied electromotive force. Hence, if IR and IX_L are the potential differences across the resistance and inductive reactance, respectively,

$$E = \sqrt{(IR)^2 + (IX_L)^2} \qquad (33)$$

or $\qquad E = \sqrt{60^2 + 80^2} = 100 \text{ v}$

The phase angle θ between voltage and current can be found by using any of the trigonometric functions. For example,

$$\tan \theta = \frac{IX_L}{IR} = \frac{80}{60} = 1.33$$

$$\therefore \theta = 53.1°$$

and it is apparent from the vector diagram that the current through the circuit lags the applied voltage by this amount.

Although the foregoing demonstrates that the *vector sum* of the voltage across the resistance and the voltage across the reactance is equal to the applied electromotive force, no relation between applied voltage and circuit current has been given as yet.

Since $\qquad E = \sqrt{(IR)^2 + (IX_L)^2}$

then $\qquad E = \sqrt{I^2R^2 + I^2X_L^2}$

Factoring, $\qquad E = \sqrt{I^2(R^2 + X_L^2)}$

Hence, $\qquad E = I \sqrt{R^2 + X_L^2} \qquad (34)$

As previously stated, the applied voltage divided by the current results in a quotient that represents the opposition offered to the flow of current. Hence, from Eq. (34),

$$\frac{E}{I} = \sqrt{R^2 + X_L^2} \qquad (35)$$

The expression $\sqrt{R^2 + X_L^2}$ is called the *impedance* of the circuit. It is denoted by Z and measured in ohms. Therefore

$$Z = \sqrt{R^2 + X_L^2} \qquad (36)$$

Applying Eq. (36) to the circuit of Fig. 29-15,

$$Z = \sqrt{6^2 + 8^2} = 10 \ \Omega$$

and $\qquad I = \dfrac{E}{Z} = 10 \text{ a}$

From Eq. (35), Eq. (36) may be written

$$E = IZ = I \sqrt{R^2 + X_L^2}$$

The foregoing illustrates that the factor I is common to all expressions, which is the same as saying that the current is the same in all parts of the circuit. Because this condition exists, it is permissible to plot the resistance and reactance as rectangular components as shown in Fig. 29-17. Hence the impedance of a series circuit is simply the vector sum of the resistance and reactance. The various methods used in solving for the impedance are the same as those given for vector addition of rectangular components in the example of Art. 27-4. Note that the values are identical.

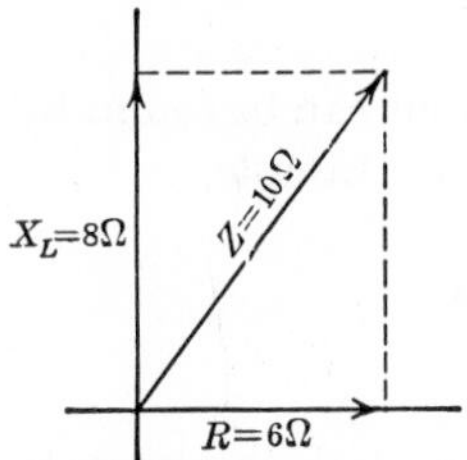

$X_L = 8\Omega$

$Z = 10\Omega$

$R = 6\Omega$

FIG. 29-17.

Example. A circuit consisting of 120 ohms resistance in series with an inductance of 0.35 henry is connected across a 440-volt 60-cycle alternator. Determine

(a) The phase angle between voltage and current.

(b) The impedance of the circuit.

(c) The current through the circuit.

Solution: (a) Drawing and labeling the circuit is left to the student. The inductive reactance is

$$X_L = 2\pi f L = 2\pi \times 60 \times 0.35 = 132 \ \Omega$$

Draw the vector diagram as shown in Fig. 29-18. Then, since

$$\tan \theta = \frac{X_L}{R} = \frac{132}{120} = 1.10$$
$$\therefore \theta = 47.7°$$

Note that the phase angle denotes the position of the applied voltage with respect to the current which is taken as a reference. Thus an inductive series circuit always has a "lagging" phase angle which is a *positive*

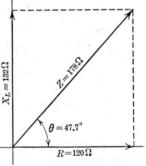

FIG. 29-18.

angle when resistance, reactance, and impedance are plotted vectorially.

(b)
$$Z = \frac{R}{\cos \theta} = \frac{120}{\cos 47.7°} = 178 \ \Omega$$

or
$$Z = \frac{X_L}{\sin \theta} = \frac{132}{\sin 47.7°} = 178 \ \Omega$$

(c)
$$I = \frac{E}{Z} = \frac{440}{178} = 2.47 \ a$$

29-8. Resistance and Capacity in Series. Figure 29-19 represents a circuit in which an alternating electromotive force of 100 volts is applied across a combination of 6 ohms resistance in series with 8 ohms capacitive reactance. Note the similarity between the circuits of Fig. 29-15 and Fig. 29-19. Both have the same values of resistance and absolute values of reactance. However, in the circuit of Fig. 29-19, the voltage drop across the capacitive reactance is 90° behind the current. Again using the current as a reference, because it is the same in all parts of the circuit, the voltage across the resistance and the voltage across the capacitive reactance are plotted as shown in Fig. 29-20 and treated as rectangular components of the applied electromotive force. The impedance of the circuit is found in the same manner

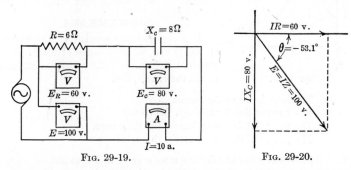

Fig. 29-19.   Fig. 29-20.

as that of the inductive circuit, that is, by vector addition of the rectangular components. The phase angle is found by the same method.

$$\tan \theta = \frac{X_c}{R} = \frac{8}{6} = 1.33$$
$$\therefore \ \theta = -53.1°$$

In the capacitive circuit the current leads the voltage, and we prefix the phase angle with a minus sign because of its position (Art. 22-2).

Example. A circuit consisting of 175 ohms resistance in series with a condenser of 5.0 microfarads is connected across a source of 150 volts, 120 cycles. Determine

(a) The phase angle between voltage and current.
(b) The impedance of the circuit.
(c) The current through the circuit.

Solution: (a) Drawing and labeling the circuit is left to the student. The capacitive reactance is

$$X_c = \frac{1}{2\pi f C} = \frac{1}{2\pi \times 120 \times 5 \times 10^{-6}} = \frac{10^4}{2\pi \times 1.2 \times 5} = 265 \ \Omega$$

Draw the vector diagram as shown in Fig. 29-21.   Then, since

$$\tan \theta = \frac{X_c}{R} = \frac{265}{175} = 1.51$$
$$\therefore \theta = -56.6°$$

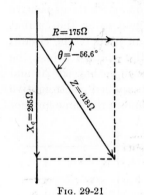

FIG. 29-21

Thus the current is leading the voltage by 56.6°, as shown by the vector diagram.

(b) $$Z = \frac{R}{\cos \theta} = \frac{175}{\cos 56.6°} = 318 \ \Omega$$

or $$Z = \frac{X_c}{\sin \theta} = \frac{265}{\sin 56.6°} = 318 \ \Omega$$

(c) $$I = \frac{E}{Z} = \frac{150}{318} = 0.472 \ a$$

PROBLEMS 29-4

1. A series circuit consists of a resistance of 150 Ω and an inductance of 0.5 h. If a potential difference of 220 v, 60 $\sim$ is applied across the circuit, find

(a) The impedance of the circuit
(b) The current flowing through the circuit.
(c) The potential difference across the resistance.
(d) The potential difference across the inductance.

2. A 0.01-h choke has an effective resistance of 22.8 Ω at 800 $\sim$.   If an alternating e m.f of 110 v, 800 $\sim$ is impressed across the choke, find

(a) The impedance of the choke.
(b) The current.

3. A circuit consists of 800 Ω resistance in series with an inductance of 360 μh.   There are 2000 v, 1000 kc impressed across the circuit.   On the assumption that the inductance is of negligible resistance, find

(a) The impedance of the circuit
(b) The current flowing through the circuit
(c) The potential difference across the resistance.
(d) The potential difference across the inductance

4. In the circuit of Prob. 3, the applied voltage is held constant while the frequency is decreased until the current is twice the value found in Prob 3.   Under this condition, find

(a) The impedance.
(b) The frequency.

5. A series circuit consists of a resistance of 125 Ω and a condenser of 12 μf   If a potential difference of 440 v, 60 $\sim$ is applied across the circuit, find

(*a*) The impedance of the circuit.
(*b*) The current flowing through the circuit.
(*c*) The potential difference across the resistance.
(*d*) The potential difference across the condenser.

6. What is the impedance at 21 Mc of a series circuit consisting of a resistance of 25 Ω and a condenser of 75 μμf?

7. What will be the impedance of the circuit of Prob. 6 if an additional condenser of 75 μμf is connected in parallel with the original condenser?

8. What will be the impedance of the circuit of Prob. 6 if an additional resistance of 50 Ω is connected in series with the original circuit?

9. A circuit consists of 100 Ω resistance in series with a condenser of 250 μμf. If 500 v, 1500 kc is impressed upon the circuit, find

(*a*) The impedance of the circuit.
(*b*) The current flowing through the circuit.
(*c*) The potential difference across the resistance.
(*d*) The potential difference across the condenser.

10. In the circuit of Prob. 9, what must be the capacity of a condenser connected in parallel with the original condenser in order to increase the current to three times the value found in Prob. 9?

29-9. Resistance, Inductance, and Capacity in Series.

It has been shown that inductive reactance causes the current to lag the voltage and that capacitive reactance causes the current to lead the voltage; hence, these two reactions are

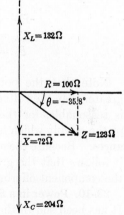

exactly opposite in effect. Figure 29-22 represents a series circuit consisting of resistance, inductance, and capacity connected across an alternator that supplies 220 volts, 60 cycles.

Now $\omega = 2\pi f = 2\pi \times 60 = 377$

Therefore, $X_L = \omega L = 377 \times 0.35 = 132\ \Omega$

and $X_c = \dfrac{1}{\omega C} = \dfrac{1}{377 \times 13 \times 10^{-6}} = \dfrac{10^3}{3.77 \times 1.3} = 204\ \Omega$

FIG. 29-22.   FIG. 29-23.

Figure 29-23 is a vector diagram of the conditions existing in the circuit. Since X_L and X_c are oppositely directed vectors, it is evident that the resultant reactance will have a magnitude equal to their algebraic sum and with the direction of the greater. Therefore, the net reactance of the circuit is a capacitive reactance of 72 ohms as illustrated in Fig. 29-23. Thus the entire circuit could be replaced by an equivalent series circuit consisting of 100 ohms resistance and 72 ohms capacitive reactance, provided that the frequency of the alternator remains constant.

The impedance, current, and potential differences are found by the usual methods.

$$\tan \theta = \frac{X_c}{R} = \frac{72}{100} = 0.72$$
$$\therefore \ \theta = -35.8°$$
$$Z = \frac{X}{\sin \theta} = \frac{72}{\sin 35.8°} = 123 \ \Omega$$
$$I = \frac{E}{Z} = \frac{220}{123} = 1.79 \ a$$
$$E_R = IR = 1.79 \times 100 = 179 \ v$$
$$E_L = IX_L = 1.79 \times 132 = 236 \ v$$
$$E_c = IX_c = 1.79 \times 204 = 365 \ v$$

Note that the potential difference across the reactances is greater than the voltage impressed across the entire circuit. This is reasonable, for the applied voltage is across the impedance of the circuit which is a smaller value, in ohms, than the reactances. Because the current is common to all circuit components, it follows that the greatest potential difference will exist across the component offering the greatest opposition.

29-10. Power in a Series Circuit of Resistance and Reactance. It has been shown that, in a circuit consisting of resistance only, no power is returned to the source of voltage. Also, it has been shown that a circuit containing reactance alone consumes no power; that is, a reactance alternately receives and returns all power to the source. It is evident, therefore, that in a circuit containing both resistance and reactance there must be some power expended in the resistance and also some returned to the source by the reactance. Figure 29-24 represents the relation among voltage, current, and power in the circuit of Fig. 29-22.

As previously stated, the instantaneous power in the circuit is equal to the product of the applied voltage and the current through the circuit. When the voltage and current are of the same sign, they are acting together and taking power from the source. When their signs are unlike, they are operating in

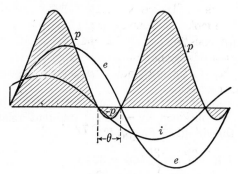

Fig. 29-24.

opposite directions and power is returned to the source. The *apparent power* is

$$P_a = EI \tag{37}$$

and the actual power taken by the circuit, which is called the *true power* or *active power*, is

$$P = I^2 R \tag{38}$$

or

$$P = E_R I \tag{39}$$

where E_R is the potential difference across the resistance of the circuit.

The *power factor* of a circuit is the ratio of the true power to the apparent power. That is,

$$\text{P.f.} = \frac{P}{P_a} \tag{40}$$

Substituting the value of P from Eq. (38) and that of P_a in Eq. (37),

$$\text{P.f.} = \frac{I^2 R}{EI} = \frac{IR}{E}$$

Then, since

$$E = IZ$$

$$\text{P.f.} = \frac{IR}{IZ}$$

or

$$\text{P.f.} = \frac{R}{Z} \tag{41}$$

Hence, the power factor of a series circuit may be obtained by dividing the resistance of a circuit by its impedance. The power factor is often expressed in terms of the angle of lead or lag. From preceding vector diagrams, it is evident that

$$\frac{R}{Z} = \cos \theta$$

$$\therefore \text{P.f.} = \cos \theta \qquad (42)$$

From Eq. (40), $P = P_a$ p.f.

Substituting for P_a, $P = EI$ p.f.

Substituting for the power factor, $P = EI \cos \theta \qquad (43)$

From the foregoing, it is seen that the power expended in a circuit may be obtained by utilizing different relations. For example, in the circuit of Fig. 29-22,

$$P = I^2 R = 1.79^2 \times 100 = 320 \text{ w}$$
$$P = E_R I = 179 \times 1.79 = 320 \text{ w}$$

and $P = EI \cos \theta = 220 \times 1.79 \times \cos 35.8° = 320 \text{ w}$

The power factor of a circuit may be expressed as a decimal or as a percentage. Thus the power factor of this circuit is

$$\cos \theta = \cos 35.8° = 0.812$$

Expressed as percentage,

$$\text{P.f.} = 100 \cos 35.8° = 81.2\%$$

29-11. Solution of Series Circuits by Employing the Tangent of the Phase Angle. A method of computing the impedance of series circuits that is convenient for slide-rule operators confines itself to the use of the tangent of the phase angle. The derivation of this method is based upon the relation

$$Z = \sqrt{R^2 + X^2}$$

Multiplying and dividing by R^2, $Z = \dfrac{R^2 \sqrt{R^2 + X^2}}{R^2}$

Then $Z = R \sqrt{\dfrac{R^2}{R^2} + \dfrac{X^2}{R^2}} = R \sqrt{1 + \left(\dfrac{X}{R}\right)^2} = R \sqrt{1 + \tan^2 \theta}$

The impedance is found on the slide rule as follows: Divide the reactance by the resistance, using scales C and D, so that the quotient, which is tan θ, appears on scale D opposite the index

of C.   Now $\tan^2 \theta$ is on scale A opposite the index of B.   Add 1
to the value of $\tan^2 \theta$, and set the index of B to $(1 + \tan^2 \theta)$ on A.

Now $\sqrt{1 + \tan^2 \theta}$ is on scale D opposite the index of C, ready
to be multiplied by the resistance.

29-12. Notation for Series Circuits.   In Art. 3-4, it was
shown that positive and negative "real" numbers could be
represented graphically by plotting them along a horizontal
line.   The positive numbers were plotted to the right of zero, and
the negative numbers were plotted to the left.   This idea was
expanded in Art. 15-2 where the original horizontal line was
made the X axis for a system of rectangular coordinates.

In Art. 17-13 the system of representation was extended to
include the "imaginary" numbers by agreeing to plot them
along the Y axis, the letter j being used as a symbol of operation.
Thus, when some number is prefixed with j, it means that the
vector which the number represents is to be rotated through an
angle of 90°.   The rotation is positive, or in a counterclockwise
direction, when the sign of j is positive; and negative, or in a
clockwise direction, when the sign of j is negative.

From the foregoing, it is evident that resistance, when plotted
on a vector diagram, is considered as a "real" number because
it is plotted along the X axis.   In this instance the term "real"
may well define resistance, for it is the only opposition to the
flow of current that consumes power.

Since reactances are displaced 90° from resistance in a vector
diagram, it follows that inductive reactance can be prefixed
with a plus j and capacitive reactance by a minus j.   Thus, an
inductive reactance of 75 ohms would be written $j75$ ohms and
plotted on the positive Y axis; a capacitive reactance of 86 ohms
would be written $-j86$ ohms and plotted on the negative Y axis.

It has been shown that a vector can be completely described
in terms of its rectangular components.   For example, the circuit of Fig. 29-15 can be described as consisting of an impedance
of 10 ohms at an angle of 53.1°, which would be written

$$Z = 10 \underline{/53.1°} \ \Omega$$

where the angle sign is included for emphasis and the number of
degrees denotes the angle that the vector makes with the positive
X axis.   This is known as *polar form*.   Since this impedance is

made up of 6 ohms of resistance and 8 ohms of inductive reactance, we may write

$$Z = R + jX_L = 6 + j8 \ \Omega$$

This is known as *rectangular form.*

The rectangular form is a very convenient method of notation.
For example, instead of writing "A series circuit of 4 ohms

Circuit	Vector	Z Rectangular Form	Z Polar Form
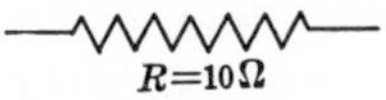 $R=10\,\Omega$	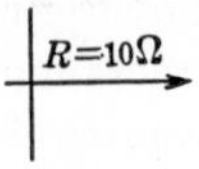 $R=10\,\Omega$	$Z=10+j0\,\Omega$	$Z=10\ \underline{/0°}\ \Omega$
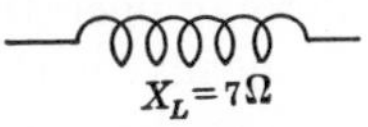 $X_L=7\,\Omega$	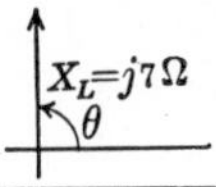 $X_L=j7\,\Omega$, θ	$Z=0+j7\,\Omega$	$Z=7\ \underline{/90°}\,\Omega$
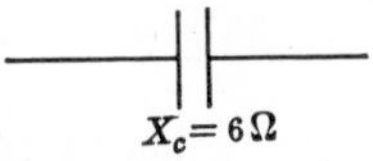 $X_c=6\,\Omega$	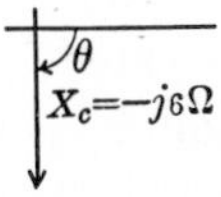 θ, $X_c=-j6\,\Omega$	$Z=0-j6\,\Omega$	$Z=6\ \underline{/-90°}\,\Omega$
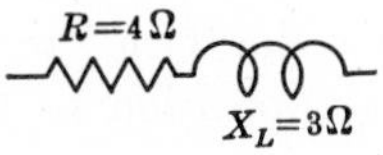 $R=4\,\Omega$, $X_L=3\,\Omega$	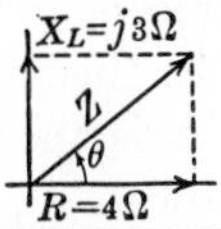 $X_L=j3\,\Omega$, θ, $R=4\,\Omega$	$Z=4+j3\,\Omega$	$Z=5\ \underline{/36.9°}\,\Omega$
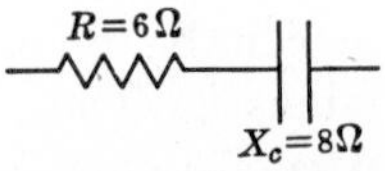 $R=6\,\Omega$, $X_c=8\,\Omega$	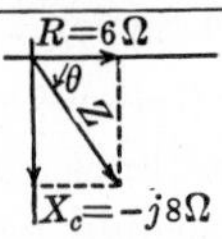 $R=6\,\Omega$, θ, $X_c=-j8\,\Omega$	$Z=6-j8\,\Omega$	$Z=10\ \underline{/-53.1°}\,\Omega$
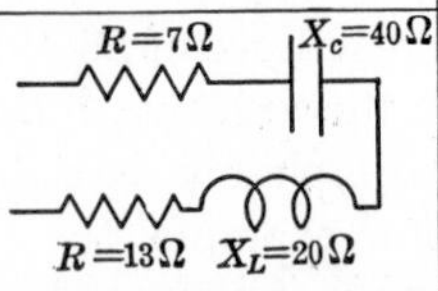 $R=7\,\Omega$ $X_c=40\,\Omega$, $R=13\,\Omega$ $X_L=20\,\Omega$	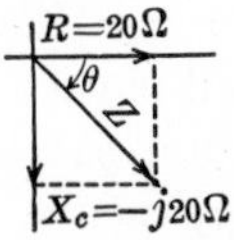 $R=20\,\Omega$, θ, $X_c=-j20\,\Omega$	$Z=20-j20\,\Omega$	$Z=28.2\ \underline{/45°}\,\Omega$

Fig. 29-25.

resistance and 3 ohms capacitive reactance," we may write
"A series circuit of $4 - j3$ ohms." Figure 29-25 shows the
various types of series circuits with their proper vector diagram
and corresponding notation.

*Note that the sign of the phase angle is the same as that of j in
the rectangular form.*

It must be understood that neither the rectangular form nor the polar form are methods for solving series circuits. They are simply convenient forms of notation that completely describe circuit conditions from both electrical and mathematical viewpoints.

29-13. Conversion from Rectangular to Polar Form and Vice Versa. In converting from rectangular to polar form, the usual methods of solution are used.

Example 1. Find the vector impedance of a series circuit of $250 - j100$ ohms.

Solution: Given $Z = R - jX = 250 - j100$ ohms.

$$\tan \theta = \frac{X}{R} = \frac{100}{250} = 0.4$$

$$\therefore \theta = -21.8°$$

$$Z = \frac{X}{\sin \theta} = \frac{100}{\sin 21.8°} = 269 \ \Omega$$

or

$$Z = \frac{R}{\cos \theta} = \frac{250}{\cos 21.8°} = 269 \ \Omega$$

Hence

$$Z = 269 \ \underline{/-21.8°} \ \Omega$$

Converting from rectangular form to polar form, which is simply vector addition of rectangular components, may be completed with a total of three movements on many types of slide rule.

Converting from polar form, in which the magnitude and angle are given, to rectangular form is simplified by making use of the trigonometric functions. Since

$$R = Z \cos \theta$$
$$X = Z \sin \theta$$

and

$$Z = R \pm jX \tag{44}$$

by substitution,

$$Z = Z \cos \theta + jZ \sin \theta \tag{45}$$

Factoring,

$$Z = Z (\cos \theta + j \sin \theta) \tag{46}$$

The $\pm$ sign is omitted in Eqs. (45) and (46) because, if the proper angles are used (positive or negative), the respective sine values will determine the proper sign of the reactance component.

Example 2. A series circuit has an impedance of 269 ohms with a leading power factor of 0.928. What are the reactance and resistance of the circuit?

Solution: Given $Z = 269$ ohms and p.f. $= 0.928$. The power factor, when expressed as a decimal, is equal to the cosine of the phase angle.

Hence, if

$$0.928 = \cos \theta$$

then
$$\theta = -21.8°$$

The angle was given the minus sign because a "leading power factor" means the current leads the voltage. Therefore,

$$Z = 269 \,\underline{/-21.8°}\ \Omega$$

Substituting these values in Eq. (45),

$$Z = 269 \cos 21.8° - j269 \sin 21.8° = 250 - j100 \ \Omega$$

29-14. The General Series Circuit. In a series circuit consisting of several resistances and reactances, the total resistance of the circuit is the sum of all the series resistances and the total reactance is the algebraic sum of the series reactances. That is, the total resistance is

$$R_t = R_1 + R_2 + R_3 + \cdots$$

and the reactance of the circuit is

$$X = j(\omega L_1 + \omega L_2 + \omega L_3 \cdots) - j\left(\frac{1}{\omega C_1} + \frac{1}{\omega C_2} + \frac{1}{\omega C_3} \cdots\right)$$

Hence, the impedance is

$$Z = R_t \pm jX$$

As an alternate method, such a circuit can always be reduced to an equivalent series circuit by combining inductances and capacitances before computing reactances. Thus, the total inductance is

$$L_t = L_1 + L_2 + L_3 \cdots$$

and the capacitance of the circuit is

$$\frac{1}{C_t} = \frac{1}{C_1} + \frac{1}{C_2} + \frac{1}{C_3} \cdots$$

However, when voltage drops across individual reactances are desired, it is best to find the equivalent circuit by combining reactances.

Example. Given the circuit of Fig. 29-26, which is supplied by 220 volts, 60 cycles. Find

(a) The equivalent series circuit.
(b) The impedance of the circuit.
(c) Current.
(d) Power factor.
(e) Power expended in the circuit.
(f) Apparent power.
(g) Voltage drop across C_1.
(h) Power expended in R_2.

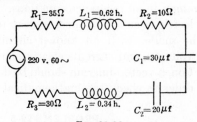

$R_1 = 35\Omega$ $L_1 = 0.62$ h. $R_2 = 10\Omega$

220 v. 60 ~ $C_1 = 30\mu f$

$R_3 = 30\Omega$ $L_2 = 0.34$ h. $C_2 = 20\mu f$

Fig. 29-26.

Solution: (a) $R_t = R_1 + R_2 + R_3 = 35 + 10 + 30 = 75\ \Omega.$
$$\omega = 2\pi f = 2\pi \times 60 = 377$$
$$L_t = L_1 + L_2 = 0.62 + 0.34 = 0.96\ \text{h}$$
$$X_L = \omega L = 377 \times 0.96 = 362\ \Omega$$
$$X_{C_1} = \frac{1}{\omega C_1} = \frac{1}{377 \times 30 \times 10^{-6}} = \frac{10^3}{3.77 \times 3} = 88.4\ \Omega$$
$$X_{C_2} = \frac{1}{\omega C_2} = \frac{1}{377 \times 20 \times 10^{-6}} = \frac{10^3}{3.77 \times 2} = 132.6\ \Omega$$
$$X_C = 88.4 + 132.6 = 221\ \Omega$$
$$X = X_L - X_C = 362 - 221 = 141\ \Omega$$

The equivalent series circuit consists of a resistance of 75 ohms and an inductive reactance of 141 ohms. That is,

$$Z = 75 + j141\ \Omega$$

The vector diagram for the equivalent circuit is shown in Fig. 29-27.

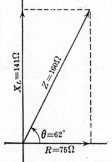

(b) $\tan \theta = \dfrac{X}{R_t} = \dfrac{141}{75} = 1.88$

         $\therefore\ \theta = 62°$

         $Z = \dfrac{R}{\cos \theta} = \dfrac{75}{\cos 62°} = 160\ \Omega$

Hence, $Z = 160\ \underline{/62°}\ \Omega$

(c) $I = \dfrac{E}{Z} = \dfrac{220}{160} = 1.38\ \text{a}$

(d)   P.f. $= \cos \theta = \cos 62° = 0.470$

Expressed as a percentage,

         P.f. $= 47.0\%$

(e) $P = EI \cos \theta = 220 \times 1.38 \times \cos 62° = 143\ \text{w}$

Fig. 29-27.

or $P = I^2R = 1.38^2 \times 75 = 143$ w

(f) $P_a = EI = 220 \times 1.38 = 304$ va

(g) $E_{C_1} = IX_{C_1} = 1.38 \times 88.4 = 122$ v

(h) $P_{R_2} = I^2R_2 = 1.38^2 \times 10 = 19$ w

The student will find it convenient to compute the value of the angular velocity $\omega = 2\pi f$ for all alternating-current problems, for this factor is common to all reactance equations.

As with all electric-circuit problems, a neat diagram of the circuit should be made, with all known circuit components, voltages, and currents clearly marked. In addition, a vector diagram should be drawn to scale in order to check the mathematical solution.

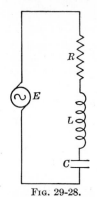

FIG. 29-28.

PROBLEMS 29-5

Given the circuit of Fig. 29-28, with the values as listed in Probs. 1 to 10. Draw a vector diagram for each circuit, and find

(a) The impedance of the circuit.

(b) The current flowing through the circuit.

(c) The equation of the current.

(d) The p.f. of the circuit.

(e) The power expended in the circuit.

Problem	E	f	R	L	C
1	440 v	60 $\sim$	500 Ω	3.5 h	12 μf
2	660 v	25 $\sim$	600 Ω	8.0 h	50 μf
3	110 v	50 $\sim$	1000 Ω	5.1 h	8.5 μf
4	110 v	800 $\sim$	50 Ω	4.8 mh	25 μf
5	1250 v	100 kc	250 Ω	800 μh	0.015 μf
6	1 v	1000 kc	20 Ω	90 μh	250 $\mu\mu$f
7	500 v	355 kc	15 Ω	375 μh	500 $\mu\mu$f
8	50 v	28 Mc	4.5 Ω	1.2 μh	25 $\mu\mu$f
9	100 v	7200 kc	10 Ω	12.5 μh	45 $\mu\mu$f
10	220 v	60 $\sim$	200 Ω	1.5 h	5 μf

11. A certain choke coil, when connected across 110 v d.c., draws 2 a from the line. When connected across 110 v, 60 $\sim$, the current is 0.25 a.

(a) What is the resistance of the coil?

(b) What is its inductive reactance?

(c) What is the inductance?

12. On the assumption that the effective resistance of the coil of Prob. 11 remains constant, how much power would it consume when connected across 120 v, 800 $\sim$?

13. The following 60-cycle impedances are connected in series:

$$Z_1 = 3 - j6 \ \Omega$$
$$Z_2 = 10 + j19 \ \Omega$$
$$Z_3 = 2 - j7 \ \Omega$$
$$Z_4 = 5 + j14 \ \Omega$$

(a) What is the vector impedance of the circuit?
(b) What value of capacitance must be added in series to make the p.f. of the circuit 70.7% leading?

14. The meters represented in Fig. 29-29 are connected such a short distance from an inductive load that line drop from meters to load is negligible. What is the equivalent series circuit of the load?

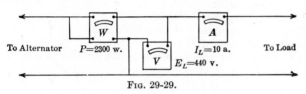

To Alternator P=2300 w. I_L=10 a. E_L=440 v.   To Load

FIG. 29-29.

15. A single-phase induction motor, with 440 v across its input terminals, delivers 10.8 mechanical horsepower at an efficiency of 90% and a p.f. of 86.6%.

(a) What is the line current?
(b) How much power is taken by the motor?

16. Given any series circuit, for example, 110 v at 60 $\sim$ applied across $3 + j4 \ \Omega$. On the same set of axes and to the same scale, plot instantaneous values of the applied voltage e, the potential difference across the resistance R, and the potential difference across the reactance X. What is your conclusion?

29-15. Series Resonance. It has been shown that the inductive reactance of a circuit varies directly as the frequency and that the capacitive reactance varies inversely as the frequency. That is, the inductive reactance will increase and the capacitive reactance will decrease as the frequency is increased, and vice versa. Then, for any value of inductance and capacitance in a circuit, there is a frequency at which the inductive reactance and the capacitive reactance are equal. This is called the *resonant frequency* of the circuit. Since, in a series circuit,

$$Z = R + j \left(\omega L - \frac{1}{\omega C} \right)$$

at resonance, $\omega L = \dfrac{1}{\omega C}$ (47)

Hence, $Z = R$

Therefore, at the resonant frequency of a series circuit, the resistance is the only circuit component that limits the flow of current, for the net reactance of the circuit is zero. Thus the current is in phase with the applied voltage which results in a circuit power factor of 100 per cent.

Example. There are impressed 10 volts, at a frequency of 1000 kilocycles across a circuit consisting of a coil of 92.2 microhenrys in series with a capacitance of 275 micromicrofarads. The effective resistance of the coil at this frequency is 10 ohms, and the resistance of the connecting wires and capacitance are negligible.

(a) What is the impedance of the circuit?

(b) How much current flows through the circuit?

(c) What is the potential difference across the reactances?

Solution: The resistance of the coil is treated as being in series with the inductive reactance.

(a) $\omega = 2\pi f = 6.28 \times 10^6$

$X_L = \omega L = 6.28 \times 10^6 \times 92.2 \times 10^{-6} = 6.28 \times 92.2 = 579\ \Omega$

$X_c = \dfrac{1}{\omega C} = \dfrac{1}{6.28 \times 10^6 \times 275 \times 10^{-12}} = \dfrac{10^4}{6.28 \times 2.75} = 579\ \Omega$

Since $X_L = X_c$

then $Z = R = 10\ \Omega$

(b) $I = \dfrac{E}{Z} = \dfrac{10}{10} = 1\ \text{a}$

(c) $E_c = IX_c = 1 \times 579 = 579\ \text{v}$

$E_L = IX_L = 1 \times 579 = 579\ \text{v}$

Note that the voltages across the inductance and capacitance are much greater than the applied voltage.

The *merit* of an inductance, denoted by Q, is defined as the ratio of its inductive reactance to its resistance. Thus,

$$Q = \frac{\omega L}{R} \qquad (48)$$

Then, at resonance, $E_c = E_L = I\omega L$

Substituting for I, $E_c = E_L = \dfrac{E\omega L}{R}$

Substituting for $\dfrac{\omega L}{R}$, $E_c = E_L = EQ$ (49)

Because the average radio circuit has purposely been designed for high Q values, it is seen that very high voltages may be developed in resonant series circuits.

29-16. Resonant Frequency.   The resonant frequency of a circuit may be determined by rewriting Eq. (47).   Thus,

$$2\pi f L = \frac{1}{2\pi f C}$$

$$\therefore f = \frac{1}{2\pi \sqrt{LC}} \tag{50}$$

where f, L, and C are in the usual units, cycles per second, henrys, and farads, respectively.

Example 1.   A series circuit consists of an inductance of 500 microhenrys and a condenser of 400 micromicrofarads.   What is the resonant frequency of the circuit?

Solution: $L = 500 \, \mu\text{h} = 5 \times 10^{-4}$ h, $C = 400 \, \mu\mu\text{f} = 4 \times 10^{-10}$ f

$$f = \frac{1}{2\pi \sqrt{LC}} = \frac{1}{2\pi \sqrt{5 \times 10^{-4} \times 4 \times 10^{-10}}} = \frac{10^7}{2\pi \sqrt{20}} = 356{,}000 \sim$$

or $f = 356$ kc

From Eq. (50) it is evident that the resonant frequency of a series circuit depends *only* upon the LC product.   This means there is an infinite number of combinations of L and C that will resonate to a particular frequency.

Example 2.   How much capacity is required to obtain resonance at 1500 kilocycles with an inductance of 45 microhenrys?

Solution: $f = 1500$ kc $= 1.5 \times 10^6 \sim$, $L = 45 \, \mu\text{h} = 4.5 \times 10^{-5}$ h
$$\omega = 2\pi f = 2\pi \times 1.5 \times 10^6 = 9.42 \times 10^6$$

From Eq. (50), $C = \dfrac{1}{(2\pi f)^2 L} = \dfrac{1}{\omega^2 L}$

$$\therefore C = \frac{1}{(9.42 \times 10^6)^2 \times 4.5 \times 10^{-5}} = 250 \, \mu\mu\text{f}$$

PROBLEMS 29-6

1. Twenty-five volts, 600 kc, is impressed across a series circuit consisting of 350 $\mu\mu$f and 201 μh.   At this frequency the effective resistance of the inductance is 13 Ω.

(a) How much current flows through the circuit?
(b) How much power is expended in the circuit?
(c) What are the voltages existing across the inductive and capacitive reactances?

2. What is the Q of the coil in Prob. 1?

3. A tuning condenser has a maximum capacity of 100 $\mu\mu$f and a minimum capacity of 10 $\mu\mu$f. What inductance must be used with the condenser if the lowest resonant frequency is to be 3750 kc? What is the highest resonant frequency?

4. A series circuit consists of an inductance of 8 μh, with an effective resistance of 5 Ω, and a condenser. A current of 0.5 a flows through the circuit at its resonant frequency of 7500 kc.

  (*a*) Wnat is the Q of the coil?
  (*b*) What is the capacitance of the condenser?
  (*c*) What is the impressed voltage across the circuit?
  (*d*) What is the potential difference across the condenser?

5. What is the equivalent circuit of a series circuit when operating at

  (*a*) Resonant frequency?
  (*b*) At a frequency less than resonant frequency?
  (*c*) At a frequency greater than resonant frequency?

CHAPTER XXX

ALTERNATING CURRENTS—PARALLEL CIRCUITS

Parallel circuits are the most commonly encountered circuits in use. The average distribution circuit has many types of loads all connected in parallel with each other, lighting circuits, motors, transformers for various uses, etc. The same is true for communication circuits which range from the most simple parallel circuits to complex networks.

This chapter deals with the solutions of parallel circuits. These solutions consist in reducing a parallel circuit to an equivalent series circuit that, when connected to the same source of electromotive force as the given parallel circuit, would result in the same line current and phase angle.

30-1. Resistances in Parallel. It was explained in Arts. 29-1 and 29-2 that, in an alternating-current circuit containing resistance only, the voltage, current, and power relations were the same as in direct-current circuits. However, in order to build a foundation from which all parallel circuits can be analyzed, the case of paralleled resistances must be considered from a vector viewpoint.

Figure 30-1 represents a 60-cycle 220-volt alternator connected to three resistances in parallel.

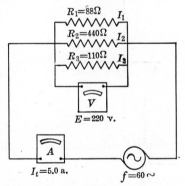

Fig. 30-1.

Neglecting the internal resistance of the alternator and the resistance of the connecting wires, the electromotive force of the alternator is impressed across each of the three resistances. Then, if I_1, I_2, and I_3 represent the currents flowing through R_1, R_2, and R_3, respectively, by Ohm's law,

$$I_1 = 2.5 \text{ a}$$
$$I_2 = 0.5 \text{ a}$$
and $$I_3 = 2.0 \text{ a}$$

457

Since all currents are in phase, the total current flowing in the line, or external circuit, will be equal to the sum of the branch currents, or 5.0 amperes. The vector diagram for the three currents is shown in Fig. 30-2. All currents are plotted in phase with the applied electromotive force which is used as a reference vector because the voltage is common to all resistances. Then, using vector notation,

$$I_1 = 2.5 + j0 \text{ a}$$
$$I_2 = 0.5 + j0 \text{ a}$$
$$I_3 = 2.0 + j0 \text{ a}$$
$$\overline{I_t = 5.0 + j0 \text{ a}}$$

or
$$I_t = 5.0 \ \underline{/0°} \text{ a}$$

As with all other circuits, the ·equivalent series impedance, which in this case is a pure resistance, is found by dividing the

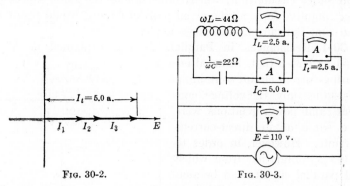

FIG. 30-2.   FIG. 30-3.

potential difference across the circuit by the total current. That is,

$$Z = \frac{E}{I_t} = \frac{220}{5} = 44 \ \Omega$$

or
$$Z = 44 \ \underline{/0°} \ \Omega$$

30-2. Inductance and Capacitance in Parallel. When a purely inductive reactance and a capacitive reactance are connected in parallel, as shown in Fig. 30-3, currents flow through these reactances that differ in phase by 180°.

The current flowing through the inductance is

$$I_L = \frac{E}{\omega L} = \frac{110}{44} = 2.5 \text{ a}$$

and that through the condenser is

$$I_c = \omega CE = \tfrac{110}{22} = 5.0 \text{ a}$$

In series circuits, the current is used as a reference vector because the current is the same in all parts of the circuit. In parallel circuits there are different values of currents in various parts of the circuit; hence, the current can no longer be used as the reference vector. However, because the same voltage exists across two or more parallel branches, this applied voltage may be used as the reference vector as shown in Fig. 30-4.

Note that the current I_L through the inductance is plotted as lagging the impressed voltage by 90° and the current I_c through the condenser is leading the voltage by 90°. The total line current I_t, which is the vector sum of the branch currents, is leading the impressed voltage by 90°. That is, using vector notation,

$$I_L = 0 - j2.5 \text{ a}$$
$$\underline{I_c = 0 + j5.0 \text{ a}}$$
$$I_t = 0 + j2.5 \text{ a}$$
or
$$I_t = 2.5 \ \underline{/90°} \text{ a}$$

Since the line current leads the impressed voltage by 90°, the equivalent series circuit consists of a condenser with a capacitive reactance of

$$\frac{E}{I_t} = \frac{110}{2.5} = 44 \ \Omega$$

Note the difference between reactances in series and reactances in parallel. In a series circuit the *greatest* reactance of the circuit results in the equivalent series circuit containing the same kind of reactance. For this reason, it is said that reactances, or voltages across reactances, are the controlling factors of series circuits. In a parallel circuit the *least* reactance of the circuit, which passes the greatest current, results in the equivalent series circuit containing the same kind of reactance. For this reason, it is said that currents are the controlling factors of parallel circuits.

30-3. Assumed Voltages. The solutions of the great majority of parallel circuits are facilitated by assuming a voltage to exist across a parallel combination. The current through each branch, due to the assumed voltage, is then added vectorially to obtain the total current. The assumed voltage is then divided by the total current, the quotient being the joint impedance of the parallel branches.

The assumed voltage should always be a power of ten in order that the slide-rule operator may utilize to the full the reciprocal scales and reciprocal relations on the rule. Choosing an assumed voltage that is a power of ten is an aid to the student even though

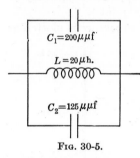

FIG. 30-5.

he does not operate a slide rule, for currents and impedances can be found by making use of reciprocal tables.

In order to avoid small decimal quantities the assumed voltage should be greater than the largest impedance of any parallel branch.

Example. Given the circuit of Fig. 30-5. What are the impedance and the power factor of the circuit at a frequency of 2500 kilocycles?

Solution: C_1 and C_2 are in parallel; hence, the total capacity is

$$C_t = C_1 + C_2 = 200 + 125 = 325 \ \mu\mu f$$

This simplifies the circuit to a condenser C of 325 $\mu\mu f$ in parallel with an inductance L of 20 μh.

$$\omega = 2\pi f = 2\pi \times 2.5 \times 10^6 = 1.57 \times 10^7$$
$$X_L = \omega L = 1.57 \times 10^7 \times 2 \times 10^{-5} = 314 \ \Omega$$
$$X_c = \frac{1}{\omega C} = \frac{1}{1.57 \times 10^7 \times 325 \times 10^{-12}} = \frac{10^3}{1.57 \times 3.25} = 196 \ \Omega$$

Assume 1000 volts across the parallel branch. Then the current through the condenser is

$$I_c = \frac{E_a}{X_c} = \frac{1000}{196} = 5.10 \ a$$

and the current through the inductance is

$$I_L = \frac{E_a}{X_L} = \frac{1000}{314} = 3.18 \ a$$

Since I_c leads the assumed voltage by 90° and I_L lags the assumed voltage by 90°, they are plotted with the assumed voltage as reference vector as shown in Fig. 30-6. Then the total current I_t, that would flow owing to the assumed voltage would be the vector sum of I_c and I_L. Adding vectorially,

$$I_c = 0 + j5.10 \ a$$
$$I_L = 0 - j3.18 \ a$$
$$\overline{I_t = 0 + j1.92 \ a}$$

or

$$I_t = 1.92 \ \underline{/90°} \ a$$

Again, since the total current leads the voltage by 90°, the equivalent series circuit consists of a condenser whose capacitive reactance is

$$\frac{E_a}{I_t} = \frac{1000}{1.92} = 521 \ \Omega$$

Since $\theta = 90°$,   p.f. $= \cos \theta = 0$.

The student should solve the circuit of Fig. 30-5, using different values of assumed voltages.

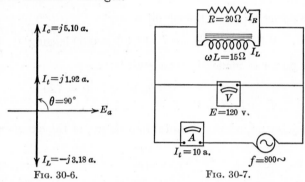

FIG. 30-6.   FIG. 30-7.

30-4. Resistance and Inductance in Parallel.

When a resistance and an inductive reactance are connected in parallel, as represented in Fig. 30-7, currents flow that differ in phase by 90°.

The current flowing through the resistance is

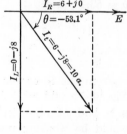

$$I_R = \frac{E}{R} = \frac{120}{20} = 6.0 \ a$$

and that through the inductance is

$$I_L = \frac{E}{\omega L} = \frac{120}{15} = 8.0 \ a$$

Since the current through the resistance   FIG. 30-8.

is in phase with the applied voltage and the current through the inductance lags the applied voltage by 90°, I_R and I_L are plotted with the applied voltage as reference vector as shown in Fig. 30-8. Then the total current I_t, or line current, is the vector sum of I_R and I_L. Adding these vectorially,

$$I_R = 6.0 + j0 \ a$$
$$I_L = 0 - j8.0 \ a$$
$$\overline{I_t = 6.0 - j8.0 \ a}$$

Hence, the total current, which consists of an "in phase" component of 6.0 amperes and a 90° lagging component of 8.0 amperes, is expressed in terms of its rectangular components. The magnitude and phase angle are then found by the usual trigonometric methods. Thus,

$$I_t = 10 \; \underline{/-53.1°} \; \text{a}$$

The power factor of the circuit is

$$\text{P.f.} = \cos \theta = \cos (-53.1°) = 0.60 \text{ lagging}$$

The power expended in the circuit is

$$P = EI \cos \theta = 120 \times 10 \times 0.60 = 720 \text{ w}$$

or $\qquad P = I_R{}^2R = 6^2 \times 20 = 720 \text{ w}$

The joint impedance, or total impedance, of the circuit is

$$Z_t = \frac{E}{I_t} = \frac{120}{10} = 12 \; \Omega$$

Since the entire circuit has a lagging power factor of 0.60, it follows that the equivalent series circuit consists of a resistance and an inductive reactance in series, the vector sum of which is 12 ohms at a phase angle θ such that $\cos \theta = 0.60$. Therefore, $\theta = 53.1°$, and

$$Z_t = 12 \; \underline{/53.1°} \; \Omega$$
$$\therefore Z_t = 12 \; (\cos 53.1° + j \sin 53.1°)$$
$$= 7.2 + j9.6 \; \Omega$$

From the foregoing, it is evident that the parallel circuit of Fig. 30-7 could be replaced by a series circuit of 7.2 ohms resistance and 9.6 ohms inductive reactance and that the alternator would be working under exactly the same load conditions as before.

In order to justify such solutions, the student should solve for the joint impedance of the circuit of Fig. 30-7 by using an assumed voltage and then using the *actual* voltage to obtain the power.

30-5. Resistance and Capacity in Parallel. When a resistance and a capacitive reactance are connected in parallel, as represented in Fig. 30-9, the current through the resistance is in phase with the voltage across the parallel combination, and the current through the capacitive reactance leads this voltage by 90°.

The circuit of Fig. 30-9 is similar to that of Fig. 30-7 except that Fig. 30-9 contains a capacitive reactance of 15 ohms in place of the inductive reactance of 15 ohms. The vector diagram of currents is shown in Fig. 30-10, and it is evident that the total current is

$$I_t = 6.0 + j8.0 \text{ a}$$

or $\qquad\qquad I_t = 10 \ \underline{/53.1°} \text{ a}$

The power factor of the circuit is

$$\text{P.f.} = \cos \theta = \cos 53.1° = 0.60 \text{ leading}$$

Similarly, the total impedance of the circuit is 12 ohms; and since the circuit has a leading power factor of 0.60, it follows that

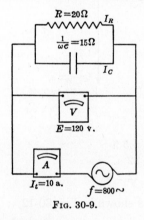

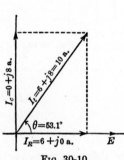

Fig. 30-9.   Fig. 30-10.

the equivalent series circuit consists of a resistance and capacitive reactance in series the vector sum of which is 12 ohms at a phase angle θ such that $\cos \theta = 0.60$. Therefore,

$$\theta = -53.1°$$

and $\qquad\qquad Z_t = 12 \ \underline{/-53.1°} \ \Omega$

$$\therefore Z_t = 7.2 - j9.6 \ \Omega$$

If the parallel circuit of Fig. 30-9 were replaced by a series circuit of 7.2 ohms resistance and 9.6 ohms capacitive reactance, the alternator would be working under exactly the same load conditions as before.

30-6. Resistance, Inductance, and Capacity in Parallel. When resistance, inductive reactance, and capacitive reactance are connected in parallel, as represented in Fig. 30-11, the line current is the vector sum of the several currents.

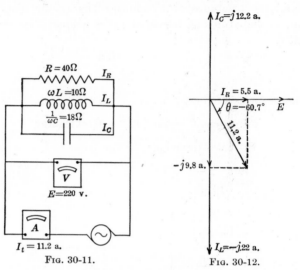

FIG. 30-11.

FIG. 30-12.

The currents through the branches are

$$I_R = \tfrac{220}{40} = 5.5 \text{ a}$$
$$I_L = \tfrac{220}{10} = 22 \text{ a}$$

and
$$I_c = \tfrac{220}{18} = 12.2 \text{ a}$$

Adding these currents vectorially as shown in Fig. 30-12,

$$I_R = 5.5 + j0 \text{ a}$$
$$I_L = 0 - j22 \text{ a}$$
$$I_c = 0 + j12.2 \text{ a}$$
$$\overline{I_t = 5.5 - j9.8 \text{ a}}$$
$$\therefore I_t = 11.2 \underline{/-60.7^\circ} \text{ a}$$
$$\text{P.f.} = \cos(-60.7^\circ) = 0.489 \text{ lagging}$$

The total impedance is

$$Z_t = \frac{E}{I_t} = \frac{220}{11.2} = 19.6 \ \Omega$$

Since the circuit has a lagging power factor of 0.489, the equivalent series circuit consists of a resistance and an inductive reactance. The vector sum of these must be 19.6 ohms at a phase angle θ such that $\cos \theta = 0.489$. Therefore, $\theta = 60.7°$ and

$$Z_t = 19.6 \ \underline{/60.7°} \ \Omega$$
$$\therefore \ Z_t = 9.59 + j17.1 \ \Omega$$

which are the values comprising the equivalent series circuit.

Example. Given the circuit represented in Fig. 30-13. Solve for the equivalent series circuit at a frequency of 5000 kilocycles.

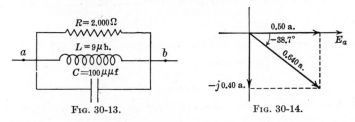

FIG. 30-13.   FIG. 30-14.

Solution: $f = 5,000 \text{ kc} = 5 \times 10^6 \sim$
$L = 9 \ \mu\text{h} = 9 \times 10^{-6} \text{ h}$
$C = 100 \ \mu\mu\text{f} = 10^{-10} \text{ f}$
$\omega = 2\pi f = 2\pi \times 5 \times 10^6 = 3.14 \times 10^7$
$X_L = \omega L = 3.14 \times 10^7 \times 9 \times 10^{-6} = 283 \ \Omega$
$X_c = \dfrac{1}{\omega C} = \dfrac{1}{3.14 \times 10^7 \times 10^{-10}} = \dfrac{10^3}{3.14} = 318 \ \Omega$

Assume $E_a = 1000$ volts applied between a and b.

$$I_R = \frac{E_a}{R} = \frac{1000}{2000} = 0.50 \text{ a}$$
$$I_L = \frac{E_a}{X_L} = \frac{1000}{283} = 3.54 \text{ a}$$
$$I_c = \frac{E_a}{X_c} = \frac{1000}{318} = 3.14 \text{ a}$$

The total current I_t is the vector sum of the three branch currents as represented in the vector diagram of Fig. 30-14. Adding vectorially,

$$I_R = 0.50 + j0 \quad \text{a}$$
$$I_L = 0 \quad - j3.54 \text{ a}$$
$$I_c = 0 \quad + j3.14 \text{ a}$$
$$\overline{I_t = 0.50 - j0.40 \text{ a}}$$
$$\therefore \ I_t = 0.640 \ \underline{/-38.7°} \text{ a}$$
$$\text{P.f.} = \cos (-38.7°) = 0.78 \text{ lagging}$$

The total impedance Z_t, which is the impedance between points a and b, is

$$Z_t = Z_{ab} = \frac{E_a}{I_t} = \frac{1000}{0.64} = 1560 \ \Omega$$

Since the current is lagging the voltage, the equivalent series circuit consists of a resistance and an inductive reactance. The vector sum of these is 1560 ohms at a phase angle θ such that $\cos \theta = 0.78$. Therefore, $\theta = 38.7°$ and

$$Z_t = 1560 \,\underline{/38.7°}\ \Omega$$
$$\therefore Z_t = 1220 + j976\ \Omega$$

That is, the equivalent series circuit is a resist-

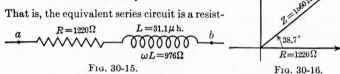

a $R=1220\Omega$ $L=31.1\mu\,\text{h.}$ b
$\omega L=976\Omega$

Fig. 30-15.

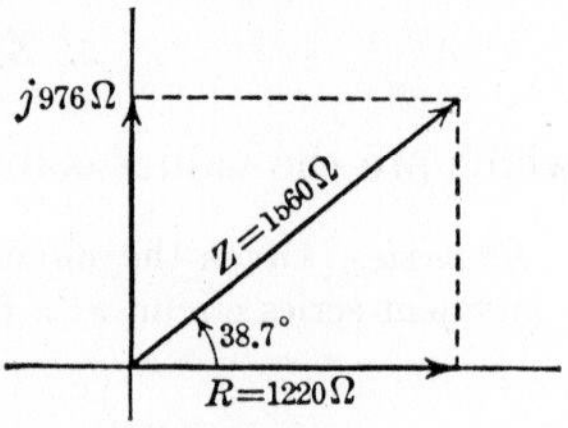

Fig. 30-16.

ance of $R = 1220\ \Omega$ and an inductive reactance of $\omega L = 976\ \Omega$. Since

$$\omega L = 976\ \Omega$$

then
$$L = \frac{976}{\omega} = \frac{976}{3.14 \times 10^7} = 31.1\ \mu\text{h}$$

which results in the equivalent circuit as represented in Fig. 30-15 with the vector diagram of Fig. 30-16.

PROBLEMS 30-1

1. In Fig. 30-17, $R = 250\ \Omega$, $L = 0.5$ h, $C = 4\ \mu\text{f}$, $f = 60 \sim$, and $E = 440$ v.

    (a) What is the reading of the ammeter?
    (b) How much power is expended in the circuit?
    (c) What is the equivalent series circuit?

2. In Fig. 30-17, $R = 8000\ \Omega$, $L = 120\ \mu\text{h}$, $C = 350\ \mu\mu\text{f}$, $f = 750$ kc, and $E = 1000$ v.

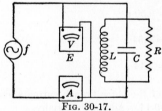

Fig. 30-17.

    (a) What is the reading of the ammeter?
    (b) What is the p.f. of the circuit?
    (c) What is the equivalent series circuit?

3. Using the values of Prob. 2, what capacitance must be connected in parallel with C in order to obtain a circuit p.f. of 1.0?

4. Using the values of Prob. 2,

    (a) At what frequency would the circuit have a p.f. of 1.0?
    (b) What is the impedance of the circuit at this frequency?

5. In Fig. 30-17, $R = 600\ \Omega$, $L = 0.03$ h, $C = 1\ \mu\text{f}$, $f = 800 \sim$ and $E = 120$ v.

    (a) What is the reading of the ammeter?
    (b) What capacitance must be connected in parallel with C in order to obtain a circuit p.f. of 1.0?

30-7. Vector Impedances in Parallel.   Figure 30-18 represents an alternator supplying 220 volts across two paralleled impedances.

The impedance of branch a is

$$Z_a = R_a + jX_L = 35 + j50 = 61 \,\underline{/55°} \; \Omega$$

and the current through this branch is

$$I_a = \frac{E}{Z_a} = \frac{220}{61} = 3.61 \text{ a}$$

Similarly, $Z_b = R_b - jX_c = 75 - j30 = 80.8 \,\underline{/-21.8°} \; \Omega$

and $I_b = \dfrac{E}{Z_b} = \dfrac{220}{80.8} = 2.72 \text{ a}$

Figure 30-19 is the vector diagram of the branch currents I_a and I_b.   The applied voltage E is used as reference vector because

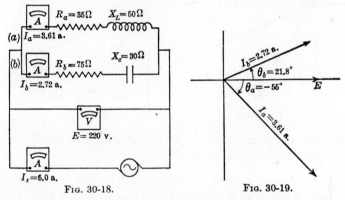

FIG. 30-18.   FIG. 30-19.

it is common to both impedances, or branches.   Note that the angles of the current vectors are opposite in sign to those of their respective impedances.   That is, I_a lags the applied voltage, whereas I_b leads the voltage.

The applied voltage E must be divided by the current I_t in order to obtain the total impedance of the circuit Z_t.   The total current, or line current, is the vector sum of the branch currents I_a and I_b and can be found by graphical methods, as explained in Art. 27-3.   However, the vector sum of two or more vectors is found readily and accurately by the addition of their respective rectangular components.   Hence, the resistive, or *inphase*, component of I_a is

$$I_a \cos \theta_a = 3.61 \cos (-55°) = 2.07 \text{ a}$$

and the reactive component is

$$I_a \sin \theta_a = 3.61 \sin (-55°) = -2.96 \text{ a}$$

Similarly, the resistive component of I_b is

$$I_b \cos \theta_b = 2.72 \cos 21.8° = 2.53 \text{ a}$$

and the reactive component is

$$I_b \sin \theta_b = 2.72 \sin 21.8° = 1.01 \text{ a}$$

The above process of determining the rectangular components of the vectors is simply a matter of converting the vectors from

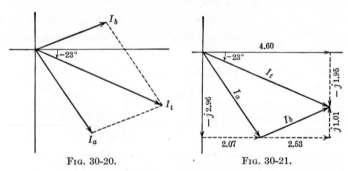

FIG. 30-20.   FIG. 30-21.

polar form to rectangular form, as explained in Art. 29-13.   This conversion is more compactly written

$$I_a = 3.61[\cos (-55°) + j \sin (-55°)] = 2.07 - j2.96 \text{ a}$$
$$I_b = 2.72(\cos 21.8° + j \sin 21.8°) \quad = 2.53 + j1.01 \text{ a}$$
$$\therefore \ I_t = 4.60 - j1.95 \text{ a}$$

The total current I_t is now expressed in terms of its rectangular components, which consist of a resistive component of 4.60 amperes and a lagging component of 1.95 amperes. The magnitude of I_t and the phase angle are found by the usual methods of vector addition. Thus,

$$I_t = 4.60 - j1.95 = 5.00 \underline{/-23°} \text{ a}$$

As with all alternating-current problems, vector diagrams should be drawn in order to clarify the various relations and to serve as an approximate check on the results obtained by computations. Thus, the magnitude and direction of I_t may be checked by graphical vector addition by either of the methods explained in Art. 27-3.   The first method is utilized in Fig. 30-20, and the second method in Fig. 30-21.

Since the current is lagging the voltage by 23° in the external circuit, the equivalent series circuit must be a resistance and an inductive reactance.   Hence,

$$Z_t = \frac{E}{I_t} = \frac{220}{5} = 44 \ \underline{/23°} \ \Omega$$

or

$$Z_t = 44(\cos 23° + j \sin 23°)$$
$$= 40.5 + j17.2 \ \Omega$$

$$\text{P.f.} = \cos 23° = 0.920 \text{ lagging}$$

$$P = EI \cos \theta$$
$$= 220 \times 5 \times \cos 23° = 1010 \text{ w}$$

or

$$P = I^2 R = 5^2 \times 40.5 = 1010 \text{ w}$$

Example.   A 60-cycle alternator delivers 110 volts to a load that consists of seventy-five 100-watt lamps and a 15-horsepower induction motor that operates at 90 per cent efficiency with a power factor of 0.80 lagging.   How much current is supplied by the alternator, and what is the power factor?

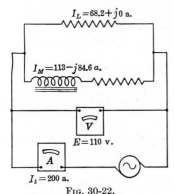

$I_L = 68.2 + j0$ a.

$I_M = 113 - j84.6$ a.

$E = 110$ v.

$I_t = 200$ a.

Fig. 30-22.

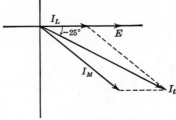

Fig. 30-23.

Solution: The current taken by the lamps, which can be considered as a resistive load, is

$$I_L = \frac{75 \times 100}{110} = 68.2 \text{ a}$$

The power delivered to the motor is

$$P = \frac{746 \times 15}{0.90} = 12.4 \text{ kw}$$

Then, since $P = EI(\text{p.f.})$

the current taken by the motor is

$$I_M = \frac{P}{E(\text{p.f.})} = \frac{12,400}{110 \times 0.80} = 141 \text{ a}$$

which consists of a resistive component and a lagging reactive component. The phase angle θ is 36.9° (power factor $=$ cos $\theta = 0.8$). That is,

$$I_M = 141 \,\underline{/-36.9°}\, a$$
$$= 141[\cos\,(-36.9°) + j \sin\,(-36.9°)]$$
$$= 113 - j84.6 \text{ a}$$

The circuit is represented in Fig. 30-22 and the vector diagram of the currents in Fig. 30-23.

The current I_t supplied by the alternator is the vector sum of the load currents I_L and I_M. Hence,

$$I_L = \quad 68.2 + j0 \quad\; a$$
$$I_M = 113 \quad - j84.6 \text{ a}$$
$$\overline{I_t \;=\; 181.2 - j84.6 \text{ a}}$$
$$= 200 \,\underline{/-25°}\, a$$

P.f. $=$ cos $(-25°) = 0.906$ lagging

or   P.f $= \dfrac{181.2}{200} = 0.906$ lagging

30-8. Summarized Procedure for Solving Parallel Circuits by the Total Current Method.

1. Draw a neat, simplified diagram of the circuit.

2. Label, on the diagram, all the known values such as voltages, currents, resistances, reactances, and impedances.

3. Carefully study the circuit so that all relations are understood.

4. Find the vector impedance (polar form) of each parallel branch.

5. If the voltage across a parallel branch is not known, assume a voltage to be across it.

6. Divide the voltage of (5), either actual or assumed, by the vector impedance of each parallel branch. The quotient is the vector current through the branch and must be assigned an angle equal in magnitude but opposite in sign to the respective impedance.

7. Resolve the currents through the parallel branches into their rectangular components, and add them. This sum represents the rectangular components of the total current through the parallel combination.

8. Find the vector current (polar form) of the total current found in (7).

9. Divide the voltage of (5) by the vector current found in (8). The quotient is the joint vector impedance of the parallel combination and must be assigned an angle equal in magnitude but opposite in sign to the total current found in (8).

10. Resolve the joint impedance found in (9) into an equivalent series circuit.

11. The equivalent series circuit found in (10) can be combined with other series resistances and reactances in order to find the total impedance of the circuit.

12. Draw vector diagrams throughout the solution. These will help in understanding circuit conditions and will serve as a valuable check to computations.

Example.   Given the circuit of Fig. 30-24.   Solve for the equivalent series circuit Z_t, the total current I_t, the power expended in the circuit, and the power factor.

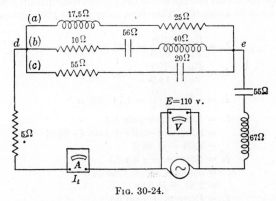

Fig. 30-24.

Solution: Although the student should be familiar with the mathematical methods involved in this solution, all steps will be shown because everything learned regarding series and parallel circuits must be utilized.

The numbered parts of the solution correspond to those in the summary above. The three parallel branches are marked (a), (b), and (c). These letters will be used as subscripts to represent quantities involved in the respective branches. Thus, Z_a is the impedance of branch (a), I_b is the current through branch (b), etc.

(4)
$$Z_a = R + jX_L = 25 + j17.5 \ \Omega$$
$$\theta_a = \text{arc tan} \frac{X_L}{R_a} = \frac{17.5}{25} = 0.700$$
$$\therefore \theta_a = 35°$$
$$Z_a = \frac{X_L}{\sin \theta_a} = \frac{17.5}{\sin 35°} = \frac{17.5}{0.574} = 30.5 \ \Omega$$
$$\therefore Z_a = 30.5 \ \underline{/35°} \ \Omega$$

$$Z_b = R + j(X_L - X_c) = 10 - j16 \ \Omega$$

$$\mathcal{E}_b = \text{arc tan} \ \frac{X_c}{R_b} = \frac{16}{10} = 1.6$$

$$\therefore \ \theta_b = -58°$$

$$Z_b = \frac{X_c}{\sin \theta_b} = \frac{16}{\sin 58°} = \frac{16}{0.848} = 18.9 \ \Omega$$

$$\therefore \ Z_b = 18.9 \ \underline{/-58°} \ \Omega$$

$$Z_c = R - jX_c = 55 - j20 \ \Omega$$

$$\theta_c = \text{arc tan} \ \frac{X_c}{R_c} = \frac{20}{55} = 0.364$$

$$\therefore \ \theta_c = -20°$$

$$Z_c = \frac{X_c}{\sin \theta_c} = \frac{20}{\sin 20°} = \frac{20}{0.342} = 58.5 \ \Omega$$

$$\therefore \ Z_c = 58.5 \ \underline{/-20°} \ \Omega$$

(5) Because the actual voltage across the parallel combination is not known, a voltage must be assumed. Therefore, assume that 100 volts exist across d and e.

(6)
$$I_a = \frac{E_{de}}{Z_a} = \frac{100}{30.5} = 3.28 \ \underline{/-35°} \ \text{a}$$

$$I_b = \frac{E_{de}}{Z_b} = \frac{100}{18.9} = 5.30 \ \underline{/58°} \ \text{a}$$

$$I_c = \frac{E_{de}}{Z_c} = \frac{100}{58.5} = 1.71 \ \underline{/20°} \ \text{a}$$

(7)
$$\begin{aligned}
I_a &= I_a(\cos \theta_a + j \sin \theta_a) \\
&= 3.28[\cos (-35°) + j \sin (-35°)] \\
&= 2.69 - j1.88 \ \text{a} \\
I_b &= I_b(\cos \theta_b + j \sin \theta_b) \\
&= 5.30(\cos 58° + j \sin 58°) \\
&= 2.81 + j4.50 \ \text{a} \\
I_c &= I_c(\cos \theta_c + j \sin \theta_c) \\
&= 1.71(\cos 20° + j \sin 20°) \\
&= 1.61 + j0.585 \ \text{a}
\end{aligned}$$

The total current I_t in rectangular form is the sum of I_a, I_b, and I_c.

$$\begin{aligned}
I_a &= 2.69 - j1.88 \ \text{a} \\
I_b &= 2.81 + j4.50 \ \text{a} \\
I_c &= 1.61 + j0.585 \ \text{a} \\
\hline
I_t &= 7.11 + j3.205 \ \text{a}
\end{aligned}$$

(8)
$$\theta_{de} = \text{arc tan} \ \frac{\text{reactive component of } I_t}{\text{resistive component of } I_t} = \frac{3.20}{7.11} = 0.450$$

$$\therefore \ \theta_{de} = \underline{/24.2°}$$

$$I_{de} = \frac{\text{reactive component of } I_{de}}{\sin \theta_{de}} = \frac{3.20}{\sin 24.2°} = 7.80 \ \text{a}$$

or
$$I_{de} = \frac{\text{resistive component of } I_{de}}{\cos \theta_{de}} = \frac{7.11}{\cos 24.2°} = 7.80 \ \text{a}$$

$$\therefore \ I_{de} = 7.80 \ \underline{/24.2°} \ \text{a}$$

(9)	$$Z_{de} = \frac{E_{de}}{I_{de}} = \frac{100}{7.80} = 12.8 \; \underline{/-24.2°} \; \Omega$$

(10)	$$\begin{aligned}Z_{de} &= Z_{de}(\cos\theta + j\sin\theta) \\ &= 12.8[\cos(-24.2°) + j\sin(-24.2°)] \\ &= 11.7 - j5.26 \; \Omega\end{aligned}$$

(11) The resistance and reactance in series with the parallel combination make up a series impedance Z_s that is in series with the equivalent series impedance Z_{de} of the paralleled branches. Therefore, the vector sum of Z_s and Z_{de} is the equivalent series impedance of the entire circuit. Thus,

$$\begin{aligned}Z_{de} &= 11.7 - j5.26 \; \Omega \\ Z_s &= 5 \quad + j12 \; \Omega \\ \hline Z_t &= 16.7 + j6.74 \; \Omega\end{aligned}$$

$$\theta_t = \text{arc tan } \frac{X_t}{R_t} = \frac{6.74}{16.7} = 0.404$$

$$\therefore \; \theta_t = 22°$$

$$Z_t = \frac{X_t}{\sin\theta_t} = \frac{6.74}{\sin 22°} = 18.0 \; \underline{/22°} \; \Omega$$

$$I_t = \frac{E}{Z_t} = \frac{110}{18.0} = 6.11 \text{ a}$$

$$P = EI_t \cos\theta_t = 110 \times 6.11 \times \cos 22° = 623 \text{ w}$$

or	$$P = I_t^2 R_t = 6.11^2 \times 16.7 = 623 \text{ w}$$

$$\text{P.f.} = \cos\theta_t = \cos 22° = 0.927 \text{ lagging}$$

Figure 30-25 is the vector diagram for the current relations in the parallel branches, and the impedance diagram for the entire circuit is shown in Fig. 30-26.

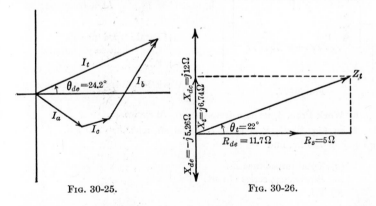

Fig. 30-25.	Fig. 30-26.

Although the solutions of such circuits involve a large number of computations, time and labor are saved in working all problems by careful planning. In addition, the student who does not use a slide rule should endeavor to become proficient in the use of the tables.

Proficiency in operating a slide rule enables one to solve such circuits in a fraction of the time required for solutions by ordinary computations.

PROBLEMS 30-2

1. Impedances $Z_a = 30 + j36$, and $Z_b = 76 - j50$ are connected in parallel. If a potential difference of 440 v is impressed across them, determine

    (*a*) The equivalent series impedance of the circuit.

    (*b*) The power expended in the circuit.

2. An alternator supplies 220 v across a load consisting of impedances $Z_a = 55 \underline{/40°}\ \Omega$ and $Z_b = 71 \underline{/-36°}\ \Omega$ in parallel. Find

    (*a*) The p.f. of the load.

    (*b*) The power expended in Z_b.

3. An induction motor, which takes 85 a at a lagging p.f. of 80% from a 440-v line, is operating in parallel with a synchronous motor that draws 50 a at a p.f. of 60% leading.

    (*a*) What is the line current?

    (*b*) What is the p.f. of the combination?

    (*c*) What is the power taken from the line?

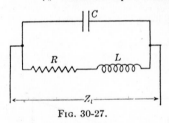

FIG. 30-27.

4. In Fig. 30-27, $R = 50\ \Omega$, $L = 0.705$ h, and $C = 10\ \mu f$. At a frequency of 50 cycles, find

    (*a*) Total impedance Z_t.

    (*b*) Equivalent series circuit.

    (*c*) P.f.

5. Work Prob. 4, using a frequency of 60 cycles.

6. Work Prob. 4, using a frequency of 70 cycles.

7. In Fig. 30-27, $R = 17\ \Omega$. $L = 180\ \mu h$, and $C = 250\ \mu\mu f$. A' a frequency of 730 kc, find

    (*a*) Total impedance Z_t.

    (*b*) Equivalent series circuit.

    (*c*) P.f.

8. Work Prob. 7, using a frequency of 750 kc.

9. Work Prob. 7, using a frequency of 770 kc.

10. An 800-cycle alternator supplies 120 v to an impedance of $9.16 \underline{/40.2°}\ \Omega$.

(a) How much current is supplied by the alternator?

(b) What sized condenser must be connected in parallel with the impedance in order to make the combination a load of unity p.f.?

(c) How much current will be taken from the alternator after the condenser is connected across the impedance?

11. A 16-μf condenser must be connected in parallel with a load Z_R in order to obtain unity p.f. This results in a current of 10 a at 120 v from an 800-cycle alternator.

(a) How much current did the alternator supply to the load before connecting the condenser?

(b) What was the p.f. of the load before connecting the condenser?

(c) What is the equivalent series impedance of Z_R?

(d) How much power is expended in the load?

12. A 60-cycle alternator supplies 440 v, 6.64 a to a coil. When a 20-μf condenser is connected in parallel with the coil, the line p.f. becomes unity.

(a) What is the effective resistance of the coil?

(b) What is the inductance of the coil?

13. Two separate shops are supplied with a-c power from the same alternator. The load taken by one shop is 64 kw at a p.f. of 0.80 lagging. The total load on the alternator is 130 kw at a power factor of 0.65 lagging. What is the p.f. of the other shop?

14. A load consisting of impedances $Z_a = 25 - j18.5$, $Z_b = 75 + j30$, and $Z_c = 10 - j15$ is connected in parallel across an alternator with an internal impedance of $Z_s = 1.5 + j2.6$. If the e.m.f. of the alternator is 260 v, find

(a) Current taken by load.

(b) Power taken by the load.

15. The load on a 230-v 60-cycle alternator consists of a 50-hp motor with a p.f. of 87% lagging and an efficiency of 85%, a lighting load of 10 kw with unity p.f., and a synchronous motor that takes 100 a with a p.f. of 55% leading.

(a) How much power is taken by the entire load?

(b) How much current is taken by the 50-hp motor?

16. An induction motor (lagging p.f.) draws 37.1 a from a 440-v 60-cycle line. A resistance across the line draws 19 a. An ammeter connected in the line reads a total of 53.6 a.

(a) What is the p.f. of the motor?

(b) How much power is taken by the motor?

(c) What sized condenser must be connected across the line in order to reduce the line current to unity p.f.?

17. In Fig. 30-28, let $R_1 = 50$ Ω, $R_2 = 100$ Ω, $R_3 = 100$ Ω, $L = 10$ μh, $C = 100$ $\mu\mu$f, and $f = 5000$ kc.

(a) What is the impedance Z_t across the alternator?

(b) If a current of 287 ma flows through R_3, what is the alternator voltage E?

18. In Fig. 30-28, let $R_1 = 10\ \Omega$, $R_2 = 250\ \Omega$, $R_3 = 200\ \Omega$, $L = 120\ \mu$h, $C = 150\ \mu\mu$f, and $f = 1200$ kc.

(a) What is the impedance across the alternator?

(b) If a potential difference of 11.3 v exists across R_1, what is the alternator voltage E?

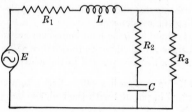

FIG. 30-28.

19. In Fig. 30-28, let $R_1 = 40\ \Omega$, $R_2 = 500\ \Omega$, $R_3 = 1000\ \Omega$, $L = 0.15$ h, $C = 2\ \mu$f, and $f = 1000$ cycles.

(a) What is the impedance of the circuit?

(b) What is the p.f. of the circuit?

(c) If a potential difference of 2.84 v exists across R_2, what is the alternator voltage E?

20. In Fig. 30-29, let $R_1 = 200\ \Omega$, $R_2 = 100\ \Omega$, $R_3 = 150\ \Omega$, $R_4 = 5\ \Omega$, $\omega L_1 = 39.6\ \Omega$, $X_c = 53.2\ \Omega$, $\omega L_2 = 450\ \Omega$, $\omega L_3 = 3\ \Omega$, and $E = 220$ v.   Find

(a) Line current I_t.

(b) Circuit p.f.

(c) Potential difference between points a and b.

(d) Current through R_3.

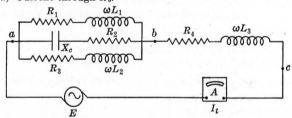

FIG. 30-29.

21. In Fig. 30-29, let $R_1 = 5\ \Omega$, $R_2 = 15\ \Omega$, $R_3 = 10\ \Omega$, $R_4 = 1.5\ \Omega$, $\omega L_1 = 22\ \Omega$, $X_c = 8\ \Omega$, $\omega L_2 = 31\ \Omega$, $\omega L_3 = 2.1\ \Omega$, and $E = 100$ v.   Find

(a) Line current I_t.

(b) Circuit p.f.

(c) Potential difference across condenser.

(d) Current through R_1.

22. In Prob. 21, if the frequency is 800 cycles, what sized condenser must be connected across points a and c in order to reduce the line current to unity p.f.?

23. In Fig. 30-29, let $R_1 = 3$ Ω, $R_2 = 5$ Ω, $R_3 = 12$ Ω, $R_4 = 4$ Ω, $\omega L_1 = 4.8$ Ω, $X_c = 4.66$ Ω, $\omega L_2 = 7.5$ Ω, and $\omega L_3 = 6$ Ω. If the potential difference across the condenser is 26.4 v, find

    (a) Line current I_t.
    (b) Alternator voltage E.
    (c) Circuit p.f.
    (d) Difference of potential across points b and c.

24. In Prob. 23, how much current will flow through R_3, if points b and c are short-circuited?

25. Given the circuit of Fig. 30-30,

    (a) What is the impedance of the circuit?
    (b) How much current is taken from the alternator?
    (c) Would the removal of the 250-$\mu\mu$f condenser cause an appreciable change in the total current?

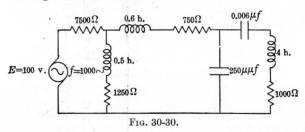

Fɪɢ. 30-30.

30-9. Parallel Resonance.

A large number of radio circuits and communication networks contain resonant parallel circuits. Figure 30-31 represents a typical parallel circuit consisting of an inductance and condenser in parallel. The resistance of the condenser, which is very small, may be neglected, and the resistance R represents the effective resistance of the inductance.

At low frequencies the inductive reactance is a low value, whereas the capacitive reactance is high. Hence, a large current flows through the inductive branch, and a small current flows through the capacitive branch. The vector sum of these currents causes a large lagging line current which, in effect, results in an equivalent series circuit of low impedance consisting of resistance and inductive reactance. At high frequencies the inductive reactance is large, and the capacitive reactance is small. This results in a large leading line current with an attendant equivalent series circuit of low impedance consisting of resistance and capacitive reactance.

There is one frequency, between those mentioned above, at which the lagging component of current through the inductive branch is equal to the leading current through the capacitive branch. This condition results in a small line current that is in phase with the voltage across the parallel circuit and therefore an impedance that is equivalent to a very high resistance.

The resonant frequency of a parallel circuit is often a source of confusion to the student studying parallel resonance for the first time. The reason for this is that different definitions for the resonant frequency are encountered in various texts. Thus, the

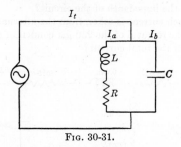

Fig. 30-31.

resonant frequency of a parallel circuit may be defined by any one of the following as:

1. The frequency at which the parallel circuit acts as a pure resistance.

2. The frequency at which the line current becomes minimum.

3. The frequency at which the inductive reactance equals the capacitive reactance. This is the same definition as that for the resonant frequency of a series circuit. That is,

$$\omega L = \frac{1}{\omega C}$$

or
$$f = \frac{1}{2\pi \sqrt{LC}} \tag{1}$$

A little consideration of these definitions will convince the student that, in high Q circuits, the three resonant frequencies differ by an amount so small as to be negligible.

In the circuit of Fig. 30-31,

$$I_b = \frac{E}{\dfrac{1}{\omega C}} = \omega C E$$

Also, $$I_a = \frac{E}{R + j\omega L}$$

Rationalizing (Art. 17-17),

$$I_a = \frac{E}{R + j\omega L} \cdot \frac{R - j\omega L}{R - j\omega L} = \frac{E(R - j\omega L)}{R^2 + (\omega L)^2}$$

$$= \frac{ER}{R^2 + (\omega L)^2} - j\,\frac{\omega L E}{R^2 + (\omega L)^2}$$

In order to satisfy the first definition for resonant frequency, the line current must be in phase with the applied voltage; that is, the out-of-phase, or quadrature, component of the current through the inductive branch must be equal to the current through the capacitive branch. Thus,

$$\frac{\omega L E}{R^2 + (\omega L)^2} = \omega C E$$

$\mathbf{D}:\omega E$, $$\frac{L}{R^2 + (\omega L)^2} = C$$

$\mathbf{M}:[R^2 + (\omega L)^2]$, $$L = [R^2 + (\omega L)^2]C \qquad (2)$$

or $$\frac{L}{C} - R^2 = (\omega L)^2$$

Hence, $$\omega = \frac{\sqrt{\dfrac{L}{C} - R^2}}{L} = \sqrt{\frac{1}{LC} - \frac{R^2}{L^2}}$$

Substituting $2\pi f$ for ω, $$2\pi f = \sqrt{\frac{1}{LC} - \frac{R^2}{L^2}}$$

Thus, the resonant frequency is $$f = \frac{1}{2\pi} \sqrt{\frac{1}{LC} - \frac{R^2}{L^2}} \qquad (3)$$

If the Q of the inductance is at all large, then $\omega L \gg R$, which, for all practical purposes, makes the term $\dfrac{R^2}{L^2}$ in Eq. (3) of such low value that it may be neglected, Eq. (3) being thus reduced to Eq.·(1).

Similarly, it may be shown that the condition of maximum impedance, as given in the second definition of parallel resonance, will be obtained when

$$f = \frac{1}{2\pi} \sqrt{\frac{1}{LC} - \frac{R^4 C}{2L^3}}$$ (4)

Equation (4) is similar to Eq. (3) in that both will reduce to Eq. (1) for nearly all radio circuits. The student should work out several examples, using different circuit values, and compare the resonant frequencies obtained from the formulas. In this connection, it is left as an exercise for the student to show that in a parallel resonant circuit, as represented in Fig. 30-31, the line current and applied voltage will be in phase (unity power factor) when

$$R^2 = X_L(X_c - X_L)$$ (5)

30-10. Impedance of Parallel Resonant Circuits. When a parallel circuit is operating at the frequency at which the circuit acts as a pure resistance, the circuit has unity power factor and the line current I_t (Fig. 30-31) consists of the inphase component of I_a. That is,

$$I_t = \frac{ER}{R^2 + (\omega L)^2}$$ (6)

Then, since $$Z_t = \frac{E}{I_t}$$

substituting in Eq. (6) for I_t,

$$\frac{E}{Z_t} = \frac{ER}{R^2 + (\omega L)^2}$$

Hence, $$Z_t = \frac{R^2 + (\omega L)^2}{R}$$ (7)

From Eq. (2), $$R^2 + (\omega L)^2 = \frac{L}{C}$$

Substituting this value in Eq. (7),

$$Z_t = \frac{L}{CR}$$ (8)

Example 1. In the circuit of Fig. 30-31, let $L = 203$ microhenrys, $C = 500$ micromicrofarads, and $R = 6.7$ ohms.

(a) What is the resonant frequency of the circuit?

(b) What is the impedance of the circuit at resonance?

Solution:

(a) $$f = \frac{1}{2\pi\sqrt{LC}} = \frac{1}{2\pi\sqrt{2.03 \times 10^{-4} \times 5 \times 10^{-10}}} = 500 \text{ kc}$$

(b) $$Z_t = \frac{L}{CR} = \frac{203 \times 10^{-6}}{500 \times 10^{-12} \times 6.7} = \frac{203}{5 \times 6.7} \times 10^4 = 60{,}600 \ \Omega$$

If the value of C is unknown, Eq. (8) may be used in different form. Thus, by multiplying both numerator and denominator by ω,

$$Z_t = \frac{\omega L}{\omega C R} = \frac{1}{\omega C} \cdot \frac{\omega L}{R}$$

Since at resonance, $$\omega L = \frac{1}{\omega C}$$

then $$Z_t = \frac{(\omega L)^2}{R} \tag{9}$$

Moreover, since $$Q = \frac{\omega L}{R}$$

substituting in Eq. (9), $Z_t = \omega L Q$ (10)

Example 2.   In the circuit of Fig. 30-31, let $L = 70.4$ microhenrys and $R = 5.31$ ohms. If the resonant frequency of the circuit is 1200 kc, determine

(a) Impedance of the circuit at resonance.

(b) The capacitance of the condenser.

Solution: $f = 1200$ kc $= 1.2 \times 10^6$ cycles

$$\omega = 2\pi f = 2\pi \times 1.2 \times 10^6 = 7.54 \times 10^6$$

(a) $$Z_t = \frac{(\omega L)^2}{R} = \frac{(7.54 \times 10^6 \times 70.4 \times 10^{-6})^2}{5.31} = 53{,}100 \ \Omega$$

(b) Since, at resonance, $\omega L = \frac{1}{\omega C}$ and $\omega L = 531 \ \Omega$,

then $$\frac{1}{\omega C} = 531 \ \Omega$$

Hence, $$C = \frac{1}{531\omega} = 250 \ \mu\mu f$$

What is the Q of this circuit?

PROBLEMS 30-3

1. An inductance of 24 μh and a condenser of 75 $\mu\mu$f are connected in parallel as shown in Fig. 30-31. If the effective resistance of the coil is 113 Ω, find

(a) Resonant frequency of circuit according to Definition 1 (Art. 30-9).

(b) Resonant frequency of circuit according to Definition 2 (Art. 30-9).

(c) Resonant frequency of circuit according to Definition 3 (Art. 30-9).

(d) Q of the inductance.

2. Repeat Prob. 1, but with the inductance having an effective resistance of 56.5 Ω.

3. An inductance of 14 μh with a Q of 100 is connected in parallel with a condenser of 32.2 $\mu\mu$f.

(a) What is the resonant frequency of the circuit?

(b) What is the impedance of the circuit at resonance?

(c) What is the effective resistance of the inductance?

4. How much power will be expended in the circuit of Prob. 3 if the impressed voltage across the parallel combination is 1000 v at the resonant frequency?

5. An inductance of 100 μh with a Q of 90 is connected in parallel with a condenser of 254 $\mu\mu$f.

(a) What is the resonant frequency of the circuit?

(b) What is the impedance of the circuit at resonance?

(c) What is the effective resistance of the inductance?

6. How much power will be expended in the circuit of Prob. 5 if the impressed voltage across the parallel combination is 100 v at the resonant frequency?

7. A condenser of 500 $\mu\mu$f is connected in parallel with an inductance. The resonant frequency was found by measurement to be 356 kc. The impedance of the circuit was measured at the resonant frequency and found to be 64,000 Ω. What is the Q of the inductance?

8. An inductance was measured with a Q meter and found to have a Q of 120. When a condenser was connected in parallel with the inductance, the resulting parallel circuit was resonant at 450 kc with an impedance of 84,000 Ω. What is the value of the inductance?

9. What is the capacity of the condenser in Prob. 8?

10. A condenser of 200 $\mu\mu$f is connected across an inductance. When 1000 v, at the resonant frequency of 1500 kc, is applied across this parallel circuit, the resulting line current is 18.9 ma. What is the Q of the inductance?

CHAPTER XXXI

VECTOR ALGEBRA

In the analysis of alternating-current circuits, it is often desirable to treat voltages, currents, and impedances algebraically in order to deal with circuit equations in general terms and simplify solutions. Moreover, many alternating-current problems are difficult to solve by the total-current method of solution described in Chap. XXX.

Because alternating currents and voltages are vector rather than scalar quantities, a form of vector algebra is introduced in this chapter to facilitate alternating-current circuit analysis.

31-1. Addition and Subtraction of Vectors in Rectangular Form. Complex numbers were introduced in Art. 17-14, and it was shown in Art. 29-12 that a vector can be completely described in terms of its rectangular components by expressing it as a complex number. For example, a vector 10 units in length and operating at an angle of 36.9° may be expressed in *polar form* by writing $10\underline{/36.9°}$. The same vector, expressed in terms of its *rectangular components*, is written as the complex number $8 + j6$.

As stated in Art. 17-15, complex numbers, or vectors in rectangular form, may be added or subtracted by treating them as ordinary binomials.

Example 1. Add $4.60 + j2.82$ and $2.11 - j8.10$.

Solution:
$$\begin{array}{r} 4.60 + j2.82 \\ 2.11 - j8.10 \\ \hline 6.71 - j5.28 \end{array}$$

Expressing the sum in polar form,

$$6.71 - j5.28 = 8.54 \underline{/-38.2°}$$

Example 2. Subtract $3.7 + j4.62$ from $14.6 - j8.84$.

Solution:
$$\begin{array}{r} 14.6 - j8.84 \\ 3.7 + j4.62 \\ \hline 10.9 - j13.46 \end{array}$$

Expressing the result in polar form,

$$10.9 - j13.46 = 17.3 \ \underline{/-51°}$$

PROBLEMS 31-1

Express the indicated sums in polar form.   Check results by graphical methods.

1. 6.4 − j 8.5
  10.3 + j19.8

2. 28.5 + j 30.0
  71.1 − j115

3. 600 − j425
  500 + j825

4. −5.43 − j16.8
  11.05 − j23.2

5.   126 + j843
  −568 − j102

6. −439 + j143
  123 − j578

Perform the following indicated subtractions, expressing the results in polar form.   Check results by graphical methods.

7. 25.9 − j46.8
  14.7 − j10.4

8.   6.73 − j 1.20
  −8.17 + j12.4

9. 600 − j 800
  900 − j1200

10. 80.9 − j45.2
  143 + j40.6

31-2. Multiplication of Vectors in Rectangular Form.   Multiplication of complex numbers was explained in Art. 17-16 where it was shown that vectors expressed in terms of their rectangular components are multiplied by treating them as ordinary binomials.

Example 1.   Multiply 8 + j5 by 10 + j9.

Solution:

$$\begin{array}{r} 8 + j5 \\ 10 + j9 \\ \hline 80 + j50 \\ + j72 + j^2 45 \\ \hline 80 + j122 + j^2 45 \end{array}$$

Since $j^2 = -1$, the product is

$$80 + j122 + (-1)45 = 80 + j122 - 45 = 35 + j122$$

Expressing the product in polar form,

$$35 + j122 = 127 \ \underline{/74°}$$

Example 2.   Multiply 80 + j39 by 35 − j50.

Solution:

$$\begin{array}{r} 80 + j39 \\ 35 - j50 \\ \hline 2800 + j1365 \\ - j4000 - j^2 1950 \\ \hline 2800 - j2635 - j^2 1950 \end{array}$$

Since $j^2 = -1$, the product is

$$2800 - j2635 - (-1)1950 = 2800 - j2635 + 1950 = 4750 - j2635$$

Expressing the product in polar form,

$$4750 - j2635 = 5430 \; \underline{/-29°}$$

31-3. Division of Vectors in Rectangular Form.

As explained in Art. 17-17, division of complex numbers, or vectors in rectangular form, is accomplished by rationalizing the denominator in order to obtain a "real" number for a divisor. Multiplying a complex number by its conjugate always results in a product that is a real number, that is, a number not affected by the operator j.

Example 1.　Find the quotient of $\dfrac{50 + j35}{8 + j5}$.

Solution: Multiply both dividend and divisor (numerator and denominator) by the conjugate of the divisor which is $8 - j5$.

Thus,　$\dfrac{50 + j35}{8 + j5} \cdot \dfrac{8 - j5}{8 - j5} = \dfrac{400 + j30 - j^2175}{64 - j^225} = \dfrac{575 + j30}{89}$

That is,　$\dfrac{575 + j30}{89} = \dfrac{575}{89} + j\dfrac{30}{89} = 6.46 + j0.337$

Expressing the quotient in polar form,

$$6.46 + j0.337 \cong 6.46 \; \underline{/3.0°}$$

Example 2.　Simplify $\dfrac{10}{3 + j4}$.

Solution: Multiply both numerator and denominator by the conjugate of the denominator which is $3 - j4$.

Thus,　$\dfrac{10}{3 + j4} \cdot \dfrac{3 - j4}{3 - j4} = \dfrac{10(3 - j4)}{9 - j^216} = \dfrac{30 - j40}{25} = 1.2 - j1.6$

Expressing the quotient in polar form,

$$1.2 - j1.6 = 2.0 \; \underline{/-53.1°}$$

PROBLEMS 31-2

Express the indicated products in polar form:

1. $(3 + j4)(3 - j6)$.

2. $(13 + j17)(23 + j11)$.

3. $(3.4 + j9.3)(1.2 + j8.7)$.

4. $(180 - j35.0)(3.20 + j0.621)$.

5. $(6.8 - j4.6)(5.5 - j7.2)$.

6. $(3 - j9)(2 - j8)$.

Express the indicated quotients in polar form:

7. $\dfrac{6 + j8}{4 + j3}$.

8. $\dfrac{90 - j20}{35 - j73}$.

9. $\dfrac{7 - j38}{5 + j13}$.

10. $\dfrac{1}{16 - j12}$.

31-4. Addition and Subtraction of Polar Vectors. As explained in previous articles, vectors expressed in polar form can be added or subtracted by graphical methods only, unless their directions are parallel. In order to add or subtract them algebraically, they must be expressed in terms of their rectangular components.

Example 1. Add $5.40 \,/31.5°$ and $8.37 \,/-75.4°$.

Solution: Converting the vectors into their rectangular components,

$$5.40 \,/31.5° = 5.40(\cos 31.5° + j \sin 31.5°) = 4.60 + j2.82$$
$$8.37 \,/-75.4° = 8.37(\cos 75.4° - j \sin 75.4°) = 2.11 - j8.10$$

Adding,   Sum $= 6.71 - j5.28$

Expressing the sum in polar form,

$$6.71 - j5.28 = 8.54 \,/-38.2°$$

Note that the vectors of this example are the same as those of Example 1 of Art. 31-1.

Example 2. Subtract $5.92 \,/51.3°$ from $17.1 \,/-31.2°$

Solution: Converting the vectors into their rectangular components,

$$17.1 \,/-31.2° = 17.1(\cos 31.2° - j \sin 31.2°) = 14.6 - j8.86$$
$$5.92 \,/51.3° = 5.92(\cos 51.3° + j \sin 51.3°) = 3.7 + j4.62$$

Subtracting,   Result $= 10.9 - j13.48$

Expressing the result in polar form,

$$10.9 - j13.48 = 17.3 \,/-51°$$

Note that the vectors of this example are the same as those of Example 2 of Art. 31-1.

PROBLEMS 31-3

Perform the indicated operations, expressing the results in polar form. Check results by graphical methods.

1. $10.6 \,/-53° + 22.3 \,/62.5°$.   2. $41.4 \,/46.5° + 135 \,/-58.2°$.
3. $735 \,/-35.3° + 965 \,/58.8°$.   4. $17.7 \,/-107.9° + 25.7 \,/-64.5°$.
5. $852 \,/81.5° + 577 \,/-169.8°$.   6. $462 \,/162° + 591 \,/-78°$.
7. $53.5 \,/-61° - 18.0 \,/-35.3°$.   8. $6.84 \,/-10.1° - 14.8 \,/123.4°$.
9. $1000 \,/-53.1° - 1500 \,/-36.9°$.   10. $92.7 \,/-29.2° - 149 \,/15.9°$.

31-5. Multiplication of Polar Vectors. In Example 1 of Art. 31-2, it was shown that

$$(8 + j5)(10 + j9) = 127 \,/74°$$

Now $$8 + j5 = 9.44 \,/32°$$

and $$10 + j9 = 13.45 \,/42°$$

Multiplying the magnitudes and adding the angles,

$$(9.44 \times 13.45) \ \underline{/32° + 42°} = 127 \ \underline{/74°}$$

which is the same product as that obtained by multiplying the vectors when expressed in terms of their rectangular components. Similarly, in Example 2 of Art. 31-2, it was shown that

$$(80 + j39)(35 - j50) = 5430 \ \underline{/-29°}$$

Now
$$80 + j39 = 89.0 \ \underline{/26°}$$

and
$$35 - j50 = 61.0 \ \underline{/-55°}$$

Multiplying the magnitudes and adding the angles,

$$(89 \times 61.0) \ \underline{/26° + (-55°)} = 5430 \ \underline{/-29°}$$

which is the same product as that obtained by multiplying the vectors when expressed in terms of their rectangular components.

From the foregoing, it is evident that *the product of two polar vectors is found by multiplying their magnitudes and adding their angles algebraically.*

31-6. Division of Polar Vectors. In Example 1 of Art. 31-3, it was shown that

$$\frac{50 + j35}{8 + j5} = 6.46 \ \underline{/3.0°}$$

Now
$$50 + j35 = 61.0 \ \underline{/35°}$$

and
$$8 + j5 = 9.44 \ \underline{/32°}$$

Dividing the magnitudes and subtracting the angle of the divisor from the angle of the dividend,

$$\frac{61.0 \ \underline{/35°}}{9.44 \ \underline{/32°}} = \frac{61.0}{9.44} \ \underline{/35° - 32°} = 6.46 \ \underline{/3.0°}$$

which is the same quotient as that obtained by dividing the vectors when expressed in terms of their rectangular components. Similarly, in Example 2 of Art. 31-3, it was shown that

$$\frac{10}{3 + j4} = 2.0 \ \underline{/-53.1°}$$

Since 10 is a positive number, it is plotted on the 0° axis (Art. 3-4) and expressed as

Now
$$\frac{10\ \underline{/0°}}{3 + j4 = 5\ \underline{/53.1°}}$$

Dividing the magnitudes and subtracting the angle of the divisor from the angle of the dividend,

$$\frac{10\ \underline{/0°}}{5\ \underline{/53.1°}} = \frac{10}{5}\ \underline{/0° - 53.1°} = 2.0\ \underline{/-53.1°}$$

which is the same quotient as that obtained by dividing the vectors when expressed in terms of their rectangular components.

From the foregoing, it is evident that *the quotient of two polar vectors is found by dividing their magnitudes and subtracting the angle of the divisor from the angle of the dividend.*

31-7. Exponential Form. In the preceding two articles, it has been demonstrated that angles are added when vectors are multiplied and that angles are subtracted when one vector is divided by another. These operations may be further justified from a consideration of the sine and cosine when expanded in series form.

By Maclaurin's theorem, a treatment of which is beyond the scope of this book, $\cos \theta$ and $\sin \theta$ may be expanded into series form as follows:

$$\cos \theta = 1 - \frac{\theta^2}{2!} + \frac{\theta^4}{4!} - \frac{\theta^6}{6!} \cdots \tag{1}$$

$$\sin \theta = \theta - \frac{\theta^3}{3!} + \frac{\theta^5}{5!} - \frac{\theta^7}{7!} \cdots \tag{2}$$

The symbol $n!$ denotes the product of $1, 2, 3, 4, \cdots n$, and is read "factorial n." Thus, $5!$ (factorial five) is

$$1 \times 2 \times 3 \times 4 \times 5.$$

Similarly, it can be shown that

$$\epsilon^{j\theta} = 1 + j\theta - \frac{\theta^2}{2!} - j\frac{\theta^3}{3!} + \frac{\theta^4}{4!} + j\frac{\theta^5}{5!} - \frac{\theta^6}{6!} - j\frac{\theta^7}{7!} \cdots \tag{3}$$

where ϵ is the base of the natural system of logarithms $\cong 2.718$. By collecting and factoring j terms, Eq. (3) may be written

$$\epsilon^{j\theta} = \left(1 - \frac{\theta^2}{2!} + \frac{\theta^4}{4!} - \frac{\theta^6}{6!} \cdots \right) + j\left(\theta - \frac{\theta^3}{3!} + \frac{\theta^5}{5!} - \frac{\theta^7}{7!} \cdots \right) \tag{4}$$

Note that the first term of the right member of Eq. (4) is $\cos \theta$ as given in Eq. (1) and that the second term in the right member of Eq. (4) is $j \sin \theta$. Therefore,

$$\epsilon^{j\theta} = \cos \theta + j \sin \theta \qquad (5)$$

Since a vector, such as $Z \underline{/\theta}$, can be expressed in terms of its rectangular components by the relation

$$Z \underline{/\theta} = Z(\cos \theta + j \sin \theta) \qquad (6)$$

it follows from Eqs. (5) and (6) that

$$Z \underline{/\theta} = Z\epsilon^{j\theta} \qquad (7)$$

Similarly, it can be shown that

$$Z \underline{/-\theta} = Z\epsilon^{-j\theta} \qquad (8)$$

Equations (7) and (8) show that *the angles of vectors can be treated as exponents.* Thus, two vectors $Z_1 \underline{/\theta}$ and $Z_2 \underline{/\phi}$ are multiplied by multiplying the magnitudes of the vectors and adding their angles algebraically. That is,

$$(Z_1 \underline{/\theta})(Z_2 \underline{/\phi}) = Z_1 Z_2 \underline{/\theta + \phi})$$

Also,

$$\frac{Z_1 \underline{/\theta}}{Z_2 \underline{/\phi}} = \frac{Z_1}{Z_2} \underline{/\theta - \phi}$$

and

$$\frac{Z_a \underline{/\theta}}{Z_b \underline{/-\phi}} = \frac{Z_a}{Z_b} \underline{/\theta + \phi}$$

Example 1. Multiply $Z_1 = 8.4 \underline{/15°}$ by $Z_2 = 10.5 \underline{/20°}$.

Solution: $Z_1 Z_2 = 8.4 \times 10.5 \underline{/15° + 20°} = 88.2 \underline{/35°}$

Example 2. Multiply $Z_a = 164 \underline{/-39°}$ by $Z_b = 2.2 \underline{/-26°}$.

Solution: $Z_a Z_b = 164 \times 2.2 \underline{/-39° + (-26°)} = 361 \underline{/-65°}$

Example 3. Divide $Z_1 = 54.2 \underline{/47°}$ by $Z_2 = 18 \underline{/16°}$.

Solution: $\dfrac{Z_1}{Z_2} = \dfrac{54.2}{18} \underline{/47° - 16°} = 3.01 \underline{/31°}$

Example 4. Divide $Z_a = 886 \underline{/18°}$ by $Z_b = 31.2 \underline{/-50°}$.

Solution: $\dfrac{Z_a}{Z_b} = \dfrac{886}{31.2} \underline{/18° - (-50°)} = 28.4 \underline{/68°}$

31-8. Powers and Roots of Polar Vectors. In addition to following the laws of exponents for multiplication and division, vectorial angles may be used as any other exponents when powers or roots of vectors are desired. For example, to square a vector, the magnitude is squared and the angle is multiplied by 2. Similarly, the root of a vector is found by extracting the root of the magnitude and dividing the angle by the index of the root.

Example 1.   Find the square of $Z_i = 14 \; \underline{/18°}$.

Solution: $Z_1{}^2 = (14 \; \underline{/18°})^2 = 14^2 \; \underline{/18° \times 2} = 196 \; \underline{/36°}$

Example 2.   Find the square root of $Z_a = 625 \; \underline{/60°}$.

Solution: $\sqrt{Z_a} = \sqrt{625 \; \underline{/60°}} = \sqrt{625} \; \underline{/60° \div 2} = 25 \; \underline{/30°}$

PROBLEMS 31-4

Multiply:

1. $5 \; \underline{/53.1°}$ by $16 \; \underline{/10.9°}$.
2. $66.8 \; \underline{/13°}$ by $4.73 \; \underline{/24°}$.
3. $1.07 \; \underline{/-37.3°}$ by $52.6 \; \underline{/31°}$.
4. $319 \; \underline{/-60°}$ by $0.242 \; \underline{/-97.3°}$.
5. $0.0924 \; \underline{/47°}$ by $185 \; \underline{/-73°}$.
6. $1.87 \; \underline{/-180°}$ by $3.54 \; \underline{/-180°}$.

Divide:

7. $77.8 \; \underline{/42°}$ by $2.87 \; \underline{/19°}$.
8. $610 \; \underline{/17°}$ by $33.5 \; \underline{/7°}$.
9. $146 \; \underline{/75°}$ by $256 \; \underline{/-12°}$.
10. $6.56 \; \underline{/-43°}$ by $3.57 \; \underline{/17°}$.
11. $45.4 \; \underline{/11°}$ by $6.74 \; \underline{/39°}$.
12. $0.297 \; \underline{/-78°}$ by $0.626 \; \underline{/-81°}$.

Perform the indicated operations:

13. $\sqrt{169 \; \underline{/16°}}$.
14. $\sqrt{576 \; \underline{/-23°}}$.
15. $(28 \; \underline{/40°})^2$.
16. $(1.7 \; \underline{/-70°})^2$.
17. $\sqrt[3]{8 \; \underline{/120°}}$.
18. $\sqrt[3]{343 \; \underline{/-18.6°}}$.
19. $(2 \; \underline{/17°})^3$.
20. $(3 \; \underline{/-18°})^4$.

31-9. Parallel Circuits. It was shown in Art. 14-2 that the reciprocal of the joint resistance R_t of several resistances in parallel is expressed by the relation

$$\frac{1}{R_t} = \frac{1}{R_1} + \frac{1}{R_2} + \frac{1}{R_3} + \frac{1}{R_4} + \cdots$$

and that when two resistances R_1 and R_2 are connected in parallel the joint resistance is

$$R_t = \frac{R_1 R_2}{R_1 + R_2}$$

An analogous condition exists when two or more impedances are connected in parallel. By following the line of reasoning used for resistances in parallel, the reciprocal of the joint impedance of several impedances in parallel is found to be

$$\frac{1}{Z_t} = \frac{1}{Z_1} + \frac{1}{Z_2} + \frac{1}{Z_3} + \frac{1}{Z_4} + \cdots \tag{9}$$

Similarly, the joint impedance Z_t of two impedances Z_1 and Z_2 connected in parallel is

$$Z_t = \frac{Z_1 Z_2}{Z_1 + Z_2} \tag{10}$$

Note that the impedances of Eqs. (9) and (10) are in polar form.

Example 1. Find the joint impedance of the circuit of Fig. 31-1.
Solution: First express the given impedances in terms of both rectangular and polar forms.

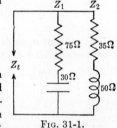

$$Z_1 = 75 - j30 = 80.8 \; \underline{/-21.8°} \; \Omega$$
$$Z_2 = 35 + j50 = 61.0 \; \underline{/55°} \; \Omega$$

As pointed out in Art. 31-4, vectors in polar form cannot be added algebraically: they must be added in terms of their rectangular components. Therefore, in substituting the given impedance values in Eq. (10), the impedances in the denominator must

Fig. 31-1.

be in rectangular form in order to carry out the indicated addition. Substituting,

$$Z_t = \frac{(80.8 \; \underline{/-21.8°})(61.0 \; \underline{/55°})}{(75 - j30) + (35 + j50)} = \frac{4930 \; \underline{/33.2°}}{110 + j20}$$

Because the denominator is in rectangular form and the numerator is in polar form, the denominator must be converted to polar form in order to complete the indicated division. Thus, by adding the terms of the denominator vectorially,

$$Z_t = \frac{4930 \; \underline{/33.2°}}{112 \; \underline{/10.3°}} = \frac{4930}{112} \; \underline{/33.2° - 10.3°} = 44 \; \underline{/22.9°} \; \Omega$$

Note that the circuit values of Fig. 31-1 are identical with those of Fig. 30-18.

Example 2. Find the joint impedance of the circuit of Fig. 31-2.
Solution: Expressing the impedance in rectangular and polar form,

$$Z_1 = 80 + j26 = 84.1 \; \underline{/18°} \; \Omega$$
$$Z_2 = 0 - j100 = 100 \; \underline{/-90°} \; \Omega$$

Substituting these values in Eq. (10),

$$Z_t = \frac{(84.1\ \underline{/18^\circ})(100\ \underline{/-90^\circ})}{(80 + j26) + (0 - j100)} = \frac{8410\ \underline{/-72^\circ}}{80 - j74}$$

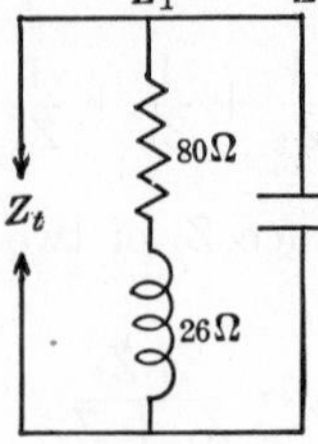

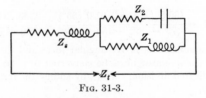

Fig. 31-2.

Performing the vector addition in the denominator,

$$Z_t = \frac{8410\ \underline{/-72^\circ}}{109\ \underline{/-42.8^\circ}}$$

$$\therefore\ Z_t = 77.2\ \underline{/-29.2^\circ}\ \Omega$$

The equivalent series circuit is found by the usual method of converting from rectangular form to polar form, namely,

$$77.2\ \underline{/-29.2^\circ} = 77.2(\cos 29.2^\circ - j \sin 29.2^\circ)$$
$$= 77.2 \cos 29.2^\circ - j77.2 \sin 29.2^\circ$$
$$= 67.4 - j37.7\ \Omega$$

31-10. Series-parallel Circuits. An equation for the joint impedance of a series-parallel circuit is obtained in the same

Fig. 31-3.

manner as the equation for the joint resistance of a combination of resistances in series and parallel as outlined in Art. 14-3. For example, in the circuit represented in Fig. 31-3, the total impedance is

$$Z_t = Z_s + \frac{Z_1 Z_2}{Z_1 + Z_2} \tag{11}$$

Example. In the circuit of Fig. 31-3, $Z_s = 12.4 + j25.6$ ohms, $Z_1 = 45 + j12.9$ ohms, and $Z_2 = 35 - j75$ ohms. Determine the equivalent impedance of the circuit.

Solution: Since Z_1 and Z_2 must be multiplied, it is necessary to express them in polar form.

$$Z_1 = 45 + j12.9 = 46.8 \,\underline{/16°}\, \Omega$$

and
$$Z_2 = 35 - j75 = 82.8 \,\underline{/-65°}\, \Omega$$

Substituting the values in Eq. (11),

$$Z_t = (12.4 + j25.6) + \frac{(46.8 \,\underline{/16°})(82.8 \,\underline{/-65°})}{(45 + j12.9) + (35 - j75)}$$

The solution is completed in the usual manner and results in

$$Z_t = 53.2 \,\underline{/20°}$$

From the foregoing examples, it is evident that an equation for the impedance of a network is expressed exactly as in direct-current problems, impedances in polar form being substituted for the resistances.

PROBLEMS 31-5

1. What is the joint impedance of two impedances $Z_1 = 58.6 \,\underline{/55°}\, \Omega$ and $Z_2 = 86 \,\underline{/-24°}\, \Omega$ connected in parallel?

2. What is the joint impedance of two impedances $Z_a = 168 \,\underline{/27°}\, \Omega$ and $Z_b = 57.2 \,\underline{/-61°}\, \Omega$ connected in parallel?

3. What is the joint impedance of two impedances $Z_1 = 100 - j27 \,\Omega$ and $Z_2 = 24.3 + j125 \,\Omega$ connected in parallel?

4. What is the joint impedance of two impedances $Z_a = 250 + j30.7 \,\Omega$ and $Z_b = 500 - j61.6 \,\Omega$ connected in parallel?

5. What is the joint impedance of an impedance of $79.3 \,\underline{/35°}\, \Omega$ connected in parallel with a resistance of $100 \,\Omega$?

6. What is the joint impedance of an impedance of $609 \,\underline{/-9°}\, \Omega$ connected in parallel with a condenser having a capacitive reactance of $100 \,\Omega$?

7. What is the joint impedance of an impedance of $201 \,\underline{/6°}\, \Omega$ connected in parallel with an inductance that has an inductive reactance of $50 \,\Omega$?

8. The joint impedance of two parallel impedances is $82 \,\underline{/-44°}\, \Omega$. One of the impedances $Z_1 = 155 \,\underline{/36°}\, \Omega$. What is the value of the other impedance? HINT: Solve Eq. (10) for Z_2.

9. What value of impedance must be connected in parallel with an impedance of $250 + j67 \,\Omega$ in order to result in a joint impedance of $146 + j27.2 \,\Omega$?

10. In the circuit of Fig. 31-4, $Z_s = 2.0 + j4.25 \,\Omega$, $Z_1 = 32.4 - j40 \,\Omega$, and $Z_2 = 35 + j18.6 \,\Omega$. Find the joint impedance Z_t.

11. In the circuit of Fig. 31-4, $Z_s = 3.0 \,\underline{/12°}\, \Omega$, $Z_1 = 15 - j7 \,\Omega$, and $Z_2 = 6 + j5 \,\Omega$. Find the joint impedance Z_t.

12. In the circuit of Fig. 31-4, $Z_s = 3.93 + j0.992$ Ω, $Z_1 = 9.22\ \underline{/-49.4°}$ Ω, and $Z_2 = 9.44\ \underline{/32°}$ Ω. Find the joint impedance Z_t.

13. The primary current I_p of a coupled circuit is expressed by the equation

$$I_p = \frac{E}{Z_p + \dfrac{(\omega M)^2}{Z_s}}.$$

Compute the value of the primary current if the applied voltage E is $10\ \underline{/0°}$ v, the primary impedance Z_p is $16 - j36$ Ω, the secondary impedance Z_s is $20 - j45$ Ω, and ωM ($2\pi f$ times the mutual inductance between primary and secondary) is 18.

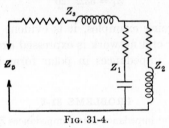

FIG. 31-4.

14. The secondary current I_s of a coupled circuit is expressed by the equation

$$I_s = \frac{-j\omega M E}{Z_p Z_s + (\omega M)^2}.$$

Compute the value of the secondary current if $\omega M = 12$, $E = 10$ v, $Z_p = 25 + j40$ Ω, and $Z_s = 40 + j13$ Ω.

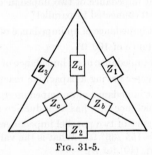

FIG. 31-5.

31-11. Equivalent Y and Δ Circuits.

When networks contain complex impedances, the equations for converting from a Δ network to an equivalent Y network, or vice versa, are derived by methods identical with those of Art. 19-8. Thus, in Fig. 31-5, each equivalent Y impedance is equal to the product of the two *adjacent* Δ impedances divided by the summation of the Δ impedances, or

$$Z_a = \frac{Z_1 Z_3}{\Sigma Z_\Delta} \tag{12}$$

$$Z_b = \frac{Z_1 Z_2}{\Sigma Z_\Delta} \tag{13}$$

and $$Z_c = \frac{Z_2 Z_3}{\Sigma Z_\Delta} \tag{14}$$

where $$\Sigma Z_\Delta = Z_1 + Z_2 + Z_3$$

and *all impedances are expressed in polar form.*

Similarly, each equivalent Δ impedance is equal to the summation of the Y impedances divided by the *opposite* Y impedance. Thus,

$$Z_1 = \frac{\Sigma Z_Y}{Z_c} \tag{15}$$

$$Z_2 = \frac{\Sigma Z_Y}{Z_a} \tag{16}$$

and $$Z_3 = \frac{\Sigma Z_Y}{Z_b} \tag{17}$$

where $$\Sigma Z_Y = Z_a Z_b + Z_b Z_c + Z_a Z_c$$

and *all impedances are expressed in polar form.*

Example 1. In Fig. 31-5, $Z_1 = 7.07 + j7.07$ ohms, $Z_2 = 4 + j3$ ohms, and $Z_3 = 6 - j8$ ohms. What are the values of the equivalent Y circuit?
Solution: Express all impedances in both rectangular and polar forms.

$$Z_1 = 7.07 + j7.07 = 10\ \underline{/45°}\ \Omega$$
$$Z_2 = 4 + j3 = 5\ \underline{/36.9°}\ \Omega$$
and $$Z_3 = 6 - j8 = 10\ \underline{/-53.1°}\ \Omega$$
$$\Sigma Z_\Delta = (7.07 + j7.07) + (4 + j3) + (6 - j8) = 17.2\ \underline{/6.91°}\ \Omega$$

Substituting in Eq. (12),

$$Z_a = \frac{(10\ \underline{/45°})(10\ \underline{/-53.1°})}{17.2\ \underline{/6.91°}} = 5.62 - j1.51\ \Omega$$

Substituting in Eq. (13),

$$Z_b = \frac{(10\ \underline{/45°})(5\ \underline{/36.9°})}{17.2\ \underline{/6.91°}} = 0.752 + j2.81\ \Omega$$

Substituting in Eq. (14),

$$Z_c = \frac{(5\ \underline{/36.9°})(10\ \underline{/-53.1°})}{17.2\ \underline{/6.91°}} = 2.67 - j1.14\ \Omega$$

The solution can be checked by converting the above Y network equivalents back to the original Δ by using Eqs. (15), (16), and (17).

Example 2.   Determine the equivalent impedance between points a and c in Fig. 31-6.

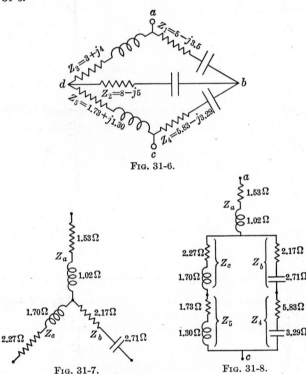

FIG. 31-6.

FIG. 31-7.   FIG. 31-8.

Solution: Convert one of the Δ circuits of Fig. 31-6 to its equivalent Y circuit.   Thus, for the delta abd,

$$Z_1 = 5 - j3.5 = 6.1 \;\underline{/-35°}\; \Omega$$
$$Z_2 = 8 - j5 = 9.44 \;\underline{/-32°}\; \Omega$$
$$Z_3 = 3 + j4 = 5 \;\underline{/53.1°}\; \Omega$$
$$\Sigma Z_\Delta = (5 - j3.5) + (8 - j5) + (3 + j4) = 16.6 \;\underline{/-15.7°}\; \Omega$$

Substituting in Eq. (12),

$$Z_a = \frac{(6.1 \;\underline{/-35°})(5 \;\underline{/53.1°})}{16.6 \;\underline{/-15.7°}} = 1.84 \;\underline{/33.8°} = 1.53 + j1.02 \; \Omega$$

Substituting in Eq. (13),

$$Z_b = \frac{(6.1 \;\underline{/-35°})(9.44 \;\underline{/-32°})}{16.6 \;\underline{/-15.7°}} = 3.47 \;\underline{/-51.3°} = 2.17 - j2.71 \; \Omega$$

Substituting in Eq. (14),

$$Z_c = \frac{(9.44\ \underline{/-32°})(5\ \underline{/53.1°})}{16.6\ \underline{/-15.7°}} = 2.84\ \underline{/36.8°} = 2.27 + j1.70\ \Omega$$

The equivalent Y impedances are shown in Fig. 31-7.

The equivalent Y impedances are connected to the remainder of the circuit as shown in Fig. 31-8 and solved as an ordinary series-parallel circuit. Thus,

$$Z_{ac} = Z_a + \frac{(Z_c + Z_5)(Z_b + Z_4)}{Z_c + Z_5 + Z_b + Z_4}$$

$$= 1.53 + j1.02$$

$$+ \frac{[(2.27 + j1.70) + (1.73 + j1.30)][(2.17 - j2.71) + (5.83 - j3.29)]}{(2.27 + j1.70) + (1.73 + j1.30) + (2.17 - j2.71) + (5.83 - j3.29)}$$

$$= 5.45 + j2.0\ \Omega$$

PROBLEMS 31-6

1. In the circuit of Fig. 31-5, $Z_1 = 56 + j47\ \Omega$, $Z_2 = 26 - j85\ \Omega$, and $Z_3 = 63 + j70\ \Omega$. Determine the impedances of the equivalent Y circuit.

2. In the circuit of Fig. 31-5, $Z_1 = 100 + j90\ \Omega$, $Z_2 = 95 - j69\ \Omega$, and $Z_3 = 31 + j90\ \Omega$. Determine the impedances of the equivalent Y circuit.

3. In the circuit of Fig. 31-5, $Z_1 = 605\ \underline{/7.5°}\ \Omega$, $Z_2 = 505\ \underline{/-8.2°}\ \Omega$, and $Z_3 = 458\ \underline{/10.7°}\ \Omega$. Determine the impedances of the equivalent Y circuit.

4. In the circuit of Fig. 31-5, $Z_1 = 5 - j4.2\ \Omega$, $Z_2 = 6.53 + j0\ \Omega$, and $Z_3 = 5 + j4.2\ \Omega$. Determine the impedances of the equivalent Y circuit.

5. In the circuit of Fig. 31-9, $Z_1 = 100\ \underline{/-36.9°}\ \Omega$, $Z_2 = 50\ \underline{/53.1°}\ \Omega$, $Z_3 = 100\ \underline{/45°}\ \Omega$, $Z_4 = 63.6\ \underline{/-42°}\ \Omega$, and $Z_5 = 27.7\ \underline{/17°}\ \Omega$. What is the equivalent impedance between points a and b?

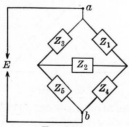

Fig. 31-9.

6. In Prob. 5, if $E = 100$ v, how much current flows through Z_4?

7. In the circuit of Fig. 31-9, $Z_1 = 217\ \underline{/61.1°}\ \Omega$, $Z_2 = 145\ \underline{/-12.7°}\ \Omega$, $Z_3 = 434\ \underline{/-28.9°}\ \Omega$, $Z_4 = 50\ \underline{/-53.1°}\ \Omega$, and $Z_5 = 100\ \underline{/-36.9°}\ \Omega$. Determine the equivalent impedance between points a and b.

8. In Prob. 7, if $E = 500$ v, how much current flows through Z_5?

9. In Prob. 7, if $E = 100$ v, how much power is expended in Z_4?

10. In Prob. 7, if $E = 250$ v, how much current flows through Z_3?

11. In the circuit of Fig. 31-9, $Z_1 = 151\ \underline{/-54°}\ \Omega$, $Z_2 = 119\ \underline{/-9°}\ \Omega$, $Z_3 = 177\ \underline{/-19°}\ \Omega$, $Z_4 = 50\ \underline{/0°}\ \Omega$, and $Z_5 = 24.5\ \underline{/90°}\ \Omega$. Determine the equivalent impedance between points a and b.

12. In Prob. 11, if $E = 100$ v, how much current flows through Z_5?

13. In Prob. 11, if $E = 150$ v, how much power is expended in Z_1?

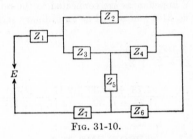

FIG. 31-10.

14. In the circuit of Fig. 31-10, $Z_1 = 5\ \underline{/36.9°}\ \Omega$, $Z_2 = 8.04 + j35.8\ \Omega$, $Z_3 = 7.13 - j40\ \Omega$, $Z_4 = 81.4\ \underline{/-37°}\ \Omega$, $Z_5 = 86.4\ \underline{/80°}\ \Omega$, $Z_6 = 53.8\ \underline{/-42°}$ Ω, $Z_7 = 8 - j6\ \Omega$, and $E = 100$ v. How much current flows through Z_1?

15. In the circuit of Fig. 31-11, $Z_1 = 548\ \underline{/35.4°}\ \Omega$, $Z_2 = 769\ \underline{/28.4°}\ \Omega$, $Z_3 = 992\ \underline{/25.4°}\ \Omega$, $Z_4 = 992\ \underline{/-25.4°}\ \Omega$, $Z_5 = 769\ \underline{/-28.4°}\ \Omega$, $Z_6 = 548$ $\underline{/-35.4°}\ \Omega$, and $Z_L = 200\ \underline{/0°}\ \Omega$. Determine the equivalent impedance between points a and b.

16. In Prob. 15, if $E = 15$ v, how much current flows through the load impedance Z_L?

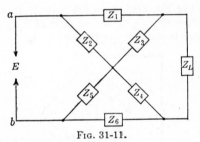

FIG. 31-11.

17. In the circuit of Fig. 31-11, $Z_1 = 295\ \underline{/40.6°}\ \Omega$, $Z_2 = 1140\ \underline{/37.6°}\ \Omega$, $Z_3 = 1000\ \underline{/28.6°}\ \Omega$, $Z_4 = 295\ \underline{/-40.6°}\ \Omega$, $Z_5 = 1140\ \underline{/-37.6°}\ \Omega$, $Z_6 = 1000$ $\underline{/-28.6°}\ \Omega$, and $Z_L = 600\ \underline{/0°}\ \Omega$. Determine the equivalent impedance between points a and b.

18. In Prob. 17, if $E = 45$ v, how much power is dissipated in the load impedance Z_L?

APPENDIX

TABLE I.—MATHEMATICAL SYMBOLS

$\times$ or $\cdot$	Multiplied by
$\div$ or $:$	Divided by
$+$	Positive. Plus. Add
$-$	Negative. Minus. Subtract
$\pm$	Positive or negative. Plus or minus
$\mp$	Negative or positive. Minus or plus
$=$ or $::$	Equals
$\equiv$	Identity
$\cong$	Is approximately equal to
$\neq$	Does not equal
$>$	Is greater than
$\gg$	Is much greater than
$<$	Is less than
$\ll$	Is much less than
$\geqq$	Greater than or equal to
$\leqq$	Less than or equal to
$\therefore$	Therefore
$\angle$	Angle
$\perp$	Perpendicular to
$\parallel$	Parallel to
$|n|$	Absolute value of n
Δ	Increment of

TABLE II.—GREEK ALPHABET

Name	Capital	Lower case	Commonly used to designate
Alpha.....	A	α	Angles. Area. Coefficients
Beta......	B	β	Angles. Flux density. Coefficients
Gamma...	Γ	γ	Conductivity. Specific gravity
Delta.....	Δ	δ	Variation. Density
Epsilon...	E	ϵ	Base of natural logarithms
Zeta.....	Z	ζ	Impedance. Coefficients. Coordinates
Eta......	H	η	Hysteresis coefficient. Efficiency
Theta.....	Θ	θ	Temperature. Phase angle
Iota......	I	ι	
Kappa....	K	κ	Dielectric constant. Susceptibility
Lambda...	Λ	λ	Wave length
Mu.......	M	μ	Micro. Amplification factor. Permeability
Nu.......	N	ν	Reluctivity
Xi........	Ξ	ξ	
Omicron..	O	o	
Pi........	Π	π	Ratio of circumference to diameter $= 3.1416$
Rho......	P	ρ	Resistivity
Sigma....	Σ	σ	Sign of summation
Tau......	T	τ	Time constant. Time phase displacement
Upsilon...	Υ	υ	
Phi.......	Φ	ϕ	Magnetic flux. Angles
Chi.......	X	χ	
Psi.......	Ψ	ψ	Dielectric flux. Phase difference
Omega....	Ω	ω	Capital, ohms. Lower case, angular velocity

TABLE III.—ABBREVIATIONS AND LETTER SYMBOLS*
General Abbreviations

Ordinarily, all words, both technical and otherwise, should be spelled out. Certain circumstances arise, however, such as in the headings of columns, in the tabulation of data, and on a very limited number of other occasions, when abbreviations are required. In such unusual circumstances, the following list of abbreviations may be used.

Many of the abbreviations are given in lower-case letters. Obviously, however, there will be occasions, such as when the abbreviations are used in titles of columns, where the original word would have been capitalized. In these cases, the abbreviations should be similarly capitalized.

A two-word adjective expression should contain a hyphen.

Term	Abbreviation
Alternating-current (adjective)	a-c
Alternating current (noun)	a.c.
Ampere	a
Antenna	ant.
Audio-frequency (adjective)	a-f
Audio frequency (noun)	a.f.
Continuous waves	cw
Cycle per second	$\sim$
Decibel	db
Direct-current (adjective)	d-c
Direct current (noun)	d.c.
Electric field intensity	ϵ
Electromotive force	e.m.f.
Frequency	f
Henry	h
High-frequency (adjective)	h-f
Intermediate-frequency (adjective)	i-f
Intermediate frequency (noun)	i.f.
Interrupted continuous waves	icw
Kilocycle (per second)	kc
Kilowatt	kw
Low-frequency (adjective)	l-f
Magnetic field intensity	H
Megacycle	Mc
Megohm	MΩ
Microfarad	μf

Term	Abbreviation
Microhenry	μh
Micromicrofarad	$\mu\mu$f
Microvolt	μv
Microvolt per meter	μv/m
Millivolt per meter	mv/m
Milliwatt	mw
Ohm	Ω
Power factor	p.f.
Radio-frequency (adjective)	r-f
Radio frequency (noun)	r.f.
Revolutions per minute	r.p.m.
Root mean square	r.m.s.
Volt	v
Watt	w

Abbreviations for Metric Prefixes

Prefix	Abbreviation
centi	c
deci	d
deka	dk
hecto	h
kilo	k
mega	M
micro	μ
milli	m

* Reprinted from "Report of the Standards Committee of The Institute of Radio Engineers."

TABLE IV.—CONVERSION FACTORS*

The symbol (δ) represents the density of a material expressed as a decimal fraction

Multiply	By	To obtain
Abamperes......................	10	amperes
Abamperes......................	3×10^{10}	statamperes
Abamperes per square centimeter...	64.52	amperes per square inch
Abampere-turns.................	10	ampere-turns
Abampere-turns.................	12.57	gilberts
Abampere-turns per centimeter.....	25.40	ampere-turns per inch
Abcoulombs.....................	10	coulombs
Abcoulombs.....................	3×10^{10}	statcoulombs
Abcoulombs per square centimeter..	64.52	coulombs per square inch
Abfarads.......................	10^9	farads
Abfarads.......................	10^{15}	microfarads
Abfarads.......................	9×10^{20}	statfarads
Abhenrys	10^{-9}	henrys
Abhenrys.......................	10^{-6}	millihenrys
Abhenrys.......................	$\frac{1}{9} \times 10^{-20}$	stathenrys
Abmhos per centimeter cube.......	$\dfrac{10^5}{\delta}$	mhos per meter-gram
Abmhos per centimeter cube.......	1.662×10^2	mhos per mil-foot
Abmhos per centimeter cube.......	10^3	megmhos per centimeter cube
Abohms........................	10^{-15}	megohms
Abohms........................	10^{-3}	microhms
Abohms........................	10^{-9}	ohms
Abohms........................	$\frac{1}{9} \times 10^{-20}$	statohms
Abohms per centimeter cube.......	10^{-3}	microhms per centimeter cube
Abohms per centimeter cube.......	6.015×10^{-3}	ohms per mil-foot
Abohms per centimeter cube.......	$10^{-5}\delta$	ohms per meter-gram
Abvolts........................	$\frac{1}{3} \times 10^{-10}$	statvolts
Abvolts........................	10^{-8}	volts
Amperes.......................	$\frac{1}{10}$	abamperes
Amperes.......................	3×10^9	statamperes
Amperes per square centimeter.....	6.452	amperes per square inch
Amperes per square inch..........	0.01550	abamperes per square centimeter
Amperes per square inch..........	0.1550	amperes per square centimeter
Amperes per square inch..........	4.650×10^8	statamperes per square centimeter

* Reprinted by permission from "The Engineers' Manual" by Hudson, published by John Wiley & Sons, Inc., New York.

TABLE IV.—CONVERSION FACTORS.—(*Continued*)

Multiply	By	To obtain
Ampere-turns.....................	$\frac{1}{10}$	abampere-turns
Ampere-turns.....................	1.257	gilberts
Ampere-turns per centimeter.......	2.540	ampere-turns per inch
Ampere-turns per inch............	0.03937	abampere-turns per centimeter
Ampere-turns per inch............	0.3937	ampere-turns per centimeter
Ampere-turns per inch............	0.4950	gilberts per centimeter
Bars.........................	10^6	dynes per square centimeter
Bars.........................	14.50	pounds per square inch
Centimeters....................	3.281×10^{-2}	feet
Centimeters....................	0.3937	inches
Centimeters....................	0.01	meters
Centimeters....................	6.214×10^{-6}	miles
Centimeters....................	10	millimeters
Centimeters....................	393.7	mils
Centimeters....................	1.094×10^{-2}	yards
Centimeters per second...........	1.969	feet per minute
Centimeters per second...........	0.03281	feet per second
Centimeters per second...........	0.036	kilometers per hour
Centimeters per second...........	0.6	meters per minute
Centimeters per second...........	0.02237	miles per hour
Centimeters per second...........	3.728×10^{-4}	miles per minute
Circular mils...................	5.067×10^{-6}	square centimeters
Circular mils...................	7.854×10^{-7}	square inches
Circular mils...................	0.7854	square mils
Coulombs per square inch..........	0.01550	abcoulombs per square centimeter
Coulombs per square inch..........	0.1550	coulombs per square centimeter
Coulombs per square inch..........	4.650×10^8	statcoulombs per square centimeter
Dynes.........................	1.020×10^{-3}	grams
Dynes.........................	7.233×10^{-5}	poundals
Dynes.........................	2.248×10^{-6}	pounds
Dynes per square centimeter.......	10^{-6}	bars
Farads.........................	10^{-9}	abfarads
Farads.........................	10^6	microfarads
Farads.........................	9×10^{11}	statfarads
Gausses........................	6.452	lines per square inch
Gilberts........................	0.07958	abampere-turns
Gilberts........................	0.7958	ampere-turns
Gilberts per centimeter...........	2.021	ampere-turns per inch

TABLE IV.—CONVERSION FACTORS.—(*Continued*)

Multiply	By	To obtain
Grams........................	980.7	dynes
Grams........................	15.43	grains
Grams........................	10^{-3}	kilograms
Grams........................	10^3	milligrams
Grams........................	0.03527	ounces
Grams........................	0.03215	ounces (troy)
Grams........................	0.07093	poundals
Grams........................	2.205×10^{-3}	pounds
Henrys.......................	10^9	abhenrys
Henrys.......................	10^3	millihenrys
Henrys.......................	$\frac{1}{9} \times 10^{-11}$	stathenrys
Inches.......................	2.540	centimeters
Inches.......................	8.333×10^{-2}	feet
Inches.......................	1.578×10^{-5}	miles
Inches.......................	10^3	mils
Inches.......................	2.778×10^{-2}	yards
Joules (international)........	9.480×10^{-4}	British thermal units
Joules (international)........	10^7	ergs
Joules (international)........	0.7378	foot-pounds
Joules (international)........	2.389×10^{-4}	kilogram-calories
Joules (international)........	0.1020	kilogram-meters
Joules (international)........	2.778×10^{-4}	watt-hours
Kilograms....................	980,665	dynes
Kilograms....................	10^3	grams
Kilograms....................	70.93	poundals
Kilograms....................	2.205	pounds
Kilograms....................	1.102×10^{-3}	tons (short)
Kilowatts....................	56.88	British thermal units per minute
Kilowatts	4.427×10^4	foot-pounds per minute
Kilowatts....................	737.8	foot-pounds per second
Kilowatts....................	1.341	horsepower
Kilowatts....................	14.33	kilogram-calories per minute
Kilowatts....................	10^3	watts
Kilowatt-hours...............	3413	British thermal units
Kilowatt-hours...............	2.656×10^6	foot-pounds
Kilowatt-hours...............	1.341	horsepower-hours
Kilowatt-hours...............	3.6×10^6	joules
Kilowatt-hours...............	860	kilogram-calories
Kilowatt-hours...............	3.672×10^5	kilogram-meters
Lines per square centimeter....	1	gausses
Lines per square inch........	0.1550	gausses

TABLE IV.—CONVERSION FACTORS.—(*Continued*)

Multiply	By	To obtain
$\log_{10} N$...............	2.303	$\log_\epsilon N$ or $\ln N$
$\log_\epsilon N$ or $\ln N$...............	0.4343	$\log_{10} N$
Lumens per square foot............	1	foot-candles
Maxwells...............	10^{-3}	kilolines
Megalines...............	10^6	maxwells
Megmhos per centimeter cube......	10^{-3}	abmhos per centimeter cube
Megmhos per centimeter cube......	2.540	megmhos per inch cube
Megmhos per centimeter cube......	$\dfrac{10^2}{\delta}$	mhos per meter-gram
Megmhos per centimeter cube......	0.1662	mhos per mil-foot
Megmhos per inch cube............	0.3937	megmhos per centimeter cube
Megohms...............	10^6	ohms
Meters...............	100	centimeters
Meters...............	3.281	feet
Meters...............	39.37	inches
Meters...............	10^{-3}	kilometers
Meters...............	6.214×10^{-4}	miles
Meters...............	10^3	millimeters
Meters...............	1.094	yards
Mhos per mil-foot...............	6.015×10^{-3}	abmhos per centimeter cube
Mhos per mil-foot...............	6.015	megmhos per centimeter cube
Mhos per mil-foot...............	15.28	megmhos per inch cube
Mhos per mil-foot...............	$\dfrac{601.5}{\delta}$	mhos per meter-gram
Microfarads...............	10^{-15}	abfarads
Microfarads...............	10^{-6}	farads
Microfarads...............	9×10^5	statfarads
Microhms...............	10^3	abohms
Microhms...............	10^{-12}	megohms
Microhms...............	10^{-6}	ohms
Microhms...............	$\frac{1}{9} \times 10^{-17}$	statohms
Miles...............	1.609×10^5	centimeters
Miles...............	5280	feet
Miles...............	6.336×10^4	inches
Miles...............	1.609	kilometers
Miles...............	1760	yards
Mil-feet...............	9.425×10^{-6}	cubic inches
Millihenrys...............	10^6	abhenrys
Millihenrys...............	10^{-3}	henrys
Millihenrys...............	$\frac{1}{9} \times 10^{-14}$	stathenrys
Ohms...............	10^9	**abohms**

TABLE IV.—CONVERSION FACTORS.—(*Continued*)

Multiply	By	To obtain
Ohms..........................	10^{-6}	megohms
Ohms..........................	10^{6}	microhms
Ohms..........................	$\frac{1}{9} \times 10^{-11}$	statohms
Ohms per mil-foot...	166.2	abohms per centimeter cube
Ohms per mil-foot..............	0.1662	microhms per centimeter cube
Ohms per mil-foot..............	0.06524	microhms per inch cube
Ohms per mil-foot..............	$1.662 \times 10^{-3}\delta$	ohms per meter-gram
Poundals......................	13,826	dynes
Poundals......................	14.10	grams
Poundals......................	0.03108	pounds
Pounds........................	444,823	dynes
Pounds........................	7000	grains
Pounds..	453.6	grams
Pounds........................	16	ounces
Pounds........................	32.17	poundals
Pounds (troy)..................	0.8229	pounds (avoirdupois)
Quadrants (angle)..............	90	degrees
Quadrants (angle)..............	5400	minutes
Quadrants (angle)..............	1.571	radians
Radians.......................	57.30	degrees
Radians.......................	3438	minutes
Radians.......................	0.6366	quadrants
Radians per second.............	57.30	degrees per second
Radians per second.............	9.549	revolutions per minute
Radians per second.............	0.1592	revolutions per second
Revolutions...................	360	degrees
Revolutions...................	4	quadrants
Revolutions...................	6.283	radians
Revolutions per minute..........	6	degrees per second
Revolutions per minute..........	0.1047	radians per second
Revolutions per minute..........	0.01667	revolutions per second
Revolutions per second..........	360	degrees per second
Revolutions per second..........	6.283	radians per second
Revolutions per second..........	60	revolutions per minute
Seconds (angle).................	4.848×10^{-6}	radians
Statamperes...................	$\frac{1}{3} \times 10^{-10}$	abamperes
Statamperes...................	$\frac{1}{3} \times 10^{-9}$	amperes
Statcoulombs..................	$\frac{1}{3} \times 10^{-10}$	abcoulombs
Statcoulombs..................	$\frac{1}{3} \times 10^{-9}$	coulombs
Statfarads....................	$\frac{1}{9} \times 10^{-20}$	abfarads
Statfarads....................	$\frac{1}{9} \times 10^{-11}$	farads
Statfarads....................	$\frac{1}{9} \times 10^{-5}$	microfarads

TABLE IV.—CONVERSION FACTORS.—*(Continued)*

Multiply	By	To obtain
Stathenrys.....................	9×10^{20}	abhenrys
Stathenrys.....................	9×10^{11}	henrys
Stathenrys.....................	9×10^{14}	millihenrys
Statohms......................	9×10^{20}	abohms
Statohms......................	9×10^{5}	megohms
Statohms......................	9×10^{17}	microhms
Statohms......................	9×10^{11}	ohms
Statvolts......................	3×10^{10}	abvolts
Statvolts......................	300	volts
Temperature (degrees centigrade) + 273.	1	absolute temperature (degrees centigrade)
Temperature (degrees centigrade) + 17.8.	1.8	temperature (degrees Fahrenheit)
Temperature (degrees Fahrenheit) + 460.	1	absolute temperature (degrees Fahrenheit)
Temperature (degrees Fahrenheit) − 32.	$\frac{5}{9}$	temperature (degrees centigrade)
Volts.........................	10^{8}	abvolts
Volts.........................	$\frac{1}{300}$	statvolts
Volts per inch.................	3.937×10^{7}	abvolts per centimeter
Volts per inch.................	1.312×10^{-3}	statvolts per centimeter
Watts.........................	0.05688	British thermal units per minute
Watts.........................	10^{7}	ergs per second
Watts.........................	44.27	foot-pounds per minute
Watts.........................	0.7378	foot-pounds per second
Watts.........................	1.341×10^{-3}	horsepower
Watts.........................	0.01433	kilogram-calories per minute
Watts.........................	10^{-3}	kilowatts
Watt-hours....................	3.413	British thermal units
Watt-hours....................	2656	foot-pounds
Watt-hours....................	1.341×10^{-3}	horsepower-hours
Watt-hours....................	0.860	kilogram-calories
Watt-hours....................	367.2	kilogram-meters
Watt-hours....................	10^{-3}	kilowatt-hours
Webers.......................	10^{8}	maxwells
Yards.........................	91.44	centimeters
Yards.........................	3	feet
Yards.........................	36	inches
Yards.........................	0.9144	meters
Yards.........................	5.682×10^{-4}	miles

TABLE V.—STANDARD ANNEALED COPPER WIRE, SOLID*

American Wire Gage (Brown and Sharpe)

Gage number	Diameter, mils	Area, circular mils	Resistance, ohms per 1000 ft, 25°C. (77°F.)	Weight, pounds per 1000 ft	Allowable current capacity,† amperes		
					Rubber insulation	Varnished cambric insulation	Other insulations
0000	460.0	211,600.0	0.0500	641.0	225	270	325
000	410.0	167,800.0	0.0630	508.0	175	210	275
00	365.0	133,100.0	0.0795	403.0	150	180	225
0	325.0	105,500.0	0.100	319.0	125	150	200
1	289.0	83,690.0	0.126	253.0	100	120	150
2	258.0	66,370.0	0.159	201.0	90	110	125
3	229.0	52,640.0	0.201	159.0	80	95	100
4	204.0	41,740.0	0.253	126.0	70	85	90
5	182.0	33,100.0	0.319	100.0	55	65	80
6	162.0	26,250.0	0.403	79.5	50	60	70
7	144.0	20,820.0	0.508	63.0			
8	128.0	16,510.0	0.641	50.0	35	40	50
9	114.0	13,090.0	0.808	39.6			
10	102.0	10,380.0	1.02	31.4	25	30	30
11	91.0	8,234.0	1.28	24.9			
12	81.0	6,530.0	1.62	19.8	20	25	25
13	72.0	5,178.0	2.04	15.7			
14	64.0	4,107.0	2.58	12.4	15	18	20
15	57.0	3,257.0	3.25	9.86			
16	51.0	2,583.0	4.09	7.82	6		
17	45.0	2,048.0	5.16	6.20			
18	40.0	1,624.0	6.51	4.92	3		
19	36.0	1,288.0	8.21	3.90			
20	32.0	1,022.0	10.4	3.09			
21	28.5	810.0	13.1	2.45			
22	25.3	642.0	16.5	1.95			
23	22.6	509.0	20.8	1.54			
24	20.1	404.0	26.2	1.22			
25	17.9	320.0	33.0	0.970			
26	15.9	254.0	41.6	0.769			
27	14.2	202.0	52.5	0.610			
28	12.6	160.0	66.2	0.484			
29	11.3	127.0	83.4	0.384			
30	10.0	100.0	105.0	0.304			
31	8.9	79.7	133.0	0.241			
32	8.0	63.2	167.0	0.191			
33	7.1	50.1	211.0	0.152			
34	6.3	39.8	266.0	0.120			
35	5.6	31.5	335.0	0.0954			
36	5.0	25.0	423.0	0.0757			
37	4.5	19.8	533.0	0.0600			
38	4.0	15.7	673.0	0.0476			
39	3.5	12.5	848.0	0.0377			
40	3.1	9.9	1070.0	0.0299			

* *Bureau of Standards Circular* 31.

† National Electrical Code.

TABLE VI.—COMMON LOGARITHMS

N	0	1	2	3	4	5	6	7	8	9
0	....	0000	3010	4771	6021	6990	7782	8451	9031	9542
1	0000	0414	0792	1139	1461	1761	2041	2304	2553	2788
2	3010	3222	3424	3617	3802	3979	4150	4314	4472	4624
3	4771	4914	5051	5185	5315	5441	5563	5682	5798	5911
4	6021	6128	6232	6335	6435	6532	6628	6721	6812	6902
5	6990	7076	7160	7243	7324	7404	7482	7559	7634	7709
6	7782	7853	7924	7993	8062	8129	8195	8261	8325	8388
7	8451	8513	8573	8633	8692	8751	8808	8865	8921	8976
8	9031	9085	9138	9191	9243	9294	9345	9395	9445	9494
9	9542	9590	9638	9685	9731	9777	9823	9868	9912	9956
10	0000	0043	0086	0128	0170	0212	0253	0294	0334	0374
11	0414	0453	0492	0531	0569	0607	0645	0682	0719	0755
12	0792	0828	0864	0899	0934	0969	1004	1038	1072	1106
13	1139	1173	1206	1239	1271	1303	1335	1367	1399	1430
14	1461	1492	1523	1553	1584	1614	1644	1673	1703	1732
15	1761	1790	1818	1847	1875	1903	1931	1959	1987	2014
16	2041	2068	2095	2122	2148	2175	2201	2227	2253	2279
17	2304	2330	2355	2380	2405	2430	2455	2480	2504	2529
18	2553	2577	2601	2625	2648	2672	2695	2718	2742	2765
19	2788	2810	2833	2856	2878	2900	2923	2945	2967	2989
20	3010	3032	3054	3075	3096	3118	3139	3160	3181	3201
21	3222	3243	3263	3284	3304	3324	3345	3365	3385	3404
22	3424	3444	3464	3483	3502	3522	3541	3560	3579	3598
23	3617	3636	3655	3674	3692	3711	3729	3747	3766	3784
24	3802	3820	3838	3856	3874	3892	3909	3927	3945	3962
25	3979	3997	4014	4031	4048	4065	4082	4099	4116	4133
26	4150	4166	4183	4200	4216	4232	4249	4265	4281	4298
27	4314	4330	4346	4362	4378	4393	4409	4425	4440	4456
28	4472	4487	4502	4518	4533	4548	4564	4579	4594	4609
29	4624	4639	4654	4669	4683	4698	4713	4728	4742	4757
30	4771	4786	4800	4814	4829	4843	4857	4871	4886	4900
31	4914	4928	4942	4955	4969	4983	4997	5011	5024	5038
32	5051	5065	5079	5092	5105	5119	5132	5145	5159	5172
33	5185	5198	5211	5224	5237	5250	5263	5276	5289	5302
34	5315	5328	5340	5353	5366	5378	5391	5403	5416	5428
35	5441	5453	5465	5478	5490	5502	5514	5527	5539	5551
36	5563	5575	5587	5599	5611	5623	5635	5647	5658	5670
37	5682	5694	5705	5717	5729	5740	5752	5763	5775	5786
38	5798	5809	5821	5832	5843	5855	5866	5877	5888	5899
39	5911	5922	5933	5944	5955	5966	5977	5988	5999	6010
40	6021	6031	6042	6053	6064	6075	6085	6096	6107	6117
41	6128	6138	6149	6160	6170	6180	6191	6201	6212	6222
42	6232	6243	6253	6263	6274	6284	6294	6304	6314	6325
43	6335	6345	6355	6365	6375	6385	6395	6405	6415	6425
44	6435	6444	6454	6464	6474	6484	6493	6503	6513	6522
45	6532	6542	6551	6561	6571	6580	6590	6599	6609	6618
46	6628	6637	6646	6656	6665	6675	6684	6693	6702	6712
47	6721	6730	6739	6749	6758	6767	6776	6785	6794	6803
48	6812	6821	6830	6839	6848	6857	6866	6875	6884	6893
49	6902	6911	6920	6928	6937	6946	6955	6964	6972	6981
50	6990	6998	7007	7016	7024	7033	7042	7050	7059	7067
N	**0**	**1**	**2**	**3**	**4**	**5**	**6**	**7**	**8**	**9**

Table VI.—Common Logarithms.—(*Continued*)

N	0	1	2	3	4	5	6	7	8	9
50	6990	6998	7007	7016	7024	7033	7042	7050	7059	7067
51	7076	7084	7093	7101	7110	7118	7126	7135	7143	7152
52	7160	7168	7177	7185	7193	7202	7210	7218	7226	7235
53	7243	7251	7259	7267	7275	7284	7292	7300	7308	7316
54	7324	7332	7340	7348	7356	7364	7372	7380	7388	7396
55	7404	7412	7419	7427	7435	7443	7451	7459	7466	7474
56	7482	7490	7497	7505	7513	7520	7528	7536	7543	7551
57	7559	7566	7574	7582	7589	7597	7604	7612	7619	7627
58	7634	7642	7649	7657	7664	7672	7679	7686	7694	7701
59	7709	7716	7723	7731	7738	7745	7752	7760	7767	7774
60	7782	7789	7796	7803	7810	7818	7825	7832	7839	7846
61	7853	7860	7868	7875	7882	7889	7896	7903	7910	7917
62	7924	7931	7938	7945	7952	7959	7966	7973	7980	7987
63	7993	8000	8007	8014	8021	8028	8035	8041	8048	8055
64	8062	8069	8075	8082	8089	8096	8102	8109	8116	8122
65	8129	8136	8142	8149	8156	8162	8169	8176	8182	8189
66	8195	8202	8209	8215	8222	8228	8235	8241	8248	8254
67	8261	8267	8274	8280	8287	8293	8299	8306	8312	8319
68	8325	8331	8338	8344	8351	8357	8363	8370	8376	8382
69	8388	8395	8401	8407	8414	8420	8426	8432	8439	8445
70	8451	8457	8463	8470	8476	8482	8488	8494	8500	8506
71	8513	8519	8525	8531	8537	8543	8549	8555	8561	8567
72	8573	8579	8585	8591	8597	8603	8609	8615	8621	8627
73	8633	8639	8645	8651	8657	8663	8669	8675	8681	8686
74	8692	8698	8704	8710	8716	8722	8727	8733	8739	8745
75	8751	8756	8762	8768	8774	8779	8785	8791	8797	8802
76	8808	8814	8820	8825	8831	8837	8842	8848	8854	8859
77	8865	8871	8876	8882	8887	8893	8899	8904	8910	8915
78	8921	8927	8932	8938	8943	8949	8954	8960	8965	8971
79	8976	8982	8987	8993	8998	9004	9009	9015	9020	9025
80	9031	9036	9042	9047	9053	9058	9063	9069	9074	9079
81	9085	9090	9096	9101	9106	9112	9117	9122	9128	9133
82	9138	9143	9149	9154	9159	9165	9170	9175	9180	9186
83	9191	9196	9201	9206	9212	9217	9222	9227	9232	9238
84	9243	9248	9253	9258	9263	9269	9274	9279	9284	9289
85	9294	9299	9304	9309	9315	9320	9325	9330	9335	9340
86	9345	9350	9355	9360	9365	9370	9375	9380	9385	9390
87	9395	9400	9405	9410	9415	9420	9425	9430	9435	9440
88	9445	9450	9455	9460	9465	9469	9474	9479	9484	9489
89	9494	9499	9504	9509	9513	9518	9523	9528	9533	9538
90	9542	9547	9552	9557	9562	9566	9571	9576	9581	9586
91	9590	9595	9600	9605	9609	9614	9619	9624	9628	9633
92	9638	9643	9647	9652	9657	9661	9666	9671	9675	9680
93	9685	9689	9694	9699	9703	9708	9713	9717	9722	9727
94	9731	9736	9741	9745	9750	9754	9759	9763	9768	9773
95	9777	9782	9786	9791	9795	9800	9805	9809	9814	9818
96	9823	9827	9832	9836	9841	9845	9850	9854	9859	9863
97	9868	9872	9877	9881	9886	9890	9894	9899	9903	9908
98	9912	9917	9921	9926	9930	9934	9939	9943	9948	9952
99	9956	9961	9965	9969	9974	9978	9983	9987	9991	9996
100	0000	0004	0009	0013	0017	0022	0026	0030	0035	0039
N	0	1	2	3	4	5	6	7	8	9

TABLE VII

Decibels Gain—Power

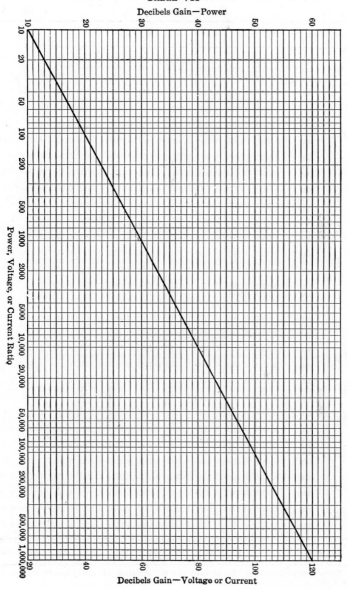

Power, Voltage, or Current Ratio

Decibels Gain—Voltage or Current

TABLE VIII.—NATURAL SINES, COSINES, AND TANGENTS*

0°–14.9°

Degs.	Function	0.0°	0.1°	0.2°	0.3°	0.4°	0.5°	0.6°	0.7°	0.8°	0.9°
0	sin	0.0000	0.0017	0.0035	0.0052	0.0070	0.0087	0.0105	0.0122	0.0140	0.0157
	cos	1.0000	1.0000	1.0000	1.0000	1.0000	1.0000	0.9999	0.9999	0.9999	0.9999
	tan	0.0000	0.0017	0.0035	0.0052	0.0070	0.0087	0.0105	0.0122	0.0140	0.0157
1	sin	0.0175	0.0192	0.0209	0.0227	0.0244	0.0262	0.0279	0.0297	0.0314	0.0332
	cos	0.9998	0.9998	0.9998	0.9997	0.9997	0.9997	0.9996	0.9996	0.9995	0.9995
	tan	0.0175	0.0192	0.0209	0.0227	0.0244	0.0262	0.0279	0.0297	0.0314	0.0332
2	sin	0.0349	0.0366	0.0384	0.0401	0.0419	0.0436	0.0454	0.0471	0.0488	0.0506
	cos	0.9994	0.9993	0.9993	0.9992	0.9991	0.9990	0.9990	0.9989	0.9988	0.9987
	tan	0.0349	0.0367	0.0384	0.0402	0.0419	0.0437	0.0454	0.0472	0.0489	0.0507
3	sin	0.0523	0.0541	0.0558	0.0576	0.0593	0.0610	0.0628	0.0645	0.0663	0.0680
	cos	0.9986	0.9985	0.9984	0.9983	0.9982	0.9981	0.9980	0.9979	0.9978	0.9977
	tan	0.0524	0.0542	0.0559	0.0577	0.0594	0.0612	0.0629	0.0647	0.0664	0.0682
4	sin	0.0698	0.0715	0.0732	0.0750	0.0767	0.0785	0.0802	0.0819	0.0837	0.0854
	cos	0.9976	0.9974	0.9973	0.9972	0.9971	0.9969	0.9968	0.9966	0.9965	0.9963
	tan	0.0699	0.0717	0.0734	0.0752	0.0769	0.0787	0.0805	0.0822	0.0840	0.0857
5	sin	0.0872	0.0889	0.0906	0.0924	0.0941	0.0958	0.0976	0.0993	0.1011	0.1028
	cos	0.9962	0.9960	0.9959	0.9957	0.9956	0.9954	0.9952	0.9951	0.9949	0.9947
	tan	0.0875	0.0892	0.0910	0.0928	0.0945	0.0963	0.0981	0.0998	0.1016	0.1033
6	sin	0.1045	0.1063	0.1080	0.1097	0.1115	0.1132	0.1149	0.1167	0.1184	0.1201
	cos	0.9945	0.9943	0.9942	0.9940	0.9938	0.9936	0.9934	0.9932	0.9930	0.9928
	tan	0.1051	0.1069	0.1086	0.1104	0.1122	0.1139	0.1157	0.1175	0.1192	0.1210
7	sin	0.1219	0.1236	0.1253	0.1271	0.1288	0.1305	0.1323	0.1340	0.1357	0.1374
	cos	0.9925	0.9923	0.9921	0.9919	0.9917	0.9914	0.9912	0.9910	0.9907	0.9905
	tan	0.1228	0.1246	0.1263	0.1281	0.1299	0.1317	0.1334	0.1352	0.1370	0.1388
8	sin	0.1392	0.1409	0.1426	0.1444	0.1461	0.1478	0.1495	0.1513	0.1530	0.1547
	cos	0.9903	0.9900	0.9898	0.9895	0.9893	0.9890	0.9888	0.9885	0.9882	0.9880
	tan	0.1405	0.1423	0.1441	0.1459	0.1477	0.1495	0.1512	0.1530	0.1548	0.1566
9	sin	0.1564	0.1582	0.1599	0.1616	0.1633	0.1650	0.1668	0.1685	0.1702	0.1719
	cos	0.9877	0.9874	0.9871	0.9869	0.9866	0.9863	0.9860	0.9857	0.9854	0.9851
	tan	0.1584	0.1602	0.1620	0.1638	0.1655	0.1673	0.1691	0.1709	0.1727	0.1745
10	sin	0.1736	0.1754	0.1771	0.1788	0.1805	0.1822	0.1840	0.1857	0.1874	0.1891
	cos	0.9848	0.9845	0.9842	0.9839	0.9836	0.9833	0.9829	0.9826	0.9823	0.9820
	tan	0.1763	0.1781	0.1799	0.1817	0.1835	0.1853	0.1871	0.1890	0.1908	0.1926
11	sin	0.1908	0.1925	0.1942	0.1959	0.1977	0.1994	0.2011	0.2028	0.2045	0.2062
	cos	0.9816	0.9813	0.9810	0.9806	0.9803	0.9799	0.9796	0.9792	0.9789	0.9785
	tan	0.1944	0.1962	0.1980	0.1998	0.2016	0.2035	0.2053	0.2071	0.2089	0.2107
12	sin	0.2079	0.2096	0.2113	0.2130	0.2147	0.2164	0.2181	0.2198	0.2215	0.2232
	cos	0.9781	0.9778	0.9774	0.9770	0.9767	0.9763	0.9759	0.9755	0.9751	0.9748
	tan	0.2126	0.2144	0.2162	0.2180	0.2199	0.2217	0.2235	0.2254	0.2272	0.2290
13	sin	0.2250	0.2267	0.2284	0.2300	0.2318	0.2334	0.2351	0.2368	0.2385	0.2402
	cos	0.9744	0.9740	0.9736	0.9732	0.9728	0.9724	0.9720	0.9715	0.9711	0.9707
	tan	0.2309	0.2327	0.2345	0.2364	0.2382	0.2401	0.2419	0.2438	0.2456	0.2475
14	sin	0.2419	0.2436	0.2453	0.2470	0.2487	0.2504	0.2521	0.2538	0.2554	0.2571
	cos	0.9703	0.9699	0.9694	0.9690	0.9686	0.9681	0.9677	0.9673	0.9668	0.9664
	tan	0.2493	0.2512	0.2530	0.2549	0.2568	0.2586	0.2605	0.2623	0.2642	0.2661
Degs.	Function	0'	6'	12'	18'	24'	30'	36'	42'	48'	54'

* Reprinted by permission from "The Engineers' Manual" by Hudson, published by John Wiley & Sons, Inc., New York.

TABLE VIII.—NATURAL SINES, COSINES, AND TANGENTS.—(*Continued*)
15°–29.9°

Degs.	Function	0.0°	0.1°	0.2°	0.3°	0.4°	0.5°	0.6°	0.7°	0.8°	0.9°
15	sin	0.2588	0.2605	0.2622	0.2639	0.2656	0.2672	0.2689	0.2706	0.2723	0.2740
	cos	0.9659	0.9655	0.9650	0.9646	0.9641	0.9636	0.9632	0.9627	0.9622	0.9617
	tan	0.2679	0.2698	0.2717	0.2736	0.2754	0.2773	0.2792	0.2811	0.2830	0.2849
16	sin	0.2756	0.2773	0.2790	0.2807	0.2823	0.2840	0.2857	0.2874	0.2890	0.2907
	cos	0.9613	0.9608	0.9603	0.9598	0.9593	0.9588	0.9583	0.9578	0.9573	0.9568
	tan	0.2867	0.2886	0.2905	0.2924	0.2943	0.2962	0.2981	0.3000	0.3019	0.3038
17	sin	0.2924	0.2940	0.2957	0.2974	0.2990	0.3007	0.3024	0.3040	0.3057	0.3074
	cos	0.9563	0.9558	0.9553	0.9548	0.9542	0.9537	0.9532	0.9527	0.9521	0.9516
	tan	0.3057	0.3076	0.3096	0.3115	0.3134	0.3153	0.3172	0.3191	0.3211	0.3230
18	sin	0.3090	0.3107	0.3123	0.3140	0.3156	0.3173	0.3190	0.3206	0.3223	0.3239
	cos	0.9511	0.9505	0.9500	0.9494	0.9489	0.9483	0.9478	0.9472	0.9466	0.9461
	tan	0.3249	0.3269	0.3288	0.3307	0.3327	0.3346	0.3365	0.3385	0.3404	0.3424
19	sin	0.3256	0.3272	0.3289	0.3305	0.3322	0.3338	0.3355	0.3371	0.3387	0.3404
	cos	0.9455	0.9449	0.9444	0.9438	0.9432	0.9426	0.9421	0.9415	0.9409	0.9403
	tan	0.3443	0.3463	0.3482	0.3502	0.3522	0.3541	0.3561	0.3581	0.3600	0.3620
20	sin	0.3420	0.3437	0.3453	0.3469	0.3486	0.3502	0.3518	0.3535	0.3551	0.3567
	cos	0.9397	0.9391	0.9385	0.9379	0.9373	0.9367	0.9361	0.9354	0.9348	0.9342
	tan	0.3640	0.3659	0.3679	0.3699	0.3719	0.3739	0.3759	0.3779	0.3799	0.3819
21	sin	0.3584	0.3600	0.3616	0.3633	0.3649	0.3665	0.3681	0.3697	0.3714	0.3730
	cos	0.9336	0.9330	0.9323	0.9317	0.9311	0.9304	0.9298	0.9291	0.9285	0.9278
	tan	0.3839	0.3859	0.3879	0.3899	0.3919	0.3939	0.3959	0.3979	0.4000	0.4020
22	sin	0.3746	0.3762	0.3778	0.3795	0.3811	0.3827	0.3843	0.3859	0.3875	0.3891
	cos	0.9272	0.9265	0.9259	0.9252	0.9245	0.9239	0.9232	0.9225	0.9219	0.9212
	tan	0.4040	0.4061	0.4081	0.4101	0.4122	0.4142	0.4163	0.4183	0.4204	0.4224
23	sin	0.3907	0.3923	0.3939	0.3955	0.3971	0.3987	0.4003	0.4019	0.4035	0.4051
	cos	0.9205	0.9198	0.9191	0.9184	0.9178	0.9171	0.9164	0.9157	0.9150	0.9143
	tan	0.4245	0.4265	0.4286	0.4307	0.4327	0.4348	0.4369	0.4390	0.4411	0.4431
24	sin	0.4067	0.4083	0.4099	0.4115	0.4131	0.4147	0.4163	0.4179	0.4195	0.4210
	cos	0.9135	0.9128	0.9121	0.9114	0.9107	0.9100	0.9092	0.9085	0.9078	0.9070
	tan	0.4452	0.4473	0.4494	0.4515	0.4536	0.4557	0.4578	0.4599	0.4621	0.4642
25	sin	0.4226	0.4242	0.4258	0.4274	0.4289	0.4305	0.4321	0.4337	0.4352	0.4368
	cos	0.9063	0.9056	0.9048	0.9041	0.9033	0.9026	0.9018	0.9011	0.9003	0.8996
	tan	0.4663	0.4684	0.4706	0.4727	0.4748	0.4770	0.4791	0.4813	0.4834	0.4856
26	sin	0.4384	0.4399	0.4415	0.4431	0.4446	0.4462	0.4478	0.4493	0.4509	0.4524
	cos	0.8988	0.8980	0.8973	0.8965	0.8957	0.8949	0.8942	0.8934	0.8926	0.8918
	tan	0.4877	0.4899	0.4921	0.4942	0.4964	0.4986	0.5008	0.5029	0.5051	0.5073
27	sin	0.4540	0.4555	0.4571	0.4586	0.4602	0.4617	0.4633	0.4648	0.4664	0.4679
	cos	0.8910	0.8902	0.8894	0.8886	0.8878	0.8870	0.8862	0.8854	0.8846	0.8838
	tan	0.5095	0.5117	0.5139	0.5161	0.5184	0.5206	0.5228	0.5250	0.5272	0.5295
28	sin	0.4695	0.4710	0.4726	0.4741	0.4756	0.4772	0.4787	0.4802	0.4818	0.4833
	cos	0.8829	0.8821	0.8813	0.8805	0.8796	0.8788	0.8780	0.8771	0.8763	0.8755
	tan	0.5317	0.5340	0.5362	0.5384	0.5407	0.5430	0.5452	0.5475	0.5498	0.5520
29	sin	0.4848	0.4863	0.4879	0.4894	0.4909	0.4924	0.4939	0.4955	0.4970	0.4985
	cos	0.8746	0.8738	0.8729	0.8721	0.8712	0.8704	0.8695	0.8686	0.8678	0.8669
	tan	0.5543	0.5566	0.5589	0.5612	0.5635	0.5658	0.5681	0.5704	0.5727	0.5750
Degs.	**Function**	**0'**	**6'**	**12'**	**18'**	**24'**	**30'**	**36'**	**42'**	**48'**	**54'**

TABLE VIII.—NATURAL SINES, COSINES, AND TANGENTS.—(*Continued*)

30°–44.9°

Degs.	Function	0.0°	0.1°	0.2°	0.3°	0.4°	0.5°	0.6°	0.7°	0.8°	0.9°
30	sin	0.5000	0.5015	0.5030	0.5045	0.5060	0.5075	0.5090	0.5105	0.5120	0.5135
	cos	0.8660	0.8652	0.8643	0.8634	0.8625	0.8616	0.8607	0.8599	0.8590	0.8581
	tan	0.5774	0.5797	0.5820	0.5844	0.5867	0.5890	0.5914	0.5938	0.5961	0.5985
31	sin	0.5150	0.5165	0.5180	0.5195	0.5210	0.5225	0.5240	0.5255	0.5270	0.5284
	cos	0.8572	0.8563	0.8554	0.8545	0.8536	0.8526	0.8517	0.8508	0.8499	0.8490
	tan	0.6009	0.6032	0.6056	0.6080	0.6104	0.6128	0.6152	0.6176	0.6200	0.6224
32	sin	0.5299	0.5314	0.5329	0.5344	0.5358	0.5373	0.5388	0.5402	0.5417	0.5432
	cos	0.8480	0.8471	0.8462	0.8453	0.8443	0.8434	0.8425	0.8415	0.8406	0.8396
	tan	0.6249	0.6273	0.6297	0.6322	0.6346	0.6371	0.6395	0.6420	0.6445	0.6469
33	sin	0.5446	0.5461	0.5476	0.5490	0.5505	0.5519	0.5534	0.5548	0.5563	0.5577
	cos	0.8387	0.8377	0.8368	0.8358	0.8348	0.8339	0.8329	0.8320	0.8310	0.8300
	tan	0.6494	0.6519	0.6544	0.6569	0.6594	0.6619	0.6644	0.6669	0.6694	0.6720
34	sin	0.5592	0.5606	0.5621	0.5635	0.5650	0.5664	0.5678	0.5693	0.5707	0.5721
	cos	0.8290	0.8281	0.8271	0.8261	0.8251	0.8241	0.8231	0.8221	0.8211	0.8202
	tan	0.6745	0.6771	0.6796	0.6822	0.6847	0.6873	0.6899	0.6924	0.6950	0.6976
35	sin	0.5736	0.5750	0.5764	0.5779	0.5793	0.5807	0.5821	0.5835	0.5850	0.5864
	cos	0.8192	0.8181	0.8171	0.8161	0.8151	0.8141	0.8131	0.8121	0.8111	0.8100
	tan	0.7002	0.7028	0.7054	0.7080	0.7107	0.7133	0.7159	0.7186	0.7212	0.7239
36	sin	0.5878	0.5892	0.5906	0.5920	0.5934	0.5948	0.5962	3.5976	0.5990	0.6004
	cos	0.8090	0.8080	0.8070	0.8059	0.8049	0.8039	0.8028	0.8018	0.8007	0.7997
	tan	0.7265	0.7292	0.7319	0.7346	0.7373	0.7400	0.7427	0.7454	0.7481	0.7508
37	sin	0.6018	0.6032	0.6046	0.6060	0.6074	0.6088	0.6101	0.6115	0.6129	0.6143
	cos	0.7986	0.7976	0.7965	0.7955	0.7944	0.7934	0.7923	0.7912	0.7902	0.7891
	tan	0.7536	0.7563	0.7590	0.7618	0.7646	0.7673	0.7701	0.7729	0.7757	0.7785
38	sin	0.6157	0.6170	0.6184	0.6198	0.6211	0.6225	0.6239	0.6252	0.6266	0.6280
	cos	0.7880	0.7869	0.7859	0.7848	0.7837	0.7826	0.7815	0.7804	0.7793	0.7782
	tan	0.7813	0.7841	0.7869	0.7898	0.7926	0.7954	0.7983	0.8012	0.8040	0.8069
39	sin	0.6293	0.6307	0.6320	0.6334	0.6347	0.6361	0.6374	0.6388	0.6401	0.6414
	cos	0.7771	0.7760	0.7749	0.7738	0.7727	0.7716	0.7705	0.7694	0.7683	0.7672
	tan	0.8098	0.8127	0.8156	0.8185	0.8214	0.8243	0.8273	0.8302	0.8332	0.8361
40	sin	0.6428	0.6441	0.6455	0.6468	0.6481	0.6494	0.6508	0.6521	0.6534	0.6547
	cos	0.7660	0.7649	0.7638	0.7627	0.7615	0.7604	0.7593	0.7581	0.7570	0.7559
	tan	0.8391	0.8421	0.8451	0.8481	0.8511	0.8541	0.8571	0.8601	0.8632	0.8662
41	sin	0.6561	0.6574	0.6587	0.6600	0.6613	0.6626	0.6639	0.6652	0.6665	0.6678
	cos	0.7547	0.7536	0.7524	0.7513	0.7501	0.7490	0.7478	0.7466	0.7455	0.7443
	tan	0.8693	0.8724	0.8754	0.8785	0.8816	0.8847	0.8878	0.8910	0.8941	0.8972
42	sin	0.6691	0.6704	0.6717	0.6730	0.6743	0.6756	0.6769	0.6782	0.6794	0.6807
	cos	0.7431	0.7420	0.7408	0.7396	0.7385	0.7373	0.7361	0.7349	0.7337	0.7325
	tan	0.9004	0.9036	0.9067	0.9099	0.9131	0.9163	0.9195	0.9228	0.9260	0.9293
43	sin	0.6820	0.6833	0.6845	0.6858	0.6871	0.6884	0.6896	0.6909	0.6921	0.6934
	cos	0.7314	0.7302	0.7290	0.7278	0.7266	0.7254	0.7242	0.7230	0.7218	0.7206
	tan	0.9325	0.9358	0.9391	0.9424	0.9457	0.9490	0.9523	0.9556	0.9590	0.9623
44	sin	0.6947	0.6959	0.6972	0.6984	0.6997	0.7009	0.7022	0.7034	0.7046	0.7059
	cos	0.7193	0.7181	0.7169	0.7157	0.7145	0.7133	0.7120	0.7108	0.7096	0.7083
	tan	0.9657	0.9691	0.9725	0.9759	0.9793	0.9827	0.9861	0.9896	0.9930	0.9965
Degs.	Function	0′	6′	12′	18′	24′	30′	36′	42′	48′	54′

TABLE VIII.—NATURAL SINES, COSINES, AND TANGENTS.—(*Continued*)
45°–59.9°

Degs.	Function	0.0°	0.1°	0.2°	0.3°	0.4°	0.5°	0.6°	0.7°	0.8°	0.9°
45	sin	0.7071	0.7083	0.7096	0.7108	0.7120	0.7133	0.7145	0.7157	0.7169	0.7181
	cos	0.7071	0.7059	0.7046	0.7034	0.7022	0.7009	0.6997	0.6984	0.6972	0.6959
	tan	1.0000	1.0035	1.0070	1.0105	1.0141	1.0176	1.0212	1.0247	1.0283	1.0319
46	sin	0.7193	0.7206	0.7218	0.7230	0.7242	0.7254	0.7266	0.7278	0.7290	0.7302
	cos	0.6947	0.6934	0.6921	0.6909	0.6896	0.6884	0.6871	0.6858	0.6845	0.6833
	tan	1.0355	1.0392	1.0428	1.0464	1.0501	1.0538	1.0575	1.0612	1.0649	1.0686
47	sin	0.7314	0.7325	0.7337	0.7349	0.7361	0.7373	0.7385	0.7396	0.7408	0.7420
	cos	0.6820	0.6807	0.6794	0.6782	0.6769	0.6756	0.6743	0.6730	0.6717	0.6704
	tan	1.0724	1.0761	1.0799	1.0837	1.0875	1.0913	1.0951	1.0990	1.1028	1.1067
48	sin	0.7431	0.7443	0.7455	0.7466	0.7478	0.7490	0.7501	0.7513	0.7524	0.7536
	cos	0.6691	0.6678	0.6665	0.6652	0.6639	0.6626	0.6613	0.6600	0.6587	0.6574
	tan	1.1106	1.1145	1.1184	1.1224	1.1263	1.1303	1.1343	1.1383	1.1423	1.1463
49	sin	0.7547	0.7559	0.7570	0.7581	0.7593	0.7604	0.7615	0.7627	0.7638	0.7649
	cos	0.6561	0.6547	0.6534	0.6521	0.6508	0.6494	0.6481	0.6468	0.6455	0.6441
	tan	1.1504	1.1544	1.1585	1.1626	1.1667	1.1708	1.1750	1.1792	1.1833	1.1875
50	sin	0.7660	0.7672	0.7683	0.7694	0.7705	0.7716	0.7727	0.7738	0.7749	0.7760
	cos	0.6428	0.6414	0.6401	0.6388	0.6374	0.6361	0.6347	0.6334	0.6320	0.6307
	tan	1.1918	1.1960	1.2002	1.2045	1.2088	1.2131	1.2174	1.2218	1.2261	1.2305
51	sin	0.7771	0.7782	0.7793	0.7804	0.7815	0.7826	0.7837	0.7848	0.7859	0.7869
	cos	0.6293	0.6280	0.6266	0.6252	0.6239	0.6225	0.6211	0.6198	0.6184	0.6170
	tan	1.2349	1.2393	1.2437	1.2482	1.2527	1.2572	1.2617	1.2662	1.2708	1.2753
52	sin	0.7880	0.7891	0.7902	0.7912	0.7923	0.7934	0.7944	0.7955	0.7965	0.7976
	cos	0.6157	0.6143	0.6129	0.6115	0.6101	0.6088	0.6074	0.6060	0.6046	0.6032
	tan	1.2799	1.2846	1.2892	1.2938	1.2985	1.3032	1.3079	1.3127	1.3175	1.3222
53	sin	0.7986	0.7997	0.8007	0.8018	0.8028	0.8039	0.8049	0.8059	0.8070	0.8080
	cos	0.6018	0.6004	0.5990	0.5976	0.5962	0.5948	0.5934	0.5920	0.5906	0.5892
	tan	1.3270	1.3319	1.3367	1.3416	1.3465	1.3514	1.3564	1.3613	1.3663	1.3713
54	sin	0.8090	0.8100	0.8111	0.8121	0.8131	0.8141	0.8151	0.8161	0.8171	0.8181
	cos	0.5878	0.5864	0.5850	0.5835	0.5821	0.5807	0.5793	0.5779	0.5764	0.5750
	tan	1.3764	1.3814	1.3865	1.3916	1.3968	1.4019	1.4071	1.4124	1.4176	1.4229
55	sin	0.8192	0.8202	0.8211	0.8221	0.8231	0.8241	0.8251	0.8261	0.8271	0.8281
	cos	0.5736	0.5721	0.5707	0.5693	0.5678	0.5664	0.5650	0.5635	0.5621	0.5606
	tan	1.4281	1.4335	1.4388	1.4442	1.4496	1.4550	1.4605	1.4659	1.4715	1.4770
56	sin	0.8290	0.8300	0.8310	0.8320	0.8329	0.8339	0.8348	0.8358	0.8368	0.8377
	cos	0.5592	0.5577	0.5563	0.5548	0.5534	0.5519	0.5505	0.5490	0.5476	0.5461
	tan	1.4826	1.4882	1.4938	1.4994	1.5051	1.5108	1.5166	1.5224	1.5282	1.5340
57	sin	0.8387	0.8396	0.8406	0.8415	0.8425	0.8434	0.8443	0.8453	0.8462	0.8471
	cos	0.5446	0.5432	0.5417	0.5402	0.5388	0.5373	0.5358	0.5344	0.5329	0.5314
	tan	1.5399	1.5458	1.5517	1.5577	1.5637	1.5697	1.5757	1.5818	1.5880	1.5941
58	sin	0.8480	0.8490	0.8499	0.8508	0.8517	0.8526	0.8536	0.8545	0.8554	0.8563
	cos	0.5299	0.5284	0.5270	0.5255	0.5240	0.5225	0.5210	0.5195	0.5180	0.5165
	tan	1.6003	1.6066	1.6128	1.6191	1.6255	1.6319	1.6383	1.6447	1.6512	1.6577
59	sin	0.8572	0.8581	0.8590	0.8599	0.8607	0.8616	0.8625	0.8634	0.8643	0.8652
	cos	0.5150	0.5135	0.5120	0.5105	0.5090	0.5075	0.5060	0.5045	0.5030	0.5015
	tan	1.6643	1.6709	1.6775	1.6842	1.6909	1.6977	1.7045	1.7113	1.7182	1.7251
Degs.	Function	0′	6′	12′	18′	24′	30′	36′	42′	48′	54′

TABLE VIII.—NATURAL SINES, COSINES, AND TANGENTS.—(*Continued*)
60°–74.9°

Degs.	Function	0.0°	0.1°	0.2°	0.3°	0.4°	0.5°	0.6°	0.7°	0.8°	0.9°
60	sin	0.8660	0.8669	0.8678	0.8686	0.8695	0.8704	0.8712	0.8721	0.8729	0.8738
	cos	0.5000	0.4985	0.4970	0.4955	0.4939	0.4924	0.4909	0.4894	0.4879	0.4863
	tan	1.7321	1.7391	1.7461	1.7532	1.7603	1.7675	1.7747	1.7820	1.7893	1.7966
61	sin	0.8746	0.8755	0.8763	0.8771	0.8780	0.8788	0.8796	0.8805	0.8813	0.8821
	cos	0.4848	0.4833	0.4818	0.4802	0.4787	0.4772	0.4756	0.4741	0.4726	0.4710
	tan	1.8040	1.8115	1.8190	1.8265	1.8341	1.8418	1.8495	1.8572	1.8650	1.8728
62	sin	0.8829	0.8838	0.8846	0.8854	0.8862	0.8870	0.8878	0.8886	0.8894	0.8902
	cos	0.4695	0.4679	0.4664	0.4648	0.4633	0.4617	0.4602	0.4586	0.4571	0.4555
	tan	1.8807	1.8887	1.8967	1.9047	1.9128	1.9210	1.9292	1.9375	1.9458	1.9542
63	sin	0.8910	0.8918	0.8926	0.8934	0.8942	0.8949	0.8957	0.8965	0.8973	0.8980
	cos	0.4540	0.4524	0.4509	0.4493	0.4478	0.4462	0.4446	0.4431	0.4415	0.4399
	tan	1.9626	1.9711	1.9797	1.9883	1.9970	2.0057	2.0145	2.0233	2.0323	2.0413
64	sin	0.8988	0.8996	0.9003	0.9011	0.9018	0.9026	0.9033	0.9041	0.9048	0.9056
	cos	0.4384	0.4368	0.4352	0.4337	0.4321	0.4305	0.4289	0.4274	0.4258	0.4242
	tan	2.0503	2.0594	2.0686	2.0778	2.0872	2.0965	2.1060	2.1155	2.1251	2.1348
65	sin	0.9063	0.9070	0.9078	0.9085	0.9092	0.9100	0.9107	0.9114	0.9121	0.9128
	cos	0.4226	0.4210	0.4195	0.4179	0.4163	0.4147	0.4131	0.4115	0.4099	0.4083
	tan	2.1445	2.1543	2.1642	2.1742	2.1842	2.1943	2.2045	2.2148	2.2251	2.2355
66	sin	0.9135	0.9143	0.9150	0.9157	0.9164	0.9171	0.9178	0.9184	0.9191	0.9198
	cos	0.4067	0.4051	0.4035	0.4019	0.4003	0.3987	0.3971	0.3955	0.3939	0.3923
	tan	2.2460	2.2566	2.2673	2.2781	2.2889	2.2998	2.3109	2.3220	2.3332	2.3445
67	sin	0.9205	0.9212	0.9219	0.9225	0.9232	0.9239	0.9245	0.9252	0.9259	0.9265
	cos	0.3907	0.3891	0.3875	0.3859	0.3843	0.3827	0.3811	0.3795	0.3778	0.3762
	tan	2.3559	2.3673	2.3789	2.3906	2.4023	2.4142	2.4262	2.4383	2.4504	2.4627
68	sin	0.9272	0.9278	0.9285	0.9291	0.9298	0.9304	0.9311	0.9317	0.9323	0.9330
	cos	0.3746	0.3730	0.3714	0.3697	0.3681	0.3665	0.3649	0.3633	0.3616	0.3600
	tan	2.4751	2.4876	2.5002	2.5129	2.5257	2.5386	2.5517	2.5649	2.5782	2.5916
69	sin	0.9336	0.9342	0.9348	0.9354	0.9361	0.9367	0.9373	0.9379	0.9385	0.9391
	cos	0.3584	0.3567	0.3551	0.3535	0.3518	0.3502	0.3486	0.3469	0.3453	0.3437
	tan	2.6051	2.6187	2.6325	2.6464	2.6605	2.6746	2.6889	2.7034	2.7179	2.7326
70	sin	0.9397	0.9403	0.9409	0.9415	0.9421	0.9426	0.9432	0.9438	0.9444	0.9449
	cos	0.3420	0.3404	0.3387	0.3371	0.3355	0.3338	0.3322	0.3305	0.3289	0.3272
	tan	2.7475	2.7625	2.7776	2.7929	2.8083	2.8239	2.8397	2.8556	2.8716	2.8878
71	sin	0.9455	0.9461	0.9466	0.9472	0.9478	0.9483	0.9489	0.9494	0.9500	0.9505
	cos	0.3256	0.3239	0.3223	0.3206	0.3190	0.3173	0.3156	0.3140	0.3123	0.3107
	tan	2.9042	2.9208	2.9375	2.9544	2.9714	2.9887	3.0061	3.0237	3.0415	3.0595
72	sin	0.9511	0.9516	0.9521	0.9527	0.9532	0.9537	0.9542	0.9548	0.9553	0.9558
	cos	0.3090	0.3074	0.3057	0.3040	0.3024	0.3007	0.2990	0.2974	0.2957	0.2940
	tan	3.0777	3.0961	3.1146	3.1334	3.1524	3.1716	3.1910	3.2106	3.2305	3.2506
73	sin	0.9563	0.9568	0.9573	0.9578	0.9583	0.9588	0.9593	0.9598	0.9603	0.9608
	cos	0.2924	0.2907	0.2890	0.2874	0.2857	0.2840	0.2823	0.2807	0.2790	0.2773
	tan	3.2709	3.2914	3.3122	3.3332	3.3544	3.3759	3.3977	3.4197	3.4420	3.4646
74	sin	0.9613	0.9617	0.9622	0.9627	0.9632	0.9636	0.9641	0.9646	0.9650	0.9655
	cos	0.2756	0.2740	0.2723	0.2706	0.2689	0.2672	0.2656	0.2639	0.2622	0.2605
	tan	3.4874	3.5105	3.5339	3.5576	3.5816	3.6059	3.6305	3.6554	3.6806	3.7062
Degs.	Function	0'	6'	12'	18'	24'	30'	36'	42'	48'	54'

Table VIII.—Natural Sines, Cosines, and Tangents.—(*Continued*)
75°–89.9°

Degs.	Function	0.0°	0.1°	0.2°	0.3°	0.4°	0.5°	0.6°	0.7°	0.8°	0.9°
75	sin	0.9659	0.9664	0.9668	0.9673	0.9677	0.9681	0.9686	0.9690	0.9694	0.9699
	cos	0.2588	0.2571	0.2554	0.2538	0.2521	0.2504	0.2487	0.2470	0.2453	0.2436
	tan	3.7321	3.7583	3.7848	3.8118	3.8391	3.8667	3.8947	3.9232	3.9520	3.9812
76	sin	0.9703	0.9707	0.9711	0.9715	0.9720	0.9724	0.9728	0.9732	0.9736	0.9740
	cos	0.2419	0.2402	0.2385	0.2368	0.2351	0.2334	0.2317	0.2300	0.2284	0.2267
	tan	4.0108	4.0408	4.0713	4.1022	4.1335	4.1653	4.1976	4.2303	4.2635	4.2972
77	sin	0.9744	0.9748	0.9751	0.9755	0.9759	0.9763	0.9767	0.9770	0.9774	0.9778
	cos	0.2250	0.2232	0.2215	0.2198	0.2181	0.2164	0.2147	0.2130	0.2113	0.2096
	tan	4.3315	4.3662	4.4015	4.4374	4.4737	4.5107	4.5483	4.5864	4.6252	4.6646
78	sin	0.9781	0.9785	0.9789	0.9792	0.9796	0.9799	0.9803	0.9806	0.9810	0.9813
	cos	0.2079	0.2062	0.2045	0.2028	0.2011	0.1994	0.1977	0.1959	0.1942	0.1925
	tan	4.7046	4.7453	4.7867	4.8288	4.8716	4.9152	4.9594	5.0045	5.0504	5.0970
79	sin	0.9816	0.9820	0.9823	0.9826	0.9829	0.9833	0.9836	0.9839	0.9842	0.9845
	cos	0.1908	0.1891	0.1874	0.1857	0.1840	0.1822	0.1805	0.1788	0.1771	0.1754
	tan	5.1446	5.1929	5.2422	5.2924	5.3435	5.3955	5.4486	5.5026	5.5578	5.6140
80	sin	0.9848	0.9851	0.9854	0.9857	0.9860	0.9863	0.9866	0.9869	0.9871	0.9874
	cos	0.1736	0.1719	0.1702	0.1685	0.1668	0.1650	0.1633	0.1616	0.1599	0.1582
	tan	5.6713	5.7297	5.7894	5.8502	5.9124	5.9758	6.0405	6.1066	6.1742	6.2432
81	sin	0.9877	0.9880	0.9882	0.9885	0.9888	0.9890	0.9893	0.9895	0.9898	0.9900
	cos	0.1564	0.1547	0.1530	0.1513	0.1495	0.1478	0.1461	0.1444	0.1426	0.1409
	tan	6.3138	6.3859	6.4596	6.5350	6.6122	6.6912	6.7720	6.8548	6.9395	7.0264
82	sin	0.9903	0.9905	0.9907	0.9910	0.9912	0.9914	0.9917	0.9919	0.9921	0.9923
	cos	0.1392	0.1374	0.1357	0.1340	0.1323	0.1305	0.1288	0.1271	0.1253	0.1236
	tan	7.1154	7.2066	7.3002	7.3962	7.4947	7.5958	7.6996	7.8062	7.9158	8.0285
83	sin	0.9925	0.9928	0.9930	0.9932	0.9934	0.9936	0.9938	0.9940	0.9942	0.9943
	cos	0.1219	0.1201	0.1184	0.1167	0.1149	0.1132	0.1115	0.1097	0.1080	0.1063
	tan	8.1443	8.2636	8.3863	8.5126	8.6427	8.7769	8.9152	9.0579	9.2052	9.3572
84	sin	0.9945	0.9947	0.9949	0.9951	0.9952	0.9954	0.9956	0.9957	0.9959	0.9960
	cos	0.1045	0.1028	0.1011	0.0993	0.0976	0.0958	0.0941	0.0924	0.0906	0.0889
	tan	9.5144	9.6768	9.8448	10.02	10.20	10.39	10.58	10.78	10.99	11.20
85	sin	0.9962	0.9963	0.9965	0.9966	0.9968	0.9969	0.9971	0.9972	0.9973	0.9974
	cos	0.0872	0.0854	0.0837	0.0819	0.0802	0.0785	0.0767	0.0750	0.0732	0.0715
	tan	11.43	11.66	11.91	12.16	12.43	12.71	13.00	13.30	13.62	13.95
86	sin	0.9976	0.9977	0.9978	0.9979	0.9980	0.9981	0.9982	0.9983	0.9984	0.9985
	cos	0.0698	0.0680	0.0663	0.0645	0.0628	0.0610	0.0593	0.0576	0.0558	0.0541
	tan	14.30	14.67	15.06	15.46	15.89	16.35	16.83	17.34	17.89	18.46
87	sin	0.9986	0.9987	0.9988	0.9989	0.9990	0.9990	0.9991	0.9992	0.9993	0.9993
	cos	0.0523	0.0506	0.0488	0.0471	0.0454	0.0436	0.0419	0.0401	0.0384	0.0366
	tan	19.08	19.74	20.45	21.20	22.02	22.90	23.86	24.90	26.03	27.27
88	sin	0.9994	0.9995	0.9995	0.9996	0.9996	0.9997	0.9997	0.9997	0.9998	0.9998
	cos	0.0349	0.0332	0.0314	0.0297	0.0279	0.0262	0.0244	0.0227	0.0209	0.0192
	tan	28.64	30.14	31.82	33.69	35.80	38.19	40.92	44.07	47.74	52.08
89	sin	0.9998	0.9999	0.9999	0.9999	0.9999	1.000	1.000	1.000	1.000	1.000
	cos	0.0175	0.0157	0.0140	0.0122	0.0105	0.0087	0.0070	0.0052	0.0035	0.0017
	tan	57.29	63.66	71.62	81.85	95.49	114.6	143.2	191.0	286.5	573.0
Degs.	Function	0′	6′	12′	18′	24′	30′	36′	42′	48′	54′

Table IX.—Squares, Cubes, Square Roots, Cube Roots, and Reciprocals of Numbers from 1 to 1000

TABLE IX   1-50

No.	Square	Cube	Sq. Root	Cu. Root	Reciprocal
1	1	1	1.0000	1.0000	1.000000000
2	4	8	1.4142	1.2599	.500000000
3	9	27	1.7321	1.4422	.333333333
4	16	64	2.0000	1.5874	.250000000
5	25	125	2.2361	1.7100	.200000000
6	36	216	2.4495	1.8171	.166666667
7	49	343	2.6458	1.9129	.142857143
8	64	512	2.8284	2.0000	.125000000
9	81	729	3.0000	2.0801	.111111111
10	100	1,000	3.1623	2.1544	.100000000
11	121	1,331	3.3166	2.2240	.090909091
12	144	1,728	3.4641	2.2894	.083333333
13	169	2,197	3.6056	2.3513	.076923077
14	196	2,744	3.7417	2.4101	.071428571
15	225	3,375	3.8730	2.4662	.066666667
16	256	4,096	4.0000	2.5198	.062500000
17	289	4,913	4.1231	2.5713	.058823529
18	324	5,832	4.2426	2.6207	.055555556
19	361	6,859	4.3589	2.6684	.052631579
20	400	8,000	4.4721	2.7144	.050000000
21	441	9,261	4.5826	2.7589	.047619048
22	484	10,648	4.6904	2.8020	.045454545
23	529	12,167	4.7958	2.8439	.043478261
24	576	13,824	4.8990	2.8845	.041666667
25	625	15,625	5.0000	2.9240	.040000000
26	676	17,576	5.0990	2.9625	.038461538
27	729	19,683	5.1962	3.0000	.037037037
28	784	21,952	5.2915	3.0366	.035714286
29	841	24,389	5.3852	3.0723	.034482759
30	900	27,000	5.4772	3.1072	.033333333
31	961	29,791	5.5678	3.1414	.032258065
32	1,024	32,768	5.6569	3.1748	.031250000
33	1,089	35,937	5.7446	3.2075	.030303030
34	1,156	39,304	5.8310	3.2396	.029411765
35	1,225	42,875	5.9161	3.2711	.028571429
36	1,296	46,656	6.0000	3.3019	.027777778
37	1,369	50,653	6.0828	3.3322	.027027027
38	1,444	54,872	6.1644	3.3620	.026315789
39	1,521	59,319	6.2450	3.3912	.025641026
40	1,600	64,000	6.3246	3.4200	.025000000
41	1,681	68,921	6.4031	3.4482	.024390244
42	1,764	74,088	6.4807	3.4760	.023809524
43	1,849	79,507	6.5574	3.5034	.023255814
44	1,936	85,184	6.6332	3.5303	.022727273
45	2,025	91,125	6.7082	3.5569	.022222222
46	2,116	97,336	6.7823	3.5830	.021739130
47	2,209	103,823	6.8557	3.6088	.021276596
48	2,304	110,592	6.9282	3.6342	.020833333
49	2,401	117,649	7.0000	3.6593	.020408163
50	2,500	125,000	7.0711	3.6840	.020000000

No.	Square	Cube	Sq. Root	Cu. Root	Reciprocal
50	2,500	125,000	7.0711	3.6840	.020000000
51	2,601	132,651	7.1414	3.7084	.019607843
52	2,704	140,608	7.2111	3.7325	.019230769
53	2,809	148,877	7.2801	3.7563	.018867925
54	2,916	157,464	7.3485	3.7798	.018518519
55	3,025	166,375	7.4162	3.8030	.018181818
56	3,136	175,616	7.4833	3.8259	.017857143
57	3,249	185,193	7.5498	3.8485	.017543860
58	3,364	195,112	7.6158	3.8709	.017241379
59	3,481	205,379	7.6811	3.8930	.016949153
60	3,600	216,000	7.7460	3.9149	.016666667
61	3,721	226,981	7.8102	3.9365	.016393443
62	3,844	238,328	7.8740	3.9579	.016129032
63	3,969	250,047	7.9373	3.9791	.015873016
64	4,096	262,144	8.0000	4.0000	.015625000
65	4,225	274,625	8.0623	4.0207	.015384615
66	4,356	287,496	8.1240	4.0412	.015151515
67	4,489	300,763	8.1854	4.0615	.014925373
68	4,624	314,432	8.2462	4.0817	.014705882
69	4,761	328,509	8.3066	4.1016	.014492754
70	4,900	343,000	8.3666	4.1213	.014285714
71	5,041	357,911	8.4261	4.1408	.014084507
72	5,184	373,248	8.4853	4.1602	.013888889
73	5,329	389,017	8.5440	4.1793	.013698630
74	5,476	405,224	8.6023	4.1983	.013513514
75	5,625	421,875	8.6603	4.2172	.013333333
76	5,776	438,976	8.7178	4.2358	.013157895
77	5,929	456,533	8.7750	4.2543	.012987013
78	6,084	474,552	8.8318	4.2727	.012820513
79	6,241	493,039	8.8882	4.2908	.012658228
80	6,400	512,000	8.9443	4.3089	.012500000
81	6,561	531,441	9.0000	4.3267	.012345679
82	6,724	551,368	9.0554	4.3445	.012195122
83	6,889	571,787	9.1104	4.3621	.012048193
84	7,056	592,704	9.1652	4.3795	.011904762
85	7,225	614,125	9.2195	4.3968	.011764706
86	7,396	636,056	9.2736	4.4140	.011627907
87	7,569	658,503	9.3274	4.4310	.011494253
88	7,744	681,472	9.3808	4.4480	.011363636
89	7,921	704,969	9.4340	4.4647	.011235955
90	8,100	729,000	9.4868	4.4814	.011111111
91	8,281	753,571	9.5394	4.4979	.010989011
92	8,464	778,688	9.5917	4.5144	.010869565
93	8,649	804,357	9.6437	4.5307	.010752688
94	8,836	830,584	9.6954	4.5468	.010638298
95	9,025	857,375	9.7468	4.5629	.010526316
96	9,216	884,736	9.7980	4.5789	.010416667
97	9,409	912,673	9.8489	4.5947	.010309278
98	9,604	941,192	9.8995	4.6104	.010204082
99	9,801	970,299	9.9499	4.6261	.010101010
100	10,000	1,000,000	10.0000	4.6416	.010000000

TABLE IX   **100-150**

No.	Square	Cube	Sq. Root	Cu. Root	Reciprocal
100	10,000	1,000,000	10.0000	4.6416	.010000000
101	10,201	1,030,301	10.0499	4.6570	.009900990
102	10,404	1,061,208	10.0995	4.6723	.009803922
103	10,609	1,092,727	10.1489	4.6875	.009708738
104	10,816	1,124,864	10.1980	4.7027	.009615385
105	11,025	1,157,625	10.2470	4.7177	.009523810
106	11,236	1,191,016	10.2956	4.7326	.009433962
107	11,449	1,225,043	10.3441	4.7475	.009345794
108	11,664	1,259,712	10.3923	4.7622	.009259259
109	11,881	1,295,029	10.4403	4.7769	.009174312
110	12,100	1,331,000	10.4881	4.7914	.009090909
111	12,321	1,367,631	10.5357	4.8059	.009009009
112	12,544	1,404,928	10.5830	4.8203	.008928571
113	12,769	1,442,897	10.6301	4.8346	.008849558
114	12,996	1,481,544	10.6771	4.8488	.008771930
115	13,225	1,520,875	10.7238	4.8629	.008695652
116	13,456	1,560,896	10.7703	4.8770	.008620690
117	13,689	1,601,613	10.8167	4.8910	.008547009
118	13,924	1,643,032	10.8628	4.9049	.008474576
119	14,161	1,685,159	10.9087	4.9187	.008403361
120	14,400	1,728,000	10.9545	4.9324	.008333333
121	14,641	1,771,561	11.0000	4.9461	.008264463
122	14,884	1,815,848	11.0454	4.9597	.008196721
123	15,129	1,860,867	11.0905	4.9732	.008130081
124	15,376	1,906,624	11.1355	4.9866	.008064516
125	15,625	1,953,125	11.1803	5.0000	.008000000
126	15,876	2,000,376	11.2250	5.0133	.007936508
127	16,129	2,048,383	11.2694	5.0265	.007874016
128	16,384	2,097,152	11.3137	5.0397	.007812500
129	16,641	2,146,689	11.3578	5.0528	.007751938
130	16,900	2,197,000	11.4018	5.0658	.007692308
131	17,161	2,248,091	11.4455	5.0788	.007633588
132	17,424	2,299,968	11.4891	5.0916	.007575758
133	17,689	2,352,637	11.5326	5.1045	.007518797
134	17,956	2,406,104	11.5758	5.1172	.007462687
135	18,225	2,460,375	11.6190	5.1299	.007407407
136	18,496	2,515,456	11.6619	5.1426	.007352941
137	18,769	2,571,353	11.7047	5.1551	.007299270
138	19,044	2,628,072	11.7473	5.1676	.007246377
139	19,321	2,685,619	11.7898	5.1801	.007194245
140	19,600	2,744,000	11.8322	5.1925	.007142857
141	19,881	2,803,221	11.8743	5.2048	.007092199
142	20,164	2,863,288	11.9164	5.2171	.007042254
143	20,449	2,924,207	11.9583	5.2293	.006993007
144	20,736	2,985,984	12.0000	5.2415	.006944444
145	21,025	3,048,625	12.0416	5.2536	.006896552
146	21,316	3,112,136	12.0830	5.2656	.006849315
147	21,609	3,176,523	12.1244	5.2776	.006802721
148	21,904	3,241,792	12.1655	5.2896	.006756757
149	22,201	3,307,949	12.2066	5.3015	.006711409
150	22,500	3,375,000	12.2474	5.3133	.006666667

No.	Square	Cube	Sq. Root	Cu. Root	Reciprocal
150	22,500	3,375,000	12.2474	5.3133	.006666667
151	22,801	3,442,951	12.2882	5.3251	.006622517
152	23,104	3,511,008	12.3288	5.3368	.006578947
153	23,409	3,581,577	12.3693	5.3485	.006535948
154	23,716	3,652,264	12.4097	5.3601	.006493506
155	24,025	3,723,875	12.4499	5.3717	.006451613
156	24,336	3,796,416	12.4900	5.3832	.006410256
157	24,649	3,869,893	12.5300	5.3947	.006369427
158	24,964	3,944,312	12.5698	5.4061	.006329114
159	25,281	4,019,679	12.6095	5.4175	.006289308
160	25,600	4,096,000	12.6491	5.4288	.006250000
161	25,921	4,173,281	12.6886	5.4401	.006211180
162	26,244	4,251,528	12.7279	5.4514	.006172840
163	26,569	4,330,747	12.7671	5.4626	.006134969
164	26,896	4,410,944	12.8062	5.4737	.006097561
165	27,225	4,492,125	12.8452	5.4848	.006060606
166	27,556	4,574,296	12.8841	5.4959	.006024096
167	27,889	4,657,463	12.9228	5.5069	.005988024
168	28,224	4,741,632	12.9615	5.5178	.005952381
169	28,561	4,826,809	13.0000	5.5288	.005917160
170	28,900	4,913,000	13.0384	5.5397	.005882353
171	29,241	5,000,211	13.0767	5.5505	.005847953
172	29,584	5,088,448	13.1149	5.5613	.005813953
173	29,929	5,177,717	13.1529	5.5721	.005780347
174	30,276	5,268,024	13.1909	5.5828	.005747126
175	30,625	5,359,375	13.2288	5.5934	.005714286
176	30,976	5,451,776	13.2665	5.6041	.005681818
177	31,329	5,545,233	13.3041	5.6147	.005649718
178	31,684	5,639,752	13.3417	5.6252	.005617978
179	32,041	5,735,339	13.3791	5.6357	.005586592
180	32,400	5,832,000	13.4164	5.6462	.005555556
181	32,761	5,929,741	13.4536	5.6567	.005524862
182	33,124	6,028,568	13.4907	5.6671	.005494505
183	33,489	6,128,487	13.5277	5.6774	.005464481
184	33,856	6,229,504	13.5647	5.6877	.005434783
185	34,225	6,331,625	13.6015	5.6980	.005405405
186	34,596	6,434,856	13.6382	5.7083	.005376344
187	34,969	6,539,203	13.6748	5.7185	.005347594
188	35,344	6,644,672	13.7113	5.7287	.005319149
189	35,721	6,751,269	13.7477	5.7388	.005291005
190	36,100	6,859,000	13.7840	5.7489	.005263158
191	36,481	6,967,871	13.8203	5.7590	.005235602
192	36,864	7,077,888	13.8564	5.7690	.005208333
193	37,249	7,189,057	13.8924	5.7790	.005181347
194	37,636	7,301,384	13.9284	5.7890	.005154639
195	38,025	7,414,875	13.9642	5.7989	.005128205
196	38,416	7,529,536	14.0000	5.8088	.005102041
197	38,809	7,645,373	14.0357	5.8186	.005076142
198	39,204	7,762,392	14.0712	5.8285	.005050505
199	39,601	7,880,599	14.1067	5.8383	.005025126
200	40,000	8,000,000	14.1421	5.8480	.005000000

TABLE IX   **200-250**

No.	Square	Cube	Sq. Root	Cu. Root	Reciprocal
200	40,000	8,000,000	14.1421	5.8480	.005000000
201	40,401	8,120,601	14.1774	5.8578	.004975124
202	40,804	8,242,408	14.2127	5.8675	.004950495
203	41,209	8,365,427	14.2478	5.8771	.004926108
204	41,616	8,489,664	14.2829	5.8868	.004901961
205	42,025	8,615,125	14.3178	5.8964	.004878049
206	42,436	8,741,816	14.3527	5.9059	.004854369
207	42,849	8,869,743	14.3875	5.9155	.004830918
208	43,264	8,998,912	14.4222	5.9250	.004807692
209	43,681	9,129,329	14.4568	5.9345	.004784689
210	44,100	9,261,000	14.4914	5.9439	.004761905
211	44,521	9,393,931	14.5258	5.9533	.004739336
212	44,944	9,528,128	14.5602	5.9627	.004716981
213	45,369	9,663,597	14.5945	5.9721	.004694836
214	45,796	9,800,344	14.6287	5.9814	.004672897
215	46,225	9,938,375	14.6629	5.9907	.004651163
216	46,656	10,077,696	14.6969	6.0000	.004629630
217	47,089	10,218,313	14.7309	6.0092	.004608295
218	47,524	10,360,232	14.7648	6.0185	.004587156
219	47,961	10,503,459	14.7986	6.0277	.004566210
220	48,400	10,648,000	14.8324	6.0368	.004545455
221	48,841	10,793,861	14.8661	6.0459	.004524887
222	49,284	10,941,048	14.8997	6.0550	.004504505
223	49,729	11,089,567	14.9332	6.0641	.004484305
224	50,176	11,239,424	14.9666	6.0732	.004464286
225	50,625	11,390,625	15.0000	6.0822	.004444444
226	51,076	11,543,176	15.0333	6.0912	.004424779
227	51,529	11,697,083	15.0665	6.1002	.004405286
228	51,984	11,852,352	15.0997	6.1091	.004385965
229	52,441	12,008,989	15.1327	6.1180	.004366812
230	52,900	12,167,000	15.1658	6.1269	.004347826
231	53,361	12,326,391	15.1987	6.1358	.004329004
232	53,824	12,487,168	15.2315	6.1446	.004310345
233	54,289	12,649,337	15.2643	6.1534	.004291845
234	54,756	12,812,904	15.2971	6.1622	.004273504
235	55,225	12,977,875	15.3297	6.1710	.004255319
236	55,696	13,144,256	15.3623	6.1797	.004237288
237	56,169	13,312,053	15.3948	6.1885	.004219409
238	56,644	13,481,272	15.4272	6.1972	.004201681
239	57,121	13,651,919	15.4596	6.2058	.004184100
240	57,600	13,824,000	15.4919	6.2145	.004166667
241	58,081	13,997,521	15.5242	6.2231	.004149378
242	58,564	14,172,488	15.5563	6.2317	.004132231
243	59,049	14,348,907	15.5885	6.2403	.004115226
244	59,536	14,526,784	15.6205	6.2488	.004098361
245	60,025	14,706,125	15.6525	6.2573	.004081633
246	60,516	14,886,936	15.6844	6.2658	.004065041
247	61,009	15,069,223	15.7162	6.2743	.004048583
248	61,504	15,252,992	15.7480	6.2828	.004032258
249	62,001	15,438,249	15.7797	6.2912	.004016064
250	62,500	15,625,000	15.8114	6.2996	.004000000

No.	Square	Cube	Sq. Root	Cu. Root	Reciprocal
250	62,500	15,625,000	15.8114	6.2996	.004000000
251	63,001	15,813,251	15.8430	6.3080	.003984064
252	63,504	16,003,008	15.8745	6.3164	.003968254
253	64,009	16,194,277	15.9060	6.3247	.003952569
254	64,516	16,387,064	15.9374	6.3330	.003937008
255	65,025	16,581,375	15.9687	6.3413	.003921569
256	65,536	16,777,216	16.0000	6.3496	.003906250
257	66,049	16,974,593	16.0312	6.3579	.003891051
258	66,564	17,173,512	16.0624	6.3661	.003875969
259	67,081	17,373,979	16.0935	6.3743	.003861004
260	67,600	17,576,000	16.1245	6.3825	.003846154
261	68,121	17,779,581	16.1555	6.3907	.003831418
262	68,644	17,984,728	16.1864	6.3988	.003816794
263	69,169	18,191,447	16.2173	6.4070	.003802281
264	69,696	18,399,744	16.2481	6.4151	.003787879
265	70,225	18,609,625	16.2788	6.4232	.003773585
266	70,756	18,821,096	16.3095	6.4312	.003759398
267	71,289	19,034,163	16.3401	6.4393	.003745318
268	71,824	19,248,832	16.3707	6.4473	.003731343
269	72,361	19,465,109	16.4012	6.4553	.003717472
270	72,900	19,683,000	16.4317	6.4633	.003703704
271	73,441	19,902,511	16.4621	6.4713	.003690037
272	73,984	20,123,648	16.4924	6.4792	.003676471
273	74,529	20,346,417	16.5227	6.4872	.003663004
274	75,076	20,570,824	16.5529	6.4951	.003649635
275	75,625	20,796,875	16.5831	6.5030	.003636364
276	76,176	21,024,576	16.6132	6.5108	.003623188
277	76,729	21,253,933	16.6433	6.5187	.003610108
278	77,284	21,484,952	16.6733	6.5265	.003597122
279	77,841	21,717,639	16.7033	6.5343	.003584229
280	78,400	21,952,000	16.7332	6.5421	.003571429
281	78,961	22,188,041	16.7631	6.5499	.003558719
282	79,524	22,425,768	16.7929	6.5577	.003546099
283	80,089	22,665,187	16.8226	6.5654	.003533569
284	80,656	22,906,304	16.8523	6.5731	.003521127
285	81,225	23,149,125	16.8819	6.5808	.003508772
286	81,796	23,393,656	16.9115	6.5885	.003496503
287	82,369	23,639,903	16.9411	6.5962	.003484321
288	82,944	23,887,872	16.9706	6.6039	.003472222
289	83,521	24,137,569	17.0000	6.6115	.003460208
290	84,100	24,389,000	17.0294	6.6191	.003448276
291	84,681	24,642,171	17.0587	6.6267	.003436426
292	85,264	24,897,088	17.0880	6.6343	.003424658
293	85,849	25,153,757	17.1172	6.6419	.003412969
294	86,436	25,412,184	17.1464	6.6494	.003401361
295	87,025	25,672,375	17.1756	6.6569	.003389831
296	87,616	25,934,336	17.2047	6.6644	.003378378
297	88,209	26,198,073	17.2337	6.6719	.003367003
298	88,804	26,463,592	17.2627	6.6794	.003355705
299	89,401	26,730,899	17.2916	6.6869	.003344482
300	90,000	27,000,000	17.3205	6.6943	.003333333

TABLE IX   **300-350**

No.	Square	Cube	Sq. Root	Cu. Root	Reciprocal
300	90,000	27,000,000	17.3205	6.6943	.003333333
301	90,601	27,270,901	17.3494	6.7018	.003322259
302	91,204	27,543,608	17.3781	6.7092	.003311258
303	91,809	27,818,127	17.4069	6.7166	.003300330
304	92,416	28,094,464	17.4356	6.7240	.003289474
305	93,025	28,372,625	17.4642	6.7313	.003278689
306	93,636	28,652,616	17.4929	6.7387	.003267974
307	94,249	28,934,443	17.5214	6.7460	.003257329
308	94,864	29,218,112	17.5499	6.7533	.003246753
309	95,481	29,503,629	17.5784	6.7606	.003236246
310	96,100	29,791,000	17.6068	6.7679	.003225806
311	96,721	30,080,231	17.6352	6.7752	.003215434
312	97,344	30,371,328	17.6635	6.7824	.003205128
313	97,969	30,664,297	17.6918	6.7897	.003194888
314	98,596	30,959,144	17.7200	6.7969	.003184713
315	99,225	31,255,875	17.7482	6.8041	.003174603
316	99,856	31,554,496	17.7764	6.8113	.003164557
317	100,489	31,855,013	17.8045	6.8185	.003154574
318	101,124	32,157,432	17.8326	6.8256	.003144654
319	101,761	32,461,759	17.8606	6.8328	.003134796
320	102,400	32,768,000	17.8885	6.8399	.003125000
321	103,041	33,076,161	17.9165	6.8470	.003115265
322	103,684	33,386,248	17.9444	6.8541	.003105590
323	104,329	33,698,267	17.9722	6.8612	.003095975
324	104,976	34,012,224	18.0000	6.8683	.003086420
325	105,625	34,328,125	18.0278	6.8753	.003076923
326	106,276	34,645,976	18.0555	6.8824	.003067485
327	106,929	34,965,783	18.0831	6.8894	.003058104
328	107,584	35,287,552	18.1108	6.8964	.003048780
329	108,241	35,611,289	18.1384	6.9034	.003039514
330	108,900	35,937,000	18.1659	6.9104	.003030303
331	109,561	36,264,691	18.1934	6.9174	.003021148
332	110,224	36,594,368	18.2209	6.9244	.003012048
333	110,889	36,926,037	18.2483	6.9313	.003003003
334	111,556	37,259,704	18.2757	6.9382	.002994012
335	112,225	37,595,375	18.3030	6.9451	.002985075
336	112,896	37,933,056	18.3303	6.9521	.002976190
337	113,569	38,272,753	18.3576	6.9589	.002967359
338	114,244	38,614,472	18.3848	6.9658	.002958580
339	114,921	38,958,219	18.4120	6.9727	.002949853
340	115,600	39,304,000	18.4391	6.9795	.002941176
341	116,281	39,651,821	18.4662	6.9864	.002932551
342	116,964	40,001,688	18.4932	6.9932	.002923977
343	117,649	40,353,607	18.5203	7.0000	.002915452
344	118,336	40,707,584	18.5472	7.0068	.002906977
345	119,025	41,063,625	18.5742	7.0136	.002898551
346	119,716	41,421,736	18.6011	7.0203	.002890173
347	120,409	41,781,923	18.6279	7.0271	.002881844
348	121,104	42,144,192	18.6548	7.0338	.002873563
349	121,801	42,508,549	18.6815	7.0406	.002865330
350	122,500	42,875,000	18.7083	7.0473	.002857143

No.	Square	Cube	Sq. Root	Cu. Root	Reciprocal
350	122,500	42,875,000	18.7083	7.0473	.002857143
351	123,201	43,243,551	18.7350	7.0540	.002849003
352	123,904	43,614,208	18.7617	7.0607	.002840909
353	124,609	43,986,977	18.7883	7.0674	.002832861
354	125,316	44,361,864	18.8149	7.0740	.002824859
355	126,025	44,738,875	18.8414	7.0807	.002816901
356	126,736	45,118,016	18.8680	7.0873	.002808989
357	127,449	45,499,293	18.8944	7.0940	.002801120
358	128,164	45,882,712	18.9209	7.1006	.002793296
359	128,881	46,268,279	18.9473	7.1072	.002785515
360	129,600	46,656,000	18.9737	7.1138	.002777778
361	130,321	47,045,881	19.0000	7.1204	.002770083
362	131,044	47,437,928	19.0263	7.1269	.002762431
363	131,769	47,832,147	19.0526	7.1335	.002754821
364	132,496	48,228,544	19.0788	7.1400	.002747253
365	133,225	48,627,125	19.1050	7.1466	.002739726
366	133,956	49,027,896	19.1311	7.1531	.002732240
367	134,689	49,430,863	19.1572	7.1596	.002724796
368	135,424	49,836,032	19.1833	7.1661	.002717391
369	136,161	50,243,409	19.2094	7.1726	.002710027
370	136,900	50,653,000	19.2354	7.1791	.002702703
371	137,641	51,064,811	19.2614	7.1855	.002695418
372	138,384	51,478,848	19.2873	7.1920	.002688172
373	139,129	51,895,117	19.3132	7.1984	.002680965
374	139,876	52,313,624	19.3391	7.2048	.002673797
375	140,625	52,734,375	19.3649	7.2112	.002666667
376	141,376	53,157,376	19.3907	7.2177	.002659574
377	142,129	53,582,633	19.4165	7.2240	.002652520
378	142,884	54,010,152	19.4422	7.2304	.002645503
379	143,641	54,439,939	19.4679	7.2368	.002638522
380	144,400	54,872,000	19.4936	7.2432	.002631579
381	145,161	55,306,341	19.5192	7.2495	.002624672
382	145,924	55,742,968	19.5448	7.2558	.002617801
383	146,689	56,181,887	19.5704	7.2622	.002610966
384	147,456	56,623,104	19.5959	7.2685	.002604167
385	148,225	57,066,625	19.6214	7.2748	.002597403
386	148,996	57,512,456	19.6469	7.2811	.002590674
387	149,769	57,960,603	19.6723	7.2874	.002583979
388	150,544	58,411,072	19.6977	7.2936	.002577320
389	151,321	58,863,869	19.7231	7.2999	.002570694
390	152,100	59,319,000	19.7484	7.3061	.002564103
391	152,881	59,776,471	19.7737	7.3124	.002557545
392	153,664	60,236,288	19.7990	7.3186	.002551020
393	154,449	60,698,457	19.8242	7.3248	.002544529
394	155,236	61,162,984	19.8494	7.3310	.002538071
395	156,025	61,629,875	19.8746	7.3372	.002531646
396	156,816	62,099,136	19.8997	7.3434	.002525253
397	157,609	62,570,773	19.9249	7.3496	.002518892
398	158,404	63,044,792	19.9499	7.3558	.002512563
399	159,201	63,521,199	19.9750	7.3619	.002506266
400	160,000	64,000,000	20.0000	7.3681	.002500000

TABLE IX   **400-450**

No.	Square	Cube	Sq. Root	Cu. Root	Reciprocal
400	160,000	64,000,000	20.0000	7.3681	.002500000
401	160,801	64,481,201	20.0250	7.3742	.002493766
402	161,604	64,964,808	20.0499	7.3803	.002487562
403	162,409	65,450,827	20.0749	7.3864	.002481390
404	163,216	65,939,264	20.0998	7.3925	.002475248
405	164,025	66,430,125	20.1246	7.3986	.002469136
406	164,836	66,923,416	20.1494	7.4047	.002463054
407	165,649	67,419,143	20.1742	7.4108	.002457002
408	166,464	67,917,312	20.1990	7.4169	.002450980
409	167,281	68,417,929	20.2237	7.4229	.002444988
410	168,100	68,921,000	20.2485	7.4290	.002439024
411	168,921	69,426,531	20.2731	7.4350	.002433090
412	169,744	69,934,528	20.2978	7.4410	.002427184
413	170,569	70,444,997	20.3224	7.4470	.002421308
414	171,396	70,957,944	20.3470	7.4530	.002415459
415	172,225	71,473,375	20.3715	7.4590	.002409639
416	173,056	71,991,296	20.3961	7.4650	.002403846
417	173,889	72,511,713	20.4206	7.4710	.002398082
418	174,724	73,034,632	20.4450	7.4770	.002392344
419	175,561	73,560,059	20.4695	7.4829	.002386635
420	176,400	74,088,000	20.4939	7.4889	.002380952
421	177,241	74,618,461	20.5183	7.4948	.002375297
422	178,084	75,151,448	20.5426	7.5007	.002369668
423	178,929	75,686,967	20.5670	7.5067	.002364066
424	179,776	76,225,024	20.5913	7.5126	.002358491
425	180,625	76,765,625	20.6155	7.5185	.002352941
426	181,476	77,308,776	20.6398	7.5244	.002347418
427	182,329	77,854,483	20.6640	7.5302	.002341920
428	183,184	78,402,752	20.6882	7.5361	.002336449
429	184,041	78,953,589	20.7123	7.5420	.002331002
430	184,900	79,507,000	20.7364	7.5478	.002325581
431	185,761	80,062,991	20.7605	7.5537	.002320186
432	186,624	80,621,568	20.7846	7.5595	.002314815
433	187,489	81,182,737	20.8087	7.5654	.002309469
434	188,356	81,746,504	20.8327	7.5712	.002304147
435	189,225	82,312,875	20.8567	7.5770	.002298851
436	190,096	82,881,856	20.8806	7.5828	.002293578
437	190,969	83,453,453	20.9045	7.5886	.002288330
438	191,844	84,027,672	20.9284	7.5944	.002283105
439	192,721	84,604,519	20.9523	7.6001	.002277904
440	193,600	85,184,000	20.9762	7.6059	.002272727
441	194,481	85,766,121	21.0000	7.6117	.002267574
442	195,364	86,350,888	21.0238	7.6174	.002262443
443	196,249	86,938,307	21.0476	7.6232	.002257336
444	197,136	87,528,384	21.0713	7.6289	.002252252
445	198,025	88,121,125	21.0950	7.6346	.002247191
446	198,916	88,716,536	21.1187	7.6403	.002242152
447	199,809	89,314,623	21.1424	7.6460	.002237136
448	200,704	89,915,392	21.1660	7.6517	.002232143
449	201,601	90,518,849	21.1896	7.6574	.002227171
450	202,500	91,125,000	21.2132	7.6631	.002222222

No.	Square	Cube	Sq. Root	Cu. Root	Reciprocal
450	202,500	91,125,000	21.2132	7.6631	.002222222
451	203,401	91,733,851	21.2368	7.6688	.002217295
452	204,304	92,345,408	21.2603	7.6744	.002212389
453	205,209	92,959,677	21.2838	7.6801	.002207506
454	206,116	93,576,664	21.3073	7.6857	.002202643
455	207,025	94,196,375	21.3307	7.6914	.002197802
456	207,936	94,818,816	21.3542	7.6970	.002192982
457	208,849	95,443,993	21.3776	7.7026	.002188184
458	209,764	96,071,912	21.4009	7.7082	.002183406
459	210,681	96,702,579	21.4243	7.7138	.002178649
460	211,600	97,336,000	21.4476	7.7194	.002173913
461	212,521	97,972,181	21.4709	7.7250	.002169197
462	213,444	98,611,128	21.4942	7.7306	.002164502
463	214,369	99,252,847	21.5174	7.7362	.002159827
464	215,296	99,897,344	21.5407	7.7418	.002155172
465	216,225	100,544,625	21.5639	7.7473	.002150538
466	217,156	101,194,696	21.5870	7.7529	.002145923
467	218,089	101,847,563	21.6102	7.7584	.002141328
468	219,024	102,503,232	21.6333	7.7639	.002136752
469	219,961	103,161,709	21.6564	7.7695	.002132196
470	220,900	103,823,000	21.6795	7.7750	.002127660
471	221,841	104,487,111	21.7025	7.7805	.002123142
472	222,784	105,154,048	21.7256	7.7860	.002118644
473	223,729	105,823,817	21.7486	7.7915	.002114165
474	224,676	106,496,424	21.7715	7.7970	.002109705
475	225,625	107,171,875	21.7945	7.8025	.002105263
476	226,576	107,850,176	21.8174	7.8079	.002100840
477	227,529	108,531,333	21.8403	7.8134	.002096436
478	228,484	109,215,352	21.8632	7.8188	.002092050
479	229,441	109,902,239	21.8861	7.8243	.002087683
480	230,400	110,592,000	21.9089	7.8297	.002083333
481	231,361	111,284,641	21.9317	7.8352	.002079002
482	232,324	111,980,168	21.9545	7.8406	.002074689
483	233,289	112,678,587	21.9773	7.8460	.002070393
484	234,256	113,379,904	22.0000	7.8514	.002066116
485	235,225	114,084,125	22.0227	7.8568	.002061856
486	236,196	114,791,256	22.0454	7.8622	.002057613
487	237,169	115,501,303	22.0681	7.8676	.002053388
488	238,144	116,214,272	22.0907	7.8730	.002049180
489	239,121	116,930,169	22.1133	7.8784	.002044990
490	240,100	117,649,000	22.1359	7.8837	.002040816
491	241,081	118,370,771	22.1585	7.8891	.002036660
492	242,064	119,095,488	22.1811	7.8944	.002032520
493	243,049	119,823,157	22.2036	7.8998	.002028398
494	244,036	120,553,784	22.2261	7.9051	.002024291
495	245,025	121,287,375	22.2486	7.9105	.002020202
496	246,016	122,023,936	22.2711	7.9158	.002016129
497	247,009	122,763,473	22.2935	7.9211	.002012072
498	248,004	123,505,992	22.3159	7.9264	.002008032
499	249,001	124,251,499	22.3383	7.9317	.002004008
500	250,000	125,000,000	22.3607	7.9370	.002000000

TABLE IX 500-550

No.	Square	Cube	Sq. Root	Cu. Root	Reciprocal
500	250,000	125,000,000	22.3607	7.9370	.002000000
501	251,001	125,751,501	22.3830	7.9423	.001996008
502	252,004	126,506,008	22.4054	7.9476	.001992032
503	253,009	127,263,527	22.4277	7.9528	.001988072
504	254,016	128,024,064	22.4499	7.9581	.001984127
505	255,025	128,787,625	22.4722	7.9634	.001980198
506	256,036	129,554,216	22.4944	7.9686	.901976285
507	257,049	130,323,843	22.5167	7.9739	.001972387
508	258,064	131,096,512	22.5389	7.9791	.001968504
509	259,081	131,872,229	22.5610	7.9843	.001964637
510	260,100	132,651,000	22.5832	7.9896	.001960784
511	261,121	133,432,831	22.6053	7.9948	.001956947
512	262,144	134,217,728	22.6274	8.0000	.001953125
513	263,169	135,005,697	22.6495	8.0052	.001949318
514	264,196	135,796,744	22.6716	8.0104	.001945525
515	265,225	136,590,875	22.6936	8.0156	.001941748
516	266,256	137,388,096	22.7156	8.0208	.001937984
517	267,289	138,188,413	22.7376	8.0260	.001934236
518	268,324	138,991,832	22.7596	8.0311	.001930502
519	269,361	139,798,359	22.7816	8.0363	.001926782
520	270,400	140,608,000	22.8035	8.0415	.001923077
521	271,441	141,420,761	22.8254	8.0466	.001919386
522	272,484	142,236,648	22.8473	8.0517	.001915709
523	273,529	143,055,667	22.8692	8.0569	.001912046
524	274,576	143,877,824	22.8910	8.0620	.001908397
525	275,625	144,703,125	22.9129	8.0671	.001904762
526	276,676	145,531,576	22.9347	8.0723	.001901141
527	277,729	146,363,183	22.9565	8.0774	.001897533
528	278,784	147,197,952	22.9783	8.0825	.001893939
529	279,841	148,035,889	23.0000	8.0876	.001890359
530	280,900	148,877,000	23.0217	8.0927	.001886792
531	281,961	149,721,291	23.0434	8.0978	.001883239
532	283,024	150,568,768	23.0651	8.1028	.001879699
533	284,089	151,419,437	23.0868	8.1079	.001876173
534	285,156	152,273,304	23.1084	8.1130	.001872659
535	286,225	153,130,375	23.1301	8.1180	.001869159
536	287,296	153,990,656	23.1517	8.1231	.001865672
537	288,369	154,854,153	23.1733	8.1281	.001862197
538	289,444	155,720,872	23.1948	8.1332	.001858736
539	290,521	156,590,819	23.2164	8.1382	.001855288
540	291,600	157,464,000	23.2379	8.1433	.001851852
541	292,681	158,340,421	23.2594	8.1483	.001848429
542	293,764	159,220,088	23.2809	8.1533	.001845018
543	294,849	160,103,007	23.3024	8.1583	.001841621
544	295,936	160,989,184	23.3238	8.1633	.001838235
545	297,025	161,878,625	23.3452	8.1683	.001834862
546	298,116	162,771,336	23.3666	8.1733	.001831502
547	299,209	163,667,323	23.3880	8.1783	.001828154
548	300,304	164,566,592	23.4094	8.1833	.001824818
549	301,401	165,469,149	23.4307	8.1882	.001821494
550	302,500	166,375,000	23.4521	8.1932	.001818182

No.	Square	Cube	Sq. Root	Cu. Root	Reciprocal
550	302,500	166,375,000	23.4521	8.1932	.001818182
551	303,601	167,284,151	23.4734	8.1982	.001814882
552	304,704	168,196,608	23.4947	8.2031	.001811594
553	305,809	169,112,377	23.5160	8.2081	.001808318
554	306,916	170,031,464	23.5372	8.2130	.001805054
555	308,025	170,953,875	23.5584	8.2180	.001801802
556	309,136	171,879,616	23.5797	8.2229	.001798561
557	310,249	172,808,693	23.6008	8.2278	.001795332
558	311,364	173,741,112	23.6220	8.2327	.001792115
559	312,481	174,676,879	23.6432	8.2377	.001788909
560	313,600	175,616,000	23.6643	8.2426	.001785714
561	314,721	176,558,481	23.6854	8.2475	.001782531
562	315,844	177,504,328	23.7065	8.2524	.001779359
563	316,969	178,453,547	23.7276	8.2573	.001776199
564	318,096	179,406,144	23.7487	8.2621	.001773050
565	319,225	180,362,125	23.7697	8.2670	.001769912
566	320,356	181,321,496	23.7908	8.2719	.001766784
567	321,489	182,284,263	23.8118	8.2768	.001763668
568	322,624	183,250,432	23.8328	8.2816	.001760563
569	323,761	184,220,009	23.8537	8.2865	.001757469
570	324,900	185,193,000	23.8747	8.2913	.001754386
571	326,041	186,169,411	23.8956	8.2962	.001751313
572	327,184	187,149,248	23.9165	8.3010	.001748252
573	328,329	188,132,517	23.9374	8.3059	.001745201
574	329,476	189,119,224	23.9583	8.3107	.001742160
575	330,625	190,109,375	23.9792	8.3155	.001739130
576	331,776	191,102,976	24.0000	8.3203	.001736111
577	332,929	192,100,033	24.0208	8.3251	.001733102
578	334,084	193,100,552	24.0416	8.3300	.001730104
579	335,241	194,104,539	24.0624	8.3348	.001727116
580	336,400	195,112,000	24.0832	8.3396	.001724138
581	337,561	196,122,941	24.1039	8.3443	.001721170
582	338,724	197,137,368	24.1247	8.3491	.001718213
583	339,889	198,155,287	24.1454	8.3539	.001715266
584	341,056	199,176,704	24.1661	8.3587	.001712329
585	342,225	200,201,625	24.1868	8.3634	.001709402
586	343,396	201,230,056	24.2074	8.3682	.001706485
587	344,569	202,262,003	24.2281	8.3730	.001703578
588	345,744	203,297,472	24.2487	8.3777	.001700680
589	346,921	204,336,469	24.2693	8.3825	.001697793
590	348,100	205,379,000	24.2899	8.3872	.001694915
591	349,281	206,425,071	24.3105	8.3919	.001692047
592	350,464	207,474,688	24.3311	8.3967	.001689189
593	351,649	208,527,857	24.3516	8.4014	.001686341
594	352,836	209,584,584	24.3721	8.4061	.001683502
595	354,025	210,644,875	24.3926	8.4108	.001680672
596	355,216	211,708,736	24.4131	8.4155	001677852
597	356,409	212,776,173	24.4336	8.4202	.001675042
598	357,604	213,847,192	24.4540	8.4249	.001672241
599	358,801	214,921,799	24.4745	8.4296	.001669449
600	360,000	216,000,000	24.4949	8.4343	.001666667

TABLE IX   **600-650**

No.	Square	Cube	Sq. Root	Cu. Root	Reciprocal
600	360,000	216,000,000	24.4949	8.4343	.001666667
601	361,201	217,081,801	24.5153	8.4390	.001663894
602	362,404	218,167,208	24.5357	8.4437	.001661130
603	363,609	219,256,227	24.5561	8.4484	.001658375
604	364,816	220,348,864	24.5764	8.4530	.001655629
605	366,025	221,445,125	24.5967	8.4577	.001652893
606	367,236	222,545,016	24.6171	8.4623	.001650165
607	368,449	223,648,543	24.6374	8.4670	.001647446
608	369,664	224,755,712	24.6577	8.4716	.001644737
609	370,881	225,866,529	24.6779	8.4763	.001642036
610	372,100	226,981,000	24.6982	8.4809	.001639344
611	373,321	228,099,131	24.7184	8.4856	.001636661
612	374,544	229,220,928	24.7386	8.4902	.001633987
613	375,769	230,346,397	24.7588	8.4948	.001631321
614	376,996	231,475,544	24.7790	8.4994	.001628664
615	378,225	232,608,375	24.7992	8.5040	.001626016
616	379,456	233,744,896	24.8193	8.5086	.001623377
617	380,689	234,885,113	24.8395	8.5132	.001620746
618	381,924	236,029,032	24.8596	8.5178	.001618123
619	383,161	237,176,659	24.8797	8.5224	.001615509
620	384,400	238,328,000	24.8998	8.5270	.001612903
621	385,641	239,483,061	24.9199	8.5316	.001610306
622	386,884	240,641,848	24.9399	8.5362	.001607717
623	388,129	241,804,367	24.9600	8.5408	.001605136
624	389,376	242,970,624	24.9800	8.5453	.001602564
625	390,625	244,140,625	25.0000	8.5499	.001600000
626	391,876	245,314,376	25.0200	8.5544	.001597444
627	393,129	246,491,883	25.0400	8.5590	.001594896
628	394,384	247,673,152	25.0599	8.5635	.001592357
629	395,641	248,858,189	25.0799	8.5681	.001589825
630	396,900	250,047,000	25.0998	8.5726	.001587302
631	398,161	251,239,591	25.1197	8.5772	.001584786
632	399,424	252,435,968	25.1396	8.5817	.001582278
633	400,689	253,636,137	25.1595	8.5862	.001579779
634	401,956	254,840,104	25.1794	8.5907	.001577287
635	403,225	256,047,875	25.1992	8.5952	.001574803
636	404,496	257,259,456	25.2190	8.5997	.001572327
637	405,769	258,474,853	25.2389	8.6043	.001569859
638	407,044	259,694,072	25.2587	8.6088	.001567398
639	408,321	260,917,119	25.2784	8.6132	.001564945
640	409,600	262,144,000	25.2982	8.6177	.001562500
641	410,881	263,374,721	25.3180	8.6222	.001560062
642	412,164	264,609,288	25.3377	8.6267	.001557632
643	413,449	265,847,707	25.3574	8.6312	.001555210
644	414,736	267,089,984	25.3772	8.6357	.001552795
645	416,025	268,336,125	25.3969	8.6401	.001550388
646	417,316	269,586,136	25.4165	8.6446	.001547988
647	418,609	270,840,023	25.4362	8.6490	.001545595
648	419,904	272,097,792	25.4558	8.6535	.001543210
649	421,201	273,359,449	25.4755	8.6579	.001540832
650	422,500	274,625,000	25.4951	8.6624	.001538462

No.	Square	Cube	Sq. Root	Cu. Root	Reciprocal
650	422,500	274,625,000	25.4951	8.6624	.001538462
651	423,801	275,894,451	25.5147	8.6668	.001536098
652	425,104	277,167,808	25.5343	8.6713	.001533742
653	426,409	278,445,077	25.5539	8.6757	.001531394
654	427,716	279,726,264	25.5734	8.6801	.001529052
655	429,025	281,011,375	25.5930	8.6845	.001526718
656	430,336	282,300,416	25.6125	8.6890	.001524390
657	431,649	283,593,393	25.6320	8.6934	.001522070
658	432,964	284,890,312	25.6515	8.6978	.001519757
659	434,281	286,191,179	25.6710	8.7022	.001517451
660	435,600	287,496,000	25.6905	8.7066	.001515152
661	436,921	288,804,781	25.7099	8.7110	.001512859
662	438,244	290,117,528	25.7294	8.7154	.001510574
663	439,569	291,434,247	25.7488	8.7198	.001508296
664	440,896	292,754,944	25.7682	8.7241	.001506024
665	442,225	294,079,625	25.7876	8.7285	.001503759
666	443,556	295,408,296	25.8070	8.7329	.001501502
667	444,889	296,740,963	25.8263	8.7373	.001499250
668	446,224	298,077,632	25.8457	8.7416	.001497006
669	447,561	299,418,309	25.8650	8.7460	.001494768
670	448,900	300,763,000	25.8844	8.7503	.001492537
671	450,241	302,111,711	25.9037	8.7547	.001490313
672	451,584	303,464,448	25.9230	8.7590	.001488095
673	452,929	304,821,217	25.9422	8.7634	.001485884
674	454,276	306,182,024	25.9615	8.7677	.001483680
675	455,625	307,546,875	25.9808	8.7721	.001481481
676	456,976	308,915,776	26.0000	8.7764	.001479290
677	458,329	310,288,733	26.0192	8.7807	.001477105
678	459,684	311,665,752	26.0384	8.7850	.001474926
679	461,041	313,046,839	26.0576	8.7893	.001472754
680	462,400	314,432,000	26.0768	8.7937	.001470588
681	463,761	315,821,241	26.0960	8.7980	.001468429
682	465,124	317,214,568	26.1151	8.8023	.001466276
683	466,489	318,611,987	26.1343	8.8066	.001464129
684	467,856	320,013,504	26.1534	8.8109	.001461988
685	469,225	321,419,125	26.1725	8.8152	.001459854
686	470,596	322,828,856	26.1916	8.8194	.001457726
687	471,969	324,242,703	26.2107	8.8237	.001455604
688	473,344	325,660,672	26.2298	8.8280	.001453488
689	474,721	327,082,769	26.2488	8.8323	.001451379
690	476,100	328,509,000	26.2679	8.8366	.001449275
691	477,481	329,939,371	26.2869	8.8408	.001447178
692	478,864	331,373,888	26.3059	8.8451	.001445087
693	480,249	332,812,557	26.3249	8.8493	.001443001
694	481,636	334,255,384	26.3439	8.8536	.001440922
695	483,025	335,702,375	26.3629	8.8578	.001438849
696	484,416	337,153,536	26.3818	8.8621	.001436782
697	485,809	338,608,873	26.4008	8.8663	.001434720
698	487,204	340,068,392	26.4197	8.8706	.001432665
699	488,601	341,532,099	26.4386	8.8748	.001430615
700	490,000	343,000,000	26.4575	8.8790	.001428571

TABLE IX   700-750

No.	Square	Cube	Sq. Root	Cu. Root	Reciprocal
700	490,000	343,000,000	26.4575	8.8790	.001428571
701	491,401	344,472,101	26.4764	8.8833	.001426534
702	492,804	345,948,408	26.4953	8.8875	.001424501
703	494,209	347,428,927	26.5141	8.8917	.001422475
704	495,616	348,913,664	26.5330	8.8959	.001420455
705	497,025	350,402,625	26.5518	8.9001	.001418440
706	498,436	351,895,816	26.5707	8.9043	.001416431
707	499,849	353,393,243	26.5895	8.9085	.001414427
708	501,264	354,894,912	26.6083	8.9127	.001412429
709	502,681	356,400,829	26.6271	8.9169	.001410437
710	504,100	357,911,000	26.6458	8.9211	.001408451
711	505,521	359,425,431	26.6646	8.9253	.001406470
712	506,944	360,944,128	26.6833	8.9295	.001404494
713	508,369	362,467,097	26.7021	8.9337	.001402525
714	509,796	363,994,344	26.7208	8.9378	.001400560
715	511,225	365,525,875	26.7395	8.9420	.001398601
716	512,656	367,061,696	26.7582	8.9462	.001396648
717	514,089	368,601,813	26.7769	8.9503	.001394700
718	515,524	370,146,232	26.7955	8.9545	.001392758
719	516,961	371,694,959	26.8142	8.9587	.001390821
720	518,400	373,248,000	26.8328	8.9628	.001388889
721	519,841	374,805,361	26.8514	8.9670	.001386963
722	521,284	376,367,048	26.8701	8.9711	.001385042
723	522,729	377,933,067	26.8887	8.9752	.001383126
724	524,176	379,503,424	26.9072	8.9794	.001381215
725	525,625	381,078,125	26.9258	8.9835	.001379310
726	527,076	382,657,176	26.9444	8.9876	.001377410
727	528,529	384,240,583	26.9629	8.9918	.001375516
728	529,984	385,828,352	26.9815	8.9959	.001373626
729	531,441	387,420,489	27.0000	9.0000	.001371742
730	532,900	389,017,000	27.0185	9.0041	.001369863
731	534,361	390,617,891	27.0370	9.0082	.001367989
732	535,824	392,223,168	27.0555	9.0123	.001366120
733	537,289	393,832,837	27.0740	9.0164	.001364256
734	538,756	395,446,904	27.0924	9.0205	.001362398
735	540,225	397,065,375	27.1109	9.0246	.001360544
736	541,696	398,688,256	27.1293	9.0287	.001358696
737	543,169	400,315,553	27.1477	9.0328	.001356852
738	544,644	401,947,272	27.1662	9.0369	.001355014
739	546,121	403,583,419	27.1846	9.0410	.001353180
740	547,600	405,224,000	27.2029	9.0450	.001351351
741	549,081	406,869,021	27.2213	9.0491	.001349528
742	550,564	408,518,488	27.2397	9.0532	.001347709
743	552,049	410,172,407	27.2580	9.0572	.001345895
744	553,536	411,830,784	27.2764	9.0613	.001344086
745	555,025	413,493,625	27.2947	9.0654	.001342282
746	556,516	415,160,936	27.3130	9.0694	.001340483
747	558,009	416,832,723	27.3313	9.0735	.001338688
748	559,504	418,508,992	27.3496	9.0775	.001336898
749	561,001	420,189,749	27.3679	9.0816	.001335113
750	562,500	421,875,000	27.3861	9.0856	.001333333

No.	Square	Cube	Sq. Root	Cu. Root	Reciprocal
750	562,500	421,875,000	27.3861	9.0856	.001333333
751	564,001	423,564,751	27.4044	9.0896	.001331558
752	565,504	425,259,008	27.4226	9.0937	.001329787
753	567,009	426,957,777	27.4408	9.0977	.001328021
754	568,516	428,661,064	27.4591	9.1017	.001326260
755	570,025	430,368,875	27.4773	9.1057	.001324503
756	571,536	432,081,216	27.4955	9.1098	.001322751
757	573,049	433,798,093	27.5136	9.1138	.001321004
758	574,564	435,519,512	27.5318	9.1178	.001319261
759	576,081	437,245,479	27.5500	9.1218	.001317523
760	577,600	438,976,000	27.5681	9.1258	.001315789
761	579,121	440,711,081	27.5862	9.1298	.001314060
762	580,644	442,450,728	27.6043	9.1338	.001312336
763	582,169	444,194,947	27.6225	9.1378	.001310616
764	583,696	445,943,744	27.6405	9.1418	.001308901
765	585,225	447,697,125	27.6586	9.1458	.001307190
766	586,756	449,455,096	27.6767	9.1498	.001305483
767	588,289	451,217,663	27.6948	9.1537	.001303781
768	589,824	452,984,832	27.7128	9.1577	.001302083
769	591,361	454,756,609	27.7308	9.1617	.001300390
770	592,900	456,533,000	27.7489	9.1657	.001298701
771	594,441	458,314,011	27.7669	9.1696	.001297017
772	595,984	460,099,648	27.7849	9.1736	.001295337
773	597,529	461,889,917	27.8029	9.1775	.001293661
774	599,076	463,684,824	27.8209	9.1815	.001291990
775	600,625	465,484,375	27.8388	9.1855	.001290323
776	602,176	467,288,576	27.8568	9.1894	.001288660
777	603,729	469,097,433	27.8747	9.1933	.001287001
778	605,284	470,910,952	27.8927	9.1973	.001285347
779	606,841	472,729,139	27.9106	9.2012	.001283697
780	608,400	474,552,000	27.9285	9.2052	.001282051
781	609,961	476,379,541	27.9464	9.2091	.001280410
782	611,524	478,211,768	27.9643	9.2130	.001278772
783	613,089	480,048,687	27.9821	9.2170	.001277139
784	614,656	481,890,304	28.0000	9.2209	.001275510
785	616,225	483,736,625	28.0179	9.2248	.001273885
786	617,796	485,587,656	28.0357	9.2287	.001272265
787	619,369	487,443,403	28.0535	9.2326	.001270648
788	620,944	489,303,872	28.0713	9.2365	.001269036
789	622,521	491,169,069	28.0891	9.2404	.001267427
790	624,100	493,039,000	28.1069	9.2443	.001265823
791	625,681	494,913,671	28.1247	9.2482	.001264223
792	627,264	496,793,088	28.1425	9.2521	.001262626
793	628,849	498,677,257	28.1603	9.2560	.001261034
794	630,436	500,566,184	28.1780	9.2599	.001259446
795	632,025	502,459,875	28.1957	9.2638	.001257862
796	633,616	504,358,336	28.2135	9.2677	.001256281
797	635,209	506,261,573	28.2312	9.2716	.001254705
798	636,804	508,169,592	28.2489	9.2754	.001253133
799	638,401	510,082,399	28.2666	9.2793	.001251564
800	640,000	512,000,000	28.2843	9.2832	.001250000

TABLE IX   **800-850**

No.	Square	Cube	Sq. Root	Cu. Root	Reciprocal
800	640,000	512,000,000	28.2843	9.2832	.001250000
801	641,601	513,922,401	28.3019	9.2870	.001248439
802	643,204	515,849,608	28.3196	9.2909	.001246883
803	644,809	517,781,627	28.3373	9.2948	.001245330
804	646,416	519,718,464	28.3549	9.2986	.001243781
805	648,025	521,660,125	28.3725	9.3025	.001242236
806	649,636	523,606,616	28.3901	9.3063	.001240695
807	651,249	525,557,943	28.4077	9.3102	.001239157
808	652,864	527,514,112	28.4253	9.3140	.001237624
809	654,481	529,475,129	28.4429	9.3179	.001236094
810	656,100	531,441,000	28.4605	9.3217	.001234568
811	657,721	533,411,731	28.4781	9.3255	.001233046
812	659,344	535,387,328	28.4956	9.3294	.001231527
813	660,969	537,367,797	28.5132	9.3332	.001230012
814	662,596	539,353,144	28.5307	9.3370	.001228501
815	664,225	541,343,375	28.5482	9.3408	.001226994
816	665,856	543,338,496	28.5657	9.3447	.001225490
817	667,489	545,338,513	28.5832	9.3485	.001223990
818	669,124	547,343,432	28.6007	9.3523	.001222494
819	670,761	549,353,259	28.6182	9.3561	.001221001
820	672,400	551,368,000	28.6356	9.3599	.001219512
821	674,041	553,387,661	28.6531	9.3637	.001218027
822	675,684	555,412,248	28.6705	9.3675	.001216545
823	677,329	557,441,767	28.6880	9.3713	.001215067
824	678,976	559,476,224	28.7054	9.3751	.001213592
825	680,625	561,515,625	28.7228	9.3789	.001212121
826	682,276	563,559,976	28.7402	9.3827	.001210654
827	683,929	565,609,283	28.7576	9.3865	.001209190
828	685,584	567,663,552	28.7750	9.3902	.001207729
829	687,241	569,722,789	28.7924	9.3940	.001206273
830	688,900	571,787,000	28.8097	9.3978	.001204819
831	690,561	573,856,191	28.8271	9.4016	.001203369
832	692,224	575,930,368	28.8444	9.4053	.001201923
833	693,889	578,009,537	28.8617	9.4091	.001200480
834	695,556	580,093,704	28.8791	9.4129	.001199041
835	697,225	582,182,875	28.8964	9.4166	.001197605
836	698,896	584,277,056	28.9137	9.4204	.001196172
837	700,569	586,376,253	28.9310	9.4241	.001194743
838	702,244	588,480,472	28.9482	9.4279	.001193317
839	703,921	590,589,719	28.9655	9.4316	.001191895
840	705,600	592,704,000	28.9828	9.4354	.001190476
841	707,281	594,823,321	29.0000	9.4391	.001189061
842	708,964	596,947,688	29.0172	9.4429	.001187648
843	710,649	599,077,107	29.0345	9.4466	.001186240
844	712,336	601,211,584	29.0517	9.4503	.001184834
845	714,025	603,351,125	29.0689	9.4541	.001183432
846	715,716	605,495,736	29.0861	9.4578	.001182033
847	717,409	607,645,423	29.1033	9.4615	.001180638
848	719,104	609,800,192	29.1204	9.4652	.001179245
849	720,801	611,960,049	29.1376	9.4690	.001177856
850	722,500	614,125,000	29.1548	9.4727	.001176471

No.	Square	Cube	Sq. Root	Cu. Root	Reciprocal
850	722,500	614,125,000	29.1548	9.4727	.001176471
851	724,201	616,295,051	29.1719	9.4764	.001175088
852	725,904	618,470,208	29.1890	9.4801	.001173709
853	727,609	620,650,477	29.2062	9.4838	.001172333
854	729,316	622,835,864	29.2233	9.4875	.001170960
855	731,025	625,026,375	29.2404	9.4912	.001169591
856	732,736	627,222,016	29.2575	9.4949	.001168224
857	734,449	629,422,793	29.2746	9.4986	.001166861
858	736,164	631,628,712	29.2916	9.5023	.001165501
859	737,881	633,839,779	29.3087	9.5060	.001164144
860	739,600	636,056,000	29.3258	9.5097	.001162791
861	741,321	638,277,381	29.3428	9.5134	.001161440
862	743,044	640,503,928	29.3598	9.5171	.001160093
863	744,769	642,735,647	29.3769	9.5207	.001158749
864	746,496	644,972,544	29.3939	9.5244	.001157407
865	748,225	647,214,625	29.4109	9.5281	.001156069
866	749,956	649,461,896	29.4279	9.5317	.001154734
867	751,689	651,714,363	29.4449	9.5354	.001153403
868	753,424	653,972,032	29.4618	9.5391	.001152074
869	755,161	656,234,909	29.4788	9.5427	.001150748
870	756,900	658,503,000	29.4958	9.5464	.001149425
871	758,641	660,776,311	29.5127	9.5501	.001148106
872	760,384	663,054,848	29.5296	9.5537	.001146789
873	762,129	665,338,617	29.5466	9.5574	.001145475
874	763,876	667,627,624	29.5635	9.5610	.001144165
875	765,625	669,921,875	29.5804	9.5647	.001142857
876	767,376	672,221,376	29.5973	9.5683	.001141553
877	769,129	674,526,133	29.6142	9.5719	.001140251
878	770,884	676,836,152	29.6311	9.5756	.001138952
879	772,641	679,151,439	29.6479	9.5792	.001137656
880	774,400	681,472,000	29.6648	9.5828	.001136364
881	776,161	683,797,841	29.6816	9.5865	.001135074
882	777,924	686,128,968	29.6985	9.5901	.001133787
883	779,689	688,465,387	29.7153	9.5937	.001132503
884	781,456	690,807,104	29.7321	9.5973	.001131222
885	783,225	693,154,125	29.7489	9.6010	.001129944
886	784,996	695,506,456	29.7658	9.6046	.001128668
887	786,769	697,864,103	29.7825	9.6082	.001127396
888	788,544	700,227,072	29.7993	9.6118	.001126126
889	790,321	702,595,369	29.8161	9.6154	.001124859
890	792,100	704,969,000	29.8329	9.6190	.001123596
891	793,881	707,347,971	29.8496	9.6226	.001122334
892	795,664	709,932,288	29.8664	9.6262	.001121076
893	797,449	712,121,957	29.8831	9.6298	.001119821
894	799,236	714,516,984	29.8998	9.6334	.001118568
895	801,025	716,917,375	29.9166	9.6370	.001117318
896	802,816	719,323,136	29.9333	9.6406	.001116071
897	804,609	721,734,273	29.9500	9.6442	.001114827
898	806,404	724,150,792	29.9666	9.6477	.001113586
899	808,201	726,572,699	29.9833	9.6513	.001112347
900	810,000	729,000,000	30.0000	9.6549	.001111111

TABLE IX   **900-950**

No.	Square	Cube	Sq. Root	Cu. Root	Reciprocal
900	810,000	729,000,000	30.0000	9.6549	.001111111
901	811,801	731,432,701	30.0167	9.6585	.001109878
902	813,604	733,870,808	30.0333	9.6620	.001108647
903	815,409	736,314,327	30.0500	9.6656	.001107420
904	817,216	738,763,264	30.0666	9.6692	.001106195
905	819,025	741,217,625	30.0832	9.6727	.001104972
906	820,836	743,677,416	30.0998	9.6763	.001103753
907	822,649	746,142,643	30.1164	9.6799	.001102536
908	824,464	748,613,312	30.1330	9.6834	.001101322
909	826,281	751,089,429	30.1496	9.6870	.001100110
910	828,100	753,571,000	30.1662	9.6905	.001098901
911	829,921	756,058,031	30.1828	9.6941	.001097695
912	831,744	758,550,528	30.1993	9.6976	.001096491
913	833,569	761,048,497	30.2159	9.7012	.001095290
914	835,396	763,551,944	30.2324	9.7047	.001094092
915	837,225	766,060,875	30.2490	9.7082	.001092896
916	839,056	768,575,296	30.2655	9.7118	.001091703
917	840,889	771,095,213	30.2820	9.7153	.001090513
918	842,724	773,620,632	30.2985	9.7188	.001089325
919	844,561	776,151,559	30.3150	9.7224	.001088139
920	846,400	778,688,000	30.3315	9.7259	.001086957
921	848,241	781,229,961	30.3480	9.7294	.001085776
922	850,084	783,777,448	30.3645	9.7329	.001084599
923	851,929	786,330,467	30.3809	9.7364	.001083424
924	853,776	788,889,024	30.3974	9.7400	.001082251
925	855,625	791,453,125	30.4138	9.7435	.001081081
926	857,476	794,022,776	30.4302	9.7470	.001079914
927	859,329	796,597,983	30.4467	9.7505	.001078749
928	861,184	799,178,752	30.4631	9.7540	.001077586
929	863,041	801,765,089	30.4795	9.7575	.001076426
930	864,900	804,357,000	30.4959	9.7610	.001075269
931	866,761	806,954,491	30.5123	9.7645	.001074114
932	868,624	809,557,568	30.5287	9.7680	.001072961
933	870,489	812,166,237	30.5450	9.7715	.001071811
934	872,356	814,780,504	30.5614	9.7750	.001070664
935	874,225	817,400,375	30.5778	9.7785	.001069519
936	876,096	820,025,856	30.5941	9.7819	.001068376
937	877,969	822,656,953	30.6105	9.7854	.001067236
938	879,844	825,293,672	30.6268	9.7889	.001066098
939	881,721	827,936,019	30.6431	9.7924	.001064963
940	883,600	830,584,000	30.6594	9.7959	.001063830
941	885,481	833,237,621	30.6757	9.7993	.001062699
942	887,364	835,896,888	30.6920	9.8028	.001061571
943	889,249	838,561,807	30.7083	9.8063	.001060445
944	891,136	841,232,384	30.7246	9.8097	.001059322
945	893,025	843,908,625	30.7409	9.8132	.001058201
946	894,916	846,590,536	30.7571	9.8167	.001057082
947	896,809	849,278,123	30.7734	9.8201	.001055966
948	898,704	851,971,392	30.7896	9.8236	.001054852
949	900,601	854,670,349	30.8058	9.8270	.001053741
950	902,500	857,375,000	30.8221	9.8305	.001052632

No.	Square	Cube	Sq. Root	Cu. Root	Reciprocal
950	902,500	857,375,000	30.8221	9.8305	.001052632
951	904,401	860,085,351	30.8383	9.8339	.001051525
952	906,304	862,801,408	30.8545	9.8374	.001050420
953	908,209	865,523,177	30.8707	9.8408	.001049318
954	910,116	868,250,664	30.8869	9.8443	.001048218
955	912,025	870,983,875	30.9031	9.8477	.001047120
956	913,936	873,722,816	30.9192	9.8511	.001046025
957	915,849	876,467,493	30.9354	9.8546	.001044932
958	917,764	879,217,912	30.9516	9.8580	.001043841
959	919,681	881,974,079	30.9677	9.8614	.001042753
960	921,600	884,736,000	30.9839	9.8648	.001041667
961	923,521	887,503,681	31.0000	9.8683	.001040583
962	925,444	890,277,128	31.0161	9.8717	.001039501
963	927,369	893,056,347	31.0322	9.8751	.001038422
964	929,296	895,841,344	31.0483	9.8785	.001037344
965	931,225	898,632,125	31.0644	9.8819	.001036269
966	933,156	901,428,696	31.0805	9.8854	.001035197
967	935,089	904,231,063	31.0966	9.8888	.001034126
968	937,024	907,039,232	31.1127	9.8922	.001033058
969	938,961	909,853,209	31.1288	9.8956	.001031992
970	940,900	912,673,000	31.1448	9.8990	.001030928
971	942,841	915,498,611	31.1609	9.9024	.001029866
972	944,784	918,330,048	31.1769	9.9058	.001028807
973	946,729	921,167,317	31.1929	9.9092	.001027749
974	948,676	924,010,424	31.2090	9.9126	.001026694
975	950,625	926,859,375	31.2250	9.9160	.001025641
976	952,576	929,714,176	31.2410	9.9194	.001024590
977	954,529	932,574,833	31.2570	9.9227	.001023541
978	956,484	935,441,352	31.2730	9.9261	.001022495
979	958,441	938,313,739	31.2890	9.9295	.001021450
980	960,400	941,192,000	31.3050	9.9329	.001020408
981	962,361	944,076,141	31.3209	9.9363	.001019368
982	964,324	946,966,168	31.3369	9.9396	.001018330
983	966,289	949,862,087	31.3528	9.9430	.001017294
984	968,256	952,763,904	31.3688	9.9464	.001016260
985	970,225	955,671,625	31.3847	9.9497	.001015228
986	972,196	958,585,256	31.4006	9.9531	.001014199
987	974,169	961,504,803	31.4166	9.9565	.001013171
988	976,144	964,430,272	31.4325	9.9598	.001012146
989	978,121	967,361,669	31.4484	9.9632	.001011122
990	980,100	970,299,000	31.4643	9.9666	.001010101
991	982,081	973,242,271	31.4802	9.9699	.001009082
992	984,064	976,191,488	31.4960	9.9733	.001008065
993	986,049	979,146,657	31.5119	9.9766	.001007049
994	988,036	982,107,784	31.5278	9.9800	.001006036
995	990,025	985,074,875	31.5436	9.9833	.001005025
996	992,016	988,047,936	31.5595	9.9866	.001004016
997	994,009	991,026,973	31.5753	9.9900	.001003009
998	996,004	994,011,992	31.5911	9.9933	.001002004
999	998,001	997,002,999	31.6070	9.9967	.001001001
1000	1,000,000	1,000,000,000	31.6228	10.0000	.001000000

INDEX

541

ANSWERS TO PROBLEMS

NOTE: The accuracy of answers to numerical computations is in general that obtainable with a ten-inch slide rule in accordance with Art. 8-16.

Problems 2-1

1. 8 times E, 3 times i, 11 times R.   **2.** 32 volts, 2 volts.

3. $21.00. 3n dollars.   **4.** 25 cents.

5. $\dfrac{\$2.50}{n}$. $\dfrac{\$2.50q}{n}$.   **6.** $24E$ volts.

7. $\dfrac{x}{2}$ cents per kilowatt-hour.

8. (a) $\dfrac{1}{8}$. (b) $\dfrac{1}{6}$. (c) $\dfrac{1}{3}$. (d) $\dfrac{1}{R}$. (e) $\dfrac{1}{24}$.

9. E volts, $5E$ volts, $30E$ volts.

10. I amperes, $\dfrac{I}{2}$ amperes, $\dfrac{3I}{2}$ amperes, $15I$ amperes.

11. 13.   **12.** 5.   **13.** 80.   **14.** 4.
15. 2.   **16.** 10.   **17.** 2.   **18.** 4.
19. 1.   **20.** 1.

21. $E + 10$ volts.   **22.** $60I - 6$ amperes.

23. $25 - R$ ohms.   **24.** $60 - I$ amperes.

25. $E - 220$ volts.

Problems 2-2

1. 27.	**2.** 60.	**3.** 900.	**4.** 1080.
5. 18.	**6.** 1.	**7.** 0.	**8.** 0.055.
9. 95.	**10.** 52.	**11.** Monomial.	**12.** Binomial.
13. Trinomial.	**14.** Trinomial.	**15.** Monomial.	**16.** Monomial.
17. Trinomial.	**18.** Binomial.	**19.** Monomial.	**20.** Trinomial.
21. Monomial.	**22.** Trinomial.	**23.** Monomial.	**24.** Trinomial.

25. Trinomial.

26. 6, 7, 8, 9, 10, 12, 13, 14, 17, 18, 20, 22, 24, 25.

27. (a) 12.56 square inches. (b) 0.785 square inch.

28. (a) 150 watts. (b) 2 watts.

29. (a) 16 feet. (b) 400 feet. (c) $16t^2$ feet.

30. (a) 60.5 watts. (b) 968 watts.

31. I^2R.   **32.** $\dfrac{E^2}{R}$.   **33.** $E - IR$.

34. $Z = \sqrt{R^2 + X^2}$.   **35.** $4x^3 - y^2$.   **36.** $(x + y)^2$.

37. $R^2 = Z^2 - X^2$.   **38.** $\dfrac{R + X}{R - X}$.

39. (a) 15.   (b) 6.   (c) 1.   (d) $\frac{1}{3}$.   (e) $\frac{1}{2}$.

40. 62,800,000.   **41.** 3450.   **42.** 4 times

43. (a) Power is increased by a factor of 4.
   (b) Power is increased by a factor of 9.

44. (a) Power is increased by a factor of 4.
   (b) Power is increased by a factor of 9.
   (c) Power is increased by a factor of 16.

45. Power is reduced by a factor of $\frac{1}{2}$.

Problems 3-1

1. -11.   **2.** -14.   **3.** 17.   **4.** -17.

5. 58.   **6.** -21.   **7.** -107.   **8.** -139.

9. -252.   **10.** 58.   **11.** 208.   **12.** -17.05.

13. -0.0999.   **14.** -38.596.   **15.** $\frac{2}{3}$.   **16.** $-\frac{3}{10}$.

17. -1.66.   **18.** $-56\frac{13}{24}$.   **19.** $4\frac{13}{8}$.

   20. Yes.   By adding a number of opposite sign that is less than twice the absolute value of the original number.

Problems 3-2

1. -50.   **2.** -57.   **3.** -31.   **4.** 251.

5. -50.   **6.** -8.   **7.** 73.89.   **8.** -0.6375.

9. $7\frac{5}{8}$.   **10.** $-\frac{7}{8}$.   **11.** -31.99.   **12.** 1.81.

13. -9677.   **14.** $25\frac{7}{15}$.   **15.** 112.32.   **16.** $-13\frac{7}{24}$.

17. $11°$.   **18.** $16°$.   **19.** $24°$.   **20.** $27°$.

21. $10°$.   **22.** $11°$.   **23.** $21°$.   **24.** $78°$.

   25. Yes.   This may be accomplished by subtracting, from some number, another number of opposite sign or of the same sign but greater than 2 times the absolute value of the minuend.

   26. No.   In arithmetic the negative number is not defined.

27. Yes.   **28.** 660 v.   **29.** 60 v.

Problems 3-3

1. $33x$.   **2.** $-13a^2b$.

3. $16I^2R$.   **4.** 0.

5. $13iz$.   **6.** $8ab^2 - 3a^2b$.

7. $4E - 2IX.$

8. $5a^3b + 9a^2b^2 - 10ab^3.$

9. $2(R + r).$

10. $16xyz^2.$

11. $3x - 4y - 2z.$

12. $x - a + c - 11.$

13. $4x^2 + 7x - 18.$

14. $9x^2 + 5x - 10.$

15. $3c^4 - 2a^2c^2 - 4a^2 + a^4.$

16. $12x - 17y + 3z.$

17. $a + 5c - 3x - 4.$

18. $7d - 2a + 4(b - c).$

19. $4r + 8\sqrt{R^2 + X^2} + 4Z + 6.$

20. $11a - 2(x - y) + z + 1.$

21. $8IR + 9E - 4IX - 6.$

22. $5W - 9EI - I^2R + 1.$

23. $x - 3x^2 + 3.$

24. $5.54xy + 6.5x.$

25. $\dfrac{3x}{5} + \dfrac{9y^3}{10}.$

26. $25IX - 4E.$

27. $17ab - 14xy.$

28. $6r - 3\sqrt{R^2 + X^2} - 4Z$

29. $10Ix + 5E - 18IR.$

30. $I^2R - 4EI + 6W.$

31. $-3a^3 - 3a^2 - 2a.$

32. $20x^2 - 19xy - 6y^2.$

33. $y^2 - x^2.$

34. $1 - a^3 + 4ab - b^2.$

35. $\dfrac{5s}{4} - \dfrac{p}{2} - \dfrac{3q}{10}.$

36. $6ir - 14e + 5iz.$

37. $0.012b^2 - 1.34ab - 5.5a^2.$

38. $5.2EI + 5I^2R + 5W.$

39. $\dfrac{5ir}{6} - \dfrac{e}{2} + \dfrac{ix}{5}.$

40. $63.11s^2 - 0.0011t - 12.09u.$

Problems 3–4

1. $2y - 2x - z.$

2. $3x^2 + xy.$

3. $a^2 - 5ab - 2b^2.$

4. $22b - 19a.$

5. $y + z - x.$

6. $10x - 2y.$

7. $2p - 14q.$

8. $0.$

9. $0.$

10. $7ab^2 - a^2b - 2b^3.$

11. $e.$

12. $11ei - 36w.$

13. $\dfrac{z}{4} - \dfrac{y}{3}.$

14. $e.$

15. $2x - 2b.$

Problems 3–5

1. $a + (b - c + d).$

2. $e + (E - ir - ix).$

3. $\dfrac{E}{R} + \left(\dfrac{e}{z} + 3I - 2i\right).$

4. $\dfrac{E^2}{R} + (-i^2r + 6EI - 5W).$

5. $\omega L + \left(-\dfrac{1}{\omega C} - X + Z\right).$

6. $Z^2 + (R^2 - 2RX + X^2).$

7. $y^2 + (-x^2 + 2xy - y^2).$

8. $p + (-q - r - s).$

9. $\dfrac{1}{\omega C} + (-\omega L + 2\omega M - X).$

10. $a + (-y + b - c).$

11. $E - (e - IR).$

12. $P - (I^2R + EI).$

13. $65 - x.$

14. $10e - (E + 3IR).$

15. $12ei - (4P + I^2R).$

16. $16 + p.$

Problems 4-1

1. -20. **2.** -18. **3.** -17.92.

4. $\frac{2}{5}$. **5.** -72. **6.** 0.075852.

7. $-1\frac{8}{35}$. **8.** 14. **9.** $\frac{1}{40}$.

10. 0.0028125. **11.** xyz. **12.** $pqrst$.

13. a^2b^2c. **14.** $-\dfrac{1}{\omega c}$. **15.** $-\dfrac{1}{abc^3d}$.

Problems 4-2

1. x^8. **2.** $-a^5$. **3.** b^{10}.

4. r^{10}. **5.** $14x^3$. **6.** $-12a^5x$.

7. $-18x^4$. **8.** $-90b$. **9.** a^2.

10. $-30a^4x^3$. **11.** $-26b^{a+n}$. **12.** $9a^4b^2$.

13. $-8e^3x^2y$. **14.** $15a^4b^3c^4d^6x$. **15.** $8a^3y^6$.

16. $-\dfrac{a^3b^4c}{3}$. **17.** $0.75s^4t^3u$. **18.** $-\dfrac{20e^5r^5i}{3}$.

19. $\dfrac{a^3b^4cde}{6}$. **20.** $p^3qr^3s^2$. **21.** $-x^3y^4z^2$.

22. 10^5. **23.** 10^4. **24.** $I^2Z^3R^2$.

25. $7W \cdot X^5Y^2Z$. **26.** $-6a^4b^3c^3de$. **27.** $6ax^3y^2z^3$.

28. $18a^2b^3c^2d^3e^3f$. **29.** $-1.25e^7i^3x^2y^4$. **30.** $a^4b^4c^4d^4e^4$.

Problems 4-3

1. $4x + jx^2$. **2.** $2x^3 - 6x$.

3. $3IR_1 + 6IR_2$. **4.** $4i^2R - 6I^2R$.

5. $4x^2y - 16y^2 - 8y$. **6.** $2y^6 - 3y^5 + 4y^4 - 3y^3$.

7. $5a^5 - 3a^4 + 4a^3$. **8.** $-15b^4 + 20b^3 - 15b^2$.

9. $10c^4 - 20c^3 - 15c^2$. **10.** $-6d^7 + 24d^6 + 18d^4$.

11. $-4y^4 + 8y^5 + 6y^6$. **12.** $4j^2x^2 - j^2xy + 2j^2x^3y^2$.

13. $-b^6d^2 + b^4d^4 - b^2d^6$. **14.** $12ar^3s^2 - 6ar^2s^2 + 9ars^3 + 3ars^4$.

15. $\dfrac{a^4b^2}{4} - \dfrac{a^3b^3}{3} + \dfrac{a^2b^4}{3}$. **16.** $\dfrac{a^4x^3}{3} - \dfrac{3a^3x^4}{4} + \dfrac{a^2x^5}{3}$.

17. $17x + 16y$. **18.** $9a - 22b$.

19. $-2jsx$. **20.** $x^3 - y^3$.

21. $8a^2 - 10ab + 17ac$. **22.** 0.

23. $2a - b + \dfrac{c}{2}$. **24.** $2 - 20x$.

25. $\dfrac{33b^2}{2} - 10$. **26.** $6s$.

27. $10x^2 - 8$. **28.** $a^3x - 2a^2x^2 - 4ax^3$.

29. $-3x^5y^2 + x^4y^3 - 2x^3y^4$. **30.** $-2a^2b^3 - a^2b^4 + 3ab^5 + ab^2$.

Problems 4-4

1. $c^2 + 2c + 1$.　　**2.** $c^2 - 2c + 1$.　　**3.** $c^2 - 1$.

4. $r^2 + 4r + 4$.　　**5.** $r^2 - 4r + 4$.　　**6.** $r^2 - 4$.

7. $i^2 + 5i + 6$.　　**8.** $i^2 + i - 6$.　　**9.** $j^2 - 2j - 35$.

10. $x^2 - 17x + 72$.　　**11.** $a^2 + 7a + 12$.　　**12.** $12C^2 + 29C + 14$.

13. $9i^2 + 9i - 40$.　　**14.** $6r^2 + 8r - 8$.

15. $30 - 15y - 24z + 12yz$.　　**16.** $2x^2 - 7xy - 4y^2$.

17. $6a^2 - 13ab + 6b^2$.　　**18.** $6b^2 - 22b + 12$.

19. $acx^2 + adx^2 - bcx^2 - bdx^2$.　　**20.** $12a^2 + 8ab^2 - 3ab - 2b^3$.

21. $10a^3 - 30ab - 6a^2b^2 + 18b^3$.

22. $3a^3 + 9a^2 - 7a - 4ax - 12x - 21$.

23. $x^3 + y^3$.　　**24.** $a^3 + 3a^2b + 3ab^2 + b^3$.

25. $a^3 + 3a^2b + 3ab^2 + b^3$.　　**26.** $3a^3 - 5a^2 + 3a^2b - 5ab - b - a$.

27. $3a^4 - 5a^3 - a^2 + 5a - 2$.　　**28.** $4a^2 + 4ab - 4a + b^2 - 2b + 1$.

29. $9a^4 + 30a^2 - 18a^2x - 30x + 9x^2 + 25$.

30. $3a^3 + 12a^2b - 18ab^2 + 3b^3$.　　**31.** $\dfrac{x^2}{9} - \dfrac{xy}{6} + \dfrac{y^2}{16}$.

32. $a^2 - \dfrac{145ab}{72} + b^2$.　　**33.** $2m^2 + \dfrac{2mn}{3} - \dfrac{n^2}{6}$.

34. $11x^2 - 22x - 32$.　　**35.** $3a^2 - 27a + 36$.

36. $2b^2 - 4b + 9$.　　**37.** $16y^2 - 38y + 14$.

38. $-a^2 + 4ab + 13b^2$.　　**39.** $2x^2y + 2xy^2$.

40. $30a^2 - 33ab - 39ac - 18b^2 + 30bc + 12c^2 - a - b + c$.

Problems 5-1

1. -2.　　**2.** -4.　　**3.** 4.　　**4.** 9.

5. 700.　　**6.** $-\frac{2}{3}$.　　**7.** $-\frac{20}{21}$.　　**8.** $\dfrac{a}{b^2}$.

9. $-\dfrac{xy}{36}$.　　**10.** $-\dfrac{1}{\omega c}$.　　**11.** -4.　　**12.** -4.

13. 100.　　**14.** 256.　　**15.** -81.

Problems 5-2

1. $-3y$.　　**2.** $3z$.　　**3.** $-4a^2b$.

4. $-12m^2p^3$.　　**5.** $4er^2$.　　**6.** $2ac$.

7. $-2x^2yz$.　　**8.** $9ce$.　　**9.** $13qr$.

10. $-3ab^2d$　　**11.** $-4a^2d$.　　**12.** $-\dfrac{2y^2}{x^2}$.

13. $\dfrac{s^2}{2r^2t}$.　　**14.** $\dfrac{1}{3a^2d}$.　　**15.** $-\dfrac{ei}{4r}$.

16. $\dfrac{b^7}{3c^5}$.

17. $-\dfrac{3xy^6}{w^4}$.

18. $\dfrac{rt^8}{3u}$.

19. $-\dfrac{a^8}{4b^{12}d^2}$.

20. $-\dfrac{7y^4}{x^4z^9}$.

Problems 5-3

1. $2x - 3y$.

2. $4a - 2b$.

3. $4m^2 - 3n^2$.

4. $4 - 2z$.

5. $a^4 - a^2 + 1$.

6. $xz^2 - y^2 + z^2$.

7. $-am^2 + bm - c$.

8. $1 - 2a^2b + 3a^4b^3$.

9. $-5 - 3r^2s + 10r^4s^2$.

10. $6 + 10ac - 5a^2c^2 - 3a^4b^4$.

11. $-\dfrac{r^2s}{3} + \dfrac{5s^2t}{2} - 2st^2$.

12. $-4x^4y^2 + 7 + 6y^6$.

13. $\dfrac{3m^8}{10} - \dfrac{7m^6}{5} + \dfrac{6m^4}{5} + \dfrac{m^2}{2} - 1$.

14. $3 + c$.

15. $4 + 2x$.

16. $R - r$.

17. $I + i$.

18. $6(c + d)^2 - a$.

19. $b - a$.

20. $a + b$.

Problems 5-4

1. $x + 2$.

2. $a - 4$.

3. $x - 6$.

4. $b - 24$.

5. $3t + 1$.

6. $a + 5$.

7. $4n^2 - n$.

8. $3b + 1$.

9. $3s - 7t$.

10. $3x + 4y$.

11. $a^2 + 7a + 14 + \dfrac{6}{a - 1}$.

12. $x^2 - 1 + \dfrac{2}{x^2 + 1}$.

13. $x + y$.

14. $x^2 + xy + y^2$.

15. $x^3 + x^2y + xy^2 + y^3$.

16. $x^2 - xy + y^2$.

17. $x^4 - x^3y + x^2y^2 - xy^3 + y^4$.

18. $x^6 - x^5y + x^4y^2 - x^3y^3 + x^2y^4 - xy^5 + y^6$.

19. $x - y$.

20. $x^3 - x^2y + xy^2 - y^3$.

21. $x^5 - x^4y + x^3y^2 - x^2y^3 + xy^4 - y^5$.

22. $2a - 3$.

23. $b^3 - 3b^2 + 2b - 1$.

24. $2x^2 + x - 1 + \dfrac{3x + 4}{x^2 - x + 3}$.

25. $10c^2 - 3c - 12 + \dfrac{7c - 45}{3c^2 + 2c - 4}$.

26. $\dfrac{x^2}{4} - 3xy + 9y^2$.

27. $\dfrac{b^2}{9} - \dfrac{b}{6} + \dfrac{1}{16}$.

28. $3a + \frac{1}{3}$.

29. $n - 3$.

30. $6d - \dfrac{e}{3} - \dfrac{1}{2}$.

Problems 6-1

1. $y = 4$.

2. $r = -5$.

3. $i = 1$.

4. $e = 6$.

5. $x = 1$.

6. $e = 5$.

7. $r = 2$.

8. $x = 4$.

9. $Z = 0.8$.   **10.** $i = \frac{2}{3}$.   **11.** $p = \frac{1}{3}$.   **12.** $r = -5$.

13. $e = -10$.   **14.** $i = 7$.   **15.** $p = -12$.   **16.** $r = -2$.

17. $p = 1.25$.   **18.** $R = 2$.   **19.** $I = 5$.   **20.** $E = -1.4$.

Problems 6-2

1. $R - 10 \ \Omega$.

2. $R + 6 \ \Omega$.

3. $E + e$.

4. (a) $x - y$.
(b) $x + z$.

5. (a) $40 - x$.
(b) $x - y$.

6. 49.

7. 31.

8. 110 v.

9. 12.

10. 12.

11. (a) 48 ft.
(b) 24 ft.

12. (a) $50.50.
(b) $24.50.

13. (a) 187.5 ft.
(b) 112.5 ft.

14. 10 in.
11 in.
12 in.

15. First side, 15 ft.
Second side, 20 ft.
Third side, 10 ft.

16. $x - y = b - a$.

17. $b + x + 13$.

18. $\frac{y}{bx}$ ft.

19. $\frac{x^2}{2} + 2y^2$.

20. 23, 24.

21. $35°$.
$65°$.
$80°$.

22. Charles is 13 years old.
John is 17 years old.

23. $90°$.
$60°$.
$30°$.

24. 40, 42, 44.

25. Frank is 4 months old.
Paul is 16 months old.

Problems 6-3

1. $R_2 = R_t - R_1 - R_3$.

2. $R^2 = Z^2 - X^2$.

3. $I = \dfrac{E}{Z}$.

4. $P = \dfrac{120f}{N}$.

5. $L = \dfrac{Rm}{K}$.

6. $f = \dfrac{1}{2\pi C X_c}$

7. $L = \dfrac{X_L}{2\pi f}$.

8. $N_s = \dfrac{E_s N_p}{E_p}$.

9. $N_s = \dfrac{I_p N_p}{I_s}$.

10. $I_s = \dfrac{I_p E_p}{E_s}$.

11. $R = \dfrac{\omega L}{Q}$.

12. $Q = CV$.

13. $L = \dfrac{F}{Hi}$.

14. $B = \dfrac{E10^8}{Lv}$.

15. $R = \dfrac{E - e}{I}$.

16. $R = \dfrac{P}{I^2}.$

17. $R = \dfrac{E^2}{P}.$

18. $N = \dfrac{Hl}{4\pi i}.$

19. $H = \dfrac{\phi}{A}.$

20. $\mu = \dfrac{B^2Al}{8w}.$

21. $t = \dfrac{Q}{0.24EI}.$

22. $e_1 = E + e_2 - IR_1 - IR_2.$

23. $v = \lambda f.$

24. $P = \dfrac{L10^8}{1.25N^2}.$

25. $K = \dfrac{Cd}{0.08842A}.$

26. $\mu = G_mR_p.$

27. $\mu_{sg} = \dfrac{-E_{sg}}{E_c}.$

28. $R_L = \dfrac{E_b - e_b}{i}.$

29. $R = \dfrac{H}{0.057I^2t}.$

30. $Y_b = Y_f + 2m.$

31. $m = \dfrac{F\mu d^2}{m'}.$

32. $T = \dfrac{2\pi}{W}.$

33. $\theta = \omega t.$

34. $n = \dfrac{\omega}{2\pi}.$

35. $h = \dfrac{V^2}{2g}.$

36. $m = \dfrac{2\ \text{K.E.}}{V^2}.$

37. $V_0 = 2V - V_t.$

38. $\text{K.E.} = \dfrac{IW^2}{2}.$

39. $m = \dfrac{F}{w^2r}.$

40. $r = \dfrac{F}{4\pi^2n^2m}.$

41. $C = \dfrac{N + n}{2P}.$

42. $P = \dfrac{N - 2}{I}.$

43. $K = \dfrac{C - D}{2}.$

44. $D = 2C - d.$

45. $C = \dfrac{D + d}{2}.$

46. $P = \dfrac{L}{n}.$

47. $P = \dfrac{N}{D}.$

48. $T = \dfrac{Ct}{C - F}.$

49. $c = a + b - d.$

50. $H = \dfrac{N + 2}{P}.$

51. $I = A - P.$

52. $r = \dfrac{I}{Pt}.$

53. $l = \dfrac{Mr}{K}.$

54. $t = \dfrac{I}{Ad}.$

55. $a = \dfrac{G^2}{b}.$

56. $a = \dfrac{A}{\pi b}.$

57. $A = \dfrac{T - ph}{2}.$

58. $r = \dfrac{S}{2\pi h}.$

59. $a^2 = c^2 - b^2.$

60. $A = \dfrac{ab}{2}.$

Problems 7-1

1. $6.43 \times 10^8.$　　**2.** $4.356 \times 10^3.$　　**3.** $1.36 \times 10^{-2}.$

4. $1.4 \times 10.$　　**5.** $2.5 \times 10^{-4}.$　　**6.** $3.69 \times 10^{-2}.$

7. $4.89 \times 10^4.$　　**8.** $6.43 \times 10^{-7}.$　　**9.** $1.25 \times 10^{-11}.$

10. $5.93 \times 10^4.$　　**11.** $2.59 \times 10^{-1}.$　　**12.** $1.89 \times 10^6.$

13. $2.59 \times 10^{-2}.$　　**14.** $8.6 \times 10^{-11}.$　　**15.** $5.65 \times 10^7.$

16. $1.684 \times 10^9.$　　**17.** $3.67 \times 10^{-7}.$　　**18.** $8.42 \times 10^{-9}.$

19. $2.56 \times 10^{-6}.$　　**20.** $3.99 \times 10^4.$

Problems 7-2

1. $10^5.$　　**2.** $10^3.$　　**3.** $2.60 \times 10.$

4. $2.07 \times 10.$　　**5.** $7.14 \times 10^{-14}.$　　**6.** $1.31 \times 10^{-3}.$

7. 2.38×10^2.　　**8.** 1.45×10^{-9}.　　**9.** 9.23×10^{-5}.
10. 9.70×10^{-2}.

Problems 7-3

1. 5.00×10^{-9}.　　**2.** 1.00.　　**3.** 1.68×10^3.
4. 2.27×10^{-3}.　　**5.** 1.14×10^{19}.　　**6.** 4.25×10^5.
7. 1.63×10^{-4}.　　**8.** 4.90×10^{-2}.　　**9.** 8.03×10^{-1}.
10. 7.93×10^{-2}.　　**11.** 4.99×10^4.　　**12.** 1.63×10^5.
13. 1.26×10^3.　　**14.** 6.05×10^{-7}.　　**15.** 6.54×10^{-9}.
16. 2.81×10.　　**17.** 1.25×10^2.　　**18.** 1.94×10^{10}.
19. 5.30×10^{-11}.　　**20.** 5.34×10^{13}.

Problems 7-4

1. 10^{12}.　　**2.** 10^{15}.　　**3.** 10^{-12}.
4. 9×10^{-6}.　　**5.** 1.25×10^{14}.　　**6.** 3.43×10^{-7}.
7. 2.56×10^{20}.　　**8.** 1.60×10^3.　　**9.** 10^{-3}.
10. 2.7×10^{-3}.　　**11.** 4×10^3.　　**12.** 9.52×10^{-1}.
13. 1.50×10^{10}.　　**14.** 6.54×10^{11}.　　**15.** 3.23×10^7.

Problems 8-1

1. (a) 2×10 ma.
　　(b) 2×10^4 μa.
3. (a) 3.5×10^2 ma.
　　(b) 3.5×10^5 μa.

5. (a) 2.5×10^{-2} a.
　　(b) 2.5×10^4 μa.
7. (a) 3.58×10^5 μh.
　　(b) 3.58×10^{-1} h.

9. (a) 1.5×10^{-4} h.
　　(b) 1.5×10^{-1} mh.
11. (a) 4.5×10^3 Ω.
　　(b) 4.5×10^9 $\mu\Omega$.
13. (a) 2.5×10^{-1} kw.
　　(b) 2.5×10^5 mw.
15. (a) 3.5×10^{-2} μf.
　　(b) 3.5×10^4 $\mu\mu$f.
17. (a) 3×10^{-11} f.
　　(b) 3×10^{-5} μf.
19. (a) 1.25×10^{-1} mh.
　　(b) 1.25×10^{-4} h.

2. (a) 3.42×10^6 μa.
　　(b) 3.42×10^3 ma.
4. (a) 4.2×10 mv.
　　(b) 4.2×10^4 μv.
　　(c) 4.2×10^{-5} kv.

6. (a) 2.5×10^{-10} f.
　　(b) 2.5×10^2 $\mu\mu$f.
8. (a) 1.35×10^4 v.
　　(b) 1.35×10^{10} μv.
　　(c) 1.35×10^7 mv.

10. (a) 3.5×10^{-10} f.
　　(b) 3.5×10^{-4} μf.
12. (a) 1.65×10^{-1} MΩ.
　　(b) 1.65×10^{11} $\mu\Omega$.
14. (a) 4.3×10^3 v.
　　(b) 4.3×10^6 mv.
16. (a) 3.64×10^4 w.
　　(b) 3.64×10^7 mw.
18. (a) 1.62×10^{-2} ma.
　　(b) 1.62×10^{-5} a.
20. (a) 2×10^{-9} f.
　　(b) 2×10^3 $\mu\mu$f.

21. (a) 5×10^{-4} μf.
(b) 5×10^{-10} f.

23. (a) 3×10^3 Ω.
(b) 3×10^9 μΩ.

25. (a) 2×10^5 μv.
(b) 2×10^2 mv.

27. (a) 4.35×10^6 cycles.
(b) 4.35×10^3 kc.

29. 3.4×10^4 micromhos

22. (a) 6.5×10^2 mh.
(b) 6.5×10^5 μh.

24. (a) 1.25×10^{-5} a.
(b) 1.25×10^{-2} ma.

26. (a) 10 kc.
(b) 10^{-2} Mc.

28. (a) 4.135 Mc.
(b) 4.135×10^6 cycles.

30. 1.26×10^{-3} mho.

Problems 9-1

1. 34.4 Ω.
4. 0.423 a.
7. 300 Ω.
10. 1.4×10^{10} μv.
13. 43.2 Ω.
16. 111 v.

19. 0.550 a cold.
0.579 a hot.

2. 220 v.
5. 8.75 v.
8. 81 v.
11. 750 a.
14. 8.125 v.
17. 21.75 v.

20. 25 v.

3. 5.5 a.
6. 4.4 a.
9. 0.783 a.
12. 4.4×10^{-3} a.
15. 2.88 ma.
18. 50 v at 3.05 Ω.
12.3 v at 0.750 Ω.

21. 16.7 Ω.

Problems 9-2

1. (a) 2.5 kw.
(b) 3.35 hp.

4. 35.4 hp.

7. 2.5 a.

10. 5 w.

13. (a) 6 mw.
(b) 2 ma.

16. 238 hr.

19. (a) 8.33×10^{-12} w.
(b) 1.67×10^{-7} a.

22. 7 kw.

25. (a) 3.07 kw.
(b) 6.98 a.
(c) 1.77 kw.
(d) 500 ma.
(e) 57.6%.

2. (a) 30 kw.
(b) 40.2 hp.

5. 373 kw.

8. 278 v.

11. 80.7 mw.

14. (a) 78.1 mw.
(b) 6.25 v.

17. 16 cents.

20. (a) 79.9%.
(b) $44.45.

23. (a) 4.91 kw.
(b) 22.3 a.
(c) 9.86 Ω.
(d) $17.75.

3. (a) 3.92 kw.
(b) 3920 w.

6. 495 w.

9. 1460 w.

12. 16.9 w.

15. (a) 28.6 a.
(b) $7.56.

18. 50.9 a.

21. 80.4%.

24. 8.38 kw.

Problems 9-3

1. 5.24 a.

2. $E_{R_1} = 41.4$ v.
$E_{R_2} = 55$ v.
$E_{R_3} = 123.6$ v.

3. 28.9 w.

4. (a) 40.3 Ω.
(b) 300 w.

5. 216 Ω.

6. (a) 22.7 Ω.
(b) 6.5 Ω.
(c) 1.54 a.
(d) 53.8 w.

7. 25.4 Ω.

8. 20 Ω.

9. (a) 22.7 Ω.
(b) 187.4 w.

10. (a) 467 v.
(b) 1246 w.
(c) 236 v.

Problems 10-1

1. 5.3856 Ω.

2. 3.57 Ω.

3. (a) 0.153 Ω.
(b) 0.0612 Ω.

4. 2.58 Ω.

5. (a) 0.386 Ω.
(b) 0.129 Ω.

6. 0.0756 Ω.

7. 0.403 Ω.

8. 0.025 Ω.

9. 430 ft.

10. 656 ft.

Problems 10-2

1. 1020 cir mils.

2. 133,000 cir mils.

3. 404 cir mils.

4. 25.3 mils.

5. 410 mils.

6. 0.0142 in.

7. 5130 sq mils.

8. 1620 cir mils.

9. 0.0157 sq in.

10. 318,000 cir mils.

Problems 10-3

1. 12.9 Ω.

2. 21.1 Ω.

3. 29.4 Ω.

4. 250 Ω/mil-foot.

5. 104 Ω.

6. 394 ft.

7. 3.23 ft.

8. 2.98 miles.

9. 500 ft.

10. 16.7 Ω.

Problems 10-4

1. 9.89 Ω.

2. 19.5 Ω.

3. 13.9 Ω.

4. 86.5°C.

5. No.

Problems 10-5

1. (a) 0.25 Ω.
(b) 798 lb.

2. (a) 3.38 Ω.
(b) 264 lb.

3. (a) 0.516 Ω.
(b) 2.48 lb.

4. (a) 0.391 Ω.
(b) 0.295 lb.

5. 31.1 Ω.

6. 3120 Ω.

7. (*a*) 230 v.   **8.** (*a*) No. 8 wire.   **9.** No. 00 wire.
    (*b*) 95.8%.   (*b*) 95.8%.

10. (*a*) No. 6 wire
     (*b*) 230.9 v.

Problems 11-1

1. e^2i^2.

2. i^3r^3.

3. $a^4b^2c^6$.

4. $\dfrac{4e^2}{z^2}$

5. $9x^6y^2$.

6. $16i^4R^2$.

7. $-8a^6b^3$.

8. $9x^4y^6z^2$.

9. $-64I^6R^3$.

10. $256s^4t^6$.

11. $121W^4x^6y^8$.

12. $169p^4q^2r^6$.

13. $-125c^9d^3e^6$.

14. $64a^6b^9c^3$.

15. $144x^2y^6z^4$.

16. $\dfrac{a^4}{9}$

17. $-\dfrac{x^3y^6}{8}$.

18. $-\dfrac{27a^3b^9}{64}$.

19. $\dfrac{9r^2s^4t^2}{25}$.

20. $\dfrac{x^4y^2z^6}{a^2b^4c^2}$.

21. $-\dfrac{e^3d^9e^6}{p^6r^3s^9}$.

22. $-\dfrac{64r^3s^6t^3}{125}$.

23. $-\dfrac{25p^4r^2}{64}$.

24. $\dfrac{a^6b^3c^9}{8}$.

25. $-\dfrac{8m^6n^9}{27}$.

26. $\dfrac{a^{12}b^9c^3}{r^6s^{12}t^9}$.

27. $\dfrac{64c^9b^9e^{15}}{27}$.

28. $\dfrac{25x^6y^{10}z^{12}}{36}$.

29. $-\dfrac{27a^6b^{12}c^9}{343}$.

30. $-\dfrac{9m^4n^{10}p^2}{64}$.

31. $-\dfrac{4r^2s^6t^4u^3}{9}$.

Problems 11-2

1. 3.

2. 5.

3. 16.

4. 12.

5. 20.

6. $\pm 3a$.

7. $\pm 2e^2$.

8. $\pm 4r^2$.

9. $\pm 3x^4$.

10. $\pm 2ei$.

11. $\pm 5cd^2$.

12. $\pm 9r^3s^5$.

13. $\pm 6pq^2$.

14. -2.

15. 4.

16. $\pm 7mn^7$.

17. $5xy^3$.

18. $\pm 15r^5s^6$.

19. $\pm 10xy^5$.

20. $\pm 2r^4$.

21. -6.

22. $\pm 12c^4d^5$.

23. $3a^2bc^4$.

24. $10x^4y^2z$.

25. $\pm 14a^3x^9$.

26. $\pm 3ab^2$.

27. 8.

28. $\pm 11x^9y^5z^2$.

29. $2z^3$.

30. $\pm 17mn^3p^2$.

31. $-3r^4$.

32. $\pm c^2b^6$.

33. $2p^2qr^3$.

34. $\pm \dfrac{n}{2}$.

35. $-6az$.

36. $\pm \dfrac{5mnp^3}{4}$.

37. $\pm \dfrac{xy^2}{3}$.

38. $\tfrac{1}{3}$.

39. $\pm \dfrac{3c^2de^4}{5x}$.

40. $\pm \dfrac{e}{2}$.

41. $\pm \dfrac{1}{5a^2}$.

42. $\pm \dfrac{8hi^2k^5}{11a^4bc^3}$.

43. $\pm \dfrac{16a^4bx^2}{5y^2z^3}$.

44. $\pm \dfrac{13vt}{12a^3z^2}$.

45. $\pm \dfrac{14m^2np^4}{15ab^2c^6}$.

46. $-\dfrac{ab^2c^5}{3}$.

47. $\dfrac{x^2yz^6}{5}$.

48. $\pm \dfrac{8c^2d^3e}{11xz^3}$.

49. $-\dfrac{1}{6x^2y^4z}$.

50. $\dfrac{3a^5bc^3}{7xy^4z^2}$.

Problems 11-3

1. $2(x + 3)$.

2. $\frac{1}{6}(2r + R)$.

3. $e(e + 2i + 3)$.

4. $\frac{cd}{20}(4c - 2cd^3 + d)$.

5. $3a^3(1 - 5a)$.

6. $5a(b^3 - 3b^2c + 3bc^2 - c^3)$.

7. $6i(5 - 2r)$.

8. $12r^2s^2(4 - 12rs + 9s^2)$.

9. $3x^3(x + 2y - 1)$.

10. $\frac{x^2y}{18}(2y + 6x - 3x^2)$.

11. $e(e + e^2 - e^3 + 2)$.

12. $\frac{cd}{24}(6d^2 + 3c - 2c^3d^4)$.

13. $5e(e + 2 - 3e^2)$.

14. $p(q^6 - 5q^3 + 6)$.

15. $3y(3x^2 - 2x - 21)$.

16. $13v^2t^2x(3v^4tx^3 - 2tx^3 - 4)$.

17. $3a(b - 2bc + b^2 - x)$

18. $14mn^2(2mn - 3n^2 + 5m^2)$.

19. $\frac{ir}{8}(4i - 2r - z)$.

20. $\frac{c^2d}{162}(9c^2d - 6d^2 - 2)$.

21. $15abc(2a^3bc^2d - 15ac^3d^2 + 3)$.

22. $x = c + d$.

23. $y = c + d$.

Problems 11-4

1. $e^2 + 6e + 9$.

2. $4r^2 - 4rR + R^2$.

3. $9i^2 - 12iI + 4I^2$.

4. $p^2 + 4p + 4$.

5. $i^4 - 6i^2 + 9$.

6. $i^4 + 6i^2 + 9$.

7. $b^2 - 8b + 16$.

8. $z^2 + 12z + 36$.

9. $t^6 - 14t^3 + 49$.

10. $\lambda^2 - 4\lambda + 4$.

11. $9x^2 - 6xy + y^2$.

12. $4i^2r^2 + 24ir + 36$.

13. $36 + 12b + b^2$.

14. $R^2 + 2Rr + r^2$.

15. $F^2 - 2Ff + f^2$.

16. $81 - 18\alpha + \alpha^2$.

17. $\alpha^2 - 2\alpha\beta + \beta^2$.

18. $c^2 - 2ca + a^2$.

19. $121 - 22m + m^2$.

20. $25x^2 - 10xy + y^2$.

21. $49m^2 + 14mp + p^2$.

22. $9a^2 - 12ab + 4b^2$.

23. $144r^2 - 24rs + s^2$.

24. $a^2 + 2a + 1$.

25. $\mu^2 + 20\mu + 100$.

26. $m^6 + 2m^3n^2 + n^4$.

27. $x^2 - 2x + 1$.

28. $36a^2b^2 - 36abcd + 9c^2d^2$.

29. $25 - 30x^2 + 9x^4$.

30. $81v^4 - 108v^2t^2 + 36t^4$.

31. $16s^4 + 80s^2r + 100r^2$.

32. $81c^4 + 108c^2d^2 + 36d^4$.

33. $16a^4 - 24a^2b + 9b^2$.

34. $25p^2 - 110pq + 121q^2$.

35. $9c^2 + 48cd^2e^3 + 64d^4e^6$.

36. $1 + 2e^4 + e^8$.

37. $1 - 2a^2b^3 + a^4b^6$.

38. $25p^2 - 60pqr^2 + 36q^2r^4$.

39. $x^4 - 8x^2z + 16z^2$.

40. $9a^4b^4 - 6a^2b^2c^2d^2 + c^4d^4$.

41. $R^2 + R + \frac{1}{4}$.

42. $e^2 - \frac{2e}{3} + \frac{1}{9}$.

43. $r^2 - \dfrac{r}{2} + \dfrac{1}{16}.$

44. $d^2 + \dfrac{6d}{5} + \dfrac{9}{25}.$

45. $Z^2 - \dfrac{4Z}{3} + \dfrac{4}{9}.$

46. $B^2 - \dfrac{3B}{2} + \dfrac{9}{16}.$

47. $r^2 - \dfrac{2r}{5} + \dfrac{1}{25}.$

48. $E^2 + \dfrac{2E}{9} + \dfrac{1}{81}.$

49. $\mu^2 + \dfrac{\mu}{3} + \dfrac{1}{36}.$

50. $R^2 - \dfrac{4R}{7} + \dfrac{4}{49}.$

51. $y^4 + \dfrac{4y^2}{5} + \dfrac{4}{25}.$

52. $c^4 + \dfrac{5c^2}{3} + \dfrac{25}{36}.$

53. $a^4 - \dfrac{3a^2}{4} + \dfrac{9}{64}.$

54. $b^2 - \dfrac{8b}{5} + \dfrac{16}{25}.$

55. $x^6 - \dfrac{5x^3}{4} + \dfrac{25}{64}.$

58. 441.   **59.** 361.   **60.** 1296.   **61.** 1849.

62. 2809.   **63.** 1089.   **64.** 484.   **65.** 1521.

66. 841.   **67.** 324.   **68.** 784.   **69.** 3721.

70. 3481.   **72.** 4225.   **73.** 3025.   **74.** 7225.

75. 5625.   **76.** 11,025.   **77.** 15,625.   **78.** 9025.

79. 13,225.   **80.** 2025.

Problems 11-5

1. $2ei.$ **2.** $-2rS.$ **3.** $12EI.$ **4.** $-6m^2n.$

5. $-56x^2y.$ **6.** $80pq.$ **7.** $-90m^2n^3$ **8.** $12ab.$

9. $-\dfrac{XY}{3}.$ **10.** $-\dfrac{C^2d}{4}.$ **11.** $4e^3.$ **12.** $-a.$

13. 4.   **14.** 25.   **15.** $9d^2.$ **16.** $-48p.$

17. $4m.$ **18.** 16.   **19.** $\frac{1}{9}.$ **20.** $\frac{1}{49}.$

21. $x - 5y.$ **22.** $Z + \frac{1}{2}.$ **23.** $ab + 9.$ **24.** $r - \dfrac{x}{3}.$

25. $8mn + pq.$ **26.** $\dfrac{2v^2}{3} + \dfrac{3t^2}{5}.$ **27.** $7a - 5b.$ **28.** $3p + \dfrac{2q}{5}.$

29. $\dfrac{2c}{5} + d.$ **30.** $\dfrac{2x}{7} + \dfrac{5y}{6}.$

Problems 11-6

1. $3a(x + y)(x + y).$

2. $4(x^2 + 6y)(x^2 + 6y).$

3. $6i(e - 5E)(e - 5E).$

4. $2r(3 - i)(3 - i).$

5. $5c(ab + 7)(ab + 7).$

6. $\dfrac{3}{R}(3E - 2e)(3E - 2e).$

7. $3c(d - e)(d - e).$

8. $3m(5n - 4p)(5n - 4p).$

9. $\dfrac{5e}{Z}(3E - 5)(3E - 5).$

10. $11a(bc + 2)(bc + 2).$

Problems 11-7

1. $e^2 - 4$.

2. $r^2 - 16$.

3. $E^2 - e^2$.

4. $9Z^2 - 4R^2$.

5. $\dfrac{4i^2}{9} - \dfrac{1}{s^2}$.

6. $\dfrac{49P^2}{64} - \dfrac{9}{25}$.

7. $\dfrac{16\alpha^2}{81} - \dfrac{25\beta^2}{121}$.

8. $\dfrac{9\theta^4}{16} - \dfrac{4\phi^2}{25}$.

9. $\dfrac{R^4}{36} - \dfrac{9Z^4}{100}$.

10. $\dfrac{E^4}{R^2} - I^4R^2$.

Problems 11-8

1. $(Z + R)(Z - R)$.

2. $(2E + 4e)(2E - 4e)$.

3. $(6 + 3b^2)(6 - 3b^2)$.

4. $(1 + 6r)(1 - 6r)$.

5. $(Z + \tfrac{1}{2})(Z - \tfrac{1}{2})$.

6. $(cd^2 + e)(cd^2 - e)$.

7. $(2F + f_o)(2F - f_o)$.

8. $(5a + 4B)(5a - 4B)$.

9. $(8vt + 1)(8vt - 1)$.

10. $(1 + 15\theta)(1 - 15\theta)$.

11. $\left(\dfrac{5}{\phi} + \dfrac{\alpha}{6}\right)\left(\dfrac{5}{\phi} - \dfrac{\alpha}{6}\right)$.

12. $\left(\dfrac{1}{R} + \dfrac{1}{r}\right)\left(\dfrac{1}{R} - \dfrac{1}{r}\right)$.

13. $\left(\dfrac{E}{I} + \dfrac{9}{i}\right)\left(\dfrac{E}{I} - \dfrac{9}{i}\right)$.

14. $\left(\dfrac{2Z}{5} + \dfrac{R}{7}\right)\left(\dfrac{2Z}{5} - \dfrac{R}{7}\right)$.

15. $\left(\dfrac{1}{c} + \dfrac{V}{Q}\right)\left(\dfrac{1}{c} - \dfrac{V}{Q}\right)$.

16. $(3c + a - b)(3c - a + b)$.

17. $(a + 2b + x)(a + 2b - x)$.

18. $(4x + y - 7z)(4x - y + 7z)$.

19. $9(2e - cd - 3xy)(2e - cd + 3xy)$.

20. $(5ab + 10cd + 12c)(5ab + 10cd - 12c)$.

Problems 11-9

1. $e^2 + 3e + 2$.

2. $r^2 + 8r + 15$.

3. $i^2 + 8i + 15$.

4. $x^2 + 10x + 24$.

5. $\alpha^2 - 10\alpha + 21$.

6. $R^2 - 14R + 48$.

7. $E^2 + 7E - 30$.

8. $\beta^2 - 6\beta - 72$.

9. $Z^2 + 8Z - 20$.

10. $t^2 + 8t - 33$.

11. $v^2t^2 - 13vt + 36$.

12. $\theta^4 + 4\theta^2 - 60$.

13. $\alpha^2t^4 - 8\alpha t^2 + 15$.

14. $a^2 - 16ab + 48b^2$.

15. $I^2 - \dfrac{4EI}{R} - \dfrac{12E^2}{R^2}$.

16. $\theta^2 + \dfrac{74\theta}{5} - 3$.

17. $\alpha^4 - \dfrac{\alpha^2}{4} - \dfrac{1}{8}$.

18. $\beta^4 + \dfrac{10\beta^2}{3} + 1$.

19. $t^2e^2 - tei^2R - 12i^4R^2$.

20. $\phi^4 + \dfrac{3\phi^2}{10} + \dfrac{1}{50}$.

Problems 11-10

1. $(e + 3)(e + 2)$.
2. $(r - 6)(r - 2)$.
3. $(i + 3)(i + 4)$.
4. $(E - 7)(E - 2)$.
5. $(P - 8)(P - 3)$.
6. $(Z - 7)(Z + 5)$.
7. $(R + 5)(R - 9)$.
8. $(X - 9)(X - 6)$.
9. $(\alpha + 2)(\alpha - 1)$.
10. $(V + 12t)(V + 3t)$.
11. $(\theta + 9)(\theta - 7)$.
12. $(B - 11)(B + 4)$.
13. $(I - 11R)(I + 5R)$.
14. $(\phi^3 - 6)(\phi^3 - 12)$.
15. $(X - 10)(X - 15)$.
16. $(a - 25)(a - 2)$.
17. $(Q - 12)(Q + 2)$.
18. $(j - 15x)(j + 8x)$.
19. $(ab - 16)(ab + 6)$.
20. $(e - 10j)(e - 11j)$.
21. $(j + 12)(j - 5)$.
22. $(xy - 14Z)(xy - 2Z)$.
23. $(E + 9I)(E - 8I)$
24. $(R - 16)(R - 10)$.
25. $(\alpha + 12)(\alpha - 8)$.
26. $(I + 14)(I + 6)$.
27. $(B + 7)(B - 10)$.
28. $(\theta - 25)(\theta - 2)$.
29. $(xy - 3)(xy + 2)$.
30. $(\phi + 9)(\phi + 1)$.

Problems 11-11

1. $8e^2 - 2e - 15$.
2. $9Z^2 + 18Z + 8$.
3. $12j^2 - 5j - 2$.
4. $4E^2 - 13E - 12$.
5. $10r^2 - 31r + 15$.
6. $6R^2 + 11R + 3$.
7. $6I^2 + 13I + 6$.
8. $21P^2 + 4P - 12$.
9. $40a^2 - 18a - 7$.
10. $45x^2 - 30x - 40$.
11. $42e^2i^2 - 45ei + 12$.
12. $20\theta^2 + 3\theta - 9$.
13. $4r^2 - 31r - 8$.
14. $5E^2 - 6E + 1$.
15. $6j^2 - 5jb - b^2$.
16. $4I^4 + 9I^2 - 9$.
17. $3x^2 + 8xy - 3y^2$.
18. $4c^2 - 9cj + 5j^2$.
19. $6\phi^2 + \phi - 5$.
20. $42r^2 + 11rR - 20R^2$.
21. $72v^2 - 35vt + 3t^2$.
22. $4\alpha^2 - 12\alpha\beta + 9\beta^2$.
23. $27e^2i^2 + 42eiw - 5w^2$.
24. $30a^2b^2 + aby - 42y^2$.
25. $54x^2y^4 - 3xy^2 - 12$.
26. $54r^2 + r - \frac{2}{3}$.
27. $6 + 31E + 18E^2$.
28. $14i^2 + 4.8i + 0.18$
29. $30 + 3Z^2 - 63Z^4$.
30. $\dfrac{5R^2}{8} - \dfrac{8}{5}$.
31. $80 - 2\theta - 12\theta^2$.
32. $3\alpha^4 + 1.8\alpha^2 - 0.81$.
33. $4R^2 - 45Ri + 11i^2$.
34. $\dfrac{3a^2}{4} + a - \dfrac{8}{3}$.
35. $90x^4y^2 - 74x^2yZ + 12Z^2$.
36. $42 + 27E - 24E^2$.
37. $60\alpha^4 - 13\alpha^2 - 28$.
38. $10v^2 - vt - 2t^2$.
39. $63E^4 + 10E^2e^2 - 25e^4$.
40. $\theta^2 + \dfrac{3\theta}{4} + \dfrac{1}{8}$.

41. $32\alpha^4 + 4\alpha^2 - 45.$

42. $120R^2 - \dfrac{4R}{3i} \cdots \dfrac{4}{9i^2}.$

43. $ac + bc + ad + bd.$

44. $72a^2 - \dfrac{10a}{b} + \dfrac{1}{3b^2}.$

45. $50\theta^2 + \dfrac{3\theta}{2} - \dfrac{1}{50}.$

46. $24I^2 + \dfrac{4I}{r} + \dfrac{1}{6r^2}.$

47. $35e^4 + e^2E^2 - 6E^4.$

48. $32Z^4 + 4Z^2R^2 - 45R^4.$

49. $160x^2 + 4xy - 21y^2$

50. $35e^2i^2 + 12eiI^2R - 36I^4R^2.$

Problems 11-12

1. $(3a + 1)(3a + 2).$

2. $(2e - 1)(e - 3).$

3. $(3b + 8)(3b + 4).$

4. $(5r - 1)(r - 3).$

5. $(3I + 6)(2I - 10).$

6. $(3Z + 1)(Z - 19).$

7. $(2a + b)(a - 11b).$

8. $(7x - 3)(4x - 1).$

9. $(10\theta - 3)(\theta + 1).$

10. $(4e - 5i)(3e + 7i).$

11. $(2R + 7)(4R - 5).$

12. $(4a + 3)(3a + 2).$

13. $(3E - 7)(3E + 5).$

14. $(2i + 5r)(i - 4r).$

15. $(3v - 5t)(2v - 5t).$

16. $(5x + 3)(3x + 2).$

17. $(7r + 2i)(3r - 5i).$

18. $(2xy + 5)(2xy - 3).$

19. $(3\theta + 4)(5\theta + 3).$

20. $(5e - 3)(2e + 5).$

21. $(7a + 2b)(a - 4b).$

22. $(4\theta - 5)(6\theta + 3).$

23. $(3x - 7y)(5x + 3y).$

24. $(3p + 5q)(2p + 7q).$

25. $(3R + 1)(R + 7).$

26. $(7B + 2)(2B - 5).$

27. $(a^2 + \frac{1}{2})(a^2 - \frac{1}{4}).$

28. $(2c - 7d)(2c - 5d).$

29. $(4t - 5)(3t + 7).$

30. $(e - \frac{1}{3})(e - \frac{1}{3}).$

31. $(a + 0.5)(a - 0.3).$

32. $(x - \frac{1}{2})(x - \frac{1}{2}).$

33. $(5v - 15t)(v + 10t).$

34. $(3c - 7d)(3c + 8d).$

35. $(9B - 5)(2B + 3).$

36. $(2\theta + 0.1)(\theta - 0.5).$

37. $(m - 0.9)(m + 1).$

38. $(r + 0.7)(r - 0.2).$

39. $(5x - 3y)(2x + 3y).$

40. $(5a + 6b)(2a - 5b).$

Problems 11-13

1. $(a + 1)(a^2 - a + 1).$

2. $(x - 5)(x^2 + 5x + 25).$

3. $(x - 1)(x^2 + x + 1).$

4. $(m - 2n)(m^2 + 2mn + 4n^2)$

5. $(3e - 1)(9e^2 + 3e + 1).$

6. $(4x - 1)(16x^2 + 4x + 1).$

7. $(2a + x)(4a^2 - 2ax + x^2).$

8. $\left(a + \dfrac{1}{2}\right)\left(a^2 - \dfrac{a}{2} + \dfrac{1}{4}\right).$

9. $(4 - b)(16 + 4b + b^2).$

10. $\left(x + \dfrac{2}{3y}\right)\left(x^2 - \dfrac{2x}{3y} + \dfrac{4}{9y^2}\right).$

11. $(3r + 1)(9r^2 - 3r + 1).$

12. $\left(e - \dfrac{i}{5}\right)\left(e^2 + \dfrac{ie}{5} + \dfrac{i^2}{25}\right).$

13. $(1 - e)(1 + e + e^2)$.   **14.** $(\theta - 3)(\theta^2 + 3\theta + 9)$.

15. $[(a + b) + (c + d)][(a + b)^2 - (a + b)(c + d) + (c + d)^2]$.

16. $[(x + y) + 1][(x + y)^2 - (x + y) + 1]$.

17. $(2a - 4B)(4a^2 + 8aB + 16B^2)$.   **18.** $(1 + R)(1 - R + R^2)$.

19. $\left(\dfrac{2x}{3} - \dfrac{1}{2}\right)\left(\dfrac{4x^2}{9} + \dfrac{x}{3} + \dfrac{1}{4}\right)$.   **20.** $(5\theta - \frac{1}{5})(25\theta^2 + \theta + \frac{1}{25})$.

Problems 11-14

1. $-27\dfrac{e^6}{Z^3}$.   **2.** $16a^8b^4x^{20}y^{12}$.

3. $\dfrac{64d^6e^3f^9}{729x^6y^{12}z^3}$.   **4.** $\pm 5x^2yz^3$.

5. $-9a^4b^5c$.   **6.** $\pm\dfrac{7e^2ir^3}{25xy^4z^3}$.

7. $3ab^2c^4$.   **8.** $-\frac{2}{3}x^2yz^3$.

9. $\dfrac{5cd^3e^2}{6x^2y^4z}$.   **10.** $\pi(R - r)(R + r)$.

11. $\dfrac{r}{3}(i - 4e + 2i^2)$.   **12.** $p(1 + rt)$.

13. $\dfrac{I}{2}(R - 1 - 3E)$.   **14.** $\dfrac{1}{R}(E + e)$.

15. $0.15w(t - 3n + 4)$.   **16.** $e^2 + 20e + 100$.

17. $49R^4 - 28R^2r + 4r^2$.   **18.** $144\theta^2 - 18\theta + \frac{9}{16}$.

19. $144i^2 + 16i + \frac{4}{9}$.   **20.** $0.25\alpha^2 + 0.3\alpha\beta + 0.09\beta^2$.

21. $\frac{1}{4} - 6E^3 + 36E^6$.   **22.** $-20e$.

23. $4R^2$.   **24.** 1.   **25.** E^2.

26. 81.   **27.** B^2.   **28.** $\pm(5x - 3)$.

29. $\pm(a + 4)$.   **30.** $\pm(i + \frac{1}{2})$.   **31.** $\pm\left(1 - \dfrac{\phi}{2}\right)$.

32. $\pm(R + \frac{2}{3})$.   **33.** $\pm(\frac{10}{3} - 5E)$.   **34.** $9e^2 - 16i^2$.

35. $x^4 - 9y^2$.   **36.** $\dfrac{9Z^2}{25} - 49$.   **37.** $25E^2 - 81e^2$.

38. $x + y$.   **39.** $6 - Z$.   **40.** $2I + 3i$.

41. $e - \frac{1}{2}$.   **42.** $\frac{1}{2} - 0.3a$.   **43.** $x + y + 5$.

44. $\frac{2}{9} + 0.4w$.   **45.** $a + b + 1$.   **46.** $(9 - V)(9 + V)$.

47. $(2\alpha - 7\beta)(2\alpha + 7\beta)$.   **48.** $(xy - ab^3c^2)(xy + ab^3c^2)$.

49. $(e - 0.4)(e + 0.4)$.   **50.** $\left(0.3i - \dfrac{7I}{2}\right)\left(0.3i + \dfrac{7I}{2}\right)$.

51. $(0.4R - 0.05Z)(0.4R + 0.05Z)$.   **52.** $\left(\dfrac{\theta}{9} - \dfrac{\phi}{5}\right)\left(\dfrac{\theta}{9} + \dfrac{\phi}{5}\right)$.

53. $24 + 6\alpha - 9\alpha^2$.   **54.** $15R^2 + 31R - 24$.

55. $e^4 + 0.3e^2 - 0.1$.   **56.** $i^2 - \dfrac{i}{4} - \dfrac{1}{8}$.

57. $\dfrac{3E^2}{4} + E - \dfrac{8}{3}$.

58. $50I^2 + 1.5I - 0.02$.

59. $0.8Z^2 + 0.1Z - 0.15$.

60. $\dfrac{5\theta^2}{8} - \dfrac{8}{5}$.

61. $(R - 10)(R - 1)$.

62. $(a + 5)(a - 2)$.

63. $(i + 7)(i + 7)$.

64. $(x - 7)(x + 5)$.

65. $(e - 0.3)(e + 0.2)$.

66. $(I + \frac{1}{3})(I - \frac{1}{4})$.

67. $3x^2 - 13x + 12$.

68. $8R^2 - 30R + 25$.

69. $110a^4 - a^2b - 132b^2$.

70. $0.01e^2 + 0.06e + 0.08$.

71. $(5a - 3)(2a - 5)$.

72. $(\alpha + \frac{1}{3})(\alpha + \frac{1}{2})$.

73. $(3i + 7)(3i - 10)$.

74. $(3r + 1)(5r - 1)$.

75. $(3x - 2y)(5x + 4y)$.

76. $(3w - 0.5)(w + 0.3)$.

77. $(E - 0.6I)(E - 0.3I)$.

78. $(9y - 4x)(3y - x)$.

79. $(7\theta - 5)(8\theta + 7)$.

80. $(\alpha + 0.5\beta)(\alpha - 0.4\beta)$.

81. $\left(x + \dfrac{1}{y}\right)\left(x + \dfrac{1}{y}\right)$.

82. $(e + 3E)(e^2 - 3eE + 9E^2)$.

83. $7(i - 1)(i^2 + i + 1)$.

84. $3(b + 2)(b - 2)(b^2 + 3)$.

85. $x(x^2 + 5)(x + 1)(x - 1)$.

86. $2e(5 - e)(25 + 5e + e^2)$.

87. $xy(x - y)(x^2 + xy + y^2)$.

88. $R(R - r)(R + r)$.

89. $(1 + I)(1 - I + I^2)$.

90. $(a + \frac{1}{9})(a + \frac{1}{9})$.

91. $3(10x^2 - 9y)(10x^2 + 9y)$.

92. $\left(\dfrac{5e}{13} - 14E\right)\left(\dfrac{5e}{13} + 14E\right)$.

93. $(x^2 - 11)(x^2 - 7)$.

94. $(\alpha - 4\beta)(\alpha^2 + 4\alpha\beta + 16\beta^2)$.

95. $b(b - c)(b + c)$.

96. $3x(x - 6)(x + 6)$.

97. $3(E + 3)(E + 8)$.

98. $(c^3 + 7)(c^3 + 7)$.

99. $(13m + 3n)(13m + 3n)$.

100. $3(a + 2b)(a^2 - 2ab + 4b^2)$.

Problems 12-1

1. 12.

2. 16.

3. $3xy$.

4. $5ab^2$.

5. $6ei^2$.

6. $8x^2y^2$.

7. $9vt$.

8. $x - y$.

9. $m - n$.

10. $2c(d - e)$.

11. $2x^2(3x + y)$.

12. $a^2(a - b)(a - 2b)$.

13. $a^2(x - y)$.

14. $mn(x + y)$.

15. $3x + 2y$.

Problems 12-2

1. 100.

2. 360.

3. 1575.

4. a^2b^3.

5. $12bxy$.

6. $42x^2y^2$.

7. $48m^3n^5$.

8. $64x^3y^4$.

9. $84r^2st^3$.

10. $a^2(a - 3)$.

11. $21r^3(r + 1)$.

12. $x^4 - y^4$.

13. $(a - 2)(a - 3)(a + 3)$.

14. $(e + 7)(e - 5)(e - 6)$.

15. $(a + b)(a - b)^2(a^2 + ab + b^2)$.

16. $(1 - 8i)(1 + 3i)(1 - 3i + 9i^2)$.

17. $x(x + 1)(x - 1)(x - 10)$.

18. $(1 + a^2)(1 + a)^2(1 - a + a^2)$.

19. $2r(r - 3)(r + 3)(r^2 + 3r + 9)$.

20. $2b(b - 4)(b + 2)(2b + 1)(b - 2)$.

Problems 12-3

1. 9.

2. 8.

3. x.

4. $4ei$.

5. $r^2 - 16$.

6. $6x + 12y$.

7. $8E - E^2$.

8. $(x - 2)(x + 3)$.

9. $i - 3e$.

10. $12x$.

11. $\frac{3}{8}$.

12. $\frac{28}{42}$.

13. $\dfrac{24E^2I^2}{3I^2R}$.

14. $\dfrac{2f}{4\pi f^2 C}$.

15. $\dfrac{\sqrt{LC}}{2\pi LC}$.

Problems 12-4

1. $\frac{2}{5}$.

2. $\frac{1}{3}$.

3. $\frac{7}{9}$.

4. $\dfrac{x}{x + y}$.

5. $\dfrac{2}{(a - 1)(3a + 1)}$.

6. $\dfrac{a - b}{a + b}$.

7. $\dfrac{2a - b}{3b}$.

8. $\dfrac{r - 7}{r + 4}$.

9. $\dfrac{2i + 5}{2i - 5}$.

10. $\dfrac{a + b - c}{a - b + c}$.

11. $\dfrac{e^2 - e + 1}{e}$.

12. $\dfrac{a(x - 4)}{x + 5}$.

13. $\dfrac{r + 2s}{r^2 + rs + s^2}$.

14. $\dfrac{a}{a + 1}$.

15. $\dfrac{3(m^2 - n^2)}{m^2 + n^2}$.

16. $\dfrac{d(c^2 + 2c + 4)}{(c + 2)(c - 1)}$.

17. $\dfrac{E^2 - 17}{E^2 - 5}$.

18. $\dfrac{x^2 - y^2}{x^2 + 2y^2}$.

19. $\dfrac{I + 7}{3I^2 - 6I}$.

20. $x^4 + x^2 + 1$.

Problems 12-5

1. $\dfrac{6}{b^2 - a^2}$.

2. $\dfrac{8E^2}{R - r}$.

3. $\dfrac{E}{R_2 - R_1}$.

4. $\dfrac{a + b}{y^2 - x^2}$.

5. $\dfrac{c + d}{f - e}$.

6. $\dfrac{b - a}{23}$.

7. $\dfrac{e - E}{r}$.

8. $\dfrac{E^2 + e^2}{3r}$.

9. -1.

10. $-\dfrac{1}{x + y}$.

11. $\dfrac{r}{s + 2t}$.

12. $\dfrac{1 - m}{1 + m}$.

13. $\dfrac{1}{a + 5}$.

14. $\dfrac{x - y - z}{3}$.

Problems 12-6

1. $\frac{11}{3}$.

2. $\frac{45}{7}$.

3. $\frac{47}{9}$.

4. $\dfrac{x + y}{y}$.

5, $\dfrac{ce - d}{e}$.

6. $\dfrac{Ir - e}{r}$.

7. $\dfrac{I^2 Rr - e^2}{r}$.

8. $\dfrac{3R^2}{4}$.

9. $\dfrac{8V^2}{9}$.

10. $\dfrac{EIR + e^2}{R}$.

11. $-\dfrac{3w^2}{4}$.

12. $-\dfrac{2f^2}{9}$.

13. $\dfrac{3x + 8}{x + 1}$.

14. $\dfrac{IR + Ir - e}{R + r}$.

15. $\dfrac{\alpha^2 - \beta^2 - 1}{\alpha - \beta}$.

16. $\dfrac{10e^2 - 13Ee - 3E^2 - 4e}{5e + E}$.

17. $\dfrac{i^2 - 7i + 6}{i - 3}$.

18. $\dfrac{6P^2 + 18P - 16}{3P}$.

19. $\dfrac{(x - y)^2}{2}$.

20. $\dfrac{2b^3}{a + b}$.

21. $5\frac{2}{25}$.

22. $12\frac{1}{3}$.

23. $15\frac{1}{13}$.

24. $3x^2 - 9x - 6 + \dfrac{1}{x}$.

25. $3I - 4 - \dfrac{9}{4I}$.

26. $3R + 1 - \dfrac{1}{2R}$.

27. $3a - 1 + \dfrac{7}{3a + 1}$.

28. $x^2 + 2xy + 4y^2 + \dfrac{16y^3}{x - 2y}$.

29. $a^2 + 3ab + 6b^2 + \dfrac{18b^3}{a - 2b}$.

30. $3m + 14 + \dfrac{37m + 35}{m^2 - 2m - 3}$.

Problems 12-7

1. $\frac{15}{30}, \frac{20}{30}, \frac{18}{30}$.

2. $\frac{50}{60}, \frac{45}{60}, \frac{42}{60}$.

3. $\frac{42}{56}, \frac{48}{56}, \frac{35}{56}$.

4. $\dfrac{b}{ab}, \dfrac{a}{ab}$.

5. $\dfrac{ay}{xy}, \dfrac{bx}{xy}$.

6. $\dfrac{r}{Rr}, \dfrac{R}{Rr}, \dfrac{R}{Rr}$.

7. $\dfrac{Ee}{E^2 e}, \dfrac{3e}{E^2 e}, \dfrac{8E^2}{E^2 e}$.

8. $\dfrac{x - 1}{x^2 - 1}, \dfrac{bx + b}{x^2 - 1}$.

9. $\dfrac{ax + bx}{(a + b)^2(a - b)}, \dfrac{ay - by}{(a + b)^2(a - b)}$.

10. $\dfrac{15V^2xy^3}{30x^3y^4}, \dfrac{10Vt^2x^2y^2}{30x^3y^4}, \dfrac{6Vt^2}{30x^3y^4}$.

11. $\dfrac{6a}{10a - 20}, \dfrac{25}{10a - 20}$.

12. $\dfrac{e^2 + 4e}{(e - 2)(e^2 - 16)}, \dfrac{e^3 - 2e^2}{(e - 2)(e^2 - 16)}$.

13. $\dfrac{(e - r)(e^2 - er - 12r^2)}{(a + b)^2(e^2 - er - 12r^2)}, \dfrac{(a + b)^3}{(a + b)^2(e^2 - er - 12r^2)}$.

14. $\dfrac{(c^2 - c - 12)(i - 4)}{(i + 6)^2(i - 4)}, \dfrac{(c^2 - 36)(i + 6)}{(i + 6)^2(i - 4)}$.

15. $\dfrac{x^2 - 4}{(x^2 + x - 6)(x - 1)}, \dfrac{x^2 - 9}{(x^2 + x - 6)(x - 1)}, \dfrac{x^2 - 1}{(x^2 + x - 6)(x - 1)}$.

Problems 12-8

1. $\frac{7}{24}$.

2. $\frac{1}{12}$.

3. $\frac{1}{4}$.

4. $\frac{6x}{7}$.

5. $\frac{65r}{48}$.

6. $\frac{13a}{8}$.

7. $\frac{7}{4e}$.

8. $\frac{6xy + 3yz - 2az}{12}$.

9. $\frac{1 - 5e}{ei}$.

10. $\frac{16 + 20c^2}{25c^2r}$.

11. $\frac{9\theta^2 - 8\theta + 4}{\theta^3}$.

12. $\frac{bcx - acy - abz}{abc}$.

13. $\frac{7x - 11}{14}$.

14. $\frac{r + 8}{12}$.

15. $\frac{2e}{e^2 - 16}$.

16. $\frac{3r - 26}{r^2 - 8r + 12}$.

17. $\frac{7x + 22}{3x^2 - 12}$.

18. $\frac{x - y}{xy}$.

19. $\frac{(a + b)^2}{b(a - b)}$.

20. $\frac{10}{b^2 + b - 6}$.

21. $\frac{14a^2 + 7a + 5}{(4a^2 - 1)(4a^2 + 2a + 1)}$.

22. $\frac{21}{14 - i}$.

23. $\frac{23r + 133}{r(r^2 - 49)}$.

24. $\frac{11E - 2}{3E^2 - 3}$.

25. $\frac{3b^2 - 6a^2}{2a^2b^2}$.

26. $\frac{xy + xz + yz}{xyz}$.

27. $\frac{a^3 - 2b^3}{(a + b)(a^3 - b^3)}$.

28. 0.

29. $\frac{2}{R + r}$.

30. $\frac{4x^2 + y^2}{4x^2 - 9y^2}$.

31. $\frac{4x^2 - 12xy - y^2}{4x^2 - 9y^2}$.

32. $\frac{2}{\theta^2 - 10\theta + 24}$.

33. $\frac{b^2x^2 - a^2x^2 - 2b^2xy + 2a^2xy - b^2y^2 + a^2y^2 - 2x^2y^2 + 2y^4}{(x^2 - y^2)(b^2 - a^2)}$.

34. $\frac{2}{(2r + 1)(2r + 3)(r - 1)}$.

35. $\frac{\alpha + 2}{\alpha^2 + 4\alpha + 3}$.

36. $\frac{e - 3}{e^2 - e + 1}$.

37. $\frac{1}{R + 2}$.

38. $\frac{9w^2 + 17w - 8}{w(w + 3)(w + 5)}$.

39. $\frac{9I^2 - 9}{3I - 2}$.

40. $\frac{2i^2 - 11}{i - 4}$.

41. 1.

42. $\dfrac{4e^2 - 80e - 1}{16}$.

43. $\dfrac{6\theta^2 + 19\theta + 37}{6\theta + 6}$.

44. $\dfrac{12d^2}{d^3 + 27}$.

45. $\dfrac{2ab}{b^2 - a^2}$.

46. $\dfrac{2a}{a + b}$.

47. $\dfrac{32}{4 - 3R}$.

48. $\dfrac{a^3}{2 - 2a^4}$.

49. $\dfrac{3}{r^2 + r - 2}$.

50. $\dfrac{1}{x + y}$.

Problems 12-9

1. $\frac{5}{12}$.

2. 4.

3. $\frac{2}{5}$.

4. -1.

5. $\dfrac{s^2}{r^2}$.

6. $2xyz$.

7. $\dfrac{400a}{441b^3}$.

8. $3er$.

9. $\dfrac{8Rr^2}{9}$.

10. $\dfrac{r}{6}$.

11. $2\pi r^2 h$.

12. $xy - 2y^2$.

13. $\frac{7}{12}$.

14. $\dfrac{2w - 1}{w - 4}$.

15. $\dfrac{(\theta + \phi)^2}{\theta - \phi}$.

16. $\dfrac{4}{x - y}$.

17. $\dfrac{(Z + 11)^2(Z - 11)}{(Z + 2)^2(Z - 2)}$.

18. 2.

19. $\dfrac{a + 1}{a + 5}$.

20. $\dfrac{2I - 1}{2I - 3}$.

21. $\dfrac{1 + 3R + 2R^2}{1 - R^3}$.

22. $-\frac{3}{2}$.

23. -1.

24. $\dfrac{(c + 2d)(c - 5d)}{(c + 8d)(c + 4d)}$.

25. θ.

26. $\dfrac{m}{m - n}$.

27. $\dfrac{a^2(x + y)^4(x - y)}{b^2(x^2 + xy + y^2)^2}$.

28. ar.

29. $\dfrac{1}{a + b}$.

30. $\dfrac{2y - 3x}{2y + 3x}$.

31. $\dfrac{2a + b}{a + 2b}$.

32. $\dfrac{x - y}{x + y}$.

33. $\dfrac{2(a^3 + b^2 - b^3)}{a(a - b)}$.

34. $\dfrac{2R(R - r)}{r(R + r)}$.

35. $\dfrac{x - 2y}{(x + y)^2}$.

36. $\dfrac{2a}{b - a}$.

37. $\dfrac{2}{n^2}$.

38. 3.

39. E.

40. $5a^2$.

Problems 12-10

1. -2.

2. $-\frac{5}{2}$.

3. $\frac{20}{27}$.

4. $\frac{c}{2a}$.

5. $\frac{2a + 1}{1 - 3a}$.

6. $\frac{abx}{a + b}$.

7. $e - 5$.

8. $\frac{1 - R}{1 + R}$.

9. $\frac{a^2 + b^2}{a^2 - b^2}$.

10. $\frac{Z_1 - Z_2}{Z_1 + Z_2}$.

11. $\frac{r + 2}{r}$.

12. $\frac{x - y}{x + y}$.

13. b.

14. $\frac{i^2 - i + 1}{2i - 1}$.

15. $\frac{2}{R^3}$.

16. $\frac{2xy}{x^2 + y^2}$.

17. $\frac{3y - y^2 - 3}{2y^2 - 3}$.

18. $\frac{y - x}{y + x}$.

19. $\frac{E^2 + e^2}{2Ee}$.

20. $a - b$.

Problems 13-1

1. $e = 12$.

2. $x = -3\frac{1}{2}$.

3. $i = 5$.

4. $R = 18$.

5. $Z = 18\frac{2}{3}$.

6. $E = 2\frac{1}{2}$.

7. $I = \frac{1}{4}$.

8. $t = 3$.

9. $r = 5$.

10. $R = -3$.

11. $a = 27$.

12. $e = -11$

13. $I = 9$.

14. $Z = -12$.

15. $r = 7\frac{1}{2}$.

16. $i = 3$.

17. $m = 20$.

18. $\alpha = \frac{3}{10}$.

19. $E = 2$.

20. $R = -4$.

Problems 13-2

1. $R = 15$.

2. $r = 20$.

3. $i = -12.5$.

4. $e = 30$.

5. $I = 3$.

6. $E = 1.4$.

7. $Z = -3.2$.

8. $R = -1$.

9. $R = 30$.

10. $E = -1$.

11. $x = 35$.

12. $I = -0.1$.

13. $R = -1.25$.

14. $e = 6$.

15. $r = 700$.

Problems 13-3

1. $x = 7$.

2. $r = 12$.

3. $e = -5$.

4. $r = -2$.

5. $I = 3$.

6. $E = 10$.

7. $Z = 40$.

8. $\theta = 4\frac{1}{2}$.

9. $y = -\frac{1}{2}$.

10. $\alpha = 2$.

11. $x = -6$.

12. $r = 7$.

13. $e = -2$.

14. $i = 2$.

15. $a = \frac{83}{84}$.

16. $r = 6$.

17. $e = -\frac{1}{2}$.

18. $Z = 5$.

19. $a = 1$.

20. $b = 4$.

21. $e = -2$.

22. $c = 13$.

23. $r = 5$.

24. $x = 1\frac{1}{3}$

25. $R = 3$.

Problems 13-4

2. 5.76 hr.

3. $16\frac{2}{13}$ min.

5. $x = \dfrac{abc}{ab + ac + bc}$ days.

6. 2.72 hr.

7. 5 hr.

8. $n = \dfrac{xyz}{xz + yz - xy}$ hr.

10. 1.64 gal.

12. 288, 12.

14. $\frac{2}{5}$.

16. Width, 8.5 ft.
Length, 34 ft.

18. Length, 18 ft.
Width, 12 ft.

20. 5.

11. 96.

13. 420, 13.

15. 24, 84.

17. 18 in., 15 in., 8 in.

19. 24, 25.

21. $\frac{11}{15}$.

Problems 13-5

1. $x = \dfrac{a^2 - b^2 - c^2}{2b}$.

2. $e = \dfrac{Er}{R + r}, r = \dfrac{Re}{E - e}$.

3. $I = \dfrac{E_g - E_t}{R}$.

4. $E_b = IR + E_c$.

5. $s = \dfrac{N(a + L)}{2}, a = \dfrac{2s}{N} - L$.

6. $t = \dfrac{d(ad + 1)}{P}$.

7. $p = \dfrac{a}{1 + rt}$.

8. $s = \dfrac{r(R + EI)}{p + e}$.

9. $m_2 = \dfrac{Fr^2}{m_1}$.

10. $F = \dfrac{9C}{5} + 32$.

11. $E_g = \dfrac{I_p R_p - E_p - m}{\mu}$.

12. $R_t = \dfrac{R_1 R_2}{R_1 + R_2}, R_1 = \dfrac{R_t R_2}{R_2 - R_t}, R_2 = \dfrac{R_t R_1}{R_1 - R_t}$.

13. $g = t(M - L), M = \dfrac{Lt + g}{t}, t = \dfrac{g}{M - L}$.

14. $a = \dfrac{1}{T - t}, t = T - \dfrac{1}{a}$.

15. $a = \dfrac{Cb}{kb + C}, b = \dfrac{Ca}{C - ka}$.

16. $M = \dfrac{m\mu}{v - \mu}, m = \dfrac{M(v - \mu)}{\mu}$.

17. $q = \dfrac{fp}{p - f}$.

18. $V_0 = \dfrac{2s - gt^2}{2t}$.

19. $V_1 = \dfrac{F_t g + wV_0}{w}$.

20. $k = \dfrac{273h}{273 + t}, t = \dfrac{273(h - k)}{k}$.

21. $a = rL - sr + s, L = \dfrac{sr - s + a}{r}$.

22. $C = Y_c p + 2m, m = \dfrac{C - Y_c p}{2}$.

23. $L = \dfrac{c - 12D}{A}$.

24. $m = \dfrac{p(d^2 - L^2)}{2L}$.

25. $\alpha = \dfrac{C\pi}{2(MH + C)}$.

26. $\mu = \dfrac{kE_p}{E_b - kE_g}, E_g = \dfrac{\mu E_b - kE_p}{k\mu}$.

27. $x = \dfrac{a - bd}{c}$.

28. $x = \dfrac{n}{b}$.

29. $x = a + 1$.

30. $L = \dfrac{WL_1 + W_g}{pA - V}$.

31. $b_1 = \dfrac{2A}{h} - b_2$.

32. $E_g' = \dfrac{\mu E_g - E_p' + E_p}{\mu}$.

33. $R = \dfrac{\omega^2 L^2}{Z - 1}$.

34. $R_b = \dfrac{2p}{I_{max}^2}$.

35. $E_b = \sqrt{2}P_{ac} + E_p$.

36. $r_1 = \dfrac{r_2 r_3}{r_4}, \; r_4 = \dfrac{r_2 r_3}{r_1}$.

37. $r_1 = \dfrac{ir - i_g r_g}{i + i_g}$.

38. $R_1 = \dfrac{R_0(E - I_2 R_2)}{I_2(R_0 + R_2)}$.

39. $x = \dfrac{b}{a}$.

40. $x = \dfrac{1}{C}$.

41. $Z_c = \dfrac{e_2 \omega C r_p Z_e}{\mu e - e_2 \omega C(Z_e + r_p)}$.

42. $L_2 = \dfrac{100Q + Q\beta - p\alpha}{p + Q}$.

43. $k_1 = \dfrac{3kE - E_2 k_2}{2E_2}$.

44. $x = \dfrac{abc}{bc + ac + ab}$.

45. $L_0 = \dfrac{L_t}{1 + \alpha t}$.

46. $L_b = \dfrac{\mu e_g - i_p(r_p + R_b)}{\omega i_p}$.

47. $M = \dfrac{F'x^4}{2m'(x - 3)}$.

48. $Z_1 = \dfrac{Ea - I_s Z_2}{I_s a^2}$.

49. $R_p = \dfrac{e_1 Z_1}{\mu e_g - e_1}$.

50. $C_{gp} = \dfrac{(C_g - C_{gf})(r_p + r_b)}{r_p + r_b + \mu R_b}, \; R_b = \dfrac{(C_g - C_{gf} - C_{gp})(r_p + r_b)}{\mu C_{gp}}$.

51. $R_1 = \dfrac{R_p[(E_b - E_c) - \mu(E_c + E_s)]}{\mu E_c - E_b + E_c}$.

52. $E = \dfrac{I_{max}(R_1 R_2 + \omega^2 M^2)}{\omega M}, \; R_1 = \dfrac{\omega M(E - I_{max}\omega M)}{I_{max}R_2}$.

53. $\alpha = \dfrac{4\pi r^2 - T^2 MH'}{8r^2}$.

54. $R_c = \dfrac{R_p(R_{gl} - R)}{R - R_{gl} - R_p}, \; R_p = \dfrac{R_c(R - R_{gl})}{R_{gl} - R + R_c}$.

55. $x = -(4a + 3b)$.

56. $d = \dfrac{0.8r^2 N^2 - 6Lr - 10Lt}{9L}$.

57. $R_2 = \dfrac{Z_1(\mu e_g Z_2 - e_z r_p)}{e_2(r_p + Z_1)}, \; Z_1 = \dfrac{e_z r_p R_2}{\mu e_g Z_2 - e_2(r_p + R_2)}$.

58. $L = \dfrac{\mu R_p R_{gl}}{\omega Q(G_m R_p R_{gl} - \mu R_{gl} - \mu R_p)}, \; R_p = \dfrac{\mu \omega L Q R_{gl}}{G_m \omega L Q R_{gl} - \mu R_{gl} - \mu \omega L Q}$.

59. $x = \dfrac{a^2(b - a)}{a + 2b}$.

60. $n = \dfrac{Ir}{E - IR}, \; R = \dfrac{nE - Ir}{nI}$.

61. $n = \dfrac{IR}{E - Ir}, \; r = \dfrac{nE - IR}{nI}$.

62. $R_t = \dfrac{R_1 R_2 R_3}{R_1 R_2 + R_1 R_3 + R_2 R_3}$.

63. $E_{max} = R_b I_{max} - R_b I_{min} + E_{min}, \; I_{min} = \dfrac{R_b I_{max} + E_{min} - E_{max}}{R_b}$.

64. $Z_1 = \dfrac{Z_t Z_2}{Z_2 - Z_t}$.

65. $e_g = \dfrac{i_p(r_p + r_b)}{\mu}, \; r_p = \dfrac{\mu e_g - r_b i_p}{i_p}$.

66. (a) I is doubled.   **67.** $r = 4\Omega$.   **68.** $p = 133\frac{1}{3}$.
(b) I is halved.

69. $R = 6$. **70.** Twice as much. **71.** No.

72. No. **73.** $F = C$ at $-40°$. **74.** $q = -20$.

75. $m = -250$. **76.** $n = \dfrac{4I}{E - 25I}$. **77.** $m = -67.8$.

78. $b_2 = 100$. **79.** $S = 1710$. **80.** $b = -4.62$.

81. $b = -47.4$. **82.** $i_p = 200$ ma. **83.** $r_3 = \dfrac{20r_4}{r_2}$.

84. $V_o = -40$. **85.** $D = 0.05$ cm. **86.** $I_1 = 102$ a.

87. $t = 0.0294$ sec. **88.** $C = 2.22$ μf. **89.** $I = 1.58$ a.

90. $l = 60$ cm. **91.** $N = 120$ turns. **92.** $t = 70.5°$.

93. $R_1 = 47.7$ Ω. **94.** $n = 10$ cells. **95.** $n = 4$ cells.

96. $N_s = 80$. **97.** $Z_2 = 6$ Ω. **98.** $\alpha = 8.33 \times 10^{-2}$

99. $F = 68°$. **100.** $R_3 = 2.14$ Ω.

Problems 14-1

1. 3.33 Ω. **2.** 20 Ω. **3.** 167 Ω. **4.** 6 Ω.

5. (a) 50 Ω. **6.** $R_t = \dfrac{R}{2}$. **7.** 110 v. **8.** 550 w.

(b) 40 Ω.

9. 4.92 Ω. **10.** 112 w. **11.** 47.4 Ω. **12.** 303 w.

13. 9.99 Ω. **14.** 426 Ω. **15.** 124 w.

Problems 14-2

1. 5 Ω. **2.** 2.35 Ω. **3.** 62.5 Ω. **4.** 10 Ω.

5. 2.4 Ω. **6.** 69.8 Ω. **7.** 5 Ω. **8.** (a) 3.33 Ω.

(b) 2.5 Ω.

9. (a) 16.7 Ω. **10.** $R_t = \dfrac{R}{n}$. **11.** 20 Ω. **12.** 4.32 kw.

(b) 12.5 Ω.

(c) 10 Ω.

13. (a) 10.75 a. **14.** (a) 162 v. **15.** (a) 12.5 a.

(b) 1.25 a. (b) 9.54 a. (b) 9.09 a.

(c) 2 a. (c) 3.96 a. (c) 10.4 a.

(d) 13.3 Ω. (d) 64.8 Ω. (d) 19.2 Ω.

Problems 14-3

1. 74 Ω. **2.** (a) 3.57 a. **3.** 11,800 w. **4.** (a) 19.8 a.

(b) 15.43 a. (b) 5.8 a.

(c) 2.59 Ω. (c) 8.56 Ω.

(d) 9.21 Ω. (d) 20.7 Ω.

(e) 175 v. (e) 94.2 v.

(f) 120 v.

5. 5350 w. **6.** 217 Ω. **7.** 600 Ω. **8.** 188 v.

9. 52.6 w.   **10.** 0.132 a.   **11.** (a) 2 Ω.   **12.** 3.65 a.
   (b) 5 Ω.
   (c) 4.35 Ω.
   (d) 1.69 a.
   (e) 2.7 a.

13. 730 w.   **14.** 18.5 a.   **15.** 13.4 kw.

Problems 14-4

1. (a) 109.2 v.   **2.** 112.6 v.   **3.** (a) 222.7 v.   **4.** (a) 115.4 v.
   (b) 107.6 v.   (b) 215 v.   (b) 103.8 v.
   (c) 174.6 w.   (c) 403.8 w.   (c) 190.4 w.

5. (a) 112.45 v.   **6.** (a) 109.9 v.   **7.** (a) 113.25 v.   **8.** 113.5 v.
   (b) 112.65 v.   (b) 110.3 v.   (b) 112.05 v.

9. (a) 109.5 v.   **10.** (a) A = 99.8 v.
   (b) 106.7 v. B = 97.3 v.
   (c) 100.7 v. C = 96.1 v.
   (d) 632.4 w. D = 97.3 v.
                      (b) E_{gen} = 114.6 v.

Problems 14-5

1. 0.0287 Ω.   **2.** 0.00943 Ω.   **3.** 3720 ft.   **4.** 19.32 miles.
5. 9524 ft.

Problems 15-1

1. When 26 radios are sold.
2. Third, sixth, ninth, fifteenth.
3. (a) 5 hr.
   (b) 25 miles and 50 miles.
   (c) 45 miles at 2 hr., 30 miles at 7 hr.
4. (a) 5 weeks.
   (b) Third and seventh weeks.
   (c) Twenty-fifth week.
5. Current through a fixed resistance varies directly as the applied voltage.
6. (a) 12 hr.
   (b) 540 miles.
   (c) 165 miles.
7. With constant applied voltage, current through a resistance varies inversely as the value of the resistance.

Problems 15-2

1. Latitude.

Problems 15-5

1. $x = 3, y = -2$.   **2.** $x = 4, y = -2$.
3. $x = 3, y = 2$.   **4.** $x = 1, y = 3$.

5. $E = 1, I = 4.$

7. $F = -2, f = 1.$

9. $a = 1, b = 2.$

6. $R = 4, I = 2.5.$

8. $a = -2, b = 3.$

10. $x = -2, y = 2.$

Problems 15-6

1. $x = 2, y = 1.$

3. $x = 2, y = 3.$

5. $a = 3, b = -2.$

7. $E = \frac{1.5}{7}, e = \frac{2.5}{7}.$

9. $I = 11, i = -5.$

11. $x = 1, y = 2.$

13. $r = -11, s = 12.$

15. $s = 4, t = 5.$

17. $k = 4, M = 5.$

19. $e = 3, i = -7.$

2. $x = 2, y = -3.$

4. $x = -3, y = 2$

6. $R = 2, r = 3.$

8. $\alpha = 8, \beta = 9.$

10. $R = -2, E = \frac{1}{4}.$

12. $a = 12, b = 1.$

14. $k = 2, p = \frac{1}{3}.$

16. $P = 10, R = 10.$

18. $p = \frac{1}{3}, q = \frac{1}{2}.$

20. $R = \frac{3}{2}, r = \frac{2}{5}.$

Problems 15-7

1. $x = 5, y = 3.$

3. $r = 3, s = 3.$

5. $\alpha = 40, \beta = 5.$

7. $E = 5, R = 3.$

9. $s = 10, t = 8.$

11. $R_1 = 12, R_2 = 10.$

13. $I = 16, r = -10.$

15. $r_1 = -3, r_2 = -2.$

17. $E = 3, E_1 = -2.$

19. $a = 2500, b = 1500.$

2. $a = 6, b = 2.$

4. $E = \frac{5}{2}, e = \frac{1}{3}.$

6. $\theta = 6, \phi = -10.$

8. $I = 3.5, i = 2.$

10. $Z_1 = 4, Z_2 = 5.$

12. $E = 4, e = \frac{1}{2}.$

14. $e_1 = 4, e_2 = 4.$

16. $\alpha = 5, \beta = 5.$

18. $x = 3000, y = 1200.$

20. $R_1 = 12, R_2 = 9.$

Problems 15-8

1. $x = 5, y = 4.$

3. $R = 2, r = 2.$

5. $\alpha = 5, \beta = -3.$

7. $I = 4, i = 7.$

9. $R_1 = 6, R_t = 7.$

2. $a = 5, b = 7.$

4. $E = -5\frac{4}{17}, I = -13\frac{10}{17}.$

6. $Z = 2, Z_1 = 13.$

8. $e_1 = \frac{3}{5}, e_2 = \frac{1}{10}.$

10. $E_1 = -\frac{7}{23}, E = \frac{21}{23}.$

Problems 15-9

1. $x = 8, y = 10.$

3. $x = 6, y = 8.$

5. $R = 2, r = -\frac{1}{2}.$

7. $Z = 3, Z_1 = 5.$

9. $I = 6.87, i = 8.23.$

2. $a = 6, b = 4.$

4. $a = 1, b = 3.$

6. $E = -4, e = 10.$

8. $a = 2.79, b = 1.03.$

10. $E = 10, E_1 = 7.$

Problems 15-10

1. $x = 2, y = 3$.

2. $a = \frac{15}{11}, b = -\frac{15}{7}$.

3. $e = 1, e_1 = \frac{2}{3}$.

4. $R = 9, r = -5$.

5. $e = 12, i = 8$.

6. $a = -2, b = 1$.

7. $e = 5, e_1 = 2$.

8. $r = 10\frac{10}{71}, r_1 = 14\frac{11}{71}$.

9. $I = 4, I_1 = 10$.

10. $E = -1, E_1 = 5$.

Problems 15-11

1. $x = \dfrac{5B + b}{2}, y = \dfrac{b - 5B}{2}$.

2. $x = \dfrac{4a}{7}, y = \dfrac{a}{7}$.

3. $x = -d, y = c$.

4. $x = 1, y = 0$.

5. $x = a, y = b$.

6. $x = \dfrac{3(r + s)}{rs}, y = \dfrac{5(r + s)}{rs}$.

7. $x = \dfrac{mn(m + n - mn)}{n - m}, y = \dfrac{m^2(m + n - n^2)}{m - n}$.

8. $x = 1, y = 1$.

9. $E = \dfrac{Ir + R}{I^2 + i}, e = \dfrac{IR - ir}{I^2 + i}$.

10. $E = \dfrac{e_1 i + e_2}{I + i}, e = \dfrac{Ie_1 - e_2}{I + i}$.

11. $E = \dfrac{Ii + i^2}{i - I}, e = \dfrac{I^2 + Ii}{i - I}$.

12. $e = R, E = r$.

Problems 15-12

1. $a = 1, b = 2, c = 3$.

2. $x = -4, y = -5, z = -6$.

3. $x = 1, y = 2, z = 3$.

4. $E = 7, E_1 = 5, E_2 = 3$.

5. $R = 20, r = 9, r_1 = 15$.

6. $I = 8, i = 5, \alpha = 4$.

7. $a = -\frac{3}{2}, b = \frac{3}{13}, c = -\frac{3}{10}$.

8. $a = 2, b = 4, c = 6$.

9. $R_1 = \dfrac{5\alpha - 3\beta - \gamma}{6}, R_2 = \dfrac{\alpha - 3\beta + \gamma}{6}, R_3 = \dfrac{\beta - \alpha + \gamma}{2}$.

10. $R_1 = \dfrac{-2}{\beta + \gamma}, R_2 = \dfrac{-2}{\alpha + \gamma}, R_3 = \dfrac{-2}{\alpha + \beta}$.

Problems 15-13

1. 55, 20.

2. $\dfrac{a + b}{2}, \dfrac{a - b}{2}$.

3. $\frac{2}{3}$.

4. $62.5°, 27.5°$.

5. $\dfrac{90° + n°}{2}, \dfrac{90° - n°}{2}$.

6. $40°, 65°, 75°$.

7. $A = 3$ m.p.h., $B = 5\frac{1}{4}$ m.p.h.

8. $A = 5$ m.p.h., $B = 4$ m.p.h.

9. $t = \dfrac{mv}{2f}$.

10. $v = \dfrac{2s}{t}$.

11. $A = \dfrac{s^2 \sqrt{3}}{4}$.

12. $Q = CE$.

13. $W = \dfrac{Q^2}{2C}$.

14. $R = \dfrac{I_a R_a}{I - I_a}$.

15. $I = 22$ a, $R = 5 \; \Omega$.

16. $H = 0.24 \, Pt$.

17. 200 v.

18. $R_1 = \dfrac{bg - cf}{bd - af}$, $R_2 = \dfrac{cd - ag}{bd - af}$.

19. $R_x = \dfrac{R_b R_c}{R_a}$.

20. 8×10^{-3} coulomb.

22. $E_p = \dfrac{\mu E_g R}{R_p + R}$.

25. $R_1 = \dfrac{R_a R_b + R_b R_c + R_a R_c}{R_c}$.

$$R_2 = \dfrac{R_a R_b + R_b R_c + R_a R_c}{R_a}.$$

$$R_3 = \dfrac{R_a R_b + R_b R_c + R_a R_c}{R_b}.$$

Problems 16-1

1. (a) 121 v.
(b) 400 w.

2. (a) 235 v.
(b) 6.46 kw.
(c) 234 v.

3. (a) 232.6 v.
(b) 29.6 kw.

4. (a) 131 v.
(b) 127.5 v.
(c) 10 kw.

5. 124.4 v.

6. 142.9 v.

7. (a) 119.7 v.
(b) 420 w.
(c) 114.6 v.

8. 119.7 v.

9. 4.35%.

10. 0.877%.

Problems 16-2

1. 112.2 v.

2. 228.2 v.

3. 4.12 Ω.

4. 50 a.

5. 3.09 Ω.

6. 0.278 Ω.

7. 7.89 Ω.

8. (a) 1.53 a.
(b) 0.1515 Ω.
(c) 224.5 v.

9. (a) 1.28 a.
(b) 0.2 Ω.
(c) 225.7 v.

10. (a) 168 Ω.
(b) 34.1 a.
(c) 0.120 Ω.

Problems 16-3

1. 1.1 v.

2. 1.5 a.

3. 5.9 Ω.

4. 31.25 mw.

5. 1.1 v.

6. (a) 0.22 Ω.
(b) 4.5 w.

7. 1.9 v.

8. 0.0333 Ω.

9. (a) 0.3 Ω.
(b) 12 w.

11. 1 a.

12. 0.12 w.

13. 3.15 w.

14. 1.28 a.

15. 4 a.

16. 0.4 w.

17. 2.7 a.

18. 81 mw. **19.** 1.4 a. **20.** 0.0733 Ω. **21.** 0.46 Ω.

22. (a) 1420 w. **23.** $r = 0.2$ Ω. **24.** $r = 0.3$ Ω. **25.** $r = 0.164$ Ω.
(b) 460 w. $E = 1.4$ v. $E = 1.2$ v. $E = 2.14$ v.

26. $r = 0.05$ Ω. **27.** $r = 0.04$ Ω. **28.** $R = 0.665$ Ω.
$I = 8$ a. $E = 1.6$ v. $E = 2.1$ v.

Problems 17-1

1. a^8. **2.** x^6. **3.** e^{10}. **4.** θ^2.

5. x^{a+b}. **6.** x^{5a}. **7.** u^{2x}. **8.** b^{2x}.

9. x^5. **10.** a^{2x}. **11.** e^{m+1}. **12.** v^9.

13. y^{2b}. **14.** x^9. **15.** e^{20}. **16.** $a^6 b^9 c^3$.

17. $x^4 y^8 z^{16}$. **18.** x^{3m}. **19.** x^{3m}. **20.** $a^{3m} b^{3n} c^{6p}$.

21. $-d^{3w} e^{3m} f^{3n}$. **22.** $x^{8a} y^{4b}$. **23.** $\dfrac{a^6}{b^6}$. **24.** $\dfrac{x^{2m}}{y^{3m}}$.

25. $\dfrac{e^{3p}}{E^{4p}}$. **26.** $-\dfrac{a^{3n}}{b^{3m}}$. **27.** $\dfrac{x^{4p}}{y^{8q}}$. **28.** 1.

29. $\dfrac{c^{6rt}}{d^{6st}}$. **30.** $-\dfrac{a^{9m}}{b^{12n}}$. **31.** $\dfrac{1}{a^b b^2}$. **32.** $\dfrac{1}{x^3 b^4}$.

33. $\dfrac{1}{I^2 R}$. **34.** $\dfrac{3}{x^4}$. **35.** $\dfrac{1}{(4a)^{2b}}$. **36.** $\dfrac{x^2}{8y^3}$.

37. $\dfrac{b}{a^3 c^2}$. **38.** $\dfrac{x^2 y^2}{2}$. **39.** $\dfrac{3E}{4i^2 r}$. **40.** $\dfrac{27 a^3 b^4}{2}$.

Problems 17-2

1. ± 2. **2.** -3. **3.** 2. **4.** 2.

5. 5. **6.** $-4iz^2$. **7.** $a^2 b$. **8.** $\dfrac{4e^2}{r}$.

9. $x^3 y$. **10.** $a^{12} b^8$. **11.** $\sqrt[3]{2}$. **12.** $\sqrt[3]{5^2}$.

13. $3\sqrt{a}$. **14.** $\sqrt[6]{x^9 y^4}$. **15.** $\sqrt{4e}$. **16.** $\sqrt[4]{a^3 b^6}$.

17. $x^{\frac{3}{4}}$. **18.** $b^{\frac{3}{8}}$. **19.** $6(3x)^{\frac{1}{3}}$. **20.** $(4x^2)^{\frac{2}{3}}$.

21. $(6a^3 b^5)^{\frac{1}{4}}$. **22.** $6y^{\frac{3}{4}}$. **23.** $5xb^{\frac{3}{8}}$. **24.** $a^3 b^{\frac{3}{4}}$.

25. $2bc^{\frac{1}{4}} d^{\frac{1}{3}}$.

Problems 17-3

1. $3\sqrt{2}$. **2.** $4\sqrt{2}$. **3.** $4\sqrt{3}$. **4.** $2\sqrt{3}$.

5. $2\sqrt{5}$. **6.** $4\sqrt{6}$. **7.** $3\sqrt{7}$. **8.** $3\sqrt{6}$.

9. $3\sqrt{11}$. **10.** $3a\sqrt{7}$. **11.** $2ei\sqrt{15}$. **12.** $6\sqrt{10}$.

13. $12xy^2\sqrt{2}$. **14.** $6I\sqrt{2z}$. **15.** $45x^2\sqrt{y}$. **16.** $36m^2 n\sqrt{3m}$.

17. $9\alpha\beta\sqrt{7\alpha}$. **18.** $8x^2 yz\sqrt{2xz}$. **19.** $112a^4 b^2 c\sqrt{2bd}$. **20.** $12xy^4 z\sqrt{3xz}$.

Problems 17-4

1. $\dfrac{\sqrt{30}}{6}$.

2. $\dfrac{\sqrt{6}}{3}$.

3. $\dfrac{\sqrt{10}}{4}$.

4. $\dfrac{\sqrt{5}}{5}$.

5. $\dfrac{\sqrt{35}}{5}$.

6. $\dfrac{16\sqrt{5}}{5}$.

7. $4\sqrt{3}$.

8. $\dfrac{\sqrt{15x}}{6x}$.

9. $\dfrac{x\sqrt{65x}}{10y}$.

10. $\dfrac{\sqrt{a}}{a}$.

11. $\dfrac{\sqrt{ab}}{b}$.

12. $\sqrt{xy}$.

13. $\dfrac{z\sqrt{5}}{5}$.

14. $\dfrac{\sqrt{ab}}{b}$.

15. $\sqrt{\theta}$.

16. $\dfrac{\sqrt{6xy}}{3y}$.

17. $\dfrac{\sqrt{x^2-y^2}}{x-y}$.

18. $\dfrac{2\sqrt{2}}{3}$.

19. $\dfrac{I\sqrt{3}}{2}$.

20. $\dfrac{2E\sqrt{2}}{3}$.

Problems 17-5

1. $4\sqrt{2}$.

2. $4\sqrt{7}$.

3. $3\sqrt{3}$.

4. $-\sqrt{2}-3\sqrt{6}$.

5. $14\sqrt{5}$.

6. $-\sqrt{6}$.

7. $\dfrac{7\sqrt{6}}{2}$.

8. $\dfrac{15\sqrt{2}}{2}$.

9. $\sqrt{6}$.

10. $\dfrac{18\sqrt{10}}{5}$.

11. $\dfrac{3E\sqrt{2}+E}{2}$.

12. $I-\dfrac{I\sqrt{3}}{2}$.

13. $\dfrac{13\sqrt{15}}{15}$.

14. $(x+1)\sqrt{xyz}$.

15. $\dfrac{2b\sqrt{a^2-b^2}}{a^2-b^2}$.

Problems 17-6

1. $5\sqrt{3}$.

2. $2\sqrt{5}$.

3. $24\sqrt{10}$.

4. $6\sqrt{6}$.

5. $12a^2b^2c$.

6. $6i^2$.

7. $3x$.

8. $\frac{3}{2}$.

9. $E-IR$.

10. $4(e-IX_L)$.

11. 23.

12. $4R^2+4R\sqrt{z}-3z$.

13. $22+8\sqrt{6}$.

14. $18-5\sqrt{10}$.

15. $a+2+2\sqrt{a+1}$.

16. $2b-3-2\sqrt{b^2-3b}$.

17. $2(x-\sqrt{x^2-1})$.

18. $\dfrac{E^2(7-4\sqrt{3})}{36}$.

19. $\dfrac{\theta(3-2\sqrt{2})}{2}$.

20. $\dfrac{E\sqrt{2(1+2\sqrt{3})}}{3}$.

Problems 17-7

1. $\dfrac{15+5\sqrt{2}}{7}$.

2. $\dfrac{16-4\sqrt{3}}{13}$.

3. $12-4\sqrt{7}$.

4. $-\dfrac{32+24\sqrt{5}}{29}$.

5. $\dfrac{35\sqrt{3}+14}{71}$.

6. $\dfrac{3(\sqrt{6}+\sqrt{3}-\sqrt{2}-1)}{4}$.

7. $11 - 6\sqrt{3}.$

8. $\dfrac{a^2 + 2a\sqrt{b} + b}{a^2 - b}.$

9. $\dfrac{R - 2\sqrt{Rr} + r}{R - r}.$

10. $\dfrac{y - 2\sqrt{x}}{y}.$

Problems 17-8

1. $j3.$ **2.** $j6.$ **3.** $j8.$ **4.** $-j7.$

5. $j12b.$ **6.** $-j\sqrt{2}.$ **7.** $j4\sqrt{2}.$ **8.** $j36\sqrt{2}.$

9. $j12\sqrt{3}.$ **10.** $-j12\sqrt{7}.$ **11.** $j\tfrac{4}{5}.$ **12.** $-j\tfrac{1}{2}.$

13. $j\tfrac{3}{2}\sqrt{3}.$ **14.** $j\tfrac{5}{2}\sqrt{3}.$ **15.** $j\tfrac{4}{5}\sqrt{2}.$

Problems 17-9

1. $8 + j6.$ **2.** $33 + j11.$ **3.** $29 + j31.$

4. $-50 - j24.$ **5.** $-55 - j198.$ **6.** $13 + j44.$

7. $-2 + j10.$ **8.** $7 - j43.$ **9.** $-43 - j53.$

10. $44 + j44.$ **11.** $229 - j52.$ **12.** $-13 + j90.$

Problems 17-10

1. $18 + j26.$ **2.** $-68 - j239.$ **3.** $71 - j17.$

4. $2.$ **5.** $c^2 + j2cd - d^2.$ **6.** $R^2 + X^2.$

7. $\tfrac{2}{5}(1 + j2).$ **8.** $\tfrac{3}{2}(1 + j1).$ **9.** $\dfrac{9 - j40}{41}.$

10. $j1.$ **11.** $\dfrac{1 + j13}{10}.$ **12.** $\dfrac{38 + j34}{65}.$

13. $\dfrac{4 + j2b}{4 + b^2}.$ **14.** $\dfrac{a^2 - j2ab - b^2}{a^2 + b^2}.$ **15.** $\dfrac{R^2 + j2RX - X^2}{R^2 + X^2}.$

Problems 17-11

1. $x = 4.$ **2.** $e = 16.$ **3.** $I = 81.$ **4.** $x = 4.$

5. $r = 36.$ **6.** $i = 13.$ **7.** $E = 50.$ **8.** $I = 7$

9. $\theta = 48.$ **10.** $z = 3.$ **11.** $x = 3.$

12. $h = 150$ ft. **13.** $A = 12.56$ sq in.

14. $h = 5590.$ **15.** $K = \dfrac{mV^2}{2}, \; m = \dfrac{2K}{V^2}.$

16. $F = \dfrac{mm'}{r^2}.$ **17.** $\dfrac{d_o}{d_1} = \left(\dfrac{r}{R_t} + 1\right)^2.$

18. 5.17×10^{-5} h. **19.** 4.69×10^{-8} f.

20. $C_a = \dfrac{C_b}{4\pi^2 f^2 L C_b - 1}.$ **21.** $C_b = 3.75 \times 10^{-8}$ f.

Problems 18-1

1. $x = \pm 5.$ **2.** $R = \pm 0.3.$ **3.** $r = \pm 17.$ **4.** $I = \pm 1.3.$

5. $e = \pm 2.24.$ **6.** $y = \pm \tfrac{5}{8}.$ **7.** $i = \pm 6.$ **8.** $\theta = \pm 0.3.$

9. $Z = \pm\frac{5}{8}$.   **10.** $R = \pm 3.87$.   **11.** $R = \pm 2$.   **12.** $I = \sqrt{\dfrac{P}{R}}$.

13. $R = \pm\frac{5}{8}$.   **14.** $E = \pm 6$.   **15.** $x = \pm\frac{3}{2}$.

Problems 18-2

1. $x = -4$ or 1.   **2.** $x = 1$ or 3.   **3.** $R = -5$ or 7.

4. $R = -9$ or 2.   **5.** $I = \pm\frac{4}{5}$.   **6.** $R = -3$ or 6.

7. $E = 3$ or 4.   **8.** $r = -\frac{5}{2}$ or $\frac{3}{4}$.   **9.** $R = -2$ or 3.

10. $y = -\frac{1}{6}$ or $\frac{1}{4}$.   **11.** $I = -\frac{1}{2}$ or $\frac{1}{7}$.   **12.** $E = 5\frac{1}{3}$ or 5.

13. $R = 13$ or 2.   **14.** $i = -5$ or 0.   **15.** $E = -7$ or $\frac{3}{2}$.

Problems 18-3

1. $x = 1$ or 2.   **2.** $x = -6$ or 5.   **3.** $E = -4$ or -6.

4. $I = -5 \pm \sqrt{10}$.   **5.** $R = \dfrac{9 \pm 5\sqrt{5}}{2}$.   **6.** $r = \dfrac{-5 \pm \sqrt{29}}{2}$

7. $R = \dfrac{-3 \pm \sqrt{401}}{14}$.   **8.** $I = \dfrac{-3 \pm \sqrt{41}}{16}$.   **9.** $E = 2$ or $\frac{1}{3}$.

10. $e = \dfrac{7 \pm \sqrt{129}}{4}$.   **11.** $Z = \dfrac{3 \pm \sqrt{129}}{12}$.   **12.** $R = \dfrac{-1 \pm \sqrt{15}}{6}$.

13. $R = 15$ or $\frac{10}{3}$.   **14.** $I = \dfrac{2 \pm \sqrt{3}}{3}$.   **15.** $E = \dfrac{-7 \pm \sqrt{6}}{4}$.

Problems 18-4

1. $x = -1$.   **2.** $x = -4$ or 2.   **3.** $x = -3$ or 1.

4. $x = -\frac{3}{4}$ or $\frac{2}{3}$.   **5.** $R = -\frac{3}{2}$ or $\frac{4}{3}$.   **6.** $R = \dfrac{-5 \pm \sqrt{13}}{6}$.

7. $I = 2$ or $\frac{1}{3}$.   **8.** $E = -\frac{1}{5}$ or $\frac{5}{6}$.   **9.** $r = 2 \pm \sqrt{2}$.

10. $e = \dfrac{-1 \pm \sqrt{5}}{2}$.   **11.** $\theta = \dfrac{2 \pm \sqrt{19}}{5}$.   **12.** $d = \pm\sqrt{19}$.

13. $i = \pm\sqrt{2}$.   **14.** $x = \dfrac{b-2}{a}$ or 0.   **15.** $R = -1$ or 2.

16. $R = \dfrac{5 \pm 5\sqrt{5}}{2}$.   **17.** $I = 2$ or 9.   **18.** $E = -5$ or $\frac{5}{6}$.

19. $R = -\frac{9}{5}$ or $\frac{2}{3}$.   **20.** $R = \dfrac{-5 \pm \sqrt{7}}{3}$.   **22.** $24, 25$.

23. $\frac{4}{3}$ or $\frac{3}{4}$.   **24.** 63 by 38 ft.   **25.** $a = 24$ ft., $b = 32$ ft.

26. $14, 9$.   **27.** Yes. $6, 8$ and 10.   **28.** $v = 2 \times 10^3$.

29. $v = \pm 4\sqrt{\dfrac{2Fr}{W}}$,

     v is divided by $\sqrt{2}$.

30. $t = -6 \pm \sqrt{36 + 2L}$.

31. $X = 91.6 \; \Omega.$　　　　**32.** $X = 100 \; \Omega.$　　　　**33.** (a) 6.7 sec.

　　　　　　　　　　　　　　　　　　　　　　　　　　　　　　　　(b) 93.3 sec.

34. $f = \dfrac{1}{2\pi \sqrt{LC}}.$　　　　**35.** 712 kc.　　　　**36.** 264 mh.

37. $d = 3.51$ in.　　　　**38.** $I = \sqrt{\dfrac{WN}{R}}.$　　　　**39.** $v = \sqrt{2sg}.$

40. $r = \dfrac{-PXx \pm x \sqrt{P^2X^2 + 4R^2(P-1)}}{2R(P-1)}.$

　　　$x = \dfrac{PXr \pm r \sqrt{P^2X^2 + 4R^2(P-1)}}{2R}.$

41. $R = 44.7 \; \Omega.$

42. $c_1 = \pm \dfrac{1}{\omega R_1} \sqrt{\dfrac{R_b - R_2}{R_2 R_a}}.$

　　　$c_2 = \pm \dfrac{1}{\omega} \sqrt{\dfrac{R_a}{R_2(R_b - R_2)}}.$

44. 111 v.

45. 234.3 v.

Problems 19-1

1. 1 a.　　　　**2.** 1.35 a.　　　　**3.** 2.95 v.　　　　**4.** 1.43 $\Omega.$

5. 120 v.　　　　**6.** 230 v.　　　　**7.** 0.5 a.　　　　**8.** 2.15 a.

9. 6.2 $\Omega.$　　　　**10.** Zero.

Problems 19-2

1. 60 v.　　　　**2.** 12 v.　　　　**3.** 4.5 a.　　　　**4.** 1.46 a.

5. 7.62 a.　　　　**6.** 0.916 a.

7. (a) 1.0 a.　　　　　　**8.** (a) 2.22 a which is furnished by batteries.

　　(b) From a to b.　　　　　(b) From b to a.

Problems 19-3

1. (a) 119 v.　　　　**2.** (a) 114.25 v.　　　　**3.** (a) 122.5 v.

　　(b) 117.5 v.　　　　　(b) 113.5 v.　　　　　(b) 4680 w.

4. (a) 123.6 v.　　　　**5.** $E_1 = 118.8$ v.　　　　**6.** $E_2 = 117.6$ v.

　　(b) 1210 w.　　　　　　$E_2 = 114.6$ v.　　　　　$E_3 = 112.8$ v.

　　　　　　　　　　　　　$E_3 = 114.8$ v.　　　　　$E_4 = 110.2$ v.

　　　　　　　　　　　　　$E_4 = 112.2$ v.

7. $E_1 = 117$ v.　　　　**8.** 1747 w.　　　　**9.** $E_1 = 117.3$ v.

　　$E_2 = 114$ v.　　　　　　　　　　　　　　　$E_2 = 113.1$ v.

　　$E_3 = 117$ v.　　　　　　　　　　　　　　　$E_3 = 113.3$ v.

　　$E_4 = 114$ v.　　　　　　　　　　　　　　　$E_4 = 110.7$ v

10. $E_1 = 116.8$ v.

　　$E_2 = 108.6$ v.

　　$E_3 = 112.8$ v.

　　$E_4 = 106.2$ v.

Problems 19-4

1. 1.33 a.

4. A = 0.906 v.
   B = 0.906 v.

7. 7.76 a.

10. (*a*) 5.17 a.
   (*b*) 107.5 w.

13. (*a*) 3.125 v.
   (*b*) 6.25 a.   Through battery from d to c.

14. (*a*) 220 v.
   (*b*) 312.5 w.

2. 0.704 a.

5. (*a*) 2.53 a.
   (*b*) 3.12 v.
   (*c*) 2.39 v.

8. (*a*) 2.28 a.
   (*b*) 5.84 v.

11. (*a*) 12.7 a.
   (*b*) 209 w.

15. None.

3. 16.4 w.

6. 22.9 a.

9. (*a*) 8.40 a.
   (*b*) 4.76 a.

12. (*a*) 5.19 a.
   (*b*) 1056 w.

Problems 19-5

1. R_a = 3.2 Ω.
   R_b = 2.8 Ω.
   R_c = 2.24 Ω.

4. R_1 = 9.4 Ω.
   R_2 = 15.7 Ω.
   R_3 = 11.8 Ω.

7. 3.06 a.

10. 0.817 a.

13. 14.7 a.

16. 12 Ω.

2. R_a = 1.32 Ω.
   R_b = 0.6 Ω.
   R_c = 1.65 Ω.

5. 4.53 a.

8. 1.92 a.

11. 22 a.

14. 25.5 ma.

17. 10.36 Ω.

3. R_1 = 16 Ω.
   R_2 = 14 Ω.
   R_3 = 20 Ω.

6. 2.55 a.

9. 0.96 a.

12. 15.6 a.

15. I_G = 14.6 a.

Problems 20-1

1. $3 = \log_{10} 1000$

4. $3 = \log_4 64$.

7. $4 = \log_5 625$.

10. $2x = \log_3 M$.

13. $7^2 = 49$.

16. $\epsilon^1 = \epsilon$.

19. $a^0 = 1$.

22. $x = 4$.

25. $x = 0.5$.

28. $b^1 = b$.

30. 1, 2, 3, 4, 5, 6.

2. $5 = \log_{10} 100{,}000$.

5. $0 = \log_6 1$.

8. $0.5 = \log_9 3$.

11. $10^2 = 100$.

14. $4^3 = 64$.

17. $a^1 = a$.

20. $10^0 = 1$.

23. $x = 5$.

26. $x = 125$.

3. $2 = \log_5 25$.

6. $0 = \log_a 1$.

9. $s = \log_r t$.

12. $10^3 = 1000$.

15. $4^{0.5} = 2$.

18. $10^1 = 10$.

21. $x = 2$.

24. $x = 3$.

27. $5 - 3 = 2$.

29. 1, 2, 3, 4, 5, 6, 7, 8, 9.

Problems 20-2

1. 1.

4. 1.

7. $\bar{1}$ or $9 - 10$.

2. 2.

5. 2.

8. 0.

3. 2.

6. 3.

9. 3.

10. $\overline{2}$ or 8 − 10. **11.** 0. **12.** 1.

13. 3. **14.** $\overline{1}$ or 9 − 10. **15.** 0.

16. 5. **17.** $\overline{4}$ or 6 − 10. **18.** $\overline{3}$ or 7 − 10.

19. 0. **20.** $\overline{1}$ or 9 − 10. **21.** $\overline{1}$ or 9 − 10.

22. 1. **23.** 1. **24.** −0.5.

25. −1.5.

27. log 3793 + log 70.2 − log 264.

28. log 9.30 + log 479 − (log 3.42 + log 4869).

29. $\frac{1}{2}$[log 893 + log 0.642 − (log 2.376 + log 20.4)].

30. $\frac{1}{4}$(log 7182 + log 17.53 + log 69.3).

31. log a + log b + log c − (log d + log e).

32. 3 log x + 4 log y − (log a + $\frac{1}{3}$ log b).

33. 0.6861. **34.** 3.6861.

35. $\overline{2}$.6861 or 8.6861 − 10. **36.** $\overline{4}$.6861 or 6.6861 − 10.

37. 4.6861. **38.** $\overline{1}$.6861 or 9.6861 − 10.

39. 7.6861. **40.** $\overline{6}$.6861 or 4.6861 − 10.

41. 8.162 × 10. **42.** 8.162 × 10^3.

43. 8.162 × 10^{-4}. **44.** 8.162 × 10^6.

45. 8.162 × 10^{-1}. **46.** 8.162 × 10^{-9}.

47. 8.162 × 10^2. **48.** 8.162 × 10^{-3}.

49. 8.162 × 10^{10}. **50.** 8.162 × 10^{-8}.

Problems 20-3

1. 0.4771. **2.** 2.4771 **3.** 1.4771. **4.** 2.5514.

5. 2.8075. **6.** 2.8733 **7.** 2.0043 **8.** 2.6990

9. 5.3838. **10.** 5.6981 − 10. **11.** 3.9256.

12. 6.6695. **13.** 9.9909 − 10. **14.** 5.1514.

15. 2.5347. **16.** 5.3915. **17.** 5.1741 − 10.

18. 9.8471. **19.** 0.7980. **20.** 0.4972.

21. 0.4343. **22.** 2.5762. **23.** 6.9921 − 10.

24. 5.8727. **25.** 4.9030. **26.** 6.7517.

27. 6.7517. **28.** 5.7782 − 10. **29.** 8.9031 − 20.

30. 6.5395 − 10.

Problems 20-4

1. 7.559. **2.** 7.559 × 10^3. **3.** 7.559 × 10^{-2}.

4. 9.881 × 10^2. **5.** 3.900 × 10. **6.** 1.359 × 10^4.

7. 1.359 × 10^{-4}. **8.** 7.389 × 10^5. **9.** 8.79 × 10^8.

10. 8.79 × 10^{-7}. **11.** 1. **12.** 2.

13. 3.14. **14.** 6.28. **15.** 5.09 × 10^{-7}.

16. 7.856. **17.** 7.104 × 10. **18.** 6.753 × 10^4.

19. 2.593 × 10^{-3}. **20.** 3.207 × 10^2. **21.** 3.894 × 10^{-1}.

22. 5.898×10^3.   **23.** 9.813×10^{-1}.   **24.** 2.902.
25. 9.196×10^5.   **26.** 3.477×10^2.   **27.** 2.692×10^{-2}.
28. 9.121×10^{-12} **29.** 1.332×10^3.   **30.** 7.178×10^{-11}.

Problems 20-5

1. 6.0139.   **2.** 9.8552.   **3.** $8.0297 - 10$.
4. $4.2510 - 10$.   **5.** 3.5795.   **6.** $6.7296 - 10$.
7. 2.1118.   **8.** 3.5789.   **9.** $6.9697 - 10$.
10. 1.5305.   **11.** 12.5108.   **12.** $9.6734 - 20$.

Problems 20-6

1. 9.6×10.   **2.** 2.52×10^2.   **3.** 10^2.
4. 10^3.   **5.** 1.   **6.** -1.596×10^3.
7. -2.584×10^2.   **8.** -1.125×10^{-1}.   **9.** 2.748×10^3.
10. -2.174×10^{-3}.   **11.** 4.401×10^4.   **12.** -2.152×10^3.
13. -1.   **14.** 1.680×10^3.   **15.** 1.291×10^5.
16. 3.197×10.   **17.** -1.744×10^3.   **18.** -3.516×10.
19. 6.588×10^8.   **20.** 1.839×10^{11}.

Problems 20-7

1. 2.   **2.** 5.   **3.** 8.
4. -7×10^2.   **5.** 9×10.   **6.** -8.335×10^{-1}.
7. -1.598×10^2.   **8.** -1.049×10^{-4}.   **9.** 3.113×10^6.
10. 9.232×10^3.

Problems 20-8

1. 2.298.   **2.** 1.336.   **3.** 2.443×10.
4. 3.183.   **5.** 3.722×10^{-1}.   **6.** 4.533×10^{-1}.
7. 1.393×10.   **8.** 6.113×10.   **9.** 1.90×10^{-2}.
10. 9.998×10^{-6}.

Problems 20-9

1. 6.539×10^3.   **2.** 6.808×10^{10}.   **3.** 7.37×10^{-7}.
4. 3.354×10^{-1}.   **5.** 9.956.   **6.** ± 5.343.
7. 1.779×10^{-1}.   **8.** 9.351×10^{-1}.   **9.** $\pm 9.220 \times 10^{-1}$.
10. ± 5.519.   **11.** 2.735×10.   **12.** 1.847×10.
13. $\pm 1.303 \times 10^2$.   **14.** 3.096×10^{-8}.   **15.** ± 3.326.
16. 1.177×10.   **17.** $\pm 6.076 \times 10^{-1}$.   **18.** 5.33.
19. $\pm 8.304 \times 10^{-1}$.   **20.** $\pm 6.963 \times 10^{13}$.

Problems 20-10

1. $x = 6.230$.   **2.** $x = 2.231 \times 10^{-1}$.   **3.** $x = 10$.
4. $x = 10^{50}$.   **5.** $x = 7.598 \times 10^4$.   **6.** $P = 4.00 \times 10^{16}$.
7. $P_1 = 1.197 \times 10^2$.   **8.** $E = 4.766$.   **9.** $x = 1.995$.

10. $x = 6.$ **11.** $x = 4.$ **12.** $x = 4.$

13. $x = 3.322.$ **14.** $x = 4.096.$ **15.** $x = 1.661.$

16. $x = 3.151.$ **18.** 0.325 a.

19. (a) $0.8 - 1.646 \times 10^{-9}$ a. **20.** 0.0347 sec.
  (b) $0.8 - 3.990 \times 10^{-18}$ a.

22. 0.208 sec. **23.** 315 words per minute.

24. 265 words per minute. **25.** (a) 0.22 a.
  (b) 0.109 a.

27. (a) 0.22 a. **28.** (a) 1.30×10^{-3} coulomb.
  (b) 0.03 sec. (b) 25.9 v.
  (c) Yes.

29. 868.6 Ω. **30.** 0.296 a.

31. 0.1091 a.

Problems 21-1

1. (a) 14.0 db. **2.** (a) 35.1 db. **3.** 1.90 v, 3.16 ma.
  (b) 16.8 db. (b) 22.9 db.
  (c) -22.9 db. (c) -41.2 db.
  (d) -15.8 db. (d) -37.6 db.

4. 1.73 v, 3.46 ma. **5.** 2.74 v, 4.56 ma. **6.** 2.50 v, 5.00 ma.

7. (a) $P_o = 19.8$ mw. **8.** (a) $P_o = 19.0$ mw. **9.** 10^9.
    $E_o = 3.45$ v. $E_o = 3.38$ v.
  (b) $P_o = 125$ mw. (b) $P_o = 95.1$ mw.
    $E_o = 8.66$ v. $E_o = 7.55$ v.
  (c) $P_o = 0.788$ mw. (c) $P_o = 1.51$ mw.
    $E_o = 0.688$ v. $E_o = 0.952$ v.
  (d) $P_o = 4.97$ mw. (d) $P_o = 0.600$ mw.
    $E_o = 1.73$ v. $E_o = 0.600$ v.

10. 3.16×10^4. **11.** 10^{-2}. **12.** 10^{-1}. **13.** 95 db.

14. 7.9 w, 2.5 w, 0.79 w, 0.25 w, 0.079 w.

15. 3 db. **16.** 13 db. **17.** 3.95×10^{-8} w.

18. 116 db. **19.** 2.58×10^6. **20.** 3.80×10^{11}.

21. 51.8 db. **22.** (a) 27.2 w. **23.** (a) 224.
  (b) 61.3 db. (b) 37.0 db.
  (c) 3500. (c) 6 mw.

24. 3.92 w. **26.** 77.7 db. **27.** 1.10 μv.

28. 1.59 db. **29.** -0.480 db/mile. **30.** 15.8.

31. 250.

32. 1 db $= 0.115$ neper, 1 neper $= 8.69$ db.

33. 12 db. **34.** 26 db. **35.** 14.0 db.

Problems 21-2

1. 0.182 h. **2.** 0.0576 h. **3.** (a) 9.03 mh.
  (b) 0.027 μf.

4. (*a*) 10.6 mh.
  (*b*) 0.0228 μf.
7. 0.311 μf/mile.
10. 2 miles.
13. (*a*) 0.0201 μh/cm.
  (*b*) 0.0554 μμf/cm.
  (*c*) 306 μh.
  (*d*) 843 μμf.

5. 35.4 in.

8. 3900 ft.
11. 115 miles.
14. (*a*) 610 μh.
  (*b*) 1690 μμf.

6. 70.4 in.

9. 0.257 μf/mile.
12. 19.2 miles.

Problems 21-3

1. 600 Ω.
4. 3.33 in.
8. No. 8.
11. ¼-in. tubing.
15. (*a*) 6.4 db.
  (*b*) 22.9%.
18. (*a*) 0.217 db.
  (*b*) 95.1%.
21. 284 μμf.
24. 20.7 Ω.

2. 606 Ω.
5. 11 in.
9. No. 15.
12. 77.8 Ω.
16. 95.5%.

19. (*a*) 0.250 db.
  (*b*) 95.1%.
22. 187 μμf.
25. 19.4%.

3. 496 Ω.
6. No.
10. ½-in. tubing.
13. 0.132 in.
17. (*a*) 0.352 db.
  (*b*) 92.2%.
20. (*a*) 0.0869 db.
  (*b*) 98.0%.
23. 6.41 Ω.
26. 39.4%.

Problems 22-1

3. (*a*) 45°.
  (*b*) 58°.
  (*c*) 5°.
  (*d*) −8°.
  (*e*) −45°.
  (*f*) 150°.
7. 30°.
10. 10,800°/sec.
14. No.

4. (*a*) 135°.
  (*b*) 86°.
  (*c*) 60°.
  (*d*) −30°.
  (*e*) −120°.
  (*f*) 265°
8. 6°/min
11. 45_π ft/sec.

6. 11.

9. 0.5°/min.
12. 0.25°/min.

Problems 22-2

1. (*a*) 2π radians.

  (*b*) π radians.

  (*c*) $\frac{\pi}{3}$ radians.

  (*d*) $\frac{\pi}{2}$ radians.

  (*e*) $\frac{\pi}{6}$ radians.

  (*f*) $\frac{\pi}{4}$ radians.

2. (*a*) $\frac{3\pi}{4}$ radians.

  (*b*) $\frac{3\pi}{2}$ radians.

  (*c*) $\frac{4\pi}{3}$ radians.

  (*d*) 4π radians.

  (*e*) $\frac{7\pi}{4}$ radians.

  (*f*) $\frac{5\pi}{3}$ radians.

3. (*a*) 114.6°.

  (*b*) 72°.

  (*c*) 18.2°.

  (*d*) 34.4°.

  (*e*) 126°.

  (*f*) 3.21°.

4. $\dfrac{15\pi}{2}$ radians.　　　**5.** $\dfrac{\pi}{8}$ radians.　　　**6.** 50π radians/sec.

7. 140π radians/sec.　　**8.** 1800 r.p.m.　　　**9.** 750 r.p.m.

10. $\dfrac{\pi}{12}$ radians/hr.

Problems 22-3

1. 20 ft., 13.3 ft.　　　　　　**2.** 87.8 ft., 103.3 ft.

3. $a = 4$, $B = 36.9°$, $C = 90°$.　　**4.** $A = 36.9°$, $B = 53.1°$, $C = 90°$.

5. $c = 4.75$, $A = 110°$, $B = 36°$.　　**6.** $b = 17.7$, $A = 33.8°$, $C = 46.2°$.

7. $a = 4.95$, $b = 4.95$, $C = 90°$.　　**8.** $c = 11$, $A = 80°$, $B = 20°$.

Problems 22-4

1. $c = 25$, $B = 53.1°$.　　　　　　**2.** $b = 28.1$, $B = 65.2°$.

3. $a = 127$, $B = 39.6°$.　　　　　　**4.** 122 nautical miles.

5. 89.3 ft.　　　　　　　　　　　　**6.** 4 ft.

7. 16.3 ft.　　　　　　　　　　　　**8.** 18.2 ft.

9. 300 ft.　　　　　　　　　　　　**10.** 86.5 ft.

Problems 23-1

1. $\sin \theta = \dfrac{a}{c}$.

$\cos \theta = \dfrac{b}{c}$.

$\tan \theta = \dfrac{a}{b}$.

$\cot \theta = \dfrac{b}{a}$.

$\sec \theta = \dfrac{c}{b}$.

$\csc \theta = \dfrac{c}{a}$.

$\sin \phi = \dfrac{b}{c}$.

$\cos \phi = \dfrac{a}{c}$.

$\tan \phi = \dfrac{b}{a}$.

$\cot \phi = \dfrac{a}{b}$.

$\sec \phi = \dfrac{c}{a}$.

$\csc \phi = \dfrac{c}{b}$.

2. (a) $\sin \alpha = \dfrac{OR}{PR}$.

(b) $\sin \beta = \dfrac{OP}{PR}$.

(c) $\cot \beta = \dfrac{OR}{OP}$.

(d) $\sec \alpha = \dfrac{PR}{OP}$.

(e) $\tan \alpha = \dfrac{OR}{OP}$.

3. (a) $\dfrac{OP}{OR} = \tan \beta$.

(b) $\dfrac{PR}{PO} = \sec \alpha$.

(c) $\dfrac{OR}{PR} = \cos \beta$.

(d) $\dfrac{OP}{RP} = \sin \beta$.

(e) $\dfrac{PR}{RO} = \csc \alpha$.

4. $\sin \theta = \frac{12}{13}$.

$\cos \theta = \frac{5}{13}$.

$\tan \theta = \frac{12}{5}$.

$\cot \theta = \frac{5}{12}$.

$\sec \theta = \frac{13}{5}$.

$\csc \theta = \frac{13}{12}$.

$\sin \phi = \frac{5}{13}$.

$\cos \phi = \frac{12}{13}$.

$\tan \phi = \frac{5}{12}$.

$\cot \phi = \frac{12}{5}$.

$\sec \phi = \frac{13}{12}$.

$\csc \phi = \frac{13}{5}$.

5. $\sin \theta = 0.333$.

$\cos \theta = 0.943$.

$\tan \theta = 0.354$.

$\cot \theta = 2.83$.

$\sec \theta = 1.06$.

$\csc \theta = 3$.

6. $\sin \theta = 0.707$.

$\cos \theta = 0.707$.

$\tan \theta = 1$.

7. $\sin \theta = 0.866$.

$\cos \theta = 0.5$.

$\tan \theta = 1.73$.

8. $\sin \phi = 0.446$.

$\cos \phi = 0.895$.

$\tan \phi = 0.5$.

9. $\sin \phi = 0.97$.

$\cos \phi = 0.243$.

$\tan \phi = 4$.

10. (a) $\sec \beta = \frac{5}{3}$.

(b) $\csc \alpha = 3$.

(c) $\cot \phi = 1$.

(d) $\cos \theta = \frac{3}{4}$.

(e) $\tan \beta = \frac{11}{3}$.

(f) $\sin \phi = \frac{1}{10}$.

11. Yes.

$\sin = \frac{40}{41}$.

$\cos = \frac{9}{41}$.

$\tan = \frac{40}{9}$.

$\cot = \frac{9}{40}$.

$\sec = \frac{41}{9}$.

$\csc = \frac{41}{40}$.

12. $\sin A = \frac{3}{5}$.

$\cos A = \frac{4}{5}$.

$\tan A = \frac{3}{4}$.

$\cot A = \frac{4}{3}$.

$\sec A = \frac{5}{4}$.

$\csc A = \frac{5}{3}$.

13. $\cos = \frac{3}{5}$.

$\tan = \frac{4}{3}$.

$\cot = \frac{3}{4}$.

$\sec = \frac{5}{3}$.

$\csc = \frac{5}{4}$.

14. $\sin B = \frac{4}{5}$.

$\cos B = \frac{3}{5}$.

$\tan B = \frac{4}{3}$.

$\cot B = \frac{3}{4}$.

$\sec B = \frac{5}{3}$.

$\csc B = \frac{5}{4}$.

15. $\sin = 0.167$.

$\cos = 0.988$.

$\tan = 0.169$.

$\cot = 5.92$.

$\sec = 1.01$.

16. (a) $\tan \theta$.

(b) $\sec \theta$.

(c) $\cot \theta$.

(d) $\csc \theta$.

Problems 23-2

1. III or IV.

2. I or II.

3. II or IV.

4. I or IV.

5. II or III.

6. I or III.

7. II.

8. I.

9. III.

10. II.

11. IV.

12. I.

13. II.

14. IV.

15. IV.

16. I or II.

17. II or III.

18. I or III.

19. I or II.

20. No.

21. -0.1026.

22. $\sin = +$.

$\cos = +$.

$\tan = +$.

23. $\sin = +$.

$\cos = +$.

$\tan = +$.

24. $\sin = -$.

$\cos = +$.

$\tan = -$.

25. $\sin = -$.

$\cos = -$.

$\tan = +$.

26. $\sin = +$.

$\cos = -$.

$\tan = -$.

27. $\sin = -$.

$\cos = +$.

$\tan = -$.

28. $\sin = -$.

$\cos = +$.

$\tan = -$.

29. sin = −.   **30.** sin = +.   **31.** sin = +.   **32.** sin = −1.
cos = −.   cos = −.   cos = +.   cos = 0.
tan = +.   tan = −.   tan = +.

33. sin = +.
cos = −.
tan = −.

36. $\sin \theta = \dfrac{3\sqrt{13}}{13}.$ **37.** $\sin \theta = -\frac{5}{13}.$ **38.** $\sin \theta = \frac{4}{5}.$

$\cos \theta = \dfrac{2\sqrt{13}}{13}.$ $\cos \theta = -\frac{12}{13}.$ $\cos \theta = \frac{3}{5}.$

$\tan \theta = \frac{3}{2}.$ $\tan \theta = \frac{5}{12}.$ $\tan \theta = \frac{4}{3}.$

$\cot \theta = \frac{2}{3}.$ $\cot \theta = 1\frac{2}{5}.$ $\cot \theta = \frac{3}{4}.$

$\sec \theta = \dfrac{\sqrt{13}}{2}.$ $\sec \theta = -1\frac{1}{12}.$ $\sec \theta = \frac{5}{3}.$

$\csc \theta = \dfrac{\sqrt{13}}{3}.$ $\csc \theta = -1\frac{3}{5}.$ $\csc \theta = \frac{5}{4}.$

39. $\sin \theta = -\frac{4}{5}.$ **40.** $\sin \theta = -\frac{4}{5}.$ **41.** $\sin \theta = -\dfrac{\sqrt{10}}{10}.$

$\cos \theta = \frac{3}{5}.$ $\cos \theta = -\frac{3}{5}.$ $\cos \theta = -\dfrac{3\sqrt{10}}{10}.$

$\tan \theta = -\frac{4}{3}.$ $\tan \theta = \frac{4}{3}.$ $\tan \theta = \frac{1}{3}.$
$\cot \theta = -\frac{3}{4}.$ $\cot \theta = \frac{3}{4}.$ $\cot \theta = 3.$

$\sec \theta = \frac{5}{3}.$ $\sec \theta = -\frac{5}{3}.$ $\sec \theta = -\dfrac{\sqrt{10}}{3}.$

$\csc \theta = -\frac{5}{4}.$ $\csc \theta = -\frac{5}{4}.$ $\csc \theta = -\sqrt{10}.$

42. $\sin \theta = \frac{4}{5}.$ **43.** $\sin \theta = -\frac{3}{5}.$ **44.** $\sin \theta = \dfrac{\sqrt{2}}{2}.$

$\cos \theta = -\frac{3}{5}.$ $\cos \theta = \frac{4}{5}.$ $\cos \theta = \dfrac{\sqrt{2}}{2}.$

$\tan \theta = -\frac{4}{3}.$ $\tan \theta = -\frac{3}{4}.$ $\tan \theta = 1.$
$\cot \theta = -\frac{3}{4}$ $\cot \theta = -\frac{4}{3}.$ $\cot \theta = 1.$
$\sec \theta = -\frac{5}{3}.$ $\sec \theta = \frac{5}{4}.$ $\sec \theta = \sqrt{2}.$
$\csc \theta = \frac{5}{4}.$ $\csc \theta = -\frac{5}{3}.$ $\csc \theta = \sqrt{2}.$

Problems 23-3

1. −1.   **2.** −1.   **3.** ∞.
4. ∞.   **5.** No.

Problems 24-1

1. (*a*) sin 13° = 0.2250, cos 13° = 0.9744, tan 13° = 0.2309.
(*b*) sin 89° = 0.9998, cos 89° = 0.0175, tan 89° = 57.29.
(*c*) sin 4.3° = 0.0750, cos 4.3° = 0.9972, tan 4.3° = 0.0752.
(*d*) sin 57.9° = 0.8471, cos 57.9° = 0.5314, tan 57.9° = 1.5941.
(*e*) sin 25.4° = 0.4289, cos 25.4° = 0.9033, tan 25.4° = 0.4748.

2. (*a*) sin 17° = 0.2924, cos 17° = 0.9563, tan 17° = 0.3057.
   (*b*) sin 78° = 0.9781, cos 78° = 0.2079, tan 78° = 4.7046.
   (*c*) sin 8.7° = 0.1513, cos 8.7° = 0.9885, tan 8.7° = 0.1530.
   (*d*) sin 63.1° = 0.8918, cos 63.1° = 0.4524, tan 63.1° = 1.9711.
   (*e*) sin 33.6° = 0.5534, cos 33.6° = 0.8329, tan 33.6° = 0.6644.

3. (*a*) sin 25.75° = 0.4344, cos 25.75° = 0.9007, tan 25.75° = 0.4823.
   (*b*) sin 73.36° = 0.9581, cos 73.36° = 0.2864, tan 73.36° = 3.3459.
   (*c*) sin 2.14° = 0.0373, cos 2.14° = 0.9993, tan 2.14° = 0.0374.
   (*d*) sin 47.72° = 0.7398, cos 47.72° = 0.6727, tan 47.72° = 1.0998.
   (*e*) sin 10.27° = 0.1783, cos 10.27° = 0.9840, tan 10.27° = 0.1812.

4. (*a*) sin 37.55° = 0.6094, cos 37.55° = 0.7928, tan 37.55° = 0.7687.
   (*b*) sin 69.93° = 0.9393, cos 69.93° = 0.3432, tan 69.93° = 2.7371.
   (*c*) sin 53.18° = 0.8005, cos 53.18° = 0.5993, tan 53.18° = 1.3357.
   (*d*) sin 7.49° = 0.1303, cos 7.49° = 0.9914, tan 7.49° = 0.1315.
   (*e*) sin 49.11° = 0.7560, cos 49.11° = 0.6546, tan 49.11° = 1.1548.

Problems 24-2

1. (*a*) 3.6°.	**2.** (*a*) 87.7°.	**3.** (*a*) 7.9°.	**4.** (*a*) 51.7°.
(*b*) 84.2°.	(*b*) 11.8°.	(*b*) 84.1°.	(*b*) 74.1°.
(*c*) 15.3°.	(*c*) 55.5°.	(*c*) 36.1°.	(*c*) 4.1°.
(*d*) 67.7°.	(*d*) 65.1°.	(*d*) 58.0°.	(*d*) 51.3°.
(*e*) 37.1°.	(*e*) 37.7°.	(*e*) 4.8°.	(*e*) 5.4°.

Problems 24-3

1. (*a*) sin 99° = 0.9877, cos 99° = −0.1564, tan 99° = −6.3138.
   (*b*) sin 164° = 0.2756, cos 164° = −0.9613, tan 164° = −0.2867.
   (*c*) sin 136.5° = 0.6884, cos 136.5° = −0.7254, tan 136.5° = −0.9490.
   (*d*) sin 159.1° = 0.3567, cos 159.1° = −0.9342, tan 159.1° = −0.3819.
   (*e*) sin 178.1° = 0.0332, cos 178.1° = −0.9995, tan 178.1° = −0.0332.

2. (*a*) sin 103° = 0.9744, cos 103° = −0.2250, tan 103° = −4.3315.
   (*b*) sin 169° = 0.1908, cos 169° = −0.9816, tan 169° = −0.1944.
   (*c*) sin 114.3° = 0.9114, cos 114.3° = −0.4115, tan 114.3° = −2.2148.
   (*d*) sin 152.3° = 0.4648, cos 152.3° = −0.8854, tan 152.3° = −0.5250.
   (*e*) sin 146.8° = 0.5476, cos 146.8° = −0.8368, tan 146.8° = −0.6544.

3. (*a*) sin 186° = −0.1045, cos 186° = −0.9945, tan 186° = 0.1051.
   (*b*) sin 261° = −0.9877, cos 261° = −0.1564, tan 261° = 6.3138.
   (*c*) sin 220.7° = −0.6521, cos 220.7° = −0.7581, tan 220.7° = 0.8601.
   (*d*) sin 197.4° = −0.2990, cos 197.4° = −0.9542, tan 197.4° = 0.3134.
   (*e*) sin 250.6° = −0.9432, cos 250.6° = −0.3322, tan 250.6° = 2.8396.

4. (*a*) sin 189° = −0.1564, cos 189° = −0.9877, tan 189° = 0.1584.
   (*b*) sin 247° = −0.9205, cos 247° = −0.3907, tan 247° = 2.3558.
   (*c*) sin 193.3° = −0.2300, cos 193.3° = −0.9732, tan 193.3° = 0.2364.
   (*d*) sin 200.4° = −0.3486, cos 200.4° = −0.9373, tan 200.4° = 0.3719.
   (*e*) sin 233.9° = −0.8080, cos 233.9° = −0.5892, tan 233.9° = 1.3713.

5. (a) $\sin 352° = -0.1392$, $\cos 352° = 0.9903$, $\tan 352° = -0.1405$.

(b) $\sin 277° = -0.9925$, $\cos 277° = 0.1219$, $\tan 277° = -8.1143$.

(c) $\sin 348.1° = -0.2062$, $\cos 348.1° = 0.9785$, $\tan 348.1° = -0.2107$.

(d) $\sin 285.7° = -0.9627$, $\cos 285.7° = 0.2706$, $\tan 285.7° = -3.5576$.

(e) $\sin 331.2° = -0.4818$, $\cos 331.2° = 0.8763$, $\tan 331.2° = -0.5498$.

6. (a) $\sin 274° = -0.9976$, $\cos 274° = 0.0698$, $\tan 274° = -14.30$.

(b) $\sin 349° = -0.1908$, $\cos 349° = 0.9816$, $\tan 349° = -0.1944$.

(c) $\sin 320.3° = -0.6388$, $\cos 320.3° = 0.7694$, $\tan 320.3° = -0.8302$.

(d) $\sin 292.4° = -0.9245$, $\cos 292.4° = 0.3811$, $\tan 292.4° = -2.4262$.

(e) $\sin 338.8° = -0.3616$, $\cos 338.8° = 0.9323$, $\tan 338.8° = -0.3879$.

7. (a) $\sin 385° = 0.4226$, $\cos 385° = 0.9063$, $\tan 385° = 0.4663$.

(b) $\sin 847° = 0.7986$, $\cos 847° = -0.6018$, $\tan 847° = -1.3270$.

(c) $\sin 1376° = -0.8988$, $\cos 1376° = 0.4384$, $\tan 1376° = -2.0503$.

(d) $\sin (-480°) = -0.8660$, $\cos (-480°) = -0.5000$,
$\tan (-480°) = 1.7321$.

(e) $\sin (-667°) = 0.7986$, $\cos (-667°) = 0.6018$,
$\tan (-667°) = 1.3270$.

8. (a) $\sin 590° = -0.7660$, $\cos 590° = -0.6428$, $\tan 590° = 1.1918$.

(b) $\sin (-1080°) = 0.0000$, $\cos (-1080°) = 1.0000$,
$\tan (-1080°) = 0.0000$.

(c) $\sin 1038° = -0.6691$, $\cos 1038° = 0.7431$, $\tan 1038° = -0.9004$.

(d) $\sin (-406°) = -0.7193$, $\cos (-406°) = 0.6947$,
$\tan (-406°) = -1.0355$.

(e) $\sin (-923°) = 0.3907$, $\cos (-923°) = -0.9205$,
$\tan (-923°) = -0.4245$.

9. (a) $21.3°$. **10.** (a) $-54.9°$ or $305.1°$.

(b) $-7.2°$ or $352.8°$. (b) $74.3°$.

(c) $-36.9°$ or $323.1°$. (c) $-24.5°$ or $335.5°$.

(d) $97.4°$. (d) $61.3°$.

(e) $1.6°$. (e) $-82.3°$ or $277.7°$.

11. $d = \sqrt{\dfrac{I \cos \theta}{E}}$, $I = \dfrac{Ed^2}{\cos \theta}$, $\theta = \text{arc cos } \dfrac{Ed^2}{I}$.

12. 3.06 ft. **13.** 0.369 ft-candle. **14.** $90°$.

15. $h = \sqrt{\dfrac{I \cos^3 \theta}{E_h}}$, $I = \dfrac{h^2 E_h}{\cos^3 \theta}$, $\theta = \text{arc cos } \sqrt[3]{\dfrac{h^2 E_h}{I}}$.

16. 0.550 ft-candle. **17.** 62,500 ft candles.

18. No. **19.** 514 cp.

20. $0°$.

Problems 25-1

1. $Z = 70$, $X = 29.6$, $\phi = 65°$.

2. $Z = 51.7$, $X = 50.6$, $\phi = 11.5°$.

3. $Z = 179$, $X = 38.2$, $\phi = 77.7°$.

4. $Z = 0.998$, $X = 0.903$, $\phi = 25.1°$.

5. $Z = 660$, $X = 401$, $\phi = 52.6°$.

6. $Z = 48.7$, $R = 5.0$, $\phi = 5.9°$.
7. $Z = 101.7$, $R = 101.2$, $\phi = 84.8°$.
8. $Z = 1025$, $R = 550$, $\phi = 32.4°$.
9. $Z = 2880$, $R = 2600$, $\phi = 64.3°$.
10. $Z = 0.403$, $R = 0.280$, $\phi = 44.0°$.
11. $Z = 159$, $X = 124$, $\theta = 51.1°$.
12. $Z = 1870$, $X = 660$, $\theta = 20.7°$.
13. $Z = 28.21$, $X = 28.17$, $\theta = 87.5°$.
14. $Z = 287$, $X = 277$, $\theta = 74.6°$.
15. $Z = 0.948$, $X = 0.171$, $\theta = 10.4°$.
16. $Z = 18.4$, $R = 18.2$, $\theta = 9.1°$.
17. $Z = 9040$, $R = 5960$, $\theta = 48.8°$.
18. $Z = 282$, $R = 131$, $\theta = 62.3°$.
19. $Z = 29.6$, $R = 23.9$, $\theta = 36.2°$.
20. $Z = 57.4$, $R = 3.2$, $\theta = 86.8°$.

Problems 25-2

1. $R = 6.42$, $X = 41.5$, $\phi = 8.8°$.
2. $R = 106$, $X = 20.4$, $\phi = 79.1°$.
3. $R = 1.47$, $X = 1.23$, $\phi = 50°$.
4. $R = 454$, $X = 1534$, $\phi = 16.5°$.
5. $R = 600$, $X = 24.1$, $\phi = 87.7°$.
6. $R = 321$, $X = 138$, $\theta = 23.3°$.
7. $R = 317$, $X = 386$, $\theta = 50.6°$.
8. $R = 7840$, $X = 6210$, $\theta = 38.4°$.
9. $R = 0.105$, $X = 0.214$, $\theta = 63.9°$.
10. $R = 4.84$, $X = 72.8$, $\theta = 86.2°$.

Problems 25-3

1. $\theta = 48.2°$, $\phi = 41.8°$, $X = 44.7$.
2. $\theta = 84.6°$, $\phi = 5.4°$, $X = 749$.
3. $\theta = 79.3°$, $\phi = 10.7°$, $X = 15$.
4. $\theta = 69°$, $\phi = 21°$, $X = 21.1$.
5. $\theta = 8.1°$, $\phi = 81.9°$, $X = 57$.
6. $\theta = 14.5°$, $\phi = 75.5°$, $R = 93$.
7. $\theta = 37.7°$, $\phi = 52.3°$, $R = 11$.
8. $\theta = 5.5°$, $\phi = 84.5°$, $R = 72.7$
9. $\theta = 5.0°$, $\phi = 85°$, $R = 498$.
10. $\theta = 77°$, $\phi = 13°$, $R = 0.230$.

Problems 25-4

1. $\theta = 12.2°$, $\phi = 77.8°$, $Z = 66.7$.

2. $\theta = 78.3°$, $\phi = 11.7°$, $Z = 523$.

3. $\theta = 23.1°$, $\phi = 66.9°$, $Z = 11.8$.

4. $\theta = 45°$, $\phi = 45°$, $Z = 45.7$.

5. $\theta = 58.6°$, $\phi = 31.4°$, $Z = 478$.

6. $\theta = 80.8°$, $\phi = 9.2°$, $Z = 1013$.

7. $\theta = 67.3°$, $\phi = 22.7°$, $Z = 56.3$.

8. $\theta = 63.8°$, $\phi = 26.2°$, $Z = 217$.

9. $\theta = 85.8°$, $\phi = 4.2°$, $Z = 431$.

10. $\theta = 48.7°$, $\phi = 41.3°$, $Z = 798$.

Problems 25-5

1. 28.6°.   **2.** 33.7°.   **3.** 14%, 7.97°.

4. 300 ft.   **5.** 66.4°.   **6.** 235 ft.

7. 30.3 ft.   **8.** 33.5 ft., 73.4°.   **9.** 65.5 ft.

10. 1296 ft.   **11.** 410 ft.   **12.** 1250 ft.

Problems 26-2

1. (a) $\dfrac{1}{21,600} \pi$ radian/sec.   **2.** (a) 12π radians/sec.

   (b) $\dfrac{1}{1800} \pi$ radian/sec.   (b) 2160°/sec.

   (c) $\dfrac{1}{30} \pi$ radian/sec.

3. 50π radians/sec.   **4.** (a) 0.12π radian.
                                   (b) 0.6π radian.
                                   (c) 36π radians.

5. (a) 0.588.
   (b) 0.951.
   (c) -0.809.
   (d) -0.951.

Problems 26-3

1. (a) 25.   **2.** (a) 32.   **3.** (a) 325.
   (b) 2π.   (b) 37.7.   (b) 314.
   (c) 1.   (c) 6.   (c) 50.
   (d) 1.   (d) $\frac{1}{6}$.   (d) 0.02.
   (e) 30° lead.   (e) 10° lag.   (e) 18° lag.

4. (a) E_m.   **5.** (a) I_m.
   (b) 157.   (b) 6.28×10^3.
   (c) 25.   (c) 1000.
   (d) 0.04.   (d) 10^{-3}.
   (e) 17° lead.   (e) 90° lag.

11. (b) $y = 10 \sin 37.7t$.
    (c) -5.88 in.
    (d) 6.37 in.
    (e) 5.4π radians.

12. (b) $y = 12 \sin (88t + 23°)$.
    (c) 4.69 in.
    (d) 10.9 in.
    (e) 84π radians.

Problems 27-1

1. 182.5 at $28.2°$.

2. 132 at $327.8°$.

3. 238 at $244.7°$.

4. 76.8 at $348.6°$.

Problems 27-2

1. $h = 12$, $v = 9$.

2. $h = 94.5$, $v = 45.7$

3. $h = 2.55$, $v = 6.68$.

4. $h = -18.2$, $v = 36.6$.

5. $h = -227$, $v = 55.8$.

6. $h = -45.9$, $v = -40.5$.

7. $h = 0$, $v = -80.7$.

8. $h = 9.22$, $v = -3.25$.

9. $h = 94.8$, $v = -351$.

10. $h = -508$, $v = 0$.

11. 1414 ft/sec.

12. 748 lb., 310 lb.

13. 37.5 miles.

14. 42 lb.. 23.2 lb.

15. 123 lb.

Problems 27-3

1. 10.7 at $32.8°$.

2. 181 at $53.3°$.

3. 46.1 at $74.9°$.

4. 766 at $17.8°$.

5. 24.5 at $0°$.

6. 83 at $165°$.

7. 44 at $90°$.

8. 65.4 at $319.9°$.

9. 114.6 at $253.8°$.

10. 233 at $120.2°$.

11. 15.4 at $270°$.

12. 110.4 at $40.3°$.

13. 43.4 at $132.5°$.

14. 215 at $328.5°$.

15. 39.6 at $315°$.

16. 47.8 at $61.9°$.

17. 111 miles, course $9.05°$ E of N.

18. (a) 5.32 m.p.h.
    (b) 2.28 miles downstream.

19. 10.4 knots at an angle of $73.3°$ to current.

20. At an angle of $73.3°$ against current.

Problems 28-1

1. (a) 62 v.
    (b) 287 v.
    (c) 209 v.
    (d) -290 v.
    (e) -111 v.

2. 300 v.

3. 80 v.

4. (a) 84 a.
    (b) -54.8 a.
    (c) -24.8 a.
    (d) 11.9 a.
    (e) 74.6 a.

5. −8.42 a.   **6.** −115 v.

7. 151 v.   **8.** 45° and 135°.

9. 193° and 347°.   **10.** −4.88 a.

Problems 28-2

1. (a) 60 cycles.
   (b) 7200.
   (c) $e = 622 \sin 377t$.

2. (a) 25 cycles.
   (b) $i = 63.6 \sin 157t$.

3. (a) 12 poles.
   (b) $e = 933 \sin 157t$.
   (c) 660 v.

4. (a) 24 poles.
   (b) $e = 170 \sin 5030t$.
   (c) −129 v.

5. 250 r.p.m.

6. 50 cycles.

7. 355 kc.

8. (a) 150 μv.
   (b) 32.2 Mc.

9. $i = (5.5 \times 10^{-5}) \sin (3.77 \times 10^{8})t$.
10. $e = (1.55 \times 10^{-4}) \sin (4.46 \times 10^{6})t$.

Problems 28-3

1. 382 v.   **2.** 300 v.   **3.** 6.6 a.   **4.** 28 v.

5. 220 v.   **6.** 622 v.   **7.** 39.6 a.   **8.** 34.7 v.

9. 161 v.   **10.** 6.76 a.

Problems 28-4

1. (a) $i = 1410 \sin (377t + 30°)$.
   (b) 1080 a.

2. (a) $i = 990 \sin (157t − 22°)$.
   (b) 465 a.

3. −906 a.

4. 306 a.

5. (a) $i = 283 \sin (314t − 25°)$.
   (b) 200 a.

6. −3140 v.

7. 22° lead, or lag.

8. −39.3 a.

9. 50° lead, or lag.

10. (a) $i = 42.4 \sin (377t \pm 50°)$.
   (b) 209 v.

Problems 29-1

1. (a) 2.75 a.
   (b) $e = 933 \sin 157t$.
     $i = 3.89 \sin 157t$.
   (c) 378 w.
   (d) 248 v.
   (e) 1.33 a.

2. (a) $e = 226 \sin \omega t$.
   (b) $i = 7.92 \sin \omega t$.
   (c) 48 v.
   (d) 165 w.
   (e) 1.20 a.
   (f) 3.42 a.

3. 66.5 v.

4. 245 v.

5. 2.45 a.

Problems 29-2

1. 71.6 Ω. **2.** 3770 Ω. **3.** 895 Ω. **4.** 5740 Ω.

5. (a) Inductive reactance is proportional to frequency.
(b) Inductive reactance is proportional to inductance.

6. 0.732 a. **7.** 3.26 h. **8.** 220 v. **9.** −540 ma.

10. −200 v.

Problems 29-3

1. 221 Ω. **2.** 442 Ω. **3.** 31.8 Ω.

4. 15.9 Ω. **5.** 7.96 Ω.

6. (a) Capacitive reactance is inversely proportional to frequency.
(b) Capacitive reactance is inversely proportional to capacitance.

7. 2.41 a. **8.** 5 μf.

9. 120 v. **10.** −192 ma.

11. 155 v. **12.** (a) 850 μμf.
(b) 206 μμf.

13. (a) 362 ma.
(b) The 4-μf condenser (larger reactance).

14. 125 ma. **15.** (a) $e = 311 \sin 377t$.
(b) $i = 0.138 \sin (377t + 90°)$.
(c) 104 v.
(d) 1.82 μf.
(e) 17.6 ma.

Problems 29-4

1. (a) 241 Ω, 51.5°. **2.** (a) 55.2 Ω, 65.6°.
(b) 0.914 a. (b) 1.99 a.
(c) 137 v.
(d) 172 v.

3. (a) 2400 Ω, 70.5°. **4.** (a) 1200 Ω, 48.2°.
(b) 0.834 a. (b) 396 kc.
(c) 667 v.
(d) 1885 v.

5. (a) 254 Ω, −60.5°. **6.** 104 Ω, −76.1°.
(b) 1.73 a.
(c) 217 v.
(d) 383 v.

7. 56.4 Ω, −63.7°. **8.** 126 Ω, −53.4°.

9. (a) 436 Ω, −76.7°. **10.** 760 μμf.
(b) 1.15 a.
(c) 115 v.
(d) 487 v.

Problems 29-5

1. (a) 1210 /65.5° Ω.
   - (b) 0.365 a.
   - (c) $i = 0.516 \sin (377t - 65.5°)$.
   - (d) 41.5%.
   - (e) 66.6 w.

2. (a) 1278 /62° Ω.
   - (b) 0.516 a.
   - (c) $i = 0.730 \sin (157t - 62°)$.
   - (d) 47%.
   - (e) 160 w.

3. (a) 1580 /50.8° Ω.
   - (b) 69.6 ma.
   - (c) $i = 0.0984 \sin (314t - 50.8°)$.
   - (d) 63.2%.
   - (e) 4.84 w.

4. (a) 52.5 /17.9° Ω.
   - (b) 2.1 a.
   - (c) $i = 2.97 \sin [(5.02 \times 10^3)t - 17.9°]$.
   - (d) 95.2%.
   - (e) 220 w.

5. (a) 468 /57.7° Ω.
   - (b) 2.67 a.
   - (c) $i = 3.78 \sin [(6.28 \times 10^5)t - 57.7°]$.
   - (d) 53.4%.
   - (e) 1.78 kw.

6. (a) 74.7 /−74.5° Ω.
   - (b) 13.4 ma.
   - (c) $i = 0.019 \sin [(6.28 \times 10^6)t + 74.5°]$.
   - (d) 26.8%.
   - (e) 3.59 mw.

7. (a) 62.8 /−76.2° Ω.
   - (b) 7.96 a.
   - (c) $i = 11.3 \sin [(2.23 \times 10^6)t + 76.2°]$.
   - (d) 23.9%.
   - (e) 950 w.

8. (a) 17.1 /−74.7° Ω.
   - (b) 2.92 a.
   - (c) $i = 4.13 \sin [(1.76 \times 10^8)t + 74.7°]$.
   - (d) 26.3%.
   - (e) 38.4 w.

9. (a) 75.0 /82.3° Ω.
   - (b) 1.33 a.

(c) $i = 1.89 \sin [(4.52 \times 10^7)t - 82.3°]$.

(d) 13.3%.

(e) 17.8 w.

10. (a) 203 $/9.9°$ Ω.

   (b) 1.08 a.

   (c) $i = 1.53 \sin (377t - 9.9°)$.

   (d) 98.5%.

   (e) 235 w.

11. (a) 55 Ω.

   (b) 437 Ω.

   (c) 1.16 h.

12. 23.3 mw.

13. (a) 28.3 $/45°$ Ω.

   (b) 66.3 μf.

14. $23 + j37.5$ Ω.

15. (a) 23.5 a.

   (b) 8.95 kw.

16. $e = v_r + v_x$.

Problems 29-6

1. (a) 1.92 a.   **2.** $Q = 58.3$

   (b) 48 w.

   (c) $E_c = E_L = 1460$ v.

3. 18 μh, 11,860 kc.   **4.** (a) 75.4

                         (b) 56.3 μμf.

                         (c) 2.5 v.

                         (d) 188 v.

5. (a) $R + j0$.

   (b) $R - jX$.

   (c) $R + jX$.

Problems 30-1

1. (a) 2.43 a.   **2.** (a) 0.174 a.

   (b) 775 w.   (b) 71.9% lagging.

   (c) $131 + j125$ Ω.   (c) $4140 + j4000$ Ω.

3. 25 μμf.   **4.** (a) 777 kc.

                         (b) 8000 Ω.

5. (a) 0.277 a.

   (b) 0.32 μf.

Problems 30-2

1. (a) $36.3 + j16.4$ Ω.   **2.** (a) 99%.

   (b) 4.44 kw.   (b) 552 w.

3. (a) 98.6 $/-6.45°$ a.   **4.** (a) 663 $/50°$ Ω.

   (b) 99.5%.   (b) $426 + j508$ Ω.

   (c) 43.1 kw.   (c) 64.3% lagging.

5. (a) 1430 $\underline{/-11.4°}$ Ω.
   (b) 1400 − j280 Ω.
   (c) 98.0% leading.

7. (a) 14,400 $\underline{/69°}$ Ω.
   (b) 5160 + j13,400 Ω.
   (c) 35.8% lagging.

9. (a) 15,300 $\underline{/-70°}$ Ω.
   (b) 5240 − j14,400 Ω.
   (c) 34.2% leading.

11. (a) 13.9 $\underline{/-43.9°}$ a.
   (b) 72%.
   (c) 6.21 + j6 Ω.
   (d) 1.2 kw.

13. 55%.

15. (a) 66.5 kw.
   (b) 219 a.

17. (a) 322 $\underline{/65°}$ Ω.
   (b) 104 v.

19. (a) 981 $\underline{/67.5°}$ Ω.
   (b) 38.2% lagging.
   (c) 8.37 v.

21. (a) 6.98 $\underline{/-36°}$ a.
   (b) 81% lagging.
   (c) 39 v.
   (d) 3.68 a.

23. (a) 10.6 a.
   (b) 110 v.
   (c) 72%.
   (d) 76.6 v.

25. (a) 8400 $\underline{/9.3°}$ Ω.
   (b) 11.9 ma.
   (c) No.

6. (a) 740 $\underline{/-68°}$ Ω.
   (b) 277 − j686 Ω.
   (c) 37.5% leading.

8. (a) 42,300 $\underline{/0°}$ Ω.
   (b) 42,300 + j0 Ω.
   (c) 100%.

10. (a) 13.1 a.
   (b) 14 μf.
   (c) 10 a.

12. (a) 57.4 Ω.
   (b) 87.5 mh.

14. (a) 24.2 a.
   (b) 5.65 kw.

16. (a) 80.5% lagging.
   (b) 13.1 kw.
   (c) 132 μf.

18. (a) 890 $\underline{/77.5°}$ Ω.
   (b) 1006 v.

20. (a) 2.75 $\underline{/2.7°}$ a.
   (b) 99.9%.
   (c) 207 v.
   (d) 436 ma.

22. 8.2 μf.

24. 7.77 a.

Problems 30-3

1. (a) 3676 kc.
   (b) 3750 kc.
   (c) 3751 kc.
   (d) $Q = 5$.

3. (a) 7.496 Mc.
   (b) 65,900 Ω.
   (c) 6.59 Ω.

2. (a) 3.733 Mc.
   (b) 3.750 Mc.
   (c) 3.751 Mc.
   (d) $Q = 10$.

4. 15.2 w.

5. (*a*) 999 kc.   **6.** 0.177 w.
    (*b*) 56,500 Ω.
    (*c*) 6.97 Ω.
7. $Q = 71.6$.   **8.** 248 μh.
9. 505 μμf.   **10.** $Q = 99.7$

Problems 31-1

1. 20.2 /34.1°.   **2.** 131 /−40.5°.
3. 1170 /20°.   **4.** 40.4 /−82°.
5. 863 /120.8°.   **6.** 538 /−126°.
7. 38.1 /−72.9°.   **8.** 20.2 /−42.4°.
9. 500 /126.9°.   **10.** 106 /−125.9°.

Problems 31-2

1. 33.6 /−10.3°.   **2.** 546 /78.2°.
3. 87 /152.1°.   **4.** 598 /0°.
5. 74.3 /−86.7°.   **6.** 78.2 /−147.5°.
7. 2 /16.25°.   **8.** 1.14 /51.9°.
9. 2.78 /−148.5°.   **10.** 0.05 /36.9°.

Problems 31-3

1. 20.2 /34°.   **2.** 131 /−40.5°.
3. 1170 /20°.   **4.** 40.4 /−82°.
5. 863 /120.8°.   **6.** 538 /−126°.
7. 38.1 /−72.9°.   **8.** 20.2 /−42.4°.
9. 608 /170.5°.   **10.** 106 /−125.9°.

Problems 31-4

1. 80 /64°.   **2.** 316 /37°.
3. 56.3 /−6.3°.   **4.** 77.2 /−157.3°.
5. 17.1 /−26°.   **6.** 6.62 /0°.
7. 27.1 /23°.   **8.** 18.2 /10°.
9. 0.57 /87°.   **10.** 1.84 /−60°.
11. 6.74 /−28°.   **12.** 0.474 /3°.
13. 13 /8°.   **14.** 24 /−11.5°.
15. 784 /80°.   **16.** 2.89 /−140°.
17. 2 /40°.   **18.** 7 /−6.2°.
19. 8 /51°.   **20.** 81 /−72°.

Problems 31-5

1. 44.6 /24.4° Ω.   **2.** 53.5 /−42.4° Ω.
3. 83.2 /25.7° Ω.   **4.** 170 /2.34° Ω.

5. 46.4 $\underline{/19.6°}$ Ω.

6. 96.4 $\underline{/-81°}$ Ω.

7. 47.4 $\underline{/76.4°}$ Ω.

8. 78.4 $\underline{/-73.8°}$ Ω.

9. 345 $\underline{/4.62°}$ Ω.

10. 30.7 $\underline{/2.88°}$ Ω.

11. 9.10 $\underline{/17.6°}$ Ω.

12. 10 $\underline{/0°}$ Ω.

13. 283 $\underline{/58.1°}$ ma.

14. 59.4 $\underline{/-162°}$ ma.

Problems 31-6

1. $Z_a = 46.4$ $\underline{/75.55°}$ Ω.
$Z_b = 43.8$ $\underline{/-45.45°}$ Ω.
$Z_c = 56.4$ $\underline{/-37.45°}$ Ω.

2. $Z_a = 50.9$ $\underline{/86.8°}$ Ω.
$Z_b = 62.7$ $\underline{/-20.2°}$ Ω.
$Z_c = 44.5$ $\underline{/8.8°}$ Ω.

3. $Z_a = 178.6$ $\underline{/14.8°}$ Ω.
$Z_b = 197$ $\underline{/-4.1°}$ Ω.
$Z_c = 149$ $\underline{/-0.9°}$ Ω.

4. $Z_a = 2.58$ $\underline{/0°}$ Ω.
$Z_b = 2.58$ $\underline{/-40°}$ Ω.
$Z_c = 2.58$ $\underline{/40°}$ Ω.

5. $Z_t = 87$ $\underline{/5.2°}$ Ω.

6. 0.505 a.

7. $Z_t = 187$ $\underline{/26.4°}$ Ω.

8. 0.64 a.

9. 5.5 w.

10. 0.52 a.

11. 89 $\underline{/-25.4°}$ Ω.

12. 0.74 a.

13. 67 w.

14. 1.7 a.

15. 600 $\underline{/0°}$ Ω.

16. 12.5 ma.

17. 820 $\underline{/-6.7°}$ Ω.

18. 290 mw.